To Philips own

from

Tony .

COASTAL
FISHES
of
OMAN

The Government of
the Sultanate of Oman
commissioned the Publisher
to produce this volume
and financed the research
in Oman upon which
it is based.

COASTAL
FISHES
of
OMAN

John E. Randall

Additional photography by
John P. Hoover

A CHP Production

Produced and published by
Crawford House Publishing Pty Ltd
PO Box 1484
Bathurst NSW 2795 Australia

Published in the United States of America by
University of Hawaii Press, 1995

Designed by David H. Barrett

National Library of Australia Cataloguing-in-Publication entry
    Randall, John E., 1924-
        Coastal fishes of Oman

        Bibliography.
        Includes index.
        ISBN 1 86333 126 3.

        1. Fishes – Oman, Gulf of – Identification. 2. Fishes –
        Persian Gulf – Identification. I. Title.

    597.092735

Printed in Hong Kong by Colorcraft Ltd

95 96 97 98 99 00 01 02 03 04   10 9 8 7 6 5 4 3 2 1

CONTENTS

His Majesty Sultan Qaboos bin Said, Sultan of Oman

كلمة افتتاحية
لصاحب الجلالة السلطان قابوس بن سعيد
سلطان عُمان
الأسماك الساحلية في عُمان

في غضون العشرين سنة الماضية، صدرت كتب كثيرة حول موضوع الحيوانات والنباتات العمانية الجميلة المتنوعة بل والفريدة أحيانا، فقد أنعم الله تعالى على بلادنا من فيض كرمه بثروة من الكائنات الحية.

ولقد كان العمانيون، ولآلاف السنين، أمة كبرى في مضمار الملاحة البحرية. فمن خطوطنا الساحلية الطويلة اكتشفنا شرق أفريقيا والهند والشرق الأقصى وتبادلنا معها التجارة، مما سمح لنا بنقل تراثنا وثقافتنا إلى بلدان أخرى كما أتاح لنا أن نستوعب في مجتمعنا تلك الجوانب من الثقافات الأجنبية التي شعرنا بأنها يمكن أن تعود بالنفع على عمان، وقد افادنا جميعا ذلك التبادل.

وبنفس القدر من الأهمية يأتي رجالنا الذين يمخرون عباب البحر «محليا» ألا وهم صيادونا. فهم منذ زمن طويل يجوبون خطوطنا الساحلية من أجل صيد السمك كوسيلة للعيش، جالبين الطعام للتجمعات البشرية على الساحل وفي داخلية البلاد. ولقد لعب هؤلاء الرجال دورا بارزا في توفير البروتين للغذاء الذي نتناوله. وربما ظن البعض أن المياه الساحلية العمانية بحار هادئة زرقاء اللون، لكن الواقع ان الطقس يتسبب احيانا في احوال معاكسة جدا، وتحديدا في أوقات الرياح الموسمية ـ الخريف ـ والرياح الشمالية والاعاصير. لذلك فإن بعض صيادي الاسماك لم يعودوا إلى أحبائهم أبدا بعد أن حاصرتهم العواصف.

إن كمية الأسماك التي يمكن صيدها باستخدام البدن والهوري وغيرها من القوارب الصغيرة التقليدية التي تدفعها الرياح كانت محدودة، لذلك عشنا في توازن مع الثروة السمكية العظيمة التي تعيش في سواحلنا أو تزورها. أما اليوم فإن المحرك القابل للربط في مؤخر الزورق، وقوارب الالياف الزجاجية الحديثة، والشباك المصنوعة من النايلون، قد مكنت صيادينا من جلب كميات أكبر بكثير، ليس من أجل اطعامنا نحن فحسب بل أيضا من أجل التصدير للبلدان الاجنبية. ومن ثم ينبغي علينا أن نلزم جانب الحرص وأن نتعلم من اخطاء الآخرين، كيلا نفسد نفس التوازن الموجود في الانظمة البيئية الساحلية العمانية. كما يجب علينا ألا نسرف في الصيد حتى ولو كان لنوع واحد لأن ذلك ربما اسفر عن عواقب وخيمة على سلسلة الغذاء البحري.

ولقد شرعنا منذ فترة في تطبيق أنظمة الحصص النسبية وتحديد مقدار السمك الممكن صيده في كل موسم، وسوف نستمر في رصد مدى تأثير الصيد المتزايد.

ولدى سلطنة عمان خطة لإدارة الحزام الساحلي، ينبغي التقيد بها، كما ينبغي أن تأخذ كل خطط تنمية المناطق الساحلية بعين الاعتبار مسألة الحفاظ على الموائل الطبيعية، وعلى وجه التحديد أماكن التناسل والغذاء للأسماك والربيان (القريدس أو الجمبري) والصفيلح (جراد البحر الشوكي).

وحتى الآن، فإنه لا يدرك قيمة التنوع الكبير للاسماك التي تعيش حول شواطئنا سوى صيادينا وغواصينا وعلمائنا المتخصصين في علم الأحياء البحرية، وأولئك الذين يرتادون بانتظام أسواق السمك الساحلية في بلادنا. لهذا شعرنا بوجوب توسيع نطاق تلك المعرفة، بحيث يصبح الجميع على دراية بجمال وتنوع الكائنات الحية الساحلية التي حبانا الله تعالى بها. ومن حسن الطالع أنه كان يوجد لدينا واحد من أكثر المتخصصين في دراسة الأسماك شهرة في العالم، يقوم بالغوص على طول خطنا الساحلي، وتصوير الأسماك في موائلها الطبيعية، وكتابة وصف علمي لما يجده، ألا وهو الدكتور جون راندول، من متحف بيشوب في هاواي. لذلك كلفناه أن يعود في مناسبتين أخريين للقيام بالغوص في الخط الساحلي الممتد بين الحدود الغربية وجزيرة مصيرة، وهي منطقة لم يسبق اجراء دراسة مفصلة لها. وبالتعاون مع مستر جون هوفر ـ الذي سبق وأن عمل بمركزنا للعلوم البحرية والابحاث السمكية بمسقط، وهو بارع في التصوير تحت الماء ـ اكتشف الدكتور راندول ما يربو على مائة نوع من الاسماك لم يكن من المعروف علميا في السابق أنها تعيش في مياه السواحل العمانية، بل إن من بينها أكثر من أربعين نوعا جديدا لم يكن العلم قد توصل إلى معرفته من قبل ـ وذلك إنجاز مرموق جدير بالاهتمام.

هذه الزيارات والأعمال السابقة للدكتور راندول وآخرين في مياهنا الشمالية، نتج عنها هذه الاضافة الرائعة إلى الكتب التي صدرت عن الكائنات العمانية الحية. لقد قام الدكتور راندول بتأليف الكثير من الكتب حول موضوع الأسماك طيلة فترة عمله الطويل المميز. وهذا المجلد الفخم لابد أن يعتبر بالتأكيد من بين أروع أعماله. وإننا إذ نوجه الشكر الجزيل إليه وإلى مستر جون هوفر، لنأمل في أن يستمتع العلماء ومن عداهم من غير المتخصصين على حد سواء بقراءة هذا الكتاب وأن يستفيدوا من المعلومات المتوفرة لنا الآن.

ان هذا الكتاب يبين بوضوح الميراث الجميل والقيم الذي تضمه بيئتنا البحرية. وبعون الله تعالى سوف نحافظ على هذه البيئة ونعمل على تنميتها بعناية من أجل المصلحة المستمرة والاستماع الدائم للأجيال القادمة.

قابوس بن سعيد

مسقط، اغسطس ١٩٩٥م

FOREWORD

BY

HIS MAJESTY SULTAN QABOOS BIN SAID
SULTAN OF OMAN

COASTAL FISHES OF OMAN

During the last twenty years many books have been published on the subject of Oman's beautiful, varied and, sometimes, unique fauna and flora. God has indeed been generous with the wealth of living things that He has bestowed upon our country.

Oman has, for thousands of years, been a great seafaring nation. From our long coastline, we have explored and traded with East Africa, India and the Far East. This has allowed us to take our heritage and culture to other lands, and to absorb into our own society those parts of foreign cultures that we felt would be beneficial to Oman. This exchange has benefitted us all.

Equally important are our "local" seafarers – our fishermen. They have long fished our coastline as a means of livelihood, bringing food for the coastal communities and those further inland. These men have played an extremely important role in the provision of protein to our diet. Some may think of Oman's coastal waters as calm, blue seas, but at times the weather creates very adverse conditions, particularly during times of monsoons, northerly winds and cyclones. Some fishermen have never returned to their loved ones after being caught by storms.

With the traditional wind-driven badan, huri and smaller craft, there were limitations to the numbers of fish that could be caught, and we lived in equilibrium with the vast wealth of fishes that live in and visit our coastal waters. Today, however, the outboard engine, modern glass fibre boats and nylon gear have enabled our fishermen to bring in greatly increased catches to feed not only our own population, but also for export to foreign countries. We must be cautious and learn from the mistakes of others, lest we upset the balance that exists in the coastal ecosystem of Oman. We must not overfish even one species, for that may have serious consequences on the marine food chain. We have already implemented quota systems and seasonal catches. We shall continue to monitor the effects of increased fishing.

Oman has a coastal zone management plan that should be adhered to. All coastal development plans must take into account the protection of the habitat, with particular reference to breeding and feeding grounds of fishes, prawns, shrimps and spiny lobsters.

Until now, only our fishermen, divers, marine biologists and those who regularly visit our coastal fish souks have appreciated the great diversity of fish species that live around our shores. We felt that this knowledge should be made more widely available, so that we all become aware of the beauty and diversity of our coastal fauna with which God has provided us. Fortunately, we already had one of the world's most renowned ichthyologists diving along our coastline, photographing the fishes in their native habitat and writing scientific descriptions of what he found. We therefore commisioned him, Dr John Randall of the Bishop Museum Hawaii, to return on two further occasions, to dive on the coastline between the western border and Masirah Island. This area had not previously been studied in any detail. Along with Mr John Hoover, who had previously worked at our Marine Sciences and Fisheries Research Centre at Muscat and is a superb underwater photographer, Dr Randall discovered more than a hundred species of fish previously scientifically unknown from Omani waters. These included more than forty species new to science – a remarkable achievement.

These visits, and the previous visit of Dr Randall and others in our northern waters, have resulted in this wonderful addition to our books on Omani fauna. Dr Randall has authored many books on the subject of fish during his long and distinguished career. This magnificent volume must surely rank among his finest works. We thank him and Mr Hoover, and hope that scientists and laymen alike will enjoy reading and learning from what is available to us.

This book clearly shows what a beautiful and valuable inheritance we have in our marine environment. With God's help we must protect it and develop it carefully for the sustainable benefit and enjoyment of future generations.

Muscat, August 1995

QABOOS BIN SAID

ACKNOWLEDGEMENTS

This book was made possible by the generosity of His Majesty Sultan Qaboos bin Said, whose strong interest in the natural history of Oman and the conservation of Oman's wildlife has stimulated and supported scientific research in many different fields.

John E. Randall has visited countries of the Arabian Peninsula 13 times for field work on fishes, commencing in 1972. The first trip to Oman took place in 1977, followed by three other lengthy visits, the last in 1993. John P. Hoover spent three years at the Marine Science and Fisheries Centre in Muscat (1987-1990) and accompanied Randall on his two most recent visits to Oman. It was largely because of Hoover's plan to publish a smaller book on Oman fishes that this comprehensive volume came about.

We thank His Excellency Qais bin Abdulmunim Al Zawawi, the Deputy Prime Minister for Financial and Economic Affairs, for his support of the book project.

Planning, coordination and logistic support in 1993 in Oman was provided primarily by the staff of the Office of the Adviser for Conservation of the Environment, Diwan of Royal Court, headed by Ralph Daly, assisted by Hamida bint Ali Al Rashdy, and by Ian and Sheila McLeish without whose devoted and untiring attention to the needs of the authors, dive crews and support personnel in the field the work could not have been done in time. We wish also to thank Elizabeth Daly for her much appreciated hospitality in Muscat.

Other supporting organizations and groups in Oman were the Ministry of Agriculture and Fishery Wealth (including the Marine Science and Fisheries Centre), the Omani-American Joint Commission, the Royal Army of Oman, the Royal Air Force of Oman, the Royal Navy of Oman, the Sultan's Special Force, the Directorate General of Civil Aviation and Meteorology, Sultan Qaboos University, Airwork Ltd., Dhofar Cattle Feed Co., Sadah Marine Products, Gulf of Oman Fishing International, Marsees Trading and Cont. Est., Oman Fisheries Co., Oman Sea Products Co., Dhofar Divers, Gulf Divers, Muscat Divers, Masirah Divers and Oman Dive Centre. Support in other Gulf countries was provided by the Food and Agriculture Organization of the United Nations, Rome; Directorate of Fisheries, Bahrain; Kuwait Institute for Scientific Research, Kuwait City; King Fahd University of Petroleum and Minerals, Dhahran; and the National Oceanic and Atmospheric Administration, Washington, D.C. We acknowledge all this help with gratitude.

We thank the following individuals for assistance in collecting fishes: Gerald R. Allen, Mohammed bin Amour Al Barwani, John E. Burchard, Nicholas Clarke, David N. Cochrane, Stephen L. Coles, Jan Copeland, Martin Day, Davaid Deeks, Nigel Downing, Vina S. Durve, James Ellis, David Hardy, Rolf Jensen, Gary Keat, John Jackson, Mark Johnson, John C. McCain, Linda J. McCarthy, Ian and Sheila McLeish, Qassim bin Said Mubarak, Christopher Potts, Gary Rhodes, Rodney V. Salm, Oliver B. Schlumberger, Hagen Schmid, Alan J. Smith, Anthony Smith, William F. Smith-Vaniz, Brock E. Stanaland, A. Bradley Tarr, Peter J. Vine and David H. Vousden. Among the collectors we are especially grateful for the help of John L. Earle, Jonathan K.L. Mee and Stephen A. Shaw who was leader of our support divers. Anthony Smith, captain of the Sultan's Special Force dhow *Shark*, is deserving of special thanks for two very successful cruises in southern Oman waters.

Others in Oman who assisted on the project include His Excellency Mohammed bin Abdullah bin Zaher Al Hinai, His Excellency Mohammed bin Mahfoudh bin Saad Al Ardhi, Thabit bin Zahran Al Abdessalaam, Salam bin Said Al Amri, Saleh bin Abdullah Al Amri, Abdul Wahab bin Pir

Mohammed Al Baluchi, Rashid bin Amour Al Barwani, Abdul Wahab bin Ahmed Al Bousi, Mohammed bin Ahmed Al Bousi, Saleh bin Abdullah Al Busaidy, Roy Carter, Steve Cary, Daz Cosway, Peter Dennison, Michael Dunn, Abdullah bin Sha'ban al Farsi, Don Fawver, John Fulford, Alex Gardiner, Reg Gay, Peter Goodman, Desley Hardwick, Peter Hogg, John Horton, Tony Hunter-Choat, Ken Jones, Roddy Jones, Bill Johnstone, Mohammed bin Abdul Aziz Al Kathiri, Mark Lawrence, Eoin O'Luasa, Bill McKay, Salam bin Ali Al Mashani, Jim Murphy, Keith Murty, Mick Peedell, Nasser bin Mohammed Al Qassmi, Colin Richardson, Ofait bin Mohammed Al Shahari, Mohammed bin Ahmed Al Shanfari, Saleh bin Mohammed Al Shanfari, B.R. Shetty, Mohammed bin Said Al Shukaily, Rod Stewart-Liddon, Gordon Trevis, Mohammed bin Abdullah Al Yafaey and Ali bin Ahmed Al Zawamari.

Thanks are also due the following ichthyologists who aided in the identification of fishes: Gerald R. Allen, Hans Bath, Eugenia B. Böhlke, John C. Briggs, Kent E. Carpenter, Bruce B. Collette, Leonard J.V. Compagno, William N. Eschmeyer, Ronald Fricke, Anthony C. Gill, Ofer Gon, Phillip C. Heemstra, Douglass F. Hoese, Wouter Holleman, J. Barry Hutchins, Jeff Johnson, Hirokazu Kishimoto, Leslie W. Knapp, Friedhelm Krupp, Helen K. Larson, Jeffrey M. Leis, John E. McCosker, R. J. McKay, Jonathan K.L. Mee, Gareth J. Nelson, Jørgen Nielsen, Giuseppe Notobartolo di Sciara, Frank Pezold, Lynne R. Parenti, William J. Richards, Barry C. Russell, Kunio Sasaki, Jeffrey A. Seigel, Hiroshi Senou, William F. Smith-Vaniz, Victor G. Springer, Wayne G. Starnes, Jeffrey T. Williams, Richard Winterbottom, Thosaporn Wongratana and David J. Woodland.

Loans of specimens of Oman fishes were made by David Catania of the California Academy of Sciences, Karsten E. Hartel of the Museum of Comparative Zoology of Harvard University and Richard Winterbottom of the Royal Ontario Museum.

Photographs were kindly provided by Ian Bailey, Robert Bedford, Mark N. Boulton, Simon A. Chater, Helmut Debelius, Nigel Downing, Richard Dudley, John L. Earle, Klaus E. Fiedler, Steven R. Hare, Phillip C. Heemstra, Tomoko Kimura, Yasuma Kobayashi, Linda J. McCarthy, Ian McLeish, Hajima Masuda, Jonathan K.L. Mee, George Michie, Klaus Payson, Robert M. Pyle, Gary Rhodes, Rodney V. Salm, Marthen Samuel, Oliver B. Schlumberger, Hagen Schmid, B.L. Simpson, A. Bradley Tarr, Ron and Valerie Taylor, Rudy van lder Elst, Philip Woodhead and Anthony Woodward.

Assistance in curating Oman fishes was given by Jane B. Culp, Loreen R. O'Hara, Richard L. Pyle and Arnold Y. Suzumoto.

Finally, but above all, we thank our wives, Helen A. Randall and Marcia A. Stone, for their encouragement, tolerance and help in many ways.

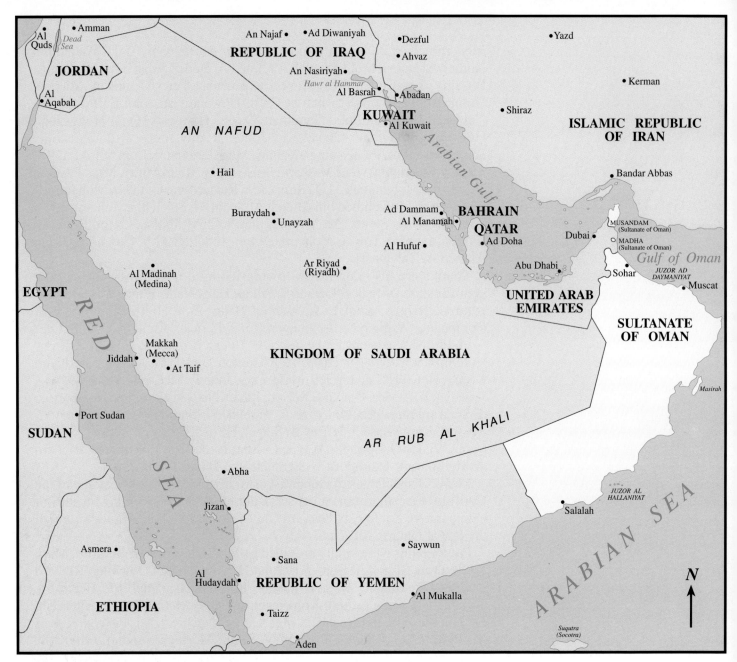

THE ARABIAN PENINSULA

This map is not an authority on international boundaries.

ISLAMIC REPUBLIC
OF IRAN

QATAR

Arabian Gulf

• Doha

Abu Dhabi •

Strait of Hormuz

*Ras ash
Shaykh Masud* • Kumzar •
Khasab •
Bukha • MUSANDAM
Tibat • (Sultanate
of Oman)

Ras Haffah
• Daba

Ash Shariqah
Dubai

Madha ⊙
(Sultanate
of Oman)

• Khawr Fakkan
• Al Fujayrah
Khatmat Milahah
Aswad •
• Shinas
• Liwa
• Sohar
• Saham

UNITED ARAB EMIRATES

Al Khaburah •

As Suwayq •
Al Masnaah •   Barka

*JUZOR AD
DAYMANIYAT*

As Seeb •
Ras al Hamra

Gulf of Oman

MUSCAT
Mutrah • *Ras al Khayran*
Sifah • *Ras Abu Daud*
Quriyat • • Al Hajir
• Dibab
• Fins
• Tiwi
Qalhat •
Sur • *Ras al Hadd*
• Al Hadd

**SULTANATE
OF OMAN**

Suwayh •   *Ras al
Khabbah*
Asylah • *Ras Asylah*
• Al Ashkarah

Ras al Jifan •
Ras Saqlah • *Ras as Sarj*
Qurun • *Ras Jibsh*

**KINGDOM OF
SAUDI ARABIA**

An Nakdah •
Ras ar Ruways
• *Ras an Nakdah*
Ras Hilf
• Qaryat Dafiyat

Masirah

*Ras
Bintawt*
Ras abu Rasas

*Khalij
Masirah*

Nafun •

Ras ad Duqm

Ras al Ani

Ras Markaz

Madrakah • *Ras Madrakah*

Al Juwayrah •

Dawhat Sawqirah

Al Lakbi •
Ras Sawqirah

Ras Qarwaw
Ras Mutaykaf

Qanawt •
As Sawda   *Shinays*
Al Hallaniyah
• *Al Qibliyah*

Hasik •
Al Hasikiyah
JUZOR AL HALLANIYAT

Sadh • *Ras Nuss*

Taqah •   Marbat •
Salalah •   *Ras Janjari*
Ras
Raysut Ras
Rakhyut • *Marbat*
Dalkut •
Ras Sajir
Ras Darbat Ali

**REPUBLIC
OF
YEMEN**

ARABIAN SEA

N ↑

**THE SULTANATE
OF OMAN**

KEY TO DEPTHS

0 to 200 metres
200 to 1000 metres
1000 to 2000 metres
2000+ metres

SCALE
1:5 000 000

0   50   100   150
Kilometres

Copyright © 1995 Crawford House Publishing Pty Ltd

INTRODUCTION

Oman, with some of the most biologically productive seas in the world, lies at the southeastern corner of the Arabian Peninsula between latitudes 16° and 27°N. It is bathed by three different bodies of the ocean: the Arabian Sea borders the long southern and central coast; the Gulf of Oman forms the northeastern coast; and the Arabian Gulf lies off the western shore of Musandam, the small detached northern part of Oman at the Strait of Hormuz. In treating the coastal fishes of Oman, it is therefore necessary to consider the marine biota of all three bodies of water.

The Arabian Gulf is unique in several respects. Its entrance is the very narrow Strait of Hormuz, thus the circulation to the Gulf of Oman is limited. It is very shallow compared to other seas of comparable size, the average depth being only 35 m, and huge expanses are only a few metres deep; the greatest depth is only 100 m (this a short distance into the Gulf from the Strait of Hormuz). As a result of these two features, the Arabian Gulf experiences an unprecedented fluctuation in sea temperature with the seasons. It varies in coastal waters from as low as 10°C in winter to 35°C in summer (even higher in shallow lagoons or flats). There is also unusually high salinity due to low rainfall and high evaporation (except in the north where moderated by the Tigris and Euphrates Rivers which empty via the Shatt al Arab into the Gulf); salinity readings may reach 40 o/oo in open water and as much as 50 o/oo in shallow lagoons. As might be expected, the marine biota of the Arabian Gulf is impoverished. Relatively few marine species of animals and plants can withstand such a huge variation of sea temperature over the course of a year, and some may be unable to tolerate the high salinity. Still another factor which may have contributed to the lack of diversity of the marine life of the Gulf is its relative youth (only 3 million to 4 million years old) and ephemeral nature. Because it is so shallow, it ceased to exist when the sea level dropped during ice ages; the most recent

(Opposite) A pair of Yellowmouth Morays (*Gymnothorax nudivomer*) at Fahl Island, off Muscat, Oman. (J. Randall)

The upwelling off Oman's southern coast results in temperate brown seaweed sharing the same habitat with corals and tropical species of fishes such as this triggerfish, *Sufflamen fraenatus*. (J. Hoover)

The rich seas of Oman support a wealth of fish life, as shown by this mixed school of six species, dominated by the porgies *Diplodus cervinus omanensis* and *Acanthopagrus bifasciatus*. (J. Hoover)

such event was a scant 20,000 years ago. The paucity of fishes in the Gulf is most apparent among the families of reef fishes. There are, for example, only four species of butterflyfishes (Chaetodontidae), two angelfishes (Pomacanthidae), 10 damselfishes (Pomacentridae), 14 wrasses (Labridae), five parrotfishes (Scaridae), two surgeonfishes (Acanthuridae), and two triggerfishes (Balistidae). Sixteen species of fishes are presently known only from the Gulf; however, like others initially believed to be endemic there, some may eventually be found to extend their distribution into the Gulf of Oman or beyond.

By contrast, the Gulf of Oman is broadly open, and much of it is deep water; more than three-fourths of this gulf has a depth of 1000 m or more, and 3000 m depths are attained in its outer part. Because of better circulation to the open ocean and limited shallow areas, the physical and chemical parameters are more benign for marine life than the Arabian Gulf. The salinity is more stable, but there is more temperature variation than might be expected. This is due to occasional upwelling along the Oman coast and the infusion of cool water from the Arabian Sea where more consistent and stronger upwelling occurs (Savidge et al., 1990). This cool upwelled water is rich in nutrients, leading to high productivity of phytoplankton and the steps up the food chain that follow (zooplankton, sardines and predatory fishes). Therefore, the Gulf of Oman is well endowed with fishery resources. However, this does not mean that the diversity of marine life is high. The fish fauna is clearly richer than that of the Arabian Gulf. For example, the number of chaetodontid fishes has doubled, but the fauna is still impoverished compared to the tropical Indian Ocean.

The Arabian Sea is the regional name for the northern part of the Indian Ocean. It borders two-thirds of the coastline of Oman from Yemen to Ra's

Four Omani fishermen coming ashore at the Batinah coast with their catch. (Richard Dudley)

al Hadd at the entrance to the Gulf of Oman. This coast is fully exposed to wave action generated by winds either locally or elsewhere in the Indian Ocean. As mentioned, there is consistent and strong upwelling to varying degrees along the coast, commencing in summer. It results from the southwest monsoon wind which drives surface water from the coast, causing cold water to rise from the depths to replace it. During the monsoon season (April to September), this cool nutrient-rich water favours the growth of phytoplankton and macroalgae in concentrations usually seen in more temperate waters.

The fish fauna of this coast is unusual in having seven different components: cosmopolitan in warm seas (a small group; examples are the sharksucker *Echeneis naucrates*, the filefish *Aluterus scriptus* and the porcupinefish *Diodon hystrix*); Indo-Pacific (a major group of species that are wide-ranging in the tropical and subtropical Indian Ocean and occur at least into the western Pacific; examples are the damselfish *Abudefduf vaigiensis*, the parrotfish *Chlorurus sordidus* and the jacks *Caranx sexfasciatus* and *Gnathanodon speciosus*); Indian Ocean (not known from the Pacific but may be wide-ranging in the Indian Ocean; examples are the scorpionfish *Pterois miles*, the grouper *Epinephelus multinotatus* and the fusilier *Caesio varilineata*); Red Sea and Gulf of Aden (including fishes once believed to be endemic there; some of these species have been recorded from southern Oman only by one or a few specimens or sightings, hence appear to be waifs rather than representatives of resident breeding populations; examples of the latter are the butterflyfishes *Chaetodon larvatus* and *C. austriacus* and the angelfish *Pomacanthus asfur*); Gulf of Oman (examples are the anthias *Pseudanthias marcia*, the hawkfish *Cirrhitichthys calliurus* and the wrasse *Thalassoma loxum*); some of these

3

Arabian Sea-Gulf of Oman fishes, such as the cardinalfish *Cheilodipterus persicus*, range into the Arabian Gulf as well, and some will no doubt be found on the coast of Yemen, Somalia, or Pakistan; southern Africa (the link here may be the cooler sea temperature on the southern Oman coast from upwelling); examples are the bullhead shark *Heterodontus ramalheira*, the porgies *Lithognathus mormyrus* and *Diplodus sargus capensis* (*Diplodus cervinus* also has a disjunct South African-Oman distribution, but it has been shown to be subspecifically different in Oman by Bauchot and Bianchi, 1984), the wrasse *Halichoeres lapillus* (which also occurs in Madagascar and Mauritius) and the blenny *Alloblennius parvus* known from South Africa, the Comoros and southern Oman. These species may eventually be found off Somalia where there is also upwelling. The seventh category is endemic species (examples are the butterflyfish *Chaetodon dialeucos*, the anemonefish *Amphiprion omanensis* and the toadfish *Bifax lacinia*). One could propose a unique eighth component for the grouper *Epinephelus marginatus* and the blenny *Parablennius pilcornis* which occur on both sides of the South Atlantic (including the Mediterranean Sea), South Africa and the south coast of Oman. Also unusual is the disjunct distribution of the croaker *Argyrosomus hololepidotus*: Australia, northwest India to the Gulf of Oman, South Africa and Madagascar and West Africa from Zaire to Namibia.

Fish collecting by the author and diving associates in recent years in Oman seas has yielded four new genera and 52 new species of inshore fishes. Undoubtedly some of these fishes will extend their range westward into Yemen and Somalia or eastward to the coast of Pakistan; on the other hand, it is expected that more undescribed species of fishes will be discovered from Oman waters.

Fahl Island, a popular site for divers from Muscat. The surrounding sea is a proposed marine reserve. (J. Hoover)

A fisherman mending his net at Raysut, Oman.
(Ian McLeish)

Such a long open coastline is not where one would expect a significant level of endemism, especially when compared to an area like the Red Sea which is more subject to isolation. Some of these endemic fishes may be glacial relics, meaning that they were once more widespread in Pleistocene time but are now confined to the Oman coast where there is upwelling. When seas become warmer after upwelling subsides, such species may retreat to the cooler water of greater depth. It is possible that the upwelling itself may have contributed to endemism by acting as a barrier to larval fish dispersal, hence isolating populations. Corals follow a similar pattern. Beach deposits indicate that some corals were more widely distributed during the Pleistocene than they are today (Salm, 1993; Salm et al., 1993).

The high productivity of Oman seas created by the upwelling has its drawbacks. One is the mortality of marine life in shallow seas which may occur from upwelling, particularly when it is followed by a period of calm. Organisms susceptible to the temperature decrease may perish. Phytoplankton blooms may exhaust nutrients; the tiny plants then die, as well as the zooplankton dependent on these plants. The decomposing dead organisms lower the oxygen level, and if wave action is insufficient to replenish it, massive kills, even of large fishes, may result. Another problem is that plankton-rich seas lack clarity which makes them less desirable for snorkeling, scuba diving, and underwater photography.

Although the seas of Oman do not attract the legions of divers and snorkelers one sees in the Red Sea and some islands of the western Indian Ocean, there is still a substantial and growing number of divers, particularly in the Muscat and Salalah areas. Divers and snorkelers are attracted to marine parks where the marine life is fully protected. Without spearfishing, fishes become more approachable, and without commercial fishing, the reef community can revert to its pristine state. Actually, marine preserves result in overall better fishing for the region because fishes within the sanctuaries can grow to full reproductive maturity, and their larvae will seed areas that may be overexploited. Some fishes such as groupers, wrasses, and parrotfishes commence their mature life as females and later change sex to males. Others like certain porgies and anemonefishes are males first and change to females later. It is obvious what will happen to the reproduction of a species when a high percentage of the initial sex form is caught before the sex reversal can take place.

Like many maritime countries, Oman needs such preserves; some sites have been proposed and are under consideration. Among those that should be established are Fahl Island, Daymaniyat Islands (extension of the nature reserve seawards), Bandar Jussah, Bandar Khayran, reefs off Masirah Island and Barr al Hikman, selected bays of the Marbat area, the Juzor al Hallaniyat (Kuria Muria Islands), and some localities in Musandam.

Oman's coast has been thoroughly studied, and detailed maps and proposals have been prepared for coastal management. If these recommendations are implemented, Oman will have a system of protected areas and effective management that will ensure the conservation of the marine life and the fisheries of the Sultanate.

Most of the Oman fishes collected by the author and associates have been deposited at the Bernice P. Bishop Museum, Honolulu (BPBM); a second series is in the California Academy of Sciences, San Francisco (CAS). Type specimens of new species have been distributed to these and other museums, generally the Natural History Museum, London (BMNH) and the U.S. National Museum of Natural History, Washington, D.C. (USNM).

As indicated by the title, this book deals only with the coastal fishes of Oman. By coastal is meant the continental shelf for which the lower depth

Bandar Jussah, a proposed nature reserve.
(Rodney V. Salm)

limit is generally taken as 200 m. Therefore, deep-sea fishes and offshore pelagic fishes such as the more oceanic flyingfishes (Exocoetidae) and the tiny but abundant lanternfishes (Myctophidae) are not treated. The larger pelagic species that may occasionally range inshore and be seen by divers or caught by fishermen are included. Species accounts are also prepared for Oman fishes that are found in brackish water, but not freshwater fishes (for these, see Krupp, 1983).

Species accounts and illustrations are given below for a total of 930 fishes. Some species recorded previously from Oman may represent misidentifications. This is particularly true of those reported in the earlier literature. Species listed by name only in publications of Oman fishes (as in a checklist) that we have not encountered in Oman waters, and for which we know of no specimens or photographs are generally not included in the present volume. Undoubtedly some of these fishes will eventually be confirmed as valid records for the country.

The first author to deal with a major part of the Oman fish fauna was Boulenger (1887) who reported on a collection of 172 species from the vicinity of Muscat made by A.S.G. Jayakar. Most were listed by name only; 14 were described as new, but only four are valid marine species: *Holapogon maximus*, *Pagellus affinis*, *Opistognathus muscatensis* and *Canthidermis macrolepis* (seven are junior synonyms, and two are freshwater species, one of which is reduced to subspecific status). Boulenger (1889) treated a second Jayakar collection, describing six more new species, two of which are junior synonyms and one, *Anthias formosus*, required a new name, *Anthias boulengeri* (Heemstra, 1973), later reclassified as *Sacura boulengeri* by Heemstra and Randall (1979). Boulenger (1892, 1895, 1900, and 1901) published four smaller papers dealing with Oman fishes; *Box lineatus* (now

Boops lineatus) was described in the first of these, and *Rhinoptera jayakari* in the second.

Steindachner (1902) reported on the fishes collected during an expedition to Socotra and the southern Arabian coast off Yemen. At the end of the paper he provided a checklist of fishes divided into two parts, south coast and east coast, the latter being primarily fishes that had been recorded by Boulenger from the Gulf of Oman.

He described five fishes as new, two of which, *Antennablennius simonyi* and *Argyrosomus heinii* range into the Arabian Gulf and one, *Scarus arabicus*, to the Gulf of Oman.

Regan (1905) recorded fishes from the Arabian Gulf, Gulf of Oman and Karachi collected by F.W. Townsend. He described 18 new species of fishes, nine of which are valid species for Oman: *Hyporhamphus sindensis, Holapogon holotaenia, Cirrhitichthys calliurus, Sorsogona nigripinna, Lepidotrigla omanensis, Callionymus muscatensis, C. margaretae, C. persicus* and *Plagiotremus townsendi*. He prepared a list of 57 fishes from the Arabian Gulf and 35 from Muscat not included on Steindachner's list for fishes of the east coast of Arabia. Regan (1908) reported on a large collection of fishes made by J. Stanley Gardiner in the Indian Ocean, mostly from insular localities; Regan included a description of *Champsodon omanensis* from F.W. Townsend material.

Norman (1939) documented the fishes obtained during the John Murray Expedition on the *Valdivia* and *Investigator* in 1933-1934. These specimens were collected from the Red Sea to the Gulf of Oman and in Zanzibar and the Maldive Islands; most are deep-water or offshore pelagic species. Eighty-six of the fishes are listed from the Gulf of Oman or Arabian Sea; only 32 of these are from less than 200 m. Seven new coastal species of

Fishing boats at Khasab. (J. Hoover)

Proposed nature reserve at Bandar Khayran.
(Rodney V. Salm)

Oman fishes are described by Norman in this publication: *Iago omanensis*, *Ichthyapus omanensis*, *Saurida longimanus*, *Chaetodon gardineri*, *C. jayakari*, *Stalix omanensis* and *Arnoglossus arabicus*.

Blegvad (1944) wrote his *Fishes of the Iranian Gulf* which included species from the Iranian side of the Gulf of Oman. Randall et al. (1994) published 51 new records of fishes from the Arabian Gulf. They reviewed the literature on Gulf fishes after Blegvad (1944).

White and Barwani (1971) reported on 199 species of fishes from a survey for the Trucial States in the southeastern Arabian Gulf and the northern Gulf of Oman in their book entitled *Common Sea Fishes of the Arabian Gulf and Gulf of Oman*. The fishes are illustrated mostly by simple line drawings, and the species accounts are brief. Localities are not given, so the reader does not know if a species occurs in one of the gulfs or both.

In 1977 the eight countries bordering the Arabian Gulf and Gulf of Oman commenced a survey of fishery resources with the assistance of the United Nations Development Programme and the Food and Agriculture Organization of the United Nations (FA0). The author, Gerald R. Allen and William F. Smith-Vaniz spent three months participating in this survey in order to prepare a pictorial guide to the commercial fishes. This was published by FAO in 1978; 82 species are figured from black and white photographs and 84 from colour photographs on nine plates. Very brief diagnoses for the species are given in English and Arabic. Unfortunately, distributional data for the species are not included.

Gubanov and Schleib served as editors for *Sharks of the Arabian Gulf* (1980) in which 19 sharks are recorded. Six of these records are doubtful (see introductory remarks on Sharks below).

Fischer and Bianchi (1984) edited fish identification sheets for commercially important fishes of the western Indian Ocean, including those of the Gulf of Oman and Arabian Gulf. Seventy-five ichthyologists, generally those recognised as specialists in the groups of which they are authors, contributed to this publication. Each species sheet has a brief section devoted to geographical distribution. Oman is specifically cited as a locality for some species. Other Oman records are to be inferred from the distributional maps of the western Indian Ocean, one of which is given for each species; the areas of occurrence of the species are crosshatched. Some authors have been very precise in preparing these maps, but others appear to have extended the crosshatching into areas where they would expect the species to be found.

Randall (l986) published a review of 43 sharks known from the waters of the Arabian Peninsula.

In their *Fishes of the Arabian Gulf*, Kuronuma and Abe (1986) compiled a list of 465 species of fishes, of which 224 were represented by specimens available to them; 134 fishes were illustrated in colour, 96 of which were published previously in their *Fishes of Kuwait* (1972). Many of the species names used by Kuronuma and Abe, in the light of revisionary studies and recent collection, are erroneous or are of species not found in the Gulf; this is particularly true of records they have taken from the literature. Most of the valid species in their book range into the Gulf of Oman or at least to Musandam.

Hare (1990) produced *Sampling Manual for Data Collectors aboard Demersal Trawlers* as Special Report No. 1 of the Oman Marine Science and Fisheries Centre. He included a list of 312 fishes by scientific name (plus others for which only generic or family names are given) that are commonly caught in bottom trawls in Oman. Though evidently not intended, some of the fishes on this list represent first records for Oman. However, no diagnostic data or illustrations are presented, nor any listing of specimens to confirm these records. Some appear to be erroneous, such as *Adiorix* (sic) *hastatus* (Cuvier) (= *Sargocentron hastatum*), otherwise known only from West Africa, and *Scarus genazonatus* Randall (= *Chlorurus genazonatus*), believed to be endemic to the Red Sea. The only other parrotfish on Hare's list is *Scarus arabicus* (Steindachner). Since the relatively common *Chlorurus sordidus* (Forsskål) is not included, it seems likely that his *S. genazonatus* represents a misidentification. Hare kindly provided an unpublished booklet containing colour prints of some of the trawl fishes from Oman; these have substantiated a few of the records.

Coastline near Bandar Khayran. (J. Hoover)

Debelius (1993) published a well-illustrated guide to tropical fishes of the Indian Ocean. The distributions given for 116 species include the Arabian Sea. Twenty-five of these are not known from Oman waters. Debelius (pers. comm.) explained that most Arabian Sea records are based on occurrence off Socotra. His recording of the following species from the Arabian Gulf, however, may be in error: *Urogymnus africanus* (Bloch and Schneider), *Gymnothorax javanicus* (Bleeker), *Cirrhitichthys calliurus* Regan and *Pomadasys furcatum* (Bloch and Schneider). He admits his records of *Myripristis xanthacrus* Randall and Guézé from Oman and *Trichonotus setiger* (Bloch and Schneider) from the Arabian Gulf are mistakes. The fish Debelius and other authors have identified as *Pomadasys furcatum* has been described as a new species; neither it nor *furcatum* are known from the Arabian Gulf.

Various Oman fishes have been treated in revisionary studies in recent years. These revisions will be cited in family or species accounts below.

Guide to the Use of this Book

The fishes in this book are presented phylogenetically by family (the names of which end in "idae"); that is, what we believe to be the most primitive

Landing fish at Mutrah. (Ian Bailey)

first and the most highly evolved last. We have followed the sequence, in general, given in the third edition of Nelson's *Fishes of the World* (1994). Within most families in the present book, the genera and species are given in alphabetical order by scientific name; however, a few with very distinct subfamilies are presented alphabetically by subfamily (in order to keep similar species in sequence).

The scientific name (given in italics) of every known animal and plant that has been formally described in the scientific literature consists of two parts, the genus (capitalized; the plural is genera) and the species. The author or authors of a scientific name may be listed after the species name. If an author's name appears in parentheses, this means that he named it in a different genus than the one in current use. The author's name most often encountered as the describer of fishes listed below is Pehr Forsskål who was the naturalist of a six-man Danish expedition to the Red Sea which commenced in 1761. He was one of five who died during the expedition. His manuscript was brought back to Denmark by the survivor, Carsten Niebuhr, and published in 1775. When Forsskål's name appears as the author of a fish name, the reader will know that the type locality (that is, the place where the fish was collected) is the Red Sea.

Our system of scientific nomenclature began in 1758 with the publication of the tenth edition of Carl Linnaeus' *Systema Naturae*. Most of the fishes in the present book were given their scientific names in the 18th or 19th centuries. Some of the common, more wide-ranging species were named more than once. In such cases, the oldest name is the valid one, and subsequent names are termed junior synonyms (or just synonyms). Most of the synonyms have been sorted out years ago, but some older names are still being unearthed which will replace currently accepted names. Synonyms which have been widely used in recent years are listed in the species accounts.

Many fishes such as damselfishes (Pomacentridae), grunts (Haemulidae) and wrasses (Labridae) have juvenile stages which are very different from adults. Understandably, some of the juveniles were given different scientific names from the adults. For some species, it is the juvenile name which is valid.

Also a reason for nomenclatorial confusion is the strikingly different colour of females and males of many wrasses (Labridae) and parrotfishes (Scaridae). The first adult form of these fishes, termed the initial phase, is usually relatively drab. For some species this form is only female. Later in life, females may change their sex to males and take on a very different colour pattern, often brightly and even gaudily coloured; these are called terminal males. The initial phase of other wrasses and parrotfishes may be either female or male, in which case the like-coloured male is termed a primary male. Terminal males of these fishes can result from either a colour change by primary males or by sex reversal and colour change of females. The different colour phases of most of these fishes were given different scientific names by early naturalists.

Fishes are divisible into two major groups that have evolved separately since mid-Devonian time (about 350,000,000 years ago), the cartilaginous fishes (Class Chondrichthyes) and the bony fishes (Class Osteichthyes). The cartilaginous fishes, which include the sharks and rays, will be treated first in this book. Each of these classes is divisible to subclasses; then to orders, suborders, and families. The family is the most convenient, best known, and stable grouping above the genus for the classification of fishes, and this will be the heading used herein within the two classes. A separate account is given for each family of fishes. This includes a listing of the characteristics (characters) held in common by all species of the family and what is known, in summarised form, of their natural history. Characteristics or habits found in all of the species of a family are generally not repeated in species accounts, so it is important for the reader to refer to the family discussions.

The distinctive shape and colour pattern of most fishes will enable one to identify the majority of them from good colour photographs. When available, we have used photographs of fishes from Oman or other countries bordering the Arabian Peninsula. When we have no publishable photograph of a fish from an Arabian locality, we have substituted one of the same species from another area when we believe it shows the same colour as in Oman. The localities of such extralimital photographs are listed at the back of this book.

Priority has been given to illustrations in this book to underwater photographs, the great majority of which were taken by the author and John P. Hoover. We used manually-operated 35-mm cameras in Ikelite housings. Many photographs were taken of fishes after we collected them or obtained them from fish markets; the photographic method was devised by the author (Randall, 1961b). Some less colourful fishes were photographed only in black and white. We used a few figures from scientific papers for fishes when we could not obtain photographs.

Some species of fishes require additional information such as the number of fin rays or scales or certain body and fin proportions to provide for their identification. Several such morphological characters may be needed to separate closely related species or to link a juvenile stage to an adult. We term the minimum amount of such information for positive identification as the diagnosis. The first part of each species account below is the diagnosis. Also included in these accounts, when known, are remarks on the habitat, distribution, size attained, what may be known of their habits, and other

Children of Omani fishermen reading *Wildlife of Oman* on a beach near Muscat. (Mark N. Boulton)

Fisherman ready to cast his throw net at Rakhyut. (Ian Bailey)

Qurm Nature Reserve of mangroves, near Muscat, from the air. (Rodney V. Salm)

information of special importance such as whether a fish has venomous spines. In order to cover 930 species in a single volume, the species accounts must be brief. Characteristics that apply to all species of a family are listed in the family accounts; these are generally not repeated for each species. Also, the first species account of a genus may include characters that apply to other species of the genus and may not be repeated. Literature references will be given in most family and many species discussions for readers wishing more detailed information.

The geographical distribution of each of the fishes is given in general terms. If a species occurs broadly throughout the Indian Ocean and ranges into the central Pacific, it is said to have an Indo-Pacific distribution. A western Pacific distribution is generally from Queensland or New South Wales north through the Indo-Malayan region to southern Japan. The Indo-Malayan region includes Indonesia, Borneo, New Guinea, Philippines and the southern part of southeast Asia. Western Indian Ocean refers to the broad tropical and subtropical area west of the southern tip of India. When a distribution such as the Arabian Gulf and Red Sea to South Africa is given, this implies that it is continental and includes the Gulf of Oman, southern coast of the Arabian Peninsula and the east coast of Africa.

The total length (TL) believed to be attained by each fish is given in centimeters (cm), except for the Whale Shark when meters (m) is used. Reliable size records are maintained for gamefishes and many of the commercial fishes, but information on the maximum size of other fishes is often lacking; therefore the length given for most of the fishes herein is an approximation.

In order to understand the terminology used in family and species accounts, it is necessary to learn the names of the different parts of fishes

and other words used in the study of fishes (Ichthyology). The following two-page plate will be helpful in this regard, and the glossary at the back of this book will provide definitions of scientific terms.

Most bony fishes have both spines and soft rays in their dorsal and anal fins. Spines are not branched, not finely segmented, generally not flexible, and usually sharp, whereas soft rays are segmented, flexible, and often branched. To differentiate these two kinds of fin rays, the count of the spines is given in Roman numerals and that of soft rays in Arabic. Thus a dorsal fin ray count of X,12 would indicate ten spines and twelve soft rays. When there are two dorsal fins, the two counts are separated by + (hence X+I,12); if broadly separated, X + I,12.

The scale count most often made on bony fishes is the number of pored scales in the lateral line from the upper end of the gill opening to the base of the caudal fin (tail), but not including those that may extend onto the base of the caudal fin. The lateral-line pores connect to a canal beneath the scales which bears sensory cells that detect low frequency vibrations such as those produced by the movement of other fishes. When the lateral line is not externally visible by pores in scales, the longitudinal series of scales on the body between the gill opening and caudal-fin base is often recorded.

A count of gill rakers on the first gill arch is sometimes helpful to separate closely related species of fishes. Gill rakers are protuberances along the inner edge of the gill arch (opposite the bright red gill filaments where respiratory exchange takes place). Usually the count is divided into two figures, the rakers of the upper part of the gill arch, this number given first, and those of the lower; the raker at the angle of the arch is included in the lower-limb count.

The shape of the trailing edge of the caudal fin is often useful in differentiating species of fishes. It may be forked, emarginate (inwardly concave), lunate (very deeply concave), truncate (the edge vertical), or rounded (outwardly convex). Occasionally, one may encounter a double emarginate caudal fin (two concavities separated by a slight middle convexity), and rarely, a pointed caudal fin (mostly on gobies).

Certain body and fin proportions may be used to characterise a fish. These are presented as percentages of a larger measurement, such as the standard length, often abbreviated as SL (the straight-line length from the tip of the snout to the base of the caudal fin), or more often as the number of times the smaller of two measurements is contained in a larger one. A common example is the depth of the body (maximum depth not counting the fins) in the standard length. A depth of 6 in the SL would indicate an elongate fish, whereas a depth of 1.5 would be a very high-bodied one. These proportions are usually given as a range to express the variation within a species. Much of this variation is due to changes in proportions that take place with growth. For example, the eye of a juvenile fish is always relatively larger than that of the adult of the same species.

In describing bands of colour on a fish, a stripe refers to a longitudinal (horizontal) band and a bar a vertical one. When irregular or oblique, it is called a band.

External Features of Fishes

Cartilaginous Fishes (Sharks and Rays)

The two illustrations below and the five on the facing page are labelled to show the principal external parts of fishes.

Whitecheek Shark
(*Carcharhinus dussumieri*)

Second dorsal fin

Upper lobe of caudal fin

First dorsal fin

Pectoral fin

Clasper

Anal fin

Pelvic Fin

Gill slits

Reef Stingray
(*Taenura lymma*)

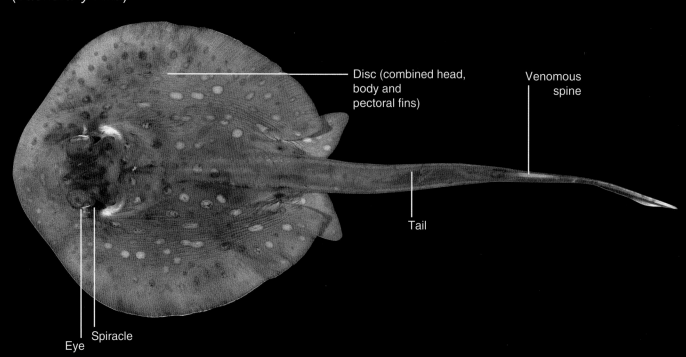

Disc (combined head, body and pectoral fins)

Venomous spine

Tail

Spiracle

Eye

Bony Fishes

Coral Hind
(*Cephalophalis miniata*)

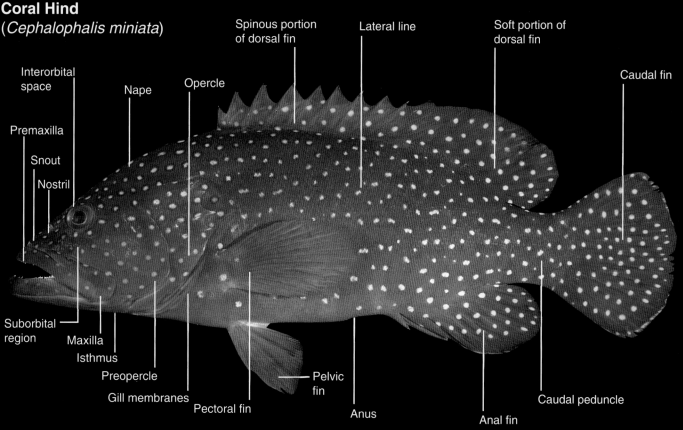

Labels (clockwise): Interorbital space, Nape, Opercle, Spinous portion of dorsal fin, Lateral line, Soft portion of dorsal fin, Caudal fin, Premaxilla, Snout, Nostril, Suborbital region, Maxilla, Isthmus, Preopercle, Gill membranes, Pectoral fin, Anus, Pelvic fin, Anal fin, Caudal peduncle

A

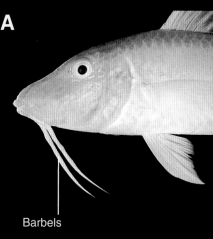

Barbels

The picture labelled **A** is the head of a goatfish (Mullidae) and shows the pair of barbels on the chin. These are moved over the bottom or thrust into the sediment during feeding to assist the fish in finding its food.

B

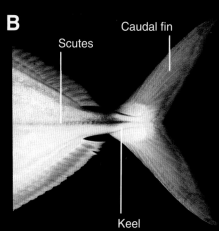

Scutes, Caudal fin, Keel

B shows the tail of a trevally (Carangidae) which has a falcate caudal fin; this shape is often found on fishes capable of swimming very rapidly. Because of the stress placed on the narrow caudal peduncle, fishes such as jacks and tunas usually reinforce it with scutes and/or keels.

C

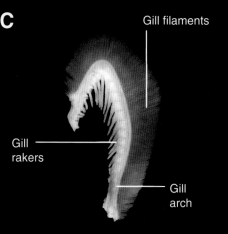

Gill filaments, Gill rakers, Gill arch

C depicts one of the gills (respiratory organs of fishes). The gill arch is the structural part. Gaseous exchange takes place in the gill filaments and the gill rakers keep food items from passing out of the gill opening along with expired water.

D

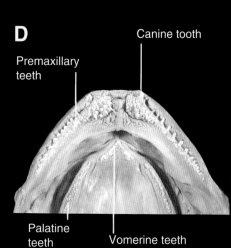

Canine tooth, Premaxillary teeth, Palatine teeth, Vomerine teeth

D is the roof of the mouth of a percomorph fish and shows the typical dentition of the premaxilla, vomer and palatine bones.

Scalloped Hammerhead, *Sphyrna lewini* (J. Randall)

School of Oman Cownose Rays, *Rhinoptera jayakari* (J. Hoover)

SHARKS AND RAYS
CHONDRICHTHYES

SHARKS

Only about 350 species of living sharks are known in the world (Compagno, 1984), compared to 21,000 estimated for bony fishes (Cohen, 1970). In spite of the paucity of species, sharks play a major role in the seas of the world. Many of the large species are the top predators of the various food chains and serve to keep Nature in balance, preying as they do on fishes, squids and octopus, the larger crustacea, sea turtles, marine mammals and sea birds. Others feed mainly on benthic invertebrates. Exceptional are the huge Basking Shark (*Cetorhinus maximus*) which feeds on zooplankton and the Whale Shark (*Rhincodon typus*) that eats zooplankton, nekton, and occasionally schooling fishes.

Some species of sharks are commercially important as food, particularly in recent years as the stocks of many of the commercially important bony fishes have dwindled from overfishing.

The fins of some sharks are valued for the preparation of soup in the Orient. This is unfortunate because it has resulted in a special effort to catch these sharks. Because sharks have relatively few young and most grow slowly, their populations can be quickly depleted by overfishing.

An enormous amount of literature, particularly the popular literature, is devoted to sharks, not to mention television and motion pictures. The one aspect of sharks that is understandably the most compelling is attack on man. Relatively few species of sharks have been shown to attack humans. The ones most responsible for injury or death are the White Shark (*Carcharodon carcharias*), Tiger Shark (*Galeocerdo cuvier*) and the Bull Shark (*Carcharhinus leucus*). As many authors have pointed out,

shark attack as a cause of serious injury or death is negligible compared to other kinds of accidents, in particular automobile accidents. Even lightning causes more deaths than sharks. When one considers the millions of people who bathe or dive in the sea every year, the chance of any one of them being bitten by a shark is extremely small. Nevertheless, there is a very special kind of horror if one contemplates being eaten alive by a shark, and this is what fuels the media when shark incidents are reported.

There is enormous variation in the size of sharks. Some such as several species of *Etmopterus* do not exceed 30 cm total length. In sharp contrast is the gargantuan but harmless Whale Shark which may be as long as 16 m.

Sharks differ in many ways from bony fishes. Their skeleton is cartilage, not bone. The jaws of sharks may seem as hard as bone, but it is only calcified cartilage. There are 5 to 7 gill openings on each side of the head of sharks, compared to a single one for bony fishes. Sharks have a spiracle, which is a rudimentary gill opening found behind or below the eye. In bottom-dwelling sharks and rays, it is functional as the incurrent opening for respiratory water. The skin of shark is rough to the touch, due to the presence of numerous, small, so-called dermal denticles which are close-set but not overlapping like the scales of most bony fishes. The mouth of most sharks is ventral on the head, thus the snout is overhanging. The teeth are modified, enlarged dermal denticles with a pulp cavity, dentine and a thin layer of hard, enamel-like vitrodentine. The teeth vary greatly in structure among the different species of sharks. Some teeth are sharp and blade-like, with or without serrae

(serrations); others long and raptorial; and still others molariform for crushing molluscs and other hard-shelled invertebrates. When teeth are broken or worn, they are replaced from intact rows behind. Sharks lack a swimbladder (also known as gas bladder), the hydrostatic organ of bony fishes. To partially offset the greater density of their bodies than seawater, sharks have a very large liver containing much oil. Also they swim with pectoral fins outstretched and angled to give them lift. All sharks have internal fertilization; the intromittent organ of the male is the pair of claspers, one developing along the medial edge of each pelvic fin (thus the sex of sharks is easily determined externally). Some sharks are oviparous; they lay eggs in leathery cases. Most sharks are ovoviviparous; the eggs develop within the uterus. The requiem sharks (Carcharhinidae, except the Tiger Shark) and hammerheads (Sphrynidae) are viviparous; the embryos are nourished by a placenta-like organ of the female. Most sharks have very few young, often only one or two (the Blue Shark and the Tiger Shark are exceptional in giving birth to as many as 80 and 135 pups, respectively, at one time). The intestine of sharks is very different from that of other vertebrates. It contains the spiral valve, much like an enclosed spiral staircase; indigestible items like squid beaks cannot easily pass through the intestine; from time to time a shark will regurgitate such items from its stomach.

Sharks have exceptional sensory systems. Well known is their keen olfaction which can detect attracting substances such as blood in minute quantities. Most sharks feed mainly at dusk or night (but may feed opportunistically during daylight hours); therefore their eyes are adapted to low levels of illumination. They have a tapetum lucidum behind the retina which reflects light (like a cat's eye at night); light passes through the light-receptor cells of the retina and is reflected back, thus doubling the stimulus. The highly developed lateralis system of sharks, a complex set of canals on the head and one along the side of the body with pores connecting to the surface, enables them to detect low frequency vibrations at considerable distances, thus they are aware of the movements of prey or predators that they may not see. The pit organs in the snout, termed ampullae of Lorenzini, have been shown to act as electroreceptors. A shark is therefore able to detect the weak electromagnetic field around a sleeping fish at night.

As mentioned above, Gubanov and Schleib (1980) recorded 19 species of sharks from the Arabian Gulf. No specimens are cited of any of these sharks, and no photographs are provided to document the records. Among the species recorded are the Common Thresher (*Alopias vulpinus*), the Grey Bamboo Shark (*Chiloscyllium griseum*), the Grey Reef Shark (as *Carcharias menisorrah*), the Silvertip Shark (*Carcharhinus albimarginatus*), the "Yellow Dog Shark" (*Scoliodon laticaudus*) and the "Common Hammerhead" (*Sphyrna zygaena*). All of these sharks were recorded for the first time from the Arabian Gulf by Gubanov and Schleib except *C. griseum* and *S. zygaena*. Blegvad (1944) and Kuronuma and Abe (1972, 1986) reported *C. griseum* from the Gulf, but their specimens were later shown to be *C. arabicum*. *Sphyrna zygaena* was recorded previously by White and Barwani (1971); however, they listed *Zygaena blochi* Blegvad (1944) and *S. zygaena* Smith (1949) in the synonymy of *S. zygaena*, and their illustration, which appears to be a copy of Smith's Fig. 21, does not resemble *zygaena*. This shark is more temperate in its distribution, and records in the tropics are spotty due probably to confusion with the more abundant and more tropical *S. lewini* (Compagno, 1984). Knowledge of the distribution and ecology of these six sharks makes the Gulf records by Gubanov and Schleib highly questionable. It is concluded that these shark records should not be recognised unless confirmed later by specimens or photographs.

BULLHEAD SHARKS
FAMILY HETERODONTIDAE

This family, also known by the common name horn sharks, contains a single very distinctive genus, *Heterodontus*, with nine species. It is classified in a separate order, the Heterodontiformes. The fossil record for the genus goes back to the Jurassic. These sharks are the only ones with both an anal fin and a stout spine at the front of each dorsal fin. Other characteristics: a prominent ridge above eye; snout short and blunt; five progressively shorter gill slits, the last three or four over base of pectoral fin; spiracle small, ventroposterior to eye; mouth small; teeth small, multiserial and close-set, those at front of jaws with one to several cusps, those at back elongate and molariform for crushing their usual prey of sea urchins, molluscs and crustaceans. Most species occur in shallow water; maximum depth recorded, 275 m. Bullhead sharks are nocturnal, slow-swimming and strongly bottom-oriented. Development is oviparous; the eggs are large and conical with a spiral flange; they may take as long as five months to hatch. These sharks are harmless unless provoked, at which time they have been known to bite their tormentors.

WHITESPOTTED BULLHEAD SHARK
Heterodontus ramalheira (Smith, 1949)

Supraorbital ridge moderately elevated; first dorsal fin nearly twice as large as second, its origin over middle of pectoral-fin base; spine at front of dorsal fins about half height of these fins; anal fin moderately pointed, its apex nearly reaching origin of ventral lobe of caudal fin; precaudal vertebrae 69-72; dark reddish brown with numerous small white spots, shading to pale yellowish ventrally. Largest female, 83 cm total length (TL); largest male 64 cm. A rare species known from only five specimens (four taken by trawl in 110-275 m) from southern Mozambique (type locality, Inhambane) and one from off southeastern Oman. Two of the Mozambique specimens had crabs in their stomach. Bass et al., (1975c: pl. 7) illustrated the dentition.

1. *Heterodontus ramalheira*, 64 cm (after Bass et al., 1975b)

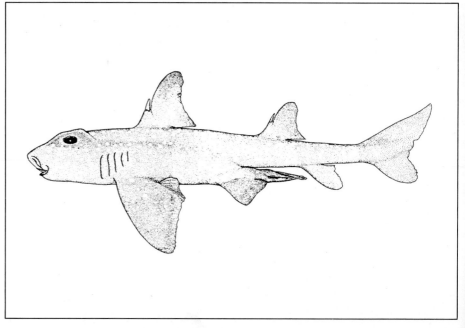

OMAN BULLHEAD SHARK
Heterodontus sp.

Supraorbital ridge moderately elevated, extending an orbit diameter anterior and posterior to eye; dorsal spines about half height of these fins; first dorsal fin slightly larger than second, its origin over middle of pectoral-fin base; apex of anal fin nearly reaching origin of lower lobe of caudal fin; teeth anteriorly in jaws with a large pointed central cusp and a small nodular cusplet on each side (better developed on lower-jaw teeth); light brown with a broad dark brown band across interorbital and broadening into a large spot below eye; a large saddle-like dark brown spot on nape; a large diffuse dark brown spot behind each dorsal fin; a dark brown spot near apex of each dorsal fin. A mature male in the Bishop Museum collection measures 52 cm in total length. Known only from trawl catches off southern Oman.

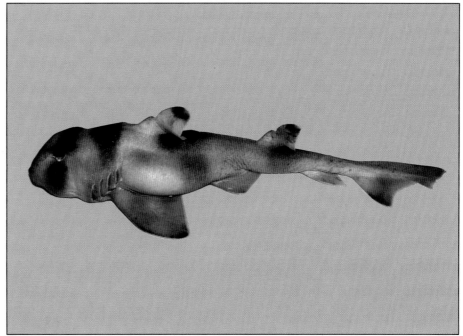

2. *Heterodontus* sp. (J. Mee)

NURSE SHARKS
FAMILY
GINGLYMOSTOMATIDAE

This family consists of only three species, two in the genus *Ginglymostoma* and one in the genus *Nebrius*. They are classified in the order Orectolobiformes, along with the carpet sharks, Zebra Shark, bamboo sharks, and the Whale Shark. They are characterised as follows: body cylindrical to slightly depressed, without ridges; head broad and depressed, without cutaneous flaps; snout short and broadly rounded; five gill slits, the fourth and fifth close together and above the pectoral-fin base; eyes small; spiracles small, each behind lower part of eye; nostrils with a barbel; mouth moderate in size; teeth in two to four functional rows, small, with a large central and small lateral cusps; two close-set dorsal fins posteriorly on body; anal fin as large or nearly as large as second dorsal fin; no precaudal pits; caudal fin with a long upper lobe, one fourth to one-third total length, and without a well-developed lower lobe. Nurse sharks are found in shallow tropical and subtropical seas; they are ovoviviparous, bottom-dwelling and nocturnal.

TAWNY NURSE SHARK
Nebrius ferrugineus (Lesson, 1830)

Characteristics of the family (see above); teeth in numerous rows, the first three or four functional; teeth with a large central cusp and four to six small cusps on each side; distal ends of dorsal and anal fins distinctly angular; second dorsal fin slightly smaller than first; origin of first dorsal fin slightly anterior to origin of pelvic fins; anal-fin origin below middle of base of second dorsal fin; caudal fin about 30% total length; pectoral fins slightly falcate; greyish to yellowish brown, paler ventrally. Attains at least 3.2 m. Wide-ranging in the Indo-Pacific region from the Red Sea and coast of East Africa to the Marshall Islands in the Northern Hemisphere and the Society Islands in the Southern; occurs at depths from less than one to at least 70 m. Feeds at night on a wide variety of benthic animals such as reef fishes, spiny lobsters, crabs and octopuses. It is reported to suck in prey with its large powerful pharynx that may be out of reach of its teeth. Shelters in caves or beneath ledges by day. Although contact by humans is usually without incident, there are a few records of bites on divers when the sharks are provoked, as by grabbing their tail. As many as four egg cases develop within the uterus at any one time; pups about 40 cm long at birth. *Nebrius concolor* Rüppell is a synonym.

3. *Nebrius ferrugineus*, about 3 m (J. Hoover)

ZEBRA SHARK
FAMILY STEGOSTOMATIDAE

For diagnosis and remarks, see account of the single species of the family below.

ZEBRA SHARK
Stegostoma varium (Seba, 1758)

Body cylindrical with a prominent median dorsal and two longitudinal ridges on each side (lower ridge lacking in juveniles); head broad and slightly depressed, without cutaneous flaps; snout short and broadly rounded; five gill slits, the last three above pectoral-fin base, the fourth and fifth very close together; eyes small; spiracles as large or larger than eye, each directly behind eye; nostrils with a short barbel; mouth moderate; teeth in several close-set functional rows, tricuspid with the cusps strongly pointed, the central one much the largest; first dorsal fin in about middle of body, its origin grading into middorsal ridge; second dorsal fin about half as large as first; anal-fin origin below rear base of second dorsal fin; caudal fin about half total length, without a lower lobe; greyish yellow with dark brown spots of variable size, few or none before eye; young whitish with black bars (hence the name Zebra Shark) which break into spots with growth. Reaches at least 2.8 m (one unconfirmed report of 3.5 m). Ranges from the Red Sea to South Africa at 34°S and east to the Samoa Islands; in the western Pacific from southern Japan to New South Wales. Despite its broad distribution, this shark is not common anywhere; occurs from the shallows to at least 30 m, often within or near coral reefs. During the day, usually at rest on the bottom; feeds at night mainly on molluscs and crustaceans, occasionally on fishes. Oviparous, the egg cases about 20 cm long, with tufts of adhesive filaments on either side for attachment to the substratum (Masuda et al., 1975: fig. 5 C); young hatch at a length of 20-30 cm (van der Elst, 1981). Some authors such as Compagno (1984) and Last and Stevens (1994) have used the name *Stegostoma fasciatum* (Hermann) for this shark in the belief that Seba's name *varium* is invalid due to many of his names being nonbinomial; however this one (as *Squalus varius*) is binomial, and Klausewitz (1960) described and illustrated the 105-cm lectotype of *S. varium*.

4. Egg of *Stegostoma varium* (R. Salm)

5. Juvenile of *Stegostoma varium*, 58 cm (J. Randall)

6. *Stegostoma varium*, 200 cm, with remoras (R. Salm)

WHALE SHARK
FAMILY RHINCODONTIDAE

For the diagnosis and remarks of the single species of the family, see the following species account.

WHALE SHARK
Rhincodon typus Smith, 1829

Body ovate in cross-section, the head strongly flattened with a truncate snout; a median dorsal and three prominent longitudinal ridges on each side, commencing above gill slits, the lowermost ending in a well-developed keel on side of caudal peduncle; mouth very large, nearly terminal; teeth minute, in over 300 rows, of which 10 to 15 are functional; five gill slits high on side, their internal openings with branchial filters; eyes small; spiracles about as large as eye; a barbel overlapping upper lip on each side; first dorsal fin much larger than second; pelvic fins below posterior half of first dorsal fin; anal fin below second dorsal fin; caudal fin with a strongly elevated upper lobe, without a subterminal notch; lower caudal lobe about half length of upper; pectoral fins long and falcate; ground colour on back varying from dark bluish grey to brown, with vertical whitish lines and rows of whitish spots, shading to whitish ventrally. The largest living fish in the world; reaches at least 16 m (unauthenticated reports to 18 m). Surface-dwelling, pelagic, in all warm seas; feeds mainly on zooplankton and nekton, sometimes on fishes and squids; takes advantage of schools of tunas which concentrate small fishes or larval fishes at the surface by rising vertically under the schools to feed, sometimes ingesting tuna as well. Believed to be ovoviviparous. Harmless to man; divers often hitch rides by holding onto the first dorsal fin.

7. *Rhincodon typus* (R. Bedford)

8. *Rhincodon typus* (T. Kimura)

BAMBOO SHARKS
FAMILY HEMISCYLLIIDAE

This family of small, slender, bottom-dwelling sharks consists of two genera, *Hemiscyllium* with five species, and *Chiloscyllium* with seven (Dingerkus and DeFino, 1983). They have cylindrical to slightly depressed bodies, sometimes with a longitudinal ridge on upper side; snout slightly pointed to broadly rounded; eyes dorsolateral on head with a slight supraorbital crest; five gill slits, the posterior three above pectoral-fin base, the last two very close together; spiracle large, ventro-posterior to eye; a conspicuous barbel medial to nasal opening; mouth small, near front of snout; teeth small, with a single cusp (*Hemiscyllium*) or with a large central cusp and a small cusp on each side (*Chiloscyllium*); two dorsal fins of nearly equal size, the origin of first near centre of body; anal fin very posterior, ending at lower origin of caudal fin; caudal fin less than one-fourth total length; no precaudal pits. Bamboo sharks are known from the western Pacific to the Arabian Gulf except for one species known only from Madagascar. They are oviparous.

ARABIAN BAMBOO SHARK
Chiloscyllium arabicum Gubanov, 1980

Orbit diameter 1.4-1.8% total length; spiracle of large adults larger than eye; teeth in jaws in 9 or 10 anterior-posterior rows, with about three or four functional; first dorsal fin slightly larger than second, but base of second dorsal fin longer than first (rarely equal to first); posterior edge of dorsal fins straight; pelvic fins slightly smaller than first dorsal fin; a prominent middorsal ridge on back anterior to second dorsal fin; caudal-fin length (measured from tip to rear base of anal fin) 17-21% total length; vertebrae 143-171; tan, becoming whitish ventrally; edges of fins (especially paired fins) sometimes orangish; juveniles coloured like adults. Largest recorded, 78 cm. Arabian Gulf to southern tip of India. A shallow-water species, generally found in about 2 to 10 m. The author opened the stomachs of 34 specimens, 462-770 mm TL, taken by trawl in Kuwait waters. Eleven were empty; food material of the others by percent of volume: fishes, 26.5; stomatopods (*Oratosquilla interrupta*), 25.8; squids, 11.0; echiuroids, 10.9; shrimps (*Metapenaeus affinis*), 7.1; crabs (*Portunus hastatoides*), 5.0; unidentified crustaceans, 4.3; unidentified animal material, 2.8. *C. confusum* Dingerkus and DeFino is a synonym. This shark was identified in early publications from the Arabian Gulf as *C. griseum* Müller and Henle by Blegvad, 1944; White and Barwani, 1971; and Kuronuma and Abe, 1972. The true *C. griseum* may not be present in the Arabian Gulf or Gulf of Oman.

SAND TIGER SHARKS
FAMILY ODONTASPIDIDAE

This family of two genera and four species is characterised as follows: body moderately stout, cylindrical to slightly compressed; head small; snout pointed, conical to somewhat depressed; spiracles small; teeth very distinctive; those anteriorly in jaws long, prong-like, smooth-edged, with one to three sharp cusplets on each side; teeth posteriorly in jaws progressively smaller, those at end of jaws tiny; gill slits large, but confined to lower half of head, all anterior to pectoral-fin base; first dorsal fin moderately large; second dorsal fin varying from nearly as large as first dorsal to about half as large; caudal fin with a long upper lobe (up to 30% total length), little elevated, with a subterminal notch and a small lower lobe; an upper but no lower precaudal pit. Sand tiger sharks are found in temperate to tropic seas; two of the species are very wide-ranging. All are ovoviviparous; uterine cannibalism is normal; typically only one pup per uterus survives.

9. *Chiloscyllium arabicum* (J. Randall)

10. Anterior end of *Chiloscyllium arabicum* (J. Randall)

SAND TIGER SHARK
Carcharias taurus Rafinesque, 1810

Snout pointed but relatively short, the preoral length about 5% total length; eyes small, about 1% total length; teeth with a single cusplet on each side, 28-38 in outer row on side of upper jaw and 26-37 in lower jaw; second dorsal fin nearly as large as first; anal and pelvic fins also nearly as large; upper lobe of caudal fin about 27% total length, the lower lobe about 11%; brown with scattered dark spots on body and caudal fin (may disappear with age). Reported to 320 cm. Widely distributed in continental waters of the Atlantic and Indo-Pacific, mainly in subtropical to temperate seas. Gubanov and Schleib (1980) wrote of this shark, "Sometimes met in the Kuwait waters, mostly in spring and summer." This record might be questioned, as have those of six other sharks by these authors, in view of the known distribution of the species; however, Leonard J.V. Compagno (pers. comm.) has examined a specimen from Karachi, Pakistan which makes the Gubanov-Schleib record more plausible. The Sand Tiger Shark feeds mainly on fishes, but it also ingests squids and crustaceans. In Australia where it is called the Grey Nurse Shark, it has an undeserved reputation as a maneater. In spite of its awesome appearance with long protruding teeth, it is relatively harmless unless provoked or attracted to a spearfisherman's catch. Unlike other sharks which sink when not swimming, the sand tiger can remain motionless in the water column. It swallows air from the surface into its stomach to give it buoyancy. This species has been classified by some authors in the genera *Odontaspis* and *Eugomphodus*. *Carcharias* was revalidated by Opinion 1459 of the International Commission on Zoological Nomenclature (1987).

11. *Carcharias taurus* (R. and V. Taylor)

12. *Alopias pelagicus*, 99 cm (J. Randall)

THRESHER SHARKS
FAMILY ALOPIIDAE

There are three species of thresher sharks, all in the genus *Alopias* for which the most obvious character is the extremely long caudal fin; the upper lobe is as long or nearly as long as the body. Other distinguishing features are the cylindrical body, short head but moderately long conical snout; moderate to large eyes; small spiracles; teeth triangular, notched on one side, with sharp edges; five short gill slits not extending onto upper half of head, the last two above pectoral-fin base; first dorsal fin in middle of body; second dorsal and anal fins extremely small; pectoral fins long and narrow; pre-caudal pits present. Thresher sharks are pelagic, but occasionally encountered in coastal waters; two are circumglobal. The Bigeye Thresher (*A. superciliosus*) ranges into deeper water (to at least 500 m). Thresher sharks feed mainly on small fishes; they are known to circle and concentrate their prey with the aid of their long caudal fins; also they are reported to stun fishes by lashing with their tail. Ovoviviparous and cannibalistic. The meat of threshers is of high quality.

PELAGIC THRESHER
Alopias pelagicus Nakamura, 1935

Head narrow, its width at first gill opening about 1.6 in head depth; interorbital space strongly convex; snout moderately long and conical; eyes lateral, moderate in size, 1.3-1.9% total length; teeth small, 21-23 on each side of upper jaw and 21 on each side of lower jaw; main cusp of teeth laterally oblique; most teeth with one or two small basal cusps on posterolateral edge; origin of first dorsal fin near centre of precaudal length, its height 5.6% total length; upper lobe of caudal fin about as long as precaudal length with a tiny terminal lobe; vertebrae of one specimen 472, of which 126 are precaudal (highest count for any shark); grey, shading to white ventrally. Attains at least 330 cm. Indo-Pacific in tropical to warm temperate seas; primarily a surface-dwelling pelagic shark, but has been taken as deep as 152 m; occasionally ventures near shore. Often misidentified as *A. vulpinus* which differs in having a broader head and shorter snout; it ranges more into temperate waters than *A. pelagicus*.

MACKEREL SHARKS
FAMILY LAMNIDAE

There are five species of lamnid sharks, the sinister White Shark (*Carcharodon carcharias*), two makos (*Isurus*), the Salmon Shark (*Lamna ditropis*), and the Porbeagle (*L. nasus*). The latter two occur in temperate seas, and the White Shark is primarily temperate in its distribution (not yet definitely known from Oman, but there are unconfirmed reports of its occurrence; it might be expected where upwelling produces cool sea temperature). These sharks share the following characters: body spindle-shaped, with a pointed snout and a narrow caudal peduncle bearing a well-developed lateral keel; mouth large; teeth large, but variable in shape; five large gill slits which extend above the midlateral line, the fifth at leading edge of pectoral fins; first dorsal fin moderately large and erect, its origin slightly anterior to middle of precaudal length; second dorsal and anal fins very small; caudal fin lunate, the upper lobe only slightly larger than lower; precaudal pits present. These swift pelagic sharks swim in tuna-like fashion by lateral strokes of the tail, rather than sinuous movement of the entire body as is typical of other sharks. They are partially warm-blooded; that is, they have a heat-exchanging circulatory system that enables them to maintain a body temperature higher than the sea in which they are swimming. Development is ovoviviparous and oviphagus (embryos feed on ova continuously produced by the female). The meat of lamnids is of high quality for food.

SHORTFIN MAKO
Isurus oxyrinchus Rafinesque, 1810

Body slender, the depth about 15% total length; snout moderately long and distinctly pointed, its length about 6.5% total length; 12 or 13 teeth on each side of jaws; anterior teeth long and slender with sharp nonserrate edges; posterior teeth progressively smaller and more triangular; pectoral fins shorter than head length (measured to last gill slit); vertebrae 183-194, of which 107-112 are precaudal; dark blue on back (fading to grey after death), white below. Reported to 394 cm. Among the most broadly distributed of all marine animals; occurs circum-globally in tropical to temperate seas (with sea temperature as low as about 16°C). Probably the fastest of all sharks; a popular gamefish famous for its spectacular leaps when hooked (all-tackle world angling record, 506 kg). Feeds mainly on small fishes and squids as its slender raptorial teeth would suggest, but large adults have been reported to feed on larger prey such as swordfish and porpoises. There are a few reports of attack on humans and boats. The Longfin Mako (*I. paulus*) was not described until 1966; it is more tropical in its distribution but it may eventually be recorded from Oman; its pectoral fins are as long or longer than its head, and its snout shorter.

13. Head of *I. oxyrinchus*, 2.3 m (J. Randall)

14. *Isurus oxyrinchus*, 2.3 m (J. Randall)

HOUNDSHARKS
FAMILY TRIAKIDAE

This family of the Carcharhini-formes consists of 9 genera and 44 species (as recognised by Compagno, 1988). They are slender with a depressed head and moderately long snout; the eyes are horizontally elongate, the eye length 1.5 to 2.5 times eye height; suprorbital crest present; spiracles small to moderately large; teeth varying from cuspidate (though not clearly blade-like) to molariform; dorsal fins broadly separated, the midbase of the first dorsal anterior to pelvic fins; outer posterior margins of dorsal and anal fins concave; ventral lobe of caudal fin small, the dorsal lobe with little elevation; no precaudal pits. These sharks are small to moderately large (largest, 170 cm); they occur in tropical to temperate seas, from inshore to depths of at least 2,000 m. Most live on or near the bottom. Development is either ovoviviparous or viviparous. Some species such as the temperate Soupfin Shark (*Galeorhinus galeus*) are commercially important.

BIGEYE HOUNDSHARK
Iago omanensis (Norman, 1939)

Body deepest at origin of first dorsal fin; dorsal profile of head posterior to interorbital space steep; snout broad and obtusely pointed; eyes large, about twice as long as high; five short gill slits, not extending onto upper half of head, the last two over pectoral-fin base; mouth subtriangular; teeth small, in numerous rows (two or three of which are functional), 23-28 on each side of upper jaw and 18-23 of lower; teeth at front of jaws with a low oblique cusp, deeply notched posterolaterally; first dorsal fin large, its origin anterior to axil of pectoral fin; caudal fin 20-22% total length; vertebrae 129-147; brown to grey, paler ventrally. Largest male 36.5 cm, largest female 58.2 cm. Known from the Red Sea and Gulf of Oman to southwest India in the depth range of 100 to at least 1000 m. Feeds on fishes (especially lanternfishes), squids, crustaceans, pelecypods and gastropods.

Viviparous, the litter size varying from two to ten.

ARABIAN HOUNDSHARK
Mustelus mosis Hemprich and Ehrenberg, 1899.

Body slender, the depth about 10% total length; head short, 17-22% total length; preoral snout length 5.5-5.6% total length; eyes larger, the horizontal diameter 2.5-3.3% total length; teeth molariform with a low cusp, in close-set alternating rows, giving a cobblestone appearance; first dorsal fin large, its origin slightly in advance of inner posterior corner of pectoral fins; height of second dorsal fin about 60% height of first; anal fin about half as large as second dorsal fin, its origin below middle of second dorsal-fin base; caudal fin about 20% total length; precaudal vertebrae 59-81; grey, shading to whitish ventrally. Reaches 150 cm. Described from the Red Sea; ranges to the Arabian Gulf and coast of India and Sri Lanka; apparently an isolated population at Natal. Occurs from near shore to moderate depths. Feeds on small benthic fishes, crustaceans and molluscs. Viviparous, with six to ten pups per litter.

15. *Iago omanensis* (A. Baranes)

16. *Mustelus mosis*, 76 cm (J. Randall)

WEASEL SHARKS
FAMILY HEMIGALEIDAE

The weasel shark family consists of four genera, the monotypic *Chaenogaleus*, *Hemigaleus*, *Hemipristis* and *Paragaleus* with three species. Prior to Compagno (1979, 1984), most authors classified them in the family Carcharhinidae. Collectively, they are moderately elongate, the body depth about 10-13% total length; snout moderately long, rounded to slightly pointed; eyes horizontally elongate; spiracles small; teeth very different in jaws; blade-like and serrate (at least basally on posterolateral edge) in upper jaw, and cuspidate and smooth-edged, but not compressed in lower; first dorsal fin moderately large, distinctly anterior to pelvic fins; second dorsal fin about one-half to two-thirds size of first and well-separated from it; caudal fin with an elevated upper lobe, a well-developed terminal lobe, and a large lower lobe; precaudal pits present. Weasel sharks occur in tropical and subtropical seas (one from the Atlantic, the others from the Indo-Pacific). Viviparous.

HOOKTOOTH SHARK
Chaenogaleus macrostoma (Bleeker, 1852)

Body moderately elongate, the depth about 12% total length; snout fairly long and angularly pointed, about 7% total length; eye slightly oval, its length about 2% total length; first four gill slits subequal, the fifth above pectoral-fin base a little shorter; mouth large; 14 teeth in outer row on each side of jaws, the upper teeth obliquely triangular with a broad angular notch, the lower half of which bears sharp cusplets (usually four); lower teeth with a long, slender, smooth-edged, incurved cusp, those at front of jaw protruding (even when mouth closed); first dorsal fin moderately large, its origin slightly anterior to inner posterior corner of pectoral fins; interdorsal space with a narrow median ridge; second dorsal fin about two-thirds as high as first dorsal; anal fin slightly smaller than second dorsal; greyish brown, the second dorsal fin broadly tipped with black. Reaches about 100 cm. A littoral species from the Arabian Gulf to southern Japan; one depth record to 59 m. Data are lacking on natural history; a report of the litter size as four. *Hemigaleus balfouri* Day is a synonym.

SNAGGLETOOTH SHARK
Hemipristis elongatus (Klunzinger, 1871)

Body moderately elongate, the depth about 14% total length; snout moderately long and broadly rounded, its preoral length 5-6% total length (longer in young than adults); 13 or 14 teeth on each side of upper jaw and 18 in lower; two pairs of medial teeth of upper jaw long and prong-like; more lateral teeth compressed, triangular with oblique cusp, and strongly serrate; teeth at front of lower jaw long and fang-like, smooth-edged and incurved with a basal cusp on each side; more lateral lower teeth progressively more triangular and oblique with two to six sharp cusplets basally on posterior edge; first dorsal fin large and apically pointed, the origin slightly posterior to inner posterior corner of pectoral fins; second dorsal fin about half as large as first; anal fin slightly smaller than second dorsal, its origin below mid-base of this fin; vertebrae of three specimens, 190-195, of which 103-107 are precaudal; grey, shading to whitish ventrally. Recorded to 240 cm total length. Shores of the Indian Ocean and western Pacific; also recorded from Madagascar, Papua New Guinea and the Philippines; not known from any oceanic islands. Occurs from depths of 1 to at least 130 m. Feeds primarily on fishes. Litters vary from two to 11. This shark was first named *Dirrhizodon elongatus* by Klunzinger from the Red Sea. Later it was shown that its fossil teeth had been the basis for the description of the genus *Hemipristis* by Agassiz in 1843. *Heterogaleus ghardaqensis* Gohar and Mazhar is a synonym.

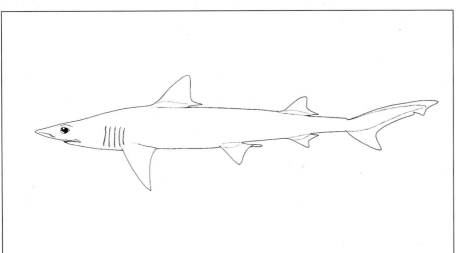

17. *Chaenogaleus macrostoma* (after Compagno, 1984)

18. *Hemipristis elongatus*, 185 cm (J. Randall)

ARABIAN WEASEL SHARK
Paragaleus sp.

Body slender, the depth about 7.7-11.4% total length; snout obtusely wedge-shaped and moderately long for the genus, the preoral length about 6.5-7.5% total length; eye slightly oval and moderately large, its greatest diameter 2.4-3.9% total length; gill slits relatively short, the third 2.5-3.1% total length; 11 or 13 upper teeth on each side of upper jaw and 12 to 15 on each side of lower (disregarding symphyseal teeth); upper teeth with a broad oblique cusp (except most medial tooth with erect cusp and posterior two or three, without a cusp) and five or six prominent sharp cusplets on basal two-thirds of concave posterolateral edge (two to four cusplets on last two or three cusped teeth); lower teeth with a narrow erect cusp on a broad base (except about five posterior teeth without cusps), at least five with oblique cusplets on posterolateral edge; dorsal fins somewhat falcate and broadly separated, the height of first dorsal 7.3-8.1% total length; height of second dorsal fin 4.4-5.6% total length; anal fin smaller than second dorsal fin, its origin clearly posterior to origin of second dorsal fin; vertebrae 165-187, of which 93-108 are precaudal; grey, paler ventrally; fins without pale edges; distal end of second dorsal fin may be dusky; a pair of black lines on underside of snout near tip. Attains about 70 cm. Known from the Arabian Gulf and Gulf of Oman to the coast of India.

REQUIEM SHARKS
FAMILY CARCHARHINIDAE

A large family of 12 genera and 49 species, mainly of tropical seas. The most important family of sharks from the standpoint of abundance, impact on marine communities and commercial importance. Body varying from robust to moderately elongate; eyes circular or nearly so; no supraorbital crest on neurocranium; nictitating eyelid present; spiracles usually absent; no nasal barbels or oronasal grooves; five gill slits, the last one or two above pectoral-fin base; mouth large; teeth of variable size, with a sharp cusp that varies from narrow to broad, smooth-edged to serrate, and with or without basal cusplets (sets of carcharhinid teeth

19. *Paragaleus* sp., 62 cm (J. Randall)

well illustrated by Springer, 1964; Bass et al., 1973, 1975a, 1975b; Garrick, 1982; and Compagno, 1988); first dorsal fin moderate to large, its base anterior to base of pelvic fins; second dorsal fin usually less than half height of first dorsal; anal fin usually about the same size as second dorsal fin; caudal fin less than 30% total length, its upper lobe elevated, with a distinct terminal lobe, its lower lobe less than half length of upper; precaudal pits present; no keel on caudal peduncle (except *Galeocerdo* and *Prionace*). Most requiem sharks are found in coastal waters of the continental shelves or around islands, but a few are pelagic such as the Blue Shark (*Prionace glauca*), the Oceanic Whitetip Shark (*Carcharhinus longimanus*), and the Silky Shark (*C. falciformis*). Most are marine, but the Bull Shark (*C. leucas*) and two species of *Glyphis* can live in fresh water for long

periods. These sharks are voracious predators which feed on a variety of animals, but mainly fishes, cephalopods, and the larger crustaceans. Large sharks of this group often prey on other sharks, rays, sea turtles, sea birds and marine mammals. The serrations of the teeth of most of them aid in their feeding on the larger animals. Several of these sharks, but in particular the Tiger Shark and Bull Shark, are among the most dangerous to divers and bathers. All except the ovoviviparous Tiger Shark are viviparous. *Carcharhinus* is the largest genus of sharks, with 30 species (revised by Garrick, 1982, modified by Compagno, 1984, 1988, and Last and Stevens, 1994). *Eulamia* and *Pterolamiops* are among its 18 generic synonyms. Many species of this genus display a narrow horizontal grey zone on the lower side invading the white of upper abdomen from anteriorly.

20. *Carcharhinus amblyrhynchos*, about 1.5 m (J. Randall)

SILVERTIP SHARK
Carcharhinus albimarginatus (Rüppell, 1837)

Snout moderately long and broadly rounded, the preoral length 6.8-9.2% total length; eyes 1.8-3.0% total length; 12 to 14 teeth on each side of jaws (usually 13 upper and 12 lower), discounting the one or two small symphyseal teeth; upper teeth broadly triangular, serrate (serrae broader basally), with a broad notch on each edge (cusp progressively more oblique laterally in jaw, and notch more pronounced on posterolateral side and less on anteriomedial); lower teeth with a narrow, erect, finely serrate cusp (becoming strongly oblique only posteriorly in jaw); interdorsal ridge present; height of first dorsal fin 7.1-10.6% total length, the apex somewhat pointed; height of second dorsal fin 1.5-2.3% total length; anal fin slightly larger than second dorsal fin; vertebrae 216-231, of which 115-125 are precaudal; dark grey dorsally, shading to white ventrally; first dorsal fin, caudal-fin lobes and pectoral fins conspicuously tipped with white, the outer posterior margins of these and other fins narrowly white (more so on smaller individuals). Reaches about 300 cm. Wide-ranging in the Indo-Pacific region and tropical eastern Pacific. One record from the Arabian Gulf is doubtful. Usually encountered on steep slopes of outer reef areas at depths greater than 30 m, but may be seen in shallow areas; maximum depth at least 600 m. Feeds mainly on a variety of fishes, including tunas. A dangerous species which has attacked humans. Litters vary from one to 11.

BIGNOSE SHARK
Carcharhinus altimus (Springer, 1950)

Snout long and slightly pointed, its preoral length 7.5-10% total length; eyes 1.3-2.3% total length; 14 to 16 (usually 15) teeth on each side of upper jaw (not counting small symphyseal teeth) and 14 or 15 in lower; upper teeth broadly triangular and moderately serrate with a slight indentation on posterolateral edge (more so posteriorly as a result of the cusp becoming more oblique); lower teeth with a narrow, erect, finely serrate cusp; interdorsal ridge prominent; first dorsal fin moderately large, its height 8.3-11.9% total length, its apex bluntly pointed; height of second dorsal fin 2.8-3.4% total length; anal fin slightly larger than second dorsal fin, its origin a little posterior to that of second dorsal; vertebrae 194-206, of which 101-110 are precaudal; grey, becoming whitish below. Reported to 285 cm. This shark was not discovered until 1950 when it was described from a small specimen from Florida, but it has since been found at scattered localities from the Red Sea and South Africa to the Mediterranean Sea. Usually occurs at depths greater than 90 m (maximum depth reported, 430 m) but has been taken near the surface. Feeds on fishes, including sharks and rays, and cephalopods. Litter size varies from three to 15.

QUEENSLAND SHARK
Carcharhinus amblyrhynchoides (Whitley, 1934)

Body moderately stout for the genus; snout short and wedge-shaped, the preoral length 5.3-6.9% total length; eyes 1.2-2.0% total length; gill slits short, 4.0-5.6% total length; 15 teeth on each side of upper jaw and 14 or 15 on lower (disregarding small symphyseals); upper teeth moderately serrate with cusps nearly as narrow as lowers (except posteriorly where obliquely triangular), the anteromedial margin concave and the posterolateral broadly notched; cusp of lower teeth erect and finely serrate; no interdorsal ridge; first dorsal fin moderately large, its height 8.6-12.6% total length, the apex somewhat pointed; height of second dorsal fin 3.1-3.7% total length; height of second dorsal fin 3.1-3.7% total length; anal fin about equal in size to second dorsal, its origin below or slightly posterior to that of second dorsal; vertebrae 168-193, of which 78-96 are precaudal; coppery, becoming white below; tips of pectoral fins (especially underside) and tips of both dorsals and lower caudal lobe black. Attains at least 170 cm. Described from Queensland where it is common; later recorded from Indonesia, Philippines, Gulf of Thailand, South China, India, Gulf of Aden and Oman (latter locality from Leonard Compagno, pers. comm.). Eats mainly fishes, occasionally cephalopods and crustaceans. A litter size of three has been reported. Also known as the Graceful Shark, an inept name since this stocky shark would not be expected to be more graceful then any other species of the genus.

21. *Carcharinus albimarginatus*, about 1.5 m (J. Randall)

22. *Carcharinus altimus*, 1.3 m (J. Randall)

23. *Carcharinus amblyrhynchoides* (after Last and Stevens, 1994)

GREY REEF SHARK
Carcharhinus amblyrhynchos (Bleeker, 1856)

Snout rounded, short to moderate in length, the preoral length 6.4-8.7% total length; eyes 1.8-3.0% total length; 13 or 14 (usually 14) teeth on each side of upper jaw and 12-14 (usually 13) on lower; upper teeth serrate with a triangular cusp, broadly notched on posterolateral edge (serrae on basal part of notch coarse); central upper teeth nearly erect, the more lateral ones progressively oblique; lower teeth finely serrate with a narrow, slightly oblique cusp; no interdorsal ridge; first dorsal fin moderately large, its height 8.6-11.3% total length, the apex slightly pointed; height of second dorsal fin 2.7-4.1% total length; anal fin about equal in size to second dorsal and directly below or slightly posterior to it; vertebrae 210-227, of which 110-119 are precaudal; grey on back (may be bronze when first caught), shading to white ventrally; trailing edge of caudal fin black, this edge becoming broader ventrally until it covers all of distal portion of lower lobe; first dorsal fin narrowly white at tip and distal part of posterior edge (white usually lacking in individuals from Pacific localities); second dorsal and anal fins blackish distally. Maximum length about 180 cm. Widespread in the Indo-Pacific from the Red Sea and east coast of Africa to the Hawaiian Islands and Pitcairn Group. More common in clear-water, coral-reef areas, hence less apt to be found in turbid inshore seas. One record from the Arabian Gulf is probably in error. Feeds mainly on fishes, occasionally on cephalopods and crustaceans. Litter size, one to six. In spite of its small size, this shark is dangerous, particularly to spearfishermen. Also it is known for its threat posturing (Johnson and Nelson, 1973) which it may exhibit when it feels threatened, as by a diver approaching too closely. This consists of exaggerated sinuous movement during slow progression, the head arched upward, the jaws moving and the pectoral fins depressed. Any overt movement toward a shark at this time could elicit an attack which can be incredibly rapid. Usually a single slashing bite results, apparently without any intention to feed. Often misidentified in the older literature as *C. menisorrah*. *C. wheeleri* Garrick is a synonym.

PIGEYE SHARK
Carcharhinus amboinensis (Müller and Henle, 1839)

A very heavy-bodied species, the depth as much as 20% total length; snout short and rounded, the preoral length 5.7-7.8% total

24. *Carcharhinus amblyrhynchos*, about 1.5 m, female with a bite mark from a male (J. Randall)

25. *Carcharhinus amboinensis*, 81 cm (J. Randall)

length; internarial distance large, 6.6-7.7% total length; eyes small, 0.7-1.6% total length; 11 to 13 (usually 12) teeth on each side of upper jaw (omitting small symphyseal teeth) and 10-12 (usually 11) on lower; upper teeth broadly triangular and coarsely serrate with only a slight emargination on posterolateral edge except the more posterior teeth in jaw with a more oblique cusp; lower teeth with a narrower, moderately serrate cusp which is slightly oblique anteriorly in jaw and shorter and more oblique posteriorly; no interdorsal ridge; first dorsal fin large, the height 10.8-13.6% total length, the distal end pointed; height of second dorsal fin 2.8-3.6% total length; anal fin about equal in size to second dorsal, its origin slightly posterior to it; vertebrae 185-195, of which 85-95 are precaudal; grey

above, white below; fins dusky-tipped, more so on young than adults. Reaches 280 cm. Often confused with the Bull Shark (*C. leucas*), differing in its higher first dorsal fin, lower second dorsal, fewer teeth, and fewer vertebrae. Because of this, its distribution is not fully known. Reliably reported from Australia, Papua New Guinea, Indonesia, Sri Lanka, Pakistan, Arabian Gulf, Gulf of Aden, Madagascar, South Africa and Gulf of Guinea, West Africa. Occurs from the surface to at least 100 m; may be found in brackish water, but not known to penetrate freshwater like *C. leucas*. Feeds on fishes, including other sharks, crustaceans, and molluscs. Potentially dangerous but not yet implicated in attack on man (possibly it has and was misidentified as the Bull Shark). Litter size, six to 13 pups.

SPINNER SHARK
Carcharhinus brevipinna (Müller and Henle, 1839)

Body slender, the depth about 13-14% total length; snout long and pointed, the preoral length 7.7-9.0% total length; eyes small, 0.8-2.0% total length; 15 to 18 (usually 16) teeth on each side of upper jaw (symphyseals excepted) and 14 to 17 (usually 15 or 16) in lower; teeth in both jaws with a narrow cusp on a broad base, erect or nearly so anteriorly in jaws, becoming oblique posteriorly (more so on upper than lower jaw); edges of upper teeth finely serrate, of lowers smooth; no interdorsal ridge; first dorsal fin relatively small, its height 6.0-10.2% total length, and moderately pointed; second dorsal fin small, its height 1.8-2.7% total length; anal fin about equal in size to second dorsal and usually slightly anterior to it; grey, shading to white ventrally, the fins usually black-tipped, especially lower caudal lobe. Maximum length recorded, 278 cm. Tropical to warm temperate in the Atlantic, Indian Ocean and western Pacific. A migratory species, moving into temperate waters during warm months; it may occur in schools. Feeds mainly on fishes, often on schooling species; it has been observed to attack a school rapidly from below, sometimes ending with a spinning leap out of the water. Gives birth to two to 15 pups. *C. maculipinnis* (Poey) is a synonym.

WHITECHEEK SHARK
Carcharhinus dussumieri (Valenciennes, 1839)

Snout moderately long and somewhat pointed, its preoral length 5.8-7.9% total length; eyes 2.0-2.7% total length; gill slits moderately long, the third 2.4-3.5% total length; 12-14 teeth on each side of upper jaw (discounting small teeth at symphysis) and 11-15 (usually 13 or 14) in lower; upper teeth with a strongly oblique, broad, serrate cusp and a deep notch on posterolateral edge, the basal part with enlarged serrae; lower teeth with a narrow, oblique, finely serrate cusp on a broad base, becoming rudimentary posteriorly; a low interdorsal ridge present; height of first dorsal fin 8.0-10.7% total length, its tip slightly rounded; height of second dorsal fin 2.6-4.0% total length; anal fin slightly larger than second dorsal, its origin a little anterior to second dorsal; vertebrae 130-150, of which 64-77 are precaudal; grey dorsally, shading to white ventrally; a conspicuous black spot covering distal part of second dorsal fin; other fins unmarked. Rarely exceeding 100 cm. A shallow-water species (maximum recorded depth, 170 m), ranging from the

26. *Carcharhinus brevipinna*, 81 cm (J. Randall)

27. *Carcharhinus dussumieri*, 71.5 cm (J. Randall)

28. *Carcharhinus falciformis*, 1.1 m (J. Randall)

Arabian Gulf to the Indo-Malayan region and northern half of Australia, north to Japan; not known from any oceanic islands; feeds mainly on small fishes, cephalopods and shrimps. Often confused with *C. sealei* (Pietschmann) which also has a black spot distally on the second dorsal fin; the latter is not known from the seas of the Arabian Peninsula. Blegvad (1944) reported *C. dussumieri* (as *C. menisorrah*) as the most common shark in the Arabian Gulf.

SILKY SHARK
Carcharhinus falciformis (Bibron, 1839)

Slender-bodied, the body depth varying from 11.5-17.5% total length; snout moderately long and pointed, the preoral length 6.9-9.3% total length; eye diameter 1.0-2.7% total length; 14-17 (usually 15) teeth on each side of jaws; upper teeth triangular with a slight indentation on anteromedial edge and a deep angular notch on postero-

lateral edge (more pronounced on teeth posteriorly in jaw where more oblique); serrae coarser on basal part of upper teeth; lower teeth with a narrow, erect, smooth-edged cusp, becoming only slightly oblique on most posterior teeth; a narrow interdorsal ridge present; first dorsal fin small, its height 5.2-9.9% total length, the apex narrowly rounded; second dorsal fin very small, its height 1.4-2.2% total length, its free inner posterior margin long (1.6-3.0 times longer than fin height); anal fin larger than second dorsal, its height 2.1-2.9% total length, the origin slightly in advance of second dorsal origin, its inner free posterior margin also long; pectoral fins long, narrow, and falcate; vertebrae 199-215, of which 98-106 are precaudal; grey to dark grey dorsally, shading to white ventrally; first dorsal and pelvic fins unmarked; remaining fins may be dusky at tips. Reported to 330 cm. This slim, swift-swimming shark is pelagic in all warm seas. Although it may be found far from land, it is usually in water masses within the influence of land; it occurs from the surface to depths as great as 500 m; sometimes ventures into relatively shallow water. Feeds mainly on fishes, especially scombrids, but also on squids and pelagic crabs. The number of embryos found in a single female have varied from two to 14. *C. menisorrah* (Valenciennes) is a synonym as a result of lectotype designation by Garrick (1982).

PONDICHERRY SHARK
Carcharhinus hemiodon (Valenciennes, 1839)

Body moderately stout; snout fairly long and somewhat pointed, its preoral length 6.5-7.4% total length; eyes 2.1-2.4% total length; 14 or 15 (usually 14) teeth on each side of upper jaw, and 12-14 on lower; upper teeth with a narrow cusp, only slightly oblique at front of jaw but strongly oblique posteriorly, with a broad deep notch on posterolateral edge, the basal part very coarsely serrate; lower teeth smooth-edged with a slender, more erect cusp; interdorsal ridge present; first dorsal fin of medium size, the height 9.4-11.6% total length, with a narrowly rounded apex; height of second dorsal fin 1.9-2.7% total length; anal fin slightly larger than second dorsal, its origin a little anterior to it; vertebrae 147-155, of which 69-71 are precaudal; grey dorsally and on sides, white ventrally; pectoral fins, lower lobe of caudal fin, and to a lesser extent second dorsal fin black-tipped; tip of first dorsal fin and upper edge of caudal fin dusky. Maximum size unknown, but probably not exceeding 2 m. Scattered records from the Gulf of Oman, coast of India, Indonesia, New Guinea, and southern China. Little is known of the biology. Sometimes classified in the genus *Hypoprion*.

BULL SHARK
Carcharhinus leucas (Valenciennes, 1839)

Heavy-bodied; snout short and broadly rounded, the preoral length 4.6-6.7% total length; internarial distance 5.9-7.0% total length; eyes small, 0.8-1.8% total length; gill slits moderately large, the third 3.1-5.5% total length; 12-14 (usually 13) teeth on each side of upper jaw (disregarding small symphyseal teeth), and 12 or 13 (usually 13) on lower; upper teeth broadly triangular, strongly serrate, and only slightly emarginate along posterolateral edge (except more posterior teeth where progressively more indented); lower teeth with a narrower, less serrate cusp (but broader and more serrate than lower teeth of other species of the genus); no interdorsal ridge; first dorsal fin moderately large, its height 7.0-11.3% total

length, the apex fairly pointed; second dorsal fin moderately large, its height 3.2-4.5% total length; anal fin about equal in size to second dorsal, its origin distinctly posterior to that of second dorsal; vertebrae 198-227, of which 101-123 are precaudal; grey, becoming white ventrally; fins of young often tipped or edged with blackish, these markings fading in adults (only the underside of paired fins dusky at tips). Largest recorded, 324 cm, but probably reaches 340 cm. Widespread in all warm seas, mainly in continental waters or those of large islands such as the Greater Antilles, Indonesia, Philippines, and Melanesia. Exceptional is a single record from Rangiroa Atoll in the Tuamotu Archipelago (Johnson, 1978). Unusual in its tolerance of both low and high salinities. Often reported in rivers far from the sea and lakes linked to the sea such as Lake Nicaragua. Typically found in shallow water, often in estuaries or harbours; however, it has been taken as deep as 152 m. Feeds on a wide variety of prey, including many kinds of bony fishes, sharks, rays, crustaceans, sea turtles, cephalopods and other molluscs, and marine mammals. One of the most dangerous sharks, only exceeded by the White Shark and Tiger Shark in the number of attacks on humans attributed to it. Attacks implicating the Sand Tiger Shark in Australia (where called the Grey Nurse Shark) were most likely the Bull Shark. The number of pups per litter vary from three to 13. Among the nine synonyms are *C. zambezensis* (Peters) and *C. nicaraguensis* (Gill and Bransford), names reflecting the occurrence in freshwater.

BLACKTIP SHARK
Carcharhinus limbatus (Valenciennes, 1839)

Snout moderately long and pointed, its preoral length 6.3-9.0% total length; eyes 1.0-2.2% total length; 14-16 (usually 15) teeth on each side of upper jaw, and 13-16

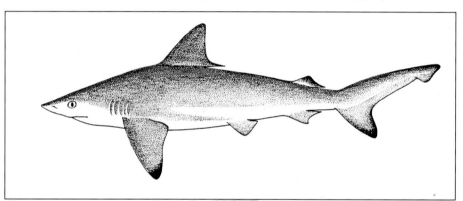
29. *Carcharhinus hemiodon* (after Compagno, 1984)

30. *Carcharhinus leucas*, 69 cm (J. Randall)

31. *Carcharhinus limbatus*, 71 cm (J. Randall)

(usually 14 or 15) in lower jaw; upper teeth narrow-cusped for the genus, progressively more oblique posteriorly, the serrae very fine apically, becoming coarse at base; lower teeth with a very narrow, erect, finely serrate cusp; no interdorsal ridge; first dorsal fin moderately large and falcate, the height 8.2-13.8% total length, the apex acute but slightly rounded; height of second dorsal fin 2.5-5.0% total length; vertebrae 174-203, of which 88-102 are precaudal; bronze dorsally in life, becoming grey after death, shading to white ventrally; pectoral fins, anal fin, and lower lobe of caudal fin tipped with black; remaining fins sometimes dusky to blackish at tips, the first dorsal and upper lobe of caudal fin often blackish at edges. Attains about 250 cm; maximum size varies with geographical area. Worldwide in tropical to warm temperate seas, generally over continental or insular shelves, but may occur far offshore. An active shark, it sometimes runs in schools and has been seen to leap free of the sea. Feeds mainly on small fishes, occasionally on cephalopods and the larger crustacea. Ordinarily not aggressive to man. The number of embryos per female varies from one to ten. Described from Martinique by Valenciennes in Müller and Henle (1839). *C. natator* Meek and Hildebrand is among its eight synonyms.

OCEANIC WHITETIP SHARK
Carcharhinus longimanus (Poey, 1861)

Snout moderately short and broadly rounded, the preoral length 5.4-7.1% total length; internarial distance 5.2-6.2% total length; eyes small, 0.9-2.5% total length; 13 or 14 (usually 14) teeth on each side of upper jaw (disregarding symphyseals) and 13-15 (usually 14) on lower jaw; upper teeth broadly triangular and strongly serrate, the cusp becoming somewhat oblique posteriorly, resulting in a concave posterolateral edge; lower teeth with a narrower cusp (but still broad for the genus), moderately serrate, and erect except posteriorly where slightly oblique; a low interdorsal ridge usually present; first dorsal fin very large and broadly rounded apically, its height 9.2-15.2% total length (average height about 12%); height of second dorsal fin 2.5-3.9% total length; anal fin slightly larger than second dorsal fin, its origin below or slightly posterior to origin of second dorsal; pectoral fins very long, broad, and distally rounded, the anterior edge up to 27% total length; vertebrae 228-244, of which 123-131 are precaudal; brownish grey, shading to white ventrally; tips of paired fins, first dorsal fin, and caudal fin lobes broadly mottled with white; anal fin usually blackish distally and second dorsal blackish; juveniles with most

fins blackish at tips. Reported to 350 cm, but rarely exceeds 300 cm. Worldwide in tropical to warm temperate seas, but most abundant in the lower 20° of latitude (Strasburg, 1958). An offshore pelagic species; however, it has been encountered near shore where the water is deep. Often seen at the surface but may occur to depths of at least 150 m. Feeds mainly on fishes and squids; its stomachs occasionally contain remains of marine mammals. The white-tipped fins have been suggested as an attractant to pelagic fishes such as tunas. Litter size, one to 15. A very dangerous shark well known to have attacked humans and boats. It is the most likely suspect in attacks on survivors from air and sea disasters in offshore tropical waters. Springer (1950) proposed a new genus for this shark, *Pterolamia* (later changed to *Pterolamiops* when he discovered *Pterolamia* is preoccupied); however, few authors have recognised this genus. As shown by Garrick (1982), *Squalus maou* Lesson is an older name for *C. longimanus*, but this name has been suppressed by the International Commission on Zoological Nomenclature in view of the much greater usage of *C. longimanus*.

HARDNOSE SHARK
Carcharhinus macloti (Müller and Henle, 1839)

Body slender; snout pointed and moderately long, its preoral length 8.7-10.2% total

length, and unusually firm as a result of heavy calcification of rostral cartilage; eyes 1.8-3.1% total length; 13-15 (usually 14) teeth on each side of upper jaw and 13 or 14 in lower (discounting small symphyseal teeth); upper teeth with a narrow, slightly oblique, smooth-edged cusp, the base with four prominent cusplets on each side; lower teeth with a slender, slightly oblique, smooth-edged cusp and no basal cusplets; low interdorsal ridge usually present; first dorsal fin small, its height 7.1-8.9% total length, the apex narrowly rounded; second dorsal fin long and low, its height 1.6-2.1% total length, the inner posterior margin more than twice fin height; origin of second dorsal fin over midbase of anal fin; anal fin slightly larger than second dorsal; vertebrae 149-156, of which 68-71 are precaudal; grey-brown, shading to white ventrally; posterior margin of pectoral fins and margin of lower caudal lobe sometimes pale; most individuals with edge of upper caudal lobe and leading edge of second dorsal fin blackish. Reaches 110 cm. Described from New Guinea; known also from the northern half of Australia and scattered continental shelf records from East Africa to southern Japan. Nothing is known of the food habits; usually one embryo per uterus. Like *C. hemiodon*, this shark has been classified by some authors in the genus *Hypoprion*.

32. *Carcharhinus longimanus* (after Last and Stevens, 1994)

33. *Carcharhinus macloti* (after Last and Stevens, 1994)

BLACKTIP REEF SHARK
Carcharhinus melanopterus (Quoy and Gaimard, 1824)

Snout moderately short and rounded, its preoral length 5.6-7.3% total length; eye diameter 1.5-3.0% total length; 11-13 (usually 12) teeth on each side of upper jaw, and 10-12 (usually 11) on each side of lower (discounting small symphyseals); upper teeth narrow-cusped, oblique (except for a few medial teeth), with a broad angular notch on posterolateral edge and a lesser notch on anteromedial edge (disappearing on posterior teeth as the cusp becomes more oblique; cusp of upper teeth finely serrate, the base strongly serrate, the first cusplet at angle notably largest; lower teeth finely serrate, with a narrow, near-erect cusp on a broad base; no interdorsal ridge; height of first dorsal fin 8.0-11.4% total length; height of second dorsal fin 3.4-5.0% total length; anal fin about equal in size to second dorsal and directly below it; vertebrae 193-214, of which 111-122 are precaudal; greyish to yellowish brown, shading to white ventrally; all fins conspicuously tipped with black, most broadly on first dorsal fin (where it may be accentuated by a broad submarginal pale band) and lower lobe of caudal fin; margin of caudal fin black except leading edge of lower lobe. Maximum length, 180 cm. Broadly distributed throughout most of the tropical and subtropical Indo-Pacific region; has invaded the eastern Mediterranean via the Suez Canal. One of the three most common sharks of Indo-Pacific islands and reefs (the others the Grey Reef Shark and the Whitetip Reef Shark). An inshore species which readily swims into very shallow water of reefs and sand flats, often with its first dorsal fin protruding above the surface; the most common inshore shark in Oman seas. Feeds on a wide variety of reef and shore fishes and cephalopods, occasionally on shrimps and stomatopods. Litters consist of two to five pups. Although generally timid and not easily approached, it can be dangerous to spearfishermen and has been known to bite the feet or legs of persons wading in the shallows (Randall and Helfman, 1973). Some authors have mis-identified this shark as *C. spallanzani* (Peron and Lesueur), now known to be a synonym of *C. sorrah*.

SANDBAR SHARK
Carcharhinus plumbeus (Nardo, 1827)

Body moderately stout; snout rounded, the preoral length 5.6-8.1% total length; eye diameter 1.4-2.9% total length; 13-15 (usually 14) teeth on each side of upper jaw and 12-15 (usually 13 or 14) on each side of lower (disregarding small symphyseal teeth); upper teeth broadly triangular, moderately serrate, and slightly oblique with a concavity on posterolateral edge (slight on medial teeth, marked on posterior ones); lower teeth with a narrow, very finely serrate, slightly oblique cusp on a broad-based root; interdorsal ridge present; first dorsal fin very large and erect, its height 13.6-16.5% total length, the tip narrowly rounded to pointed; second dorsal fin 2.6-3.9% total length; anal fin about as large as second dorsal fin, its origin below or slightly posterior to it; vertebrae 172-189, of which 88-97 are precaudal; greyish brown dorsally, white ventrally; no distinctive markings on fins (the tips and trailing edges may be dusky). Reliably reported to 240 cm. Cosmopolitan in tropical to warm temperate seas, mainly continental shelf localities but recorded from some islands such as the Bahamas, Cuba, Hawaiian Islands, New Caledonia, Seychelles, and Mauritius. Primarily an inshore species but has been taken at depths as great as 280 m. Feeds on a variety of fishes, but also crustaceans and molluscs. The number of pups of one litter varies from one to 14. Has not been implicated in attack on man but should be regarded as potentially dangerous. Wass (1973) studied the growth and reproduction in Hawaiian waters. Captive Sandbar Sharks grew an average of 31 cm the first year, 21 cm the second year, and 16 cm the third; females grew slightly faster than males. *C. milberti* (Valenciennes) is a synonym.

SPOTTAIL SHARK
Carcharhinus sorrah (Valenciennes, 1839)

Snout moderately long and pointed, its preoral length 7.1-8.4% total length; diameter of eye 1.5-2.4% total length; gill slits relatively short, the third 1.8-3.3% total length; 12 or 13 (usually 12) teeth on each side of upper jaw and 11 or 12 (usually 12)

34. *Carcharhinus melanopterus* (J. Hoover)

35. *Carcharhinus plumbeus*, about 1 m (J. Randall)

36. *Carcharhinus sorrah*, 1.1 m (J. Randall)

on lower jaw (discounting symphyseals); upper teeth broadly triangular with a large angular notch on posterolateral edge, slightly oblique medially and strongly oblique posteriorly; upper teeth serrate, strongly so on basal part of notch, the largest cusplet at angle; lower teeth with a narrow, oblique, finely serrate cusp of moderate height; interdorsal ridge present; first dorsal fin of medium size, falcate, and pointed, its height 7.7-10.9% total length; second dorsal fin small, its height 1.5-2.3% total length; anal fin larger than second dorsal fin, its origin anterior to it; vertebrae 153-175, of which 66-79 are precaudal; grey above, white below; lower lobe of caudal fin broadly tipped with black, but no dark pigment on upper lobe; pectoral fins also black-tipped; first dorsal fin usually with a small blackish spot at tip or just the edge blackish. Attains about 160 cm. Western Pacific (Queensland to Taiwan) to the western Indian Ocean (Red

37. Embryo of *G. cuvier*, 53 cm (J. Randall)

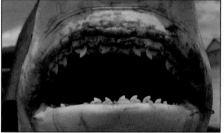

38. Jaws of *Galeocerdo cuvier* (J. Randall)

Sea to South Africa), but with some discontinuities in distribution; most records from continental waters or large islands, but has been recorded from the Seychelles, Mauritius, and the Solomon Islands. Randall (1986) published the first record from the Arabian Gulf. A shallow-water species; feeds mainly on fishes and cephalopods; litter size varies from two to six.

TIGER SHARK
Galeocerdo cuvier (Peron and Lesueur, 1822)

Head and anterior body stout, but rest of body progressively more attenuate posteriorly, with a low lateral keel on each side of the narrow caudal peduncle; snout slightly rounded and very short, its preoral length 3.7-4.8% total length; eye diameter 0.8-2.1% total length; spiracle a narrow slit behind eye; gill slits small, 1.8-2.8% total length; 10 or 11 teeth on each side of jaws (discounting a small symphyseal tooth); teeth similar in shape in both jaws, strongly serrate, the anteromedial edge convex, the posterolateral deeply notched; height of first dorsal fin 7.5-9.3% total length; vertebrae 216-233, of which 100-112 are precaudal; grey with darker grey bars or vertical rows of spots on body (markings pronounced on juveniles, faint on large adults). Reaches at least 600 cm. Worldwide in tropical to warm temperate seas, including remote islands of Oceania. Known to make migrations to higher latitudes during warm months of the year. A total of 2257 Tiger Sharks were tagged in the western Atlantic during the years 1977-1989; 135 were recovered, of which 57 had moved 100 nautical miles or more. Four of these had swum more than

1,000 nautical miles (one from New York to Costa Rica, 1853 nautical miles). Tends to move into shallow water at night for feeding, at times surprisingly shallow for such a large shark. Has been observed at the surface far from land; once it was seen from a submarine in 350 m. Feeds on a greater variety of animals than any other shark, including sharks, sea turtles, sea snakes, sea birds, and marine mammals; also frequently ingests all kinds of garbage and refuse, much of which is indigestible. The only species of the Carcharhinidae for which development is ovoviviparous; a single female can have from 10 to 80 young at one time; size at birth varies from 51-76 cm. Juvenile tiger sharks are estimated to double their length in their first year. A 131-cm tagged individual in Hawaii grew to 173 cm in 207 days. Maximum age has been estimated at 45 to 50 years. Randall (1992) has reviewed the literature on the biology of this shark. It has been implicated in 27 attacks on humans, hence second only to the White Shark in the number of attacks. Undoubtedly it is responsible for many more for which the identity of the attacking shark is unknown.

SLITEYE SHARK
Loxodon macrorhinus Müller and Henle, 1839
(Photograph on page 35)

Body slender, the depth 10-14% total length; snout long and pointed, its preoral length 8.1-9.8% total length; eyes large, 2.3-3.6% total length, with a characteristic small notch at midlevel in posterior edge of orbit; spiracles minute or absent; gill slits short, the third 1.4-2.1% total length; mouth small, its width 4.9-6.5% total length; 12-14 teeth

39. *Galeocerdo cuvier* (R. and V. Taylor)

on each side of jaws (discounting one medium-sized symphyseal tooth); teeth in both jaws smooth-edged, highly oblique, with a deep notch on posterolateral margin, the basal part of this notch convex; interdorsal ridge absent or rudimentary; height of first dorsal fin 6.2-8.7% total length; second dorsal fin small, its height 1.1-1.7% total length, its origin over rear base of anal fin; anal fin much larger than second dorsal fin, its base twice as long as that of second dorsal; precaudal pits present; vertebrae 148-191, of which 77-106 are precaudal; greyish brown, shading to white ventrally, without any prominent markings; front of snout translucent; margin of first dorsal and caudal fins may be narrowly blackish. Maximum length reported, 91 cm. Western Pacific to western Indian Ocean, mainly in continental shelf or insular shelf waters, to at least 80 m. Litter size varies from two to four.

SICKLEFIN LEMON SHARK
Negaprion acutidens (Rüppell, 1837)

Snout broadly rounded to slightly wedge-shaped, its preoral length 4.6-6.4% total length; eye diameter 0.9-2.1% total length; spiracles usually absent; gill slits large, the third 4.0-5.3% total length; 13-16 (usually 14) teeth on each side of jaws (not counting small symphyseal teeth); teeth generally not serrate (may be finely serrate basally on large individuals); upper teeth with a moderately long cusp on a broad base, a broad angular notch on each side, the two most medial teeth erect, but others progressively more oblique posteriorly until notch on anteromedial edge disappears; lower teeth similar but cusp narrow and more erect; no interdorsal ridge; first dorsal fin falcate, moderate in size, its height 6.9-10.9% total length; second dorsal fin nearly as large as first, its height 6.4-8.5% total length; anal fin smaller than second dorsal fin, its origin posterior to that of second dorsal; vertebrae 217-229, of which 135-142 are precaudal; yellowish grey to yellowish brown, paler ventrally, the fins more yellowish than body; no distinctive markings. Reaches at least 310 cm. Indo-Pacific from the Red Sea (type locality) and coast of East Africa to the Marshall Islands and French Polynesia. Primarily an inshore species, oriented to the bottom; may occur in a variety of shallow-water habitats from estuaries to exposed outer reefs; the young may be seen in very shallow water on sand flats or mangrove areas, their dorsal fins sometimes exposed. Often encountered at rest on the substratum. Feeds mainly on a wide variety of reef and shore fishes. Females give birth to one to 13 pups. Growth is slow, that of juveniles about 12 cm per year. One other species in the

40. *Loxodon macrorhinus*, 72 cm; description on page 34 (J. Randall)

41. *Negaprion acutidens* (after Last and Stevens, 1994)

42. *Prionace glauca* (R. and V. Taylor)

genus, *N. brevirostris* (Poey), a close relative from the tropical Atlantic and eastern Pacific.

BLUE SHARK
Prionace glauca (Linnaeus, 1758)

Body fusiform and slender, the depth 10-14% total length; snout long, its preoral length 8.3-9.2% total length, and moderately pointed; eye diameter 1.3-3.2% total length; usually 14 upper and 13 or 14 lower teeth on each side of jaws, discounting one or two small symphyseal teeth; upper teeth with a clearly serrate, narrow cusp, broadening onto base; upper teeth nearly erect medially but progressively more oblique posteriorly in jaw, thus becoming strongly notched on posterolateral edge; lower teeth with a narrower cusp, less serrate and less oblique; no interdorsal ridge; a low keel on side of caudal peduncle; height of first dorsal fin 7.3-8.6% total length; height of second dorsal fin 2.6-3.1% total length; anal fin

slightly larger than second dorsal, its origin a little anterior; pectoral fins long and slender (as long as head in adults); vertebrae 239-253, of which 143-150 are precaudal; deep blue on back, shading to bright blue on side, abruptly white ventrally. Maximum length, 383 cm, with unconfirmed reports of larger size. The most widely distributed of all sharks; occurs in all oceans to at least 50°N and S latitude (to 60°N in the Gulf of Alaska and nearly 70°N off Europe). Generally found where the sea temperature is 12-20°C, but can tolerate temperatures as high as 25°C. In tropical seas it descends to the cooler water of greater depth (in the Indian Ocean the greatest abundance occurs at depths of 80-220 m). Although pelagic, it sometimes comes close to shore, especially at night. Tagging in the North Atlantic has demonstrated that it has a trans-Atlantic migration route following the current system. In the Pacific one tagged off Tasmania was recaptured south of Java. Feeds mainly on fishes and squids. Litter size averages 40, with one litter reported as 135.

MILK SHARK
Rhizoprionodon acutus (Rüppell, 1837)

Body slender, the depth 11-14% total length; snout long and somewhat pointed, the preoral length 7.9-10.5% total length; eye diameter 1.5-3.0% total length; spiracles absent; 7-15 hyomandibular pores (series of pores above corner of mouth); 11-13 (usually 12) teeth on each side of jaws (disregarding a medium-sized symphyseal tooth); upper teeth with a highly oblique, blade-like cusp, finely serrate in adults, nearly straight on anteriomedial edge and strongly notched on posterolateral margin; lower teeth similar to uppers but with anteromedial edge concave and the serrae smaller; no interdorsal ridge or a faint low one; height of first dorsal fin 7.2-9.6% total length; second dorsal fin small, its height 1.6-2.2% total length, its origin over posterior half of anal-fin base; anal fin larger than second dorsal, its base nearly twice as long; pectoral fins short and broad; vertebrae 121-162, of which 55-79 are precaudal; brownish grey, shading to white ventrally; upper lobe of caudal fin often edged in black; leading edge of first dorsal fin sometimes narrowly blackish; pectoral fins with a pale trailing edge. Maximum length 178 cm, but few exceed 110 cm. Western Pacific from southern Japan to Queensland, west to the Red Sea and coast of East Africa; also West Africa from Madeira and Mauritania to Angola. Not known from oceanic islands. An inshore species (depth range about 1-200 m), usually found in turbid water. Feeds on both small benthic fishes and schooling species such as clupeoids, but also on cephalopods, crustaceans, and gastropods. The number of pups per litter varies from one to eight. Locally abundant and commercially important in some areas, especially in India. The name Milk Shark is derived from the belief that the flesh of this shark promotes lactation. Springer (1964) revised the six species of the genus and the related monotypic genera *Loxodon* and *Scoliodon*. He listed the six synonyms of *R. acutus*.

GREY SHARPNOSE SHARK
Rhizoprionodon oligolinx Springer, 1964

Similar in morphology to *R. acutus*, but a little heavier-bodied; snout shorter, but still moderately pointed, the preoral length 7.2-8.3% total length; eye diameter 2.1-3.2% total length; no spiracles; 3-8 (usually 4-7) hyomandibular pores (above corner of mouth); 11-13 (usually 11 or 12) teeth on each side of upper jaw and 10-12 (usually 11) in lower jaw; teeth much like those of *R. acutus* but serration less evident; inter-

dorsal ridge absent or very faint; height of first dorsal fin 7.3-8.6% total length; second dorsal fin small, its height 1.6-1.9% total length, its origin over posterior half of anal fin; anal fin larger than second dorsal fin, its base nearly twice as long as that of second dorsal; pectoral fins short and broad; vertebrae 151-162, of which 84-91 are precaudal; grey to brownish grey, whitish below; leading edge of upper caudal lobe and first dorsal fin often narrowly blackish; trailing margin of pectoral fins pale. Maximum length about 70 cm. Arabian Gulf along the southern coast of Asia to Sumatra and Java, and north to southern China; single records from the Gulf of Carpentaria, Palau, and southern Japan. Little is known of the bio-

logy of this small shark. Number of young per litter, three to five.

WHITETIP REEF SHARK
Triaenodon obesus (Rüppell, 1837)

Body slender, the depth 11-16% total length; head depressed, about twice as broad as deep; snout very short, its preoral length 3.1-4.5% total length; eyes horizontally elongate, the greatest diameter 1.3-2.4% total length; spiracles absent or minute; teeth small, in at least two functional rows in jaws, 20-24 on each side of upper jaw (discounting symphyseals) and 20-22 in lower; teeth similar in both jaws, smooth-edged with a

43. *Rhizoprionodon acutus*, 76 cm (J. Randall)

44. *Rhizoprionodon oligolinx*, 47.5 cm (J. Randall)

45. *Triaenodon obesus*, about 1 m (J. Randall)

large, oblique, narrow, central cusp and a small pointed basal cusp on each side (two small cusps on each side of lower teeth and two on anteromedial side of upper teeth in about posterior half of jaws); no interdorsal ridge; first dorsal fin of moderate size, 8.7-11.0% total length; second dorsal fin about two-thirds to three-fourths as large as first dorsal; anal fin nearly as large as second dorsal fin, its origin below that of second dorsal; pectoral fins broad and short; vertebrae of two specimens 208-214, of which 128-129 are precaudal; brownish grey, shading to whitish or pale yellowish ventrally; usually a few scattered, roundish, dark grey spots on body; tips of first dorsal fin and upper lobe of caudal fin white. Maximum length about 175 cm. Wide-ranging in the tropical and subtropical Indo-Pacific and eastern Pacific; among the few localities for which it is unknown are the Arabian Gulf, Easter Island, and Rapa. Rare in Oman waters. Primarily an inshore shark of coral reefs; one depth record of 330 m in the Ryukyu Islands. Usually seen at rest in caves or under ledges during the day. Feeds mainly on reef fishes, secondarily on octopuses. Litter size, one to five. Randall (1977) published on the biology of this species. The growth rate of individuals of 81-105 cm precaudal length was determined from tagging to be 2.1-4.2 cm per year. Until recently, most authors classified this shark in the Triakidae because of its dentition; but other features such as a well-developed precaudal pit, a prominent lower caudal lobe, presence of a nictitating membrane, and the structure of the intestine favor its placement in the Carcharhinidae.

HAMMERHEAD SHARKS
FAMILY SPHYRNIDAE

This distinctive family of sharks consists of nine species, here regarded as all in the genus *Sphyrna*. The head is strongly depressed and greatly expanded into blade-like extensions; eyes circular or nearly so, one at end of each lateral extension of head; nictitating eyelids present; spiracles absent; five gill slits of moderate size, the fifth above origin of pectoral fin; mouth relatively small; teeth similar to those of *Carcharhinus* (except one species with molariform posterior teeth); no interdorsal ridge; first dorsal fin moderate to large in size, falcate, and short-based, its origin over or anterior to inner rear corner of pectoral fins; second dorsal fin small, its origin posterior to anal-fin origin; precaudal pits present. Hammerheads are found throughout the tropical to warm temperate seas. Three species occur in Arabian waters. The record of a fourth, *S. zygaena* (Linnaeus), as discussed in the introductory remarks on sharks, is very doubtful. The unique laterally expanded head of these sharks is believed to have two major functions. One is to act as an anterior plane which when twisted allows for rapid turning. The other is to place the sense organs of vision and olfaction wider apart, thus giving better binocular vision and providing for better tracking of olfactory stimuli. Hammerheads share a number of characters with the requiem sharks and are believed to have evolved from carcharhinid stock. Gilbert (1967) revised the family and illustrated the dentition. Some authors have placed *S. blochii* in the monotypic genus *Eusphyra*; Gilbert (1967) is followed here in regarding *Eusphyra* as a subgenus. The Bonnethead, *S. tiburo* (Linnaeus), with its odd shovel-shaped head and posterior molariform teeth, would seem to warrant generic status if *S. blochii* is. Development is viviparous. Hammerheads are not known to be very aggressive except when enticed into action by spearfishermen who have wounded fish. There have been only a few attacks on humans; the identity of the attacking hammerhead to species was usually not known.

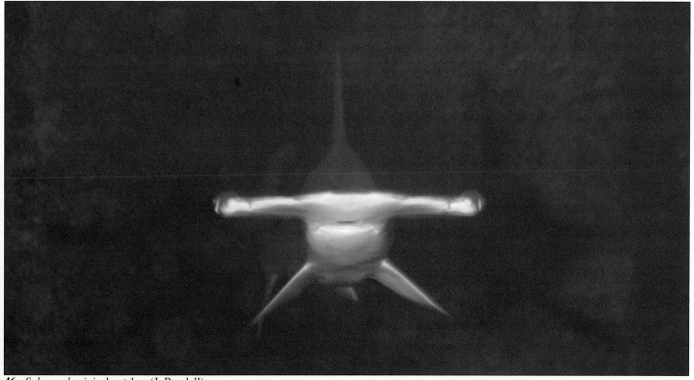

46. *Sphyrna lewini*, about 1 m (J. Randall)

WINGHEAD SHARK
Sphyrna blochii (Cuvier, 1817)

Head greatly expanded laterally, its width 42-49% head length, each lobe angling posteriorly; nostrils very large, well-separated from eyes (nearer median end of rostrum than eyes); 15 or 16 teeth on each side of upper jaw and 14 on lower (disregarding any small symphyseal teeth); teeth in jaws similar, not serrate, the cusp of each strongly oblique, thus with a deep angular notch on posterolateral edge; dorsal fin large, its apex pointed; origin of second dorsal fin over posterior third of anal fin, its posterior tip nearly reaching precaudal pit; anal-fin base more than 1.5 times longer than base of second dorsal fin; pectoral-fin length about equal to height of first dorsal fin; precaudal pit longitudinal, not crescentic and transverse; grey to brownish grey, paler ventrally, without markings. A small species, probably not exceeding 150 cm. Ranges from the Arabian Gulf to the Indo-Malayan region and northern half of Australia, north to China and Taiwan; not known from oceanic islands. Feeds mainly on small bony fishes, occasionally on crustaceans and cephalopods. Litter size varies from six to 25.

SCALLOPED HAMMERHEAD
Sphyrna lewini (Griffith and Smith, 1834)

Anterior margin of head broadly convex with a prominent median indentation and two more indentations on either side (thus giving the front of the head a scalloped effect); preoral snout length 4.6-5.8% total length; posterior edge of eyes slightly anterior to mouth; 15 or 16 teeth on each side of jaws (discounting symphyseals of moderate size); upper teeth with a narrow cusp on a broad base, slightly oblique medially and progressively more oblique posteriorly, the edges slightly serrate only on large adults; lower teeth with a narrower less-oblique cusp; first dorsal fin moderately large and erect, the height 11.9-14.5% total length; second dorsal fin small, its height 2.4-3.2% total length, its origin over midbase of anal fin; inner posterior margin of second dorsal fin nearly twice height of fin; anal fin nearly twice as large as second dorsal; vertebrae 191-203, of which 91-96 are precaudal; brownish grey, shading to white ventrally; tip of underside of pectoral fins of adults dusky; tips of these fins, lower caudal lobe, and second dorsal fin of juveniles may be black. Maximum length about 400 cm. Worldwide in tropical to warm temperate seas; the most widely distributed and probably the most common of the hammerheads. Individuals are reported from inshore to well offshore, and from the shallows to depths of at least 275 m. Kaneohe Bay, Oahu has been shown to be a major pupping and mating ground in the Hawaiian Islands (Clarke, 1971). The number of pups per litter ranges from 15 to 31. Feeds mainly on fishes, including sharks and stingrays, and cephalopods; also ingests crustaceans and gastropods. Some populations are migratory. Large semi-stationary schools are often seen, the function of which is uncertain (Klimley, 1982).

GREAT HAMMERHEAD
Sphyrna mokarran (Rüppell, 1837)

Anterior margin of head nearly straight with a median indentation and only a slight second one near lateral end of head; preoral length of snout 5.0-6.4% total length; posterior edge of eyes anterior to front of mouth; 17 teeth on each side of upper jaw and 16 or 17 on lower (discounting small teeth at symphysis); teeth similar to those of *S. lewini*, but cusp broader and serrate at all stages; first dorsal fin very high, erect, and pointed, its height 13.5-19.7% total length; second dorsal fin height 2.7-4.1% total length; anal fin slightly larger than second dorsal fin, its origin a little anterior to that of second dorsal; pelvic fins strongly falcate; brownish grey, paler below, without any markings. The largest of the hammerheads; reaches 600 cm in total length, but reports up to 8 m suggest that it may attain larger size. Widely distributed in tropical to warm temperate seas; some populations migrate to higher latitudes during warmer months; occurs both inshore and offshore. Feeds primarily on fishes, including sharks, stingrays and skates (batoids seem to be among its favorite food items), but also on cephalopods and crustaceans. Litter size, 15-42, the young 50-70 cm at birth.

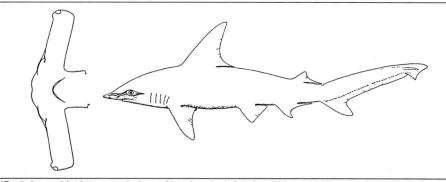

47. *Sphyrna blochii*; ventral view of head to the left (after Gilbert, 1967)

48. *Sphyrna lewini*, about 1 m (J. Randall)

49. *Sphyrna mokarran*, 241.5 cm (J. Randall)

RAYS

The various families of rays are now grouped in the order Raji-formes, along with the skates (none of which are yet known for Oman). In addition to many of the features of sharks, rays are characterised by their flattened form (except saw-fishes), with the anterior end of the enlarged pectoral fins attached to the head in front of the gill openings, ventral position of the gill slits, eyes and spiracles on dorsal surface, absence of an anal fin, no nictitating eyelid, and teeth usually flattened, close-set, and pavement-like; on some species there may be a small cusp on each tooth, but it is generally only on males (or if on females, it is larger on males). Seven families of rays have one to a few venomous spines dorsally on the tail. These spines are long and flat, tapering to a sharp point, with numerous, close-set, retrorse barbs on each side. There is a groove on each side on the ventral surface of the spine; the glandular cells which secrete the venom lie between the dermal and epidermal tissue in the groove. If contact is made on the disc, these rays can arch the tail strongly forward and drive the spine into whatever makes the contact. The pain from such wounds is excruciating, and other disabling symptoms may follow; more than a few deaths have been recorded. Those rays that live on the bottom take in respiratory water through the spiracles and pass it out the gill slits below. Many are able to bury themselves in the bottom sediment, with only their eyes and spiracles showing. The benthic species are generally white on the ventral part of their body. Rays are ovoviviparous; nutrition for development comes initially from the yolk of the egg, but later from albuminous fluid secreted from vascular filaments which line the uterine wall. The skates (Rajidae), however, lay eggs in horny capsules.

SAWFISHES
FAMILY PRISTIDAE

Sawfishes may look more like sharks than rays, but they are highly modified rays. They have elongate, near-cylindrical bodies and a long, blade-like rostrum of hardened carti-lage studded on each side with tooth-like projections (these are greatly enlarged dermal denticles, common-ly called rostral teeth); eyes and spiracles dorsal in position; two sets of five gill slits ventrally on head; two dorsal fins of similar size; broad, short pectoral fins; teeth in jaws minute and dome-shaped. There are two genera, the monotypic *Anoxy-pristis* and *Pristis* for which the exact number of species is unknown (prob-ably five or six). The long rostrum, often called the saw, is lashed back and forth among small schooling fishes to stun or kill them; it is also used to root into mud or sand for fos-sorial animals. In addition, it can be used defensively and is therefore a threat to humans coming in close contact with these fishes. Generally found in shallow water on muddy or sandy bottoms; some species enter freshwater. Like more typical rays, the development is ovoviviparous. The saws are often saved as curios. Saws "6 feet long and a foot in width across the base" were reported by Norman and Fraser (1948). Saw-fishes should not be confused with saw sharks which also have a long flat rostrum with lateral teeth; these are true sharks with gill slits on the side of the body; all have a more slender body and a long lateral bar-bel on each side of the rostrum.

NARROW SAWFISH
Anoxypristis cuspidata (Latham, 1794)

Body slender; head progressively more depressed anteriorly, ending in the blade-like saw about 26-30% total length; saw narrow and tapering slightly, its average width about one-fourth to one-third width of mouth; rostral teeth short, triangular, flat-tened, without a groove on posterior margin, 18-25 on each side, none on basal fourth of saw, those on outer half evenly spaced; spiracles behind eyes, oblique and narrow; skin naked or with widely spaced denticles; dorsal fins large, pointed, and falcate, the origin of first dorsal over posterior base of pelvic fins; each pectoral fin forming nearly an equilateral triangle; caudal fin with a distinct lower lobe, its length more than half length of upper lobe; grey, shading to whitish ventrally; rostral teeth white. Attains at least 350 cm, with unconfirmed lengths to 600 cm. Red Sea and Arabian Gulf east along the Asian continent to Indonesia, New Guinea, and northern Australia, north to Korea and southern Japan. Reported to a depth of 40 m, but usually found in shallow water; not known to enter freshwater. Some authors such as Bigelow and Schroeder (1953) classify this species in *Pristis*.

50. *Anoxypristis cuspidata* (after Last and Stevens, 1994)

OLIVE SAWFISH
Pristis zijsron Bleeker, 1851

Body robust; head progressively more flattened anteriorly, ending in a blade-like saw about 27% total length; saw tapering slightly, its average width about half width of mouth; rostral teeth 24-37 on each side; rostral teeth slender, with a groove along posterior edge, occurring along full length of saw (before it broadens basally), but shorter and more broadly spaced on proximal third; spiracles behind eyes, ovate; skin with close-set dermal denticles; dorsal fins tall, pointed, and slightly falcate, the origin of first dorsal fin above or anterior to midbase of pelvic fins; pectoral fins broadly triangular, their width (distance from body) less than half their length from origin to posterior tip; caudal fin without a distinct lower lobe; olivaceous dorsally, whitish ventrally; rostral teeth white. Maximum reported length 730 cm, but rarely over 500 cm. Arabian Gulf to Indo-Malayan region, north to southern China, south on western Australian coast to Broom, and occasionally as far south as Sydney on eastern coast; also recorded from South Africa to Mozambique; known to penetrate freshwater. The number of rostral teeth appears to vary with geographical area, 24 to 28 in Australia, 29-37 in the Arabian Gulf; the possibility exists that more than one species is involved.

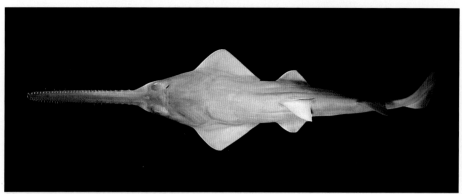

51. *Pristis zijsron*, 91 cm (J. Randall)

TORPEDO RAYS
FAMILY TORPEDINIDAE

Electric rays have been grouped by authors into from one to four families. We follow the classification of two families, the Torpedinidae (torpedo rays) and the Narcinidae (numbfishes). The Torpedinidae consists two genera, *Torpedo*, which contains at least 15 species that occur in tropical to temperate seas, mainly along continental shelves, and the monotypic *Hypnos* from Australia. The torpedos range in length from less than 50 to 180 cm. All are capable of delivering a powerful shock which may serve to stun prey or provide for defense. The shocks are produced by two large kidney-shaped organs, one on each side of the disc, the outlines of which can usually be seen (most easily on ventral side); these organs are made up of numerous columnar structures that occupy the full thickness of the disc. The disc is soft and flabby, oval, wider than long (except one species with a round disc), the anterior edge truncate, slightly emarginate or slightly double emarginate; skin naked; eyes small, vestigial in some deep-water species; spiracles just behind eyes, with or without papillae on edges; five pairs of short gill slits vetrally on disc; mouth small but distensible, without labial cartilages; teeth small with a single, sharp, curved cusp; tail strongly tapering, usually shorter than disc length, with two close-set dorsal fins and a broad caudal fin of near-symmetrical upper and lower lobes, the posterior margin truncate to rounded. Torpedo rays are usually found on mud or sand substrata and are able to bury themselves in the sediment. These slow-swimming rays do not propel themselves with undulations of the disc in the manner of stingrays but with lateral movement of the tail. They feed on crustaceans, molluscs, worms, and fishes.

LEOPARD TORPEDO
Torpedo panthera Olfers, 1831

Disc length about 87% disc width; anterior edge of disc truncate to slightly double emarginate; eyes small, their greatest diameter about 1.2-1.6 in preorbital length, 1.3-1.5 in interorbital space; spiracles about equal to or a little smaller than eyes, a short distance directly behind eyes, their rim in adults with seven or eight fleshy folds or papillae; a cutaneous fold along side of tail; dorsal fins subtriangular, very close together, the origin of the first over middle of pelvic fins, the second distinctly smaller, its origin slightly posterior to end of pelvic fins; caudal fin rounded to truncate with rounded corners; dorsal surface orangish brown, spotted or mottled with white; edge of disc, fins, and cutaneous fold on tail white. Reaches at least 35 cm. Red Sea to Arabian Gulf. Usually found inshore on sandy bottoms. Gohar and Mazhar (1964) noted in the northwestern Red Sea that "it seems to seek deeper water during the cold season."

52. *Torpedo panthera* (J. Hoover)

MARBLED TORPEDO
Torpedo sinuspersici Olfers, 1831.

Disc length about 84% disc width; anterior edge of disc slightly double emarginate; eyes small, their greatest diameter about 1.5 in preorbital length in juveniles to 2.5 in adults; interorbital space of adults about twice eye diameter; spiracles of adults larger than eyes, about a half eye diameter behind eyes, their rim usually with nine or ten papillae (four or five small ones on inner edge and four or five larger ones on posterior outer edge, according to Fraser-Brunner, 1949); dorsal fins subtriangular, very close together, the origin of the first dorsal over or slightly posterior to middle of pelvic fins; second dorsal fin about three-fourths size of first, its origin at or slightly anterior to end of pelvic fins; caudal fin truncate to slightly rounded, with broadly rounded corners; dark brown with small pale tan spots near margin of disc and tortuous pale tan bands and spots over rest of disc, tail, and fins; juveniles with large white-edged black spots. Reaches about 70 cm. Red Sea to the Gulf of Oman, Arabian Gulf, India and Sri Lanka; also recorded from the east coast of Africa south to Natal by Wallace (1967c) – this identification regarded as provisional by Compagno in Smith and Heemstra, 1986. *Torpedo suessii* Steindachner is cited by authors as a synonym based on the juvenile stage.

53. *Torpedo sinuspersici*, about 30 cm (J. Randall)

54. *Narcine* sp. (J. Mee)

NUMBFISHES
FAMILY NARCINIDAE

The numbfishes are divisible into two subfamilies, the Narcininae with four genera and about 20 species, and the Narkinae with five genera and about ten species. The species of Narcininae have a deep groove around the mouth, protrusible jaws, and two dorsal fins. The Narkinae are characterized by a shallow groove around the mouth, only slightly protractile jaws, and usually one dorsal fin (*Heteronarce* with two, and *Temera* with none). Most numbfishes are small (the largest 76 cm) with a disc which is round, oblong, or somewhat wedge-shaped. They have a strongly tapering tail longer than the disc, and a well-developed caudal fin, usually with a lateral skin fold. Eyes small, vesti-gial on some species. Mouth transverse and nearly straight, with labial cartilages; teeth small, each with a single sharp cusp. As in the Torpedinidae, there is a large kidney-shaped electric organ on each side of the disc capable of delivering a strong shock.

LARGE-EYE ELECTRIC RAY
Narcine sp.

Disc about 1.1 times wider than long, the width 46-49% total length; anterior part of disc angular, the snout tip narrowly rounded; preoral snout length 13% total length; preorbital length 9-10% total length; eyes 2.2-2.4 in preorbital length; spiracles adjacent to eyes, the margins smooth; dorsal fins large, the anterior margin of first dorsal 14-18% total length; origin of first dorsal fin anterior to rear base of pelvic fins; interdorsal space less than base of first dorsal fin; dorsal surface of disc brown to reddish orange with obscure dark brown mottling, small indistinct light blotches, and some blackish blotches anteriorly; ventral side of disk white with dusky blotches anteriorly. Only two specimens have been collected, both from the Gulf of Oman, one from 70 m and the other from a trawl haul in 106-162 m, the largest 33 cm.

GUITARFISHES
FAMILY RHINOBATIDAE

The guitarfish family consists of nine genera and about 52 species. Two of the genera, *Rhina* and *Rhynchobatus*, are often treated as a separate family (either Rhinidae or Rhynchobatidae). Norman (1926) and Compagno in Smith and Heemstra (1986) are followed here in classifying all guitarfishes in one family. Head broadly rounded and distinct from pectoral fins (*Rhina*) or narrowly wedge-shaped and merging with pectorals (*Rhinobatos* and *Rhynchobatus*); disc not as broad and flattened as other rays (sawfishes excepted); tail stout and muscular; body and fins covered with close-set dermal denticles; a middorsal row of tubercles often present; eyes small to moderate in size; spiracles large, directly behind eyes; five pairs of short gill slits, each set in an oblique row ventrally on head; teeth close-set, flattened, and pavement-like; two well-developed dorsal fins; caudal fin with no lower lobe (*Rhinobatos*) or with distinct upper and lower lobes (*Rhynchobatus*). These fishes are worldwide in tropical and subtropical seas, but most species are restricted to continental shelves or large islands. They are harmless to man, but large individuals brought alive into a boat could inflict injury as they thrash about.

BOWMOUTH GUITARFISH
Rhina ancylostoma Bloch and Schneider, 1801

Head depressed and broadly rounded, its anterior part bearing mouth and eyes clearly delimited from pectoral fins; body very thick medially; a long median ridge with a band of tubercles of variable size extending from just behind spiracles, with one or two lesser ridges to each side; another tubercle-bearing ridge medial to eye and spiracle; spiracles without cutaneous folds on their posterior edge; mouth curiously undulate, with three rounded projections of lower jaw fitting into three indentations of upper; dorsal fins erect and slightly falcate with pointed apices; origin of first dorsal fin a little anterior to origin of pelvic fins; second dorsal fin about three-fourths as large as first dorsal, midway between it and caudal fin; caudal fin large and lunate, the upper lobe extending higher than lower; pectoral fins distinctly triangular; dorsal part of body and fins with white spots; a pale-edged black spot above pectoral fins and two black bands across interorbital space; ventral part of body largely pale; juveniles more strongly marked than adults. Reported to reach

270 cm. Western Pacific from New South Wales to Korea and southern Japan, west along continental shores to the Red Sea and coast of East Africa; also recorded from the Seychelles (Smith and Smith, 1963) and Maldives (Randall and Anderson, 1993). Feeds mainly on crabs and shellfish.

GRANULATE GUITARFISH
Rhinobatos granulatus Cuvier, 1829

Width of disc 3.05-3.2 in total length; snout pointed, the lateral margin concave; snout long, its preorbital length 4.7-4.9 in total length; distance between spiracles 3.3-3.7 in preorbital length; rostral ridges close together for most their length, diverging only basally; a broad median band of enlarged denticles passing posteriorly from anterior interorbital space, with a middorsal series of large thorn-like denticles commencing a short distance behind spiracles; a transverse row of two or three large thorn-

like denticles on each side at level of greatest width of pectoral fins; a row of moderate tubercles medial to each spiracle and eye and curving anterior to eye; another smaller series on each rostral ridge; spiracles with two cutaneous folds on their posterior margin; nostrils about half width of mouth; dorsal fins about twice as high as their base; grey-brown dorsally, the entire snout translucent a short distance anterior to eyes, except for rostral ridges; median fins and outer part of paired fins light tan; ventrolateral dermal fold on tail and narrow edge of pelvic fins white. Largest reported, 215 cm in total length. Coast of India to the Arabian Gulf; also recorded from China.

HALAVI GUITARFISH
Rhinobatos halavi (Forsskål, 1775)

Width of disc 3.05-3.15 in total length; snout bluntly pointed, its lateral edge nearly straight, the preorbital length 7.0-7.4 in total

55. *Rhina ancylostoma*, 54 cm (J. Randall)

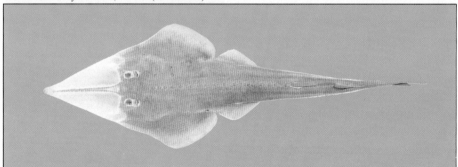

56. *Rhinobatos granulatus*, 39 cm (J. Randall)

57. *Rhinobatos halavi*, 99.5 cm (J. Randall)

length; distance between spiracles 2.6-2.7 in preorbital length; rostral ridges close together most of their length, diverging anteriorly and posteriorly; a median band of enlarged denticles commencing behind spiracles, with a middorsal row of large blunt tubercles; a row of tubercles median to spiracle and eye, curving anterior to eye; a row of small tubercles on each rostral ridge; spiracle with two cutaneous folds on posterior margin, the inner one small; nostrils about 1.5 in width of mouth; dorsal fins subequal, the first nearly twice as high as its base; uniform tan dorsally, except large translucent area on snout to each side of rostral cartilages; ventrolateral fold on tail, margin of pelvic fins (and claspers of males), and lower edge of caudal fin white. Largest reported, 171 cm. Known from the Red Sea (type locality) to Gulf of Oman (one collected in shallow water at Duqm in central Oman); also recorded from China. Gohar and Mazhar (1964) reported the food in the northwestern Red Sea as mainly crustaceans, especially prawns. This species is common along sandy shores in the northwestern Red Sea from May to October, especially females which seek shallow water to give birth to their young. Litter size up to ten; size at birth about 29 cm.

ARABIAN GUITARFISH
Rhinobatos punctifer Compagno and Randall, 1987

Width of disc 2.6-2.9 in total length; snout bluntly pointed, its lateral edge slightly concave near tip, the preorbital length 7.3-7.6 in total length; distance between spiracles 2.3-2.5 in preorbital length; eyes relatively large, the greatest diameter 3.2-3.5 in preorbital length (two specimens, 70.5-75.2 cm total length); rostral cartilages well-separated, diverging a little basally and slightly convergent anteriorly; a middorsal row of moderately large, blunt tubercles beginning an orbit diameter behind spiracles, becoming small between dorsal fins; two prominent cutaneous folds on posterior edge of spiracles, the inner one shorter; nostril length 1.3 in width of mouth; dorsal fins triangular with slightly convex anterior margin, the first dorsal slightly larger than second; base of first dorsal fin 1.75 in height of fin; dorsal surface brownish grey, the median fins, pelvic fins, outer part of disc and most of snout lateral to rostral ridges tan; widely scattered white spots the size of pupil or smaller and large diffuse dark grey spots (more evident on Gulf of Oman specimen); ventrolateral cutaneous fold, edge of pelvic fins, and lower edge of caudal fin pale. Known only from the 70.5-cm holotype

from the Gulf of Aqaba, one 75.2 cm specimen from Muscat, and four specimens from the Suez market, 62-80.5 cm (identified as *R. schlegeli* Müller and Henle by Gohar and Mazhar, 1964).

SALALAH GUITARFISH
Rhinobatos salalah Randall and Compagno, 1995

Width of disc about 2.9 in total length; disc broadly wedge-shaped anteriorly, the lateral edge slightly convex; margin of posterior half of disc strongly convex, without any angularity; tip of snout bluntly pointed; snout short, the preorbital length 8.7 in total length; distance between spiracles 2.15 in preorbital length; eye 4.2 in preorbital length; rostral ridges well-separated throughout their length, diverging slightly anteriorly and posteriorly; a middorsal row of moderately large, blunt tubercles; two prominent cutaneous folds on posterior edge of spiracles, the inner one shorter; length of nostrils about 1.6 in width of mouth; dorsal fins subequal, triangular, the height nearly twice width of base; light tan with scattered, dark-edged, bluish white spots the size of pupil or larger on outer part of disc and on pelvic fins; ventrolateral cutaneous fold on tail and edges of fins white. Known from a single specimen, 54.5 cm total length, obtained in the Salalah fish market.

GIANT GUITARFISH
Rhynchobatus djiddensis (Forsskål, 1775)

Snout long and pointed; head merging somewhat gradually with pectoral fins, but juncture apparent from a concavity in lateral margin; a long median ridge with small tubercles on back; spiracles large, adjacent to hind part of eyes, their posterior edge with two prominent cutaneous folds; lower jaw with a broad median bump fitting into a depression in upper jaw; tail longer than disc, stout and muscular; dorsal fins tall, narrow, and falcate, the origin of first slightly posterior to origin of pelvic fins; second dorsal fin about three-fourths size of first dorsal, closer to caudal fin than first dorsal; paired fins distinctly triangular; olivaceous to grey-brown dorsally, with rows of white spots along side of body and scattered white spots

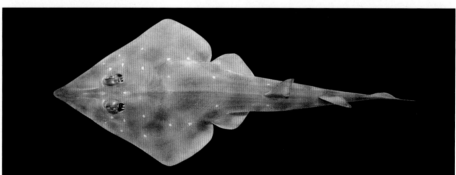

58. *Rhinobatos punctifer*, 754 cm (J. Randall)

59. *Rhinobatos salalah*, 55 cm (J. Randall)

60. *Rhynchobatis djiddensis* (O. Schlumberger)

43

on paired fins; a black spot edged with four white spots above anterior third of each pectoral fin; ventral surface whitish. Recorded to 305 cm and 227 kg. Ranges from the Mariana Islands and New Caledonia in the Pacific to the Red Sea (type locality) and coast of East Africa to Transkei, South Africa; also reported from the Seychelles and Maldives. Feeds on crabs, squids, and fishes (Gohar and Mazhar, 1964; Wallace, 1967a). Compagno in Smith and Heemstra (1986) has suggested that there may be five or six species of *Rhynchobatus*, with *djiddensis* restricted to the Red Sea and western Indian Ocean.

STINGRAYS
FAMILY DASYATIDAE

This well-known family of rays is represented by five genera: *Dasyatis* (*Trygon* is a synonym), *Himantura*, *Pastinachus* (*Hypolophus* is a synonym), *Taeniura*, and *Urogymnus*. There are more than 60 species of the family which occur in tropical to temperate seas, usually in shallow continental shelf waters on sedimentary substrata (into which they readily bury themselves). Some stingrays are found only in fresh water (Compagno and Roberts, 1982). *Dasyatis violacea* (Bonaparte) is unusual in being totally pelagic. In addition to the features mentioned under Rays above, the stingrays are characterized as follows: head, body, and pectoral fins fully fused to form a flattened disc which varies from nearly circular to rhomboidal and is often broader than long; snout rounded, angular, or apically pointed; tail slender, without dorsal or caudal fins, varying from shorter than disc to far longer, and usually armed with one or more serrate, venomous spines dorsally near base; tail may have a dorsal and/or ventral, longitudinal, cutaneous fold; skin smooth except on tail and dorsal surface of disc where it may be variously roughened with small to large, blunt to sharp tubercles, mainly middorsally on disc; mouth straight or nearly so, set well back from front of disc; teeth small, in numerous alternating rows, the surface flat to rounded or with a cusp; prominent papillae on floor of mouth. Some species reach enormous size, to over 2 m in width and a weight up to 350 kg. The larger rays are able to excavate large craters in the sediment in search of their usual fossorial prey such as various worms, crustaceans, molluscs, and fishes. Wounds from the tail spine are extremely painful and have resulted in fatalities. Immediate soaking of the injured member in water as hot as can be tolerated is advised. Probably more species of stingrays occur in Oman waters than recorded here. Because of infrequent capture and the large size of many of the species, they are not well represented in museum collections; more field work and systematic research is needed before the classification is definitive. Blegvad (1944: fig. 19) illustrated a large ray from the Arabian Gulf as *Trygon gerrardi* (Gray) (?) which does not seem to be this species (well-illustrated in his Plate II, Fig. 3). The large specimen was not retained. It might have been *Dasyatis microps* Annandale. Kuronuma and Abe (1986) recorded the long-tailed *Himantura bleekeri* (Blyth), type locality, Bay of Bengal, from the Arabian Gulf but did not collect *H. gerrardi* which is a common Gulf species, hence there is a possibility of misidentification.

OMAN MASKED STINGRAY
Dasyatis sp.

Disc rhomboidal, but with snout tip and lateral corners rounded; snout short, forming an obtuse angle; eyes large, about 2.5 in preorbital length; eyes lateral on elevated part of head, oriented more to the side than dorsally; spiracles large and oblique, adjacent to eye from behind middle of its posterior margin to below middle of its lower edge; tail longer than disc width, usually with two venomous spines on basal third, a short low dorsal cutaneous fold posterior to spines and probably a long ventral one; skin naked except for a short median row of small tubercles; light brown dorsally with numerous light blue-grey spots without dark edges over all of disc and scattered small black spots; an irregular brown band containing small black spots across interorbital space and extending lateral to eyes and spiracles; posterior part of tail with alternating black and white bands. Attains about 70 cm. This stingray appears to be an undescribed close relative of *D. kuhlii* (Müller and Henle), but it may be only a colour form of the latter. It has been observed in southern Oman and in the Gulf of Oman, but it is not common. The author has photographed what seems to be the same species off Phuket, Thailand. *D. kuhlii* has fewer and smaller pale bluish spots, and they are distinctly dark-edged; also there are fewer small black spots on the disc. Specimens are lacking from Oman for detailed study; the above diagnosis was taken from photographs.

61. *Dasyatis* sp., about 70 cm (J. Randall)

GERRARD'S STINGRAY
Himantura gerrardi (Gray, 1851)

Disc rhomboidal, the lateral corners very broadly rounded, the apex of snout acutely pointed (disregarding the produced snout tip, the angle of the snout is obtuse); disc width slightly greater than disc length, the length about 1.1 in width; preorbital length about 4.9 in disc width; eye diameter nearly as large as greatest length of spiracle, about 3.7 in preorbital length; distance between spiracles about 6 in disc width; floor of mouth behind teeth with two papillae; tail as much as 3.5 times longer than disk width, with a venomous spine about 1.5 spine lengths from base of tail; tail very slender posterior to spine, without cutaneous folds (but a midventral row of small sharp tubercles); a median band of one to three rows of tubercles as long as distance between spiracles on disc, commencing about two eye diameters behind eyes (three of the more posterior tubercles enlarged); dorsal part of disc yellowish brown, the tail with numerous alternating black and white rings (above diagnosis from a single specimen from Kuwait, 24.8 cm in disc width). Size attained by this species uncertain due to confusion with a related, apparently unnamed species. Ranges from the Arabian Gulf to Indonesia; records from the Red Sea appear to be in error. Day (1878: pl. 194, fig. 1) illustrated a small specimen from India as *Trygon uarnak*. The stingray described and figured as *Dasyatis jenkinsii* from Natal by Wallace (1967b) appears to be this species. The species illustrated by Randall et al. (1978: 80) as *Dasyatis* sp. is probably also *H. gerrardi* (Peter Last, pers. comm.).

SCALETAIL STINGRAY
Himantura imbricata (Bloch and Schneider, 1801)

Disc hemispherical to eyes, then with margins markedly concave, the snout acutely pointed; disc length equal to or slightly greater than disc width (the young with relatively wider disc); preorbital snout length about 3.5 in disc length; eyes nearly as large as spiracles, their greatest diameter about 4 in preorbital length; distance between spiracles about 1.8 in preorbital length; floor of mouth with two prominent papillae; tail short, as long or slightly longer than disc in adults (reported in young up to two times disc length), usually with two venomous spines in about middle of tail and low dorsal and ventral cutaneous folds; a broad median zone of dermal denticles from interorbital to base of spines on tail, narrower over branchial region; sometimes a median row of larger tubercles; often a row

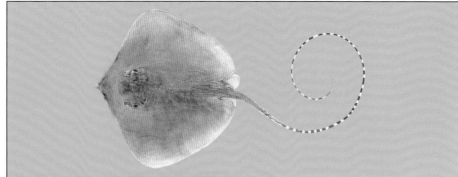

62. *Himantura gerrardi*, 63 cm (J. Randall)

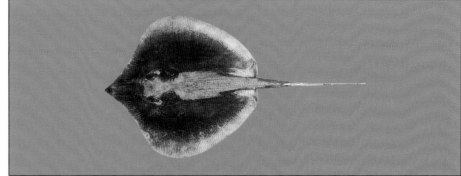

63. *Himantura imbricata*, 35 cm (J. Randall)

64. *Himantura jenkinsii* (P. Woodhead)

of about six enlarged flattened tubercles dorsally on tail before spine; orangish brown, shading to light brown distally on disc, the zone of denticles on back grey-brown; posterior edge of pelvic fins and lateral edge of tail on about its posterior half white. A small species, the maximum disc width about 22 cm. Occurs from the Arabian Gulf to the Bay of Bengal. Littoral to a maximum of about 30 m on mud or muddy sand substrata; may occur in estuarine habitats. After examining numerous specimens, Annandale (1909) concluded that *H. walga* (Müller and Henle) is a synonym.

JENKINS' STINGRAY
Himantura jenkinsii Annadale, 1909

Disc rhomboidal, the anterior margins straight, the tip slightly pointed (ignoring the tip, the front angle of the disc is broadly obtuse); lateral corners of disc broadly rounded; posterior margins of disc moderately convex; disc width about 1.2 times greater than disc length; length from snout tip to a line at greatest disc width about one-third disc length; preorbital (snout) length slightly greater than interorbital width; length of eye and spiracle combined about 2 in preorbital length; floor of mouth with four papillae; tail a little longer than disc width, nearly cylindrical without cutaneous folds, strongly tapering basally to slender whip-like form; one or two venomous spines on tail about one-fourth distance from base to tip; a broad median zone of close-set denticles from interoribtal space to and continuing onto tail; a median row of enlarged heart-shaped denticles on disc and tail to venomous spine(s); olive-brown dorsally, the margin of disc and its ventral surface white. The two type specimens measured 104 cm disc width. Ranges from Thailand to the Gulf of Oman; the types were taken in 42-50 m in the Bay of Bengal off the Ganjam coast of India. As mentioned above, the stingray from South Africa identified by Wallace (1967b) as *Dasyatis jenkinsii* appears to be *Himantura gerrardi*.

65. *Himantura uarnak* (P. Woodhead)

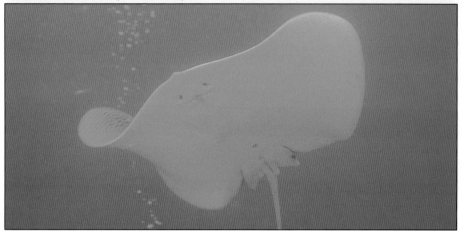

66. Ventral side of *Himantura uarnak*, 1 m wide (J. Randall)

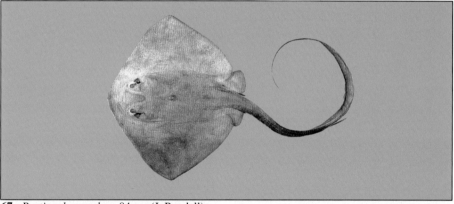

67. *Pastinachus sephen*, 84 cm (J. Randall)

DARKSPOTTED STINGRAY
Himantura uarnak (Forsskål, 1775)

Disk rhomboid in adults, the anterior margins nearly straight, ending in a pointed snout (not projecting, the snout angle obtuse); posterior margin of disc slightly rounded; anterior margins of disc of juveniles concave, the posterior margins strongly convex; disc width slightly greater than disc length; preorbital length of snout 4.7-4.9 in disc width; eye diameter 4.6-5.0 in preorbital length; distance between spiracles 5.0-5.6 in disc width; floor of mouth with five papillae; tail very long and slender, at least two times longer than disc width in adults and up to 3.5 times longer in juveniles; tail with one or two venomous spines near base (distance of first spine from base of tail about 2.5-3.0 in disc width); tail without cutaneous folds; skin smooth except for a broad median band of dermal denticles from interorbital to base of tail; one to three enlarged, flattened, heart-shaped tubercles in middorsal line; dorsal surface light yellowish brown with numerous, round to oblong, dark brown spots, some near middle of disc approaching size of eye, those near margins smaller; pale spaces between spots usually less than spot diameters; a row of dark spots on each side of base of tail; rest of tail narrowly ringed with black and white. Largest recorded from Arabian waters, 323 cm total length, 153 cm disc width, 87 kg; other records to 200 cm disc width and weight to 120 kg, but these may be other species. Reported to range throughout the Indian Ocean and western Pacific; however there are different colour forms sometimes identified as *H. uarnak* (one with a highly reticulate pattern, another with irregular pale-centred dark spots) which may eventually be shown to be distinct species. Until the classification of this complex of stingrays is sorted out, the true range of *U. uarnak* is uncertain. Unquestioned, however, is its occurrence all around the Arabian Peninsula; also, it has invaded the eastern Mediterranean via the Suez Canal. Usually found on sand at depths of 0.5-10 m, but reported to 50 m. Devadoss (1981) examined the contents of 68 stomachs of this ray, of which 43 had identifiable material; 67% by volume consisted of a wide variety of fishes of which leiognathids and engraulids were the most numerous, 27.8% crustaceans (especially shrimps), and 4.6% molluscs.

FANTAIL STINGRAY
Pastinachus sephen (Forsskål, 1775)

Disc rhomboid, the pectoral apices rounded, the snout tip slightly produced to a point; disc width about 1.2-1.3 times broader than disc length; median part of head and trunk very thick; snout short, the preorbital length 6.5-7 in disc width; eyes small, their longest diameter about 3-4.5 in preorbital length; distance between spiracles about 4.8-5.6 in disc width; floor of mouth with four or five papillae; tail broad at base and depressed, its length about twice disc width, becoming narrow and nearly cylindrical posterior to venomous spine (the anterior end of which is about one-third length of tail from its base); a broad cutaneous fold ventrally on tail, commencing a short distance before base of spine and extending about two spine lengths beyond tip of spine; a broad median zone of dermal denticles covering all of thickened part of disc and extending narrrowly onto dorsal part of tail to the spine; three or four, large, pale, circular tubercles in midline of centre of disc; grey-brown, the membranous tail fold and tail posterior to it dark grey to black. Attains a total length of at least 300 cm and a disc width of about 180 cm. Broadly distributed along continental and large island shores in the western Pacific from New South Wales to southern Japan, west to the Red Sea and coast of Africa south to Natal. Found on sand and mud substrata, sometimes in the vicinity of coral reefs. Food-habit studies revealed feeding on fishes (including leiognathids, *Nemipterus*, and soles), crustaceans, polychaete worms, sipunculids, and molluscs (including bivalves and gastropods) (Devadoss, 1981; Homma and Ishihara, 1994). Often classified in *Dasyatis* or *Hypolophus* (a synonym of *Pastinachus*).

REEF STINGRAY
Taeniura lymma (Forsskål, 1775)

Disc ovate, a little longer than wide, the snout rounded to slightly wedge-shaped, the preorbital length about 5 in disc width; median part of disc to eyes much thicker than rest of disc; eyes a little larger than spiracles, their greatest diameter about 2 in preorbital length; distance between spiracles about 6 in disc width; opening of mouth undulate, covered by internasal flap which is fringed posteriorly; two papillae in floor of mouth behind teeth; tail about 1.5 times longer than disc, depressed and tapering, the venomous spine or spines (usually two) in about centre of tail; a low cutaneous fold dorsally on tail posterior to spine; a broad membranous fold ventrally on tail commencing below base of spine and continuing to tip; surface of disc and tail usually smooth (may be a few tubercles in middorsal line); dorsal colour yellowish brown, the disc with numerous, round to oval, bright blue spots of variable size, the tail with a blue stripe on each side. Reaches at least 70 cm. Ranges from the Red Sea (type locality) and coast of East Africa to the western Pacific (from the Philippines to Queensland, east to the Solomon Islands); also recorded from Madagascar, the Seychelles, and Maldives. Nocturnal; reported to feed on molluscs, polychaete worms, and shrimps; hides on sand patches in caves or beneath ledges in reef during the day. Rare or absent in the Arabian Gulf and Gulf of Oman.

BLACKBLOTCHED STINGRAY
Taeniura meyeni Müller and Henle, 1841

Disc nearly circular, slightly broader than long, the greatest width about one-third disc length from anterior end; a very small pointed projection may be present at front of snout; snout short, the preorbital length about 5-6 in disc width; median part of disc very thick; eyes moderately large, their diameter about 3 in preorbital length; distance between spiracles about equal to preorbital length; mouth nearly straight, not covered by fringed posterior part of internasal flap; four papillae in floor of mouth; tail about as long as disc, depressed basally, the spine (usually one) in about midlength; a broad membranous fold midventrally on tail posterior to base of spine; dorsal surface of disc and tail with small flat denticles separated from others by a space greater than denticle diameter; a median row of sharp tubercles on back, extending on tail to spine, and two short oblique rows over posterior branchial region; grey, densely blotched and mottled with black. Disc width to at least 180 cm and total length to 330 cm.

68. *Taeniura lymma* (J. Hoover)

69. *Taeniura meyeni* (J. Hoover)

70. *Urogymnus africanus*, 137 cm (J. Randall)

Wide-ranging in the Indo-Pacific region from the Red Sea and East Africa to the Marquesas Islands. Generally seen in shallow water, but one record from 435 m off Mozambique (Wallace, 1967b). Two of three specimens with food in their stomachs had eaten only fishes (Randall, 1980; Homma and Ishihara, 1994). Although not aggressive, at least two humans have died from the spine wound of this large ray. *T. melanospilos* Bleeker is a synonym.

THORNY RAY
Urogymnus africanus (Bloch and Schneider, 1801)

Disc oval, a little longer than wide, very thick and mound-like centrally; eyes small, in adults much smaller than spiracles; space between spiracles 5-6 in disc width; thick central part of dorsal surface covered with numerous small flattened denticles; entire disc and tail with large thorn-like tubercles; tail about as long as disc, nearly cylindrical, strongly tapering, and without venomous spines or cutaneous folds; mouth covered by fringed posterior end of internasal flap; three to five papillae in floor of mouth; brownish grey, the tail becoming blackish distally. Reported to reach 100 cm in disc width. Type locality, Guinea coast of West Africa; much better known from the Indo-Pacific region where it ranges from the Red Sea and coast of East Africa to the Marshall Islands and Fiji. Five of seven specimens with food in their stomachs had eaten sipunculids; three of the five had also consumed polychaetes and crustaceans (Homma and Ishihara, 1994). *U. asperrimus* (Bloch and Schneider) is regarded as a synonym.

BUTTERFLYRAYS
FAMILY GYMNURIDAE

The butterflyrays consist of two genera, *Aetoplatea* with a small dorsal fin near midlength of tail, and *Gymnura*, without a dorsal fin; there are at least 12 species in the family, three in the genus *Gymnura* from the Atlantic. All have a characteristic, very broad, flat disc (at least 1.6 times broader than long) and a tail which is shorter than the disc length; a venomous spine may nor may not be present on the tail; internasal flap (transverse curtain) smooth-edged; no papillae in floor of mouth; skin usually smooth. Some authors prefer to regard these rays as a subfamily of the Dasyatidae.

VARIEGATED BUTTERFLYRAY
Gymnura poecilura (Shaw, 1804)

Disc twice as broad as long, the posterior margin convex, the anterior a slight sinuous curve; lateral corners of disc a little rounded; front of snout with a small, acutely pointed projection; preorbital length about 12 in disc width; distance between spiracles 11-12 in disc width; eyes smaller than spiracles, about 2-2.5 in preorbital length; tail about half length of disc, with a small venomous spine on its base; light brown dorsally with numerous small whitish spots, sometimes with scattered smaller dark brown spots; tail alternately banded with black and white (about 8 or 9 rings of each), the white with a dorsal dark spot (sometimes only on basal white rings). Reported to reach a maximum width of about 100 cm. Occurs from the Red Sea, Arabian Gulf, and Gulf of Oman, along continental shores of southern Asia to the Indo-Malayan region.

EAGLERAYS AND COWNOSE RAYS
FAMILY MYLIOBATIDAE

This family consists of two subfamilies, the Myliobatinae with four genera and about 22 species and the Rhinopterinae with one genus and about 10 species (some authors treat the two subfamilies as distinct families). These rays occur in all temperate to tropical seas. They have a very wide disc (at least 1.6 times wider than long), the lateral corners acutely pointed; medial part of disc very thick, the anterior part of the head protruding; the snout as viewed from above may be pointed, rounded, medially truncate, or medially indented; eyes oriented laterally more than dorsally; tail longer than disc and whiplike, with a small dorsal fin near its base, and without a caudal fin or fin folds; one or more venomous spines present or absent; five pairs of ventral gill slits, as in other rays; teeth flat, plate-like, hexagonal, closely joined, in one to seven series (the median series the longest, if more than one); several anterior-posterior rows of teeth at front of jaws functional. The food consists mainly of hard-shelled molluscs and crustaceans which are crushed by the powerful jaws. Shell fragments are ejected from the mouth. These rays can be very destructive to shellfish beds. Three species occur in Oman waters. Blegvad (1944) recorded *Aetomylaeus maculatus* (Gray and Hardwicke) from the Arabian Gulf (but retained no specimens). He described it as about the same shape as *A. nichofii* with the tail more than 4 times longer than disc; color olive-brown with lighter spots dispersed over the disc. This species may eventually be recorded from Oman. Sivasubramaniam and Ibrahim (1982) recorded *Rhinoptera adspera* Müller and Henle from Qatar; it might also be expected from Oman waters.

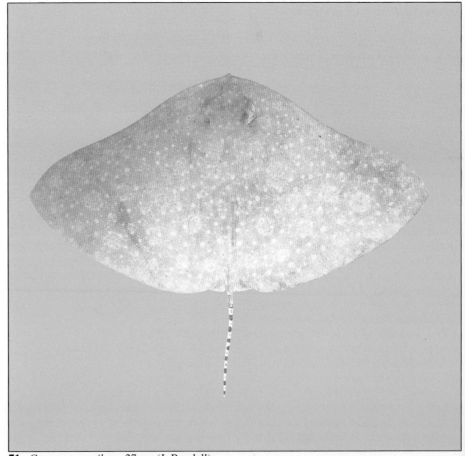

71. *Gymnura poecilura*, 27 cm (J. Randall)

SUBFAMILY MYLIOBATINAE

SPOTTED EAGLERAY
Aetobatis narinari (Euphrasen, 1790)

Disc length (including protruding part of head) 1.7-1.8 in disc width; anterior margin of disc straight for most of its length, curving posteriorly to lateral apex; posterior margin a sinuous curve with a broad anterior concave part and short posterior convex portion; head nearly circular in cross section; a prominent, flat, bluntly pointed, rostral lobe (giving rise to another common name, Duckbill Ray); rest of front of head rising steeply; tail, when intact, extremely long (as much as three times disc width); one to five venomous spines near base of tail behind dorsal fin; teeth unique in being a single series of long flat plates, those of lower jaw chevron-shaped; skin smooth; dark grey to black dorsally, with numerous white spots or rings; tail black. Largest specimen, a female, 230 cm in width. Weight to at least 200 kg. Cosmopolitan in all warm seas; migrates to higher latitudes in summer months (to Chesapeake Bay, at 37°N on the eastern coast of the United States and to Algoa Bay at 34°S in South Africa). This ray feeds heavily on both gastropods and pelecypods, but also shrimps and worms; fish remains have been found in stomachs. The author removed 41 juvenile conchs (40 of them *Strombus gigas*) from a 46-kg specimen speared in the Virgin Islands; there was not a single piece of shell or even an operculum in the stomach. Usual litter size, four. An active ray; it has often been seen to leap free of the surface.

BANDED EAGLERAY
Aetomylaeus nichofii (Bloch and Schneider, 1801)

Disc much wider than long, the length (including projecting part of head) 1.6-1.8 in width; anterior margin of disc straight except for curving posteriorly near lateral tip; posterior margin of disc concave; head flattened dorsally; a prominent rostral lobe (pointed in adults, rounded in juveniles); tail very slender and long, its length as much as 2.5 times disc width; venomous spine absent; origin of dorsal fin over or slightly anterior to rear base of pelvic fins; teeth mostly in seven series, a long median one and three smaller ones on each side, but in staggered rows; skin smooth, except in large adults which have small widely spaced denticles; grey-brown dorsally, with numerous transverse pale yellowish lines or rows of spots on disc; juveniles with chevron-shaped, purplish blue, transverse bands on disc (one of 25.2-cm disc width has five

such bands on disc and two straight transverse ones on head). Attains about 60-cm disc width; young born at about 17 cm. Ranges from the Arabian Gulf to the Indo-Malayan region and north to Japan. Littoral to depths of at least 70 m. Sivasubramaniam and Ibrahim (1982) reported the food as molluscs, crabs, lobsters, and shrimps.

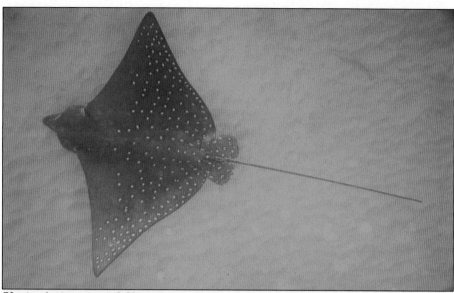

72. *Aetobatis narinari* (J. Hoover)

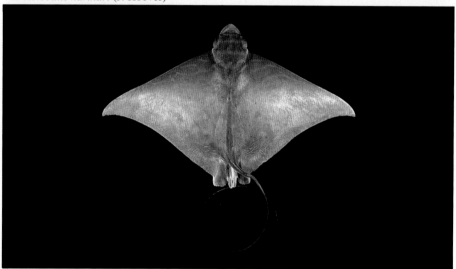

73. *Aetomylaeus nichofii*, 92 cm (J. Randall)

SUBFAMILY RHINOPTERINAE

OMAN COWNOSE RAY
Rhinoptera jayakari Boulenger, 1895

Disc length (including protruding head) about 1.75 in disc width; each anterior margin of disc nearly straight, the posterior

74. *Rhinoptera jayakari* (J. Hoover)

concave, the disc tips pointed; upper part of snout bilobed, separated from a lower, forward-projecting, and also bilobed part by a continuous deep groove around front of head; tail short, only two-thirds disc length, with a dorsal fin at its base; a serrate spine on tail behind dorsal fin; teeth flat and pavement-like, in nine series, the middle teeth of lower jaw 1.5 times broader than adjacent teeth; olivaceous above, white below, the tail black distally. This ray is known only from a single dried skin from Muscat in the Natural History Museum, London. It appears to be distinct on the basis of nine series of teeth in the jaws and its short tail. Like other species of *Rhinoptera*, it is sometimes seen in schools such as the one illustrated on page 16, which was photographed at Juzor al Hallaniyat (Kuria Muria Islands).

MANTAS AND DEVIL RAYS
FAMILY MOBULIDAE

There are only two genera of rays of this family, *Mobula* with nine species (Notarbartolo-di-Sciara, 1987), and *Manta* with an unknown number. Although it seems likely, at least from differences in colour, that there is more than one species of *Manta* in the world, Bigelow and Schroeder (1953) and Wallace (1967b) are followed here in recognising a single circumtropical species, *M. birostris*. The rays of these two genera are found in all tropical to warm temperate seas. Unlike other rays, they are plankton-feeders, hence not bottom-dwelling. The shape of the disc is much like that of myliobatids – primarily straight on anterior margins and concave posteriorly with pointed tips. However, they are not as thick-bodied, have a broader head, and a pair of unique, widely separated, cephalic flaps which they extend anteriorly from each side of the head to divert zooplankton into the broad mouth; when not feeding the flaps are coiled into a compact spiral. The eyes are lateral, at the base of the cephalic flaps. The teeth are minute, in numerous interlocking series (may be imbricated in large adults). There is a slender whip-like tail which is usually as long or longer than the disc, and a small dorsal fin on the base of the tail. Some species have one or two small serrate spines behind the dorsal fin. Also unique to these rays are the branchial filters on the inner side of the gill openings which serve to strain the zooplankton. Although it seems clear that the mobulids are derived from myliobatid-like ancestors, Nishida (1990) is not followed in placing these two groups in the same family.

MANTA
Manta birostris Donndorff, 1798

Length of disc about 2.2 in width of disc; head very broad; mouth terminal and capacious, flanked by large cephalic flaps which are about half as broad at base as their length; teeth only in lower jaw, minute, in about 270 series of 18 rows centrally, narrowing to 12 to 14 rows at corners; tail slender, about as long as disc; some specimens with one or two small serrate spines on tail behind dorsal fin; skin with small stellate tubercles; colour variable, but usually dark grey to black dorsally, sometimes with whitish areas, and white ventrally, frequently with a few dark grey to black blotches. The largest of rays and among the largest of fishes; attains a width of 7 m and weight up to 1600 kg. Occurs in all tropical and subtropical seas. Feeds mainly on pelagic crustaceans and other small animals of the zooplankton, occasionally on small schooling fishes. Often accompanied by the remora *Remorina albescens*. Capable of leaping clear of the surface of the sea.

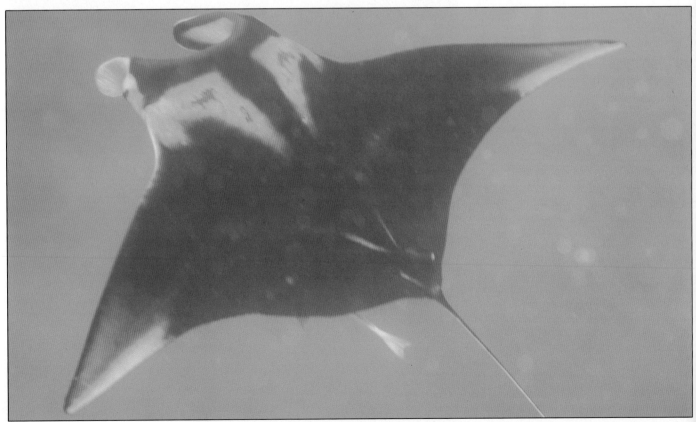

75. *Manta birostris*, 2.2 m wide (J. Randall)

KUHL'S DEVIL RAY
Mobula kuhlii (Valenciennes, 1841)

Disc length about 1.9 in disc width; anterior margin of disc straight over most its length, becoming slightly concave as it approaches head and slightly convex at tip, the posterior margin broadly concave; head broad and short, the cephalic flaps straight; mouth on lower surface of disc, its width about 12% disc width; preoral length contained about 3 times in width of mouth, less than 3.7% of disc width; bands of teeth in both jaws about 76% mouth width, the teeth wider than long, tessellated, the crown rugose; tail variable in length, without a spine, its base nearly quadrangular in cross-section; dorsal-fin height about 67% of its base; skin without denticles; dark grey, almost black dorsally, white ventrally. A small species, the maximum disc width little more than 100 cm. Notarbartolo-di-Sciara (1987) gave the range as eastern African coast to Indonesia, including the Seychelles and Sri Lanka; the illustrated specimen was obtained by the author when landed by fishermen at Mutrah; it is a female, 120 cm in disc width, 22 kg, and contained a single embryo 48 cm in disc width.

THURSTON'S DEVIL RAY
Mobula thurstoni (Lloyd, 1908)

Disc length about 1.95 in disc width; anterior margin of disc nearly straight over its initial half, then following a sinuous curve, first concave, then convex as it approaches tip of pectoral fin; posterior margin broadly concave initially, becoming nearly straight toward the back; cephalic flaps about 12.3% disc width; median part of front of head between cephalic flaps straight; mouth on lower surface of disc, its width about 12% disc width; preoral length 3.7-4.4% disc width; upper tooth band 72% and lower tooth band 76% of mouth width; teeth wider than long, those of adults imbricate, usually with two prominent posterior cusps, the slightly convex crown rugose; tail without a spine, varying in length from about half disc width to nearly disc width, its base depressed; dorsal-fin height about 80% of its base; olivaceous to dark grey on back, white below, the pectoral tips blackish distally, the leading edge of pectorals white; tip of dorsal fin white. Attains a disc width of at least 180 cm (65-85 cm at birth) and a weight of 54 kg. Recorded from Madras, India (type locality), Red Sea, Madagascar, eastern South Africa, Gulf of Thailand, Japan, Gulf of California, Gulf of Tehuantepec, and Senegal.

BONY FISHES
OSTEICHTHYES

There are two classes of living fishes, the cartilaginous sharks and rays (Chondrichthyes) and the bony fishes (Osteichthyes). As their name implies, the bony fishes have a bony skeleton. Another obvious external distinction is having a single gill opening on each side instead of the usual five for sharks and rays. The bony fishes are divisible into two major categories, usually called subclasses. One is the lobefin fishes (represented by three freshwater lungfishes, one in each southern continent, and *Latimeria*, the sole survivor in the sea of an ancient lineage that gave rise to amphibians and thence to the remaining vertebrates which colonised the land. The second group is the rayfin fishes (Actinopterygii) which have radiated into an incredible number of different forms and invaded virtually all aquatic habitats.

The living rayfin fishes are subdivided into groupings of which only the Teleostei concerns us here (the others are such freshwater fishes as sturgeons, gars, and the Bowfin). The Teleostei is divided into orders (the ordinal ending is "iformes"), and the orders into families. As mentioned, the presentation here will be by families, beginning with what we believe to be the most primitive and moving to the more highly evolved. Among the primitive characters are the low position of the pectoral fins on the side of the body; the origin of the pelvic fins in the posterior abdominal position; and the lack of true spines in the fins. Also primitive is the curious, ribbon-like, transparent leptocephalus larva which becomes smaller when it transforms to a juvenile.

76. *Mobula kuhlii*, 1.2 m wide (J. Randall)

77. *Mobula thurstoni*, 1.3 m wide (J. Randall)

TENPOUNDERS
FAMILY ELOPIDAE

This family, also known by the popular name ladyfishes, consists of a single genus, *Elops*. Whitehead (1962a) recognised six species worldwide, but some other authors believe there are fewer species. An analysis of proteins of the species of this genus, as by electrophoresis or mitochondrial DNA, would be most welcome. These fishes have an elongate body, a median ventral bone called the gular plate anteriorly between the mandibles, teeth present on maxilla; adipose eyelid present; numerous branchiostegal rays, vertebrae, and scales (which are cycloid); lateral-line tubes not branched; no spines in fins, a single dorsal fin of 20-27 rays, anal fin with 13-18 rays; pelvic fins with 12-16 rays; and a deeply forked caudal fin. The leptocephalus larva has a forked caudal fin, hence differentiated from eel leptocephali which lack a caudal fin. Regarded as the most primitive living teleost genus.

TENPOUNDER
Elops machnata (Forsskål, 1775)

Dorsal-fin origin a little posterior to midpoint of standard length, the number of rays 23-27; anal fin distinctly posterior to dorsal fin, the number of rays 15-18; pectoral rays 17-18; origin of pelvic fins slightly anterior to origin of dorsal fin; lateral-line scales 90-103; vertebrae 63-66; mouth large, the lower jaw slightly projecting, the upper jaw extending well posterior to eye; silvery, the fins a little yellowish. Reaches 90 cm. Occurs from the Red Sea south to Cape Province, South Africa, east at least to India, including Oman, Madagascar, Mauritius, Seychelles, and Sri Lanka. Marine, but freely enters tidal rivers. Most apt to be found in khawrs in Oman waters. Feeds on small fishes and shrimps. A popular gamefish, jumping repeatedly when hooked; African angling record, 11.8 kg. Flesh full of small bones, so not often eaten.

78. *Elops machnata* (R. van der Elst)

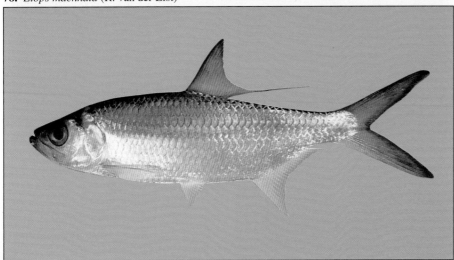

79. *Megalops cyprinoides*, 32 cm (J. Randall)

TARPONS
FAMILY MEGALOPIDAE

This family also consists of a single genus, *Megalops*, with two species: *M. atlanticus* of the Atlantic, and *M. cyprinoides* of the tropical Indo-Pacific region. Because they share many characters with *Elops*, such as the numerous branchiostegal rays and vertebrae, presence of gular plate, jaw structure, adipose eyelid, and position of the fins, they are sometimes classified in the Elopidae. However, the differences are great enough to warrant their placement in a separate family. The body is not very elongate and is strongly compressed; dorsal rays 13-21, the last very elongate; anal rays 22-31; pelvic rays 10-11; lateral-line scales 37-48; and lateral-line tubes branched.

OXEYE
Megalops cyprinoides (Broussonet, 1782)

Dorsal-fin origin in middle of standard length, the number of rays 17-21, the last ray elongate; anal fin behind dorsal fin, the rays 24-31; pectoral rays 15-16; lateral-line scales 36-42; vertebrae 67-68; body depth about 3.5 in standard length; mouth superior, the lower jaw strongly projecting; no teeth in jaws; blue-green dorsally, shading to silvery on sides and ventrally. Reaches about 60 cm. Ranges throughout the Indo-Pacific region; found mainly in shallow brackish habitats and freshwater.

BONEFISHES
FAMILY ALBULIDAE

Two subfamilies are recognised, each of a single genus; only *Albula* in the Indian Ocean. *Albula* has long been regarded as consisting of two species, the circumtropical *A. vulpes* and the tropical western Atlantic-eastern Pacific *A. nemoptera*. However, Shaklee and Tamaru (1981) have shown that there are two species in the Indo-Pacific which they identified as *A. glossodonta* Forsskål and *A. neoguinaica* Valenciennes. James B. Shaklee (pers. comm.) found a third species in the western Atlantic and still another in the eastern Atlantic, which may be *A. goreensis* Valenciennes (thus five species had previously been called *A. vulpes*). *Albula* is characterised by a moderately elongate body; small gular plate; long conical snout; ventral mouth; villiform teeth on premaxilla, vomer, and dentary, but none on maxilla; three patches of small molariform teeth on roof of mouth and one in floor of mouth (used to crush their usual prey of molluscs and crustaceans); adipose eyelid nearly covering eye; origin of dorsal fin a little in advance of mid-standard length, the rays 16-21; anal fin small and very posterior, with 7-9 rays; caudal fin deeply forked; branchiostegal rays 10-16; lateral-line scales 62-78; vertebrae 65-80. Bonefishes occur in all tropical and subtropical seas, generally in relatively shallow water on sandy substrata. They are highly prized as gamefishes but not often eaten because of the numerous small bones in the muscle tissue.

SILVER BONEFISH
Albula argentea (Forster, 1801)

Dorsal rays 16-18; anal rays 7-9; pectoral rays 16-20; lateral-line scales 62-72; vertebrae 65-72; front of lower jaw bluntly pointed; length of upper jaw from front of

80. *Albula forsteri*, 64.5 cm (J. Randall)

snout to end of maxilla 2.65-2.85 in head length; preoral snout length 7.7-8.4 in head length; silvery with a chevron-shaped black mark dorsally on tip of snout. Maximum length uncertain due to confusion with *A. glossodonta*, but at least 70 cm. Probably occurs throughout the Indo-Pacific region, though not yet recorded from the Red Sea or Arabian Gulf. The illustrated specimen was purchased in the fish market in Mutrah. Bonefish are sometimes isolated in the shallows at low tide by sandbars along the Oman coast where they are taken, along with mullet, by cast nets. The adoption of the name *A. forsteri* for this species (for which the type locality is Tahiti) is based on the examination of the holotype of *Esox argenteus* Forster which was invalid as a nomen nudum but validated by Bloch and Schneider (as *Synodus argenteus*). *A. glossodonta* (type locality, Red Sea) should be expected in Oman waters. It differs from *A. argentea* in having the lower jaw broadly rounded, a shorter upper jaw (3.05-3.25 in head length), and a shorter preoral snout length (8.6-12.0 in head length).

MORAY EELS
FAMILY MURAENIDAE

The moray eel family is one of 15 families of eels of the order Anguilliformes. The most obvious feature of eels, in general, is the very elongate body; other characters are the absence of pelvic fins and pelvic girdles; caudal fin, if present, joined with dorsal and anal fins; gill opening small; maxilla with teeth; scales usually absent (if present, as in the freshwater eels of the family Anguillidae, small and embedded); and no gill rakers. Morays have separate frontal bones, muscular compressed bodies; no pectoral fins; a large mouth with impressive dentition; anterior nostrils tubular, at front of snout; posterior nostrils usually not tubular, above front part of eye. The species of the largest genus, *Gymnothorax* (*Lycodontis* is a synonym), have long fang-like teeth in the jaws, and as might be expected, they feed mainly on fishes, occasionally on cephalopods and crustaceans. The longest teeth are usually the intermaxillary fangs; these are inwardly depressible. The species of *Siderea* have shorter but still sharp teeth and feed more on crustaceans. The species of *Echidna* and *Gymnomuraena* have low nodular to molariform teeth, well-suited for crushing hard-shelled prey such as crabs. Morays, in general, have long been regarded as nocturnal, but only a few species actively feed at night. Morays occasionally bite divers (the author has been bitten nine times), but usually this is a result of placing one's hand into a hole or crevice in the reef without knowing that a moray is lurking there. Octopus is a favorite food of many morays, and a human hand in a dark hole might well be mistaken for an octopus. Morays are tamed at some dive resorts; they are hand-fed and may be handled. However, the divemasters that do this sometimes end up being bitten. Recent research has revealed that many morays are hermaphroditic; mostly they start mature life as males and change sex later to females, but some are syn-chronous hermaphrodites, i.e. both male and female at the same time (Fishelson, 1992). Like other eels, they have a relatively large, transparent, ribbon-like larva called the leptocephalus. Juvenile morays are usually more slender than adults; this accounts for the large variation in body depth given in the diagnoses below (as total length divided by maximum body depth). Many of the morays exhibit considerable variation in colour pattern, not only with growth but also among individuals the same size. Randall et al. (1981) demonstrated the presence of a skin toxin in *Gymnothorax nudivomer*, and it is expected that the same or a similar crinotoxin will be found in other morays. Also, the bite of at least three morays (all with serrate teeth) has been shown to be mildly venomous. Randall and Golani (in press) recorded a total of 32 species of moray eels from the Red Sea. Only 15 are reported here from Oman; more are to be expected (especially some species of *Uropterygius* and the longest of morays, *Strophidon sathete*). The generic classification of morays is not yet definitive.

81. *Echidna nebulosa* (J. Randall)

82 *Enchelycore pardalis* (J. Hoover)

SNOWFLAKE MORAY
Echidna nebulosa (Ahl, 1789)

Body depth 14-20 in total length; anus in about middle of body, the preanal length 1.9-2.1 in total length; head 8.5-9.5 in total length; jaws with one or two rows of small, compressed, nodular teeth; vomerine teeth nodular, in two rows; vertebrae 121-124; white with numerous, small black spots or irregular lines and two or three longitudinal rows of large dendritic black blotches containing small yellow spots. Attains 70 cm. Indo-Pacific; typically found in shallow water on reef flats or rocky shores; rare in Oman. Feeds mainly on crabs.

DRAGON MORAY
Enchelycore pardalis (Temminck and Schlegel, 1846)

Body depth 9-16 in length; preanal length a little shorter than tail; head length 6.5-7.5 in length; jaws hooked; long canine teeth in a single row in jaws with small conical teeth between (two rows of teeth in juveniles); posterior nostrils long and tubular, longer than anterior nostrils; body brownish orange with numerous round white spots and small dark brown spots; head with irregular narrow bars of orange and white. Reaches 90 cm. Indo-Pacific, but spotty in distribution; only a few sightings in the Gulf of Oman and southern Oman.

83. *Gymnomuraena zebra* (R. Bedford)

ZEBRA MORAY
Gymnomuraena zebra (Shaw and Nodder, 1797)

Body depth 16-20 in length; tail short, the preanal length 1.45-1.55 in length; head length 9-10 in length; dorsal and anal fins very low and difficult to detect; numerous molariform teeth in jaws, those in upper jaw in two rows, those in lower jaw in three rows; intermaxillary teeth large, molariform, in three rows and adjacent to teeth at side of jaw; vomerine teeth in an elliptical patch of five or six rows, the middle ones large; dark brown to dark orangish brown with numerous narrow pale yellowish bars. Indo-Pacific and tropical eastern Pacific. Said to attain a length of 150 cm, but rarely exceeds 100 cm. The only species of the genus.

LIPSPOT MORAY
Gymnothorax chilospilus Bleeker, 1865

Body depth 15-19 in total length; anus before middle of body, the preanal length 2.1-2.3 in total length; head 6.5-8 in total length; intermaxillary canines in a single row, longest in upper jaw; other long canines anteriorly in upper jaw and an inner row at front of lower jaw; vertebrae 121-133; light brown, finely mottled with darker brown, with two or more rows of small dendritic dark brown blotches (sometimes forming short irregular dark bars); a dark brown spot at corner of mouth preceded on lower lip by a large white spot (often another white spot above and another behind dark spot at corner of mouth); each pore on side of jaws in a prominent white spot. Indo-Pacific, usually in less than 5 m, but one collected in 45 m. Largest reported, 50.5 cm. Known from Oman only from the photograph presented here (taken on the south coast of Oman near Marbat).

HONEYCOMB MORAY
Gymnothorax favagineus (Bloch and Schneider, 1801)

Body depth 13-17 in total length; anus before mid-body, the preanal length 2.1-2.2 in total length; head length 8-9 in total length; front of jaws usually with four large canines on each side, the more posterior teeth much smaller and angling backward; intermaxillary canines in a single median row, longer than lateral canines; one or two small canines may be present as a short inner row on side of upper jaw of juveniles; vertebrae 138-144; pale yellowish with numerous close-set large black spots (more numerous and relatively smaller on larger eels), the narrow pale interspaces forming a honeycomb-like pattern. One of the largest of morays, reaching at least 180 cm in length, with unconfirmed reports to 250 cm. A common species in the Gulf of Oman and the south coast.

84. *Gymnothorax chilospilus* (K. Fiedler)

85. *Gymnothorax favagineus* (J. Hoover)

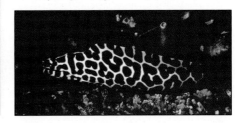

86. *G. favagineus*, juvenile (J. Randall)

YELLOWMARGIN MORAY
Gymnothorax flavimarginatus (Rüppell, 1830)

Body depth 11-18 in total length; anus before mid-body, the preanal length 2.1-2.3 in length; head 6.5-10 in total length; teeth in jaws uniserial with large canines anteriorly; intermaxillary teeth a single median row of large canines; vertebrae 129-137; body yellowish, densely mottled with dark brown; front of head purplish grey; a black spot on gill opening; a yellow-green margin posteriorly on fins. Reaches at least 120 cm. Widespread in the Indo-Pacific and eastern Pacific; observed occasionally only in southern Oman. Feeds mainly on fishes, occasionally on crustaceans.

DWARF BROWN MORAY
Gymnothorax herrei Beebe and Tee-Van, 1933

Body depth 18.5-22.5 in total length; anus before mid-length of body, the preanal length 2.15-2.2 in total length; head length 8.1-8.3 in total length; no teeth of canine proportions; two rows of conical teeth on side of upper jaw, those of outer row small, those of inner row much longer and extending to rear of jaw; inner row of teeth of lower jaw restricted to anterior part of jaw; vertebrae 109-119; brown, the head and posterior part of tail lighter brown. Largest specimen, one from the Arabian Gulf which measures 30 cm in length (usual length less than 20 cm). Western Pacific to the Red Sea, but not yet known in the Indian Ocean west of the Maldives. Generally found in shallow turbid areas. This small moray was described as *Gymnothorax brunneus* by Herre (1923) from one 16-cm specimen from the Philippines, not knowing there was already a *G. brunneus* from the western Atlantic. Beebe and Tee-Van (1933) provided the new name, *G. herrei*.

OMAN MORAY
Gymnothorax megaspilus Böhlke and Randall, 1995

Body depth 14-15 in total length; anus before mid-body, the preanal length 2.1 in total length; head length 6.6-7 in total length; teeth uniserial in jaws; long triangular canines on each side of upper jaw, decreasing slowly in size posteriorly; three rows of three long intermaxillary canines; longest teeth of lower jaw, four anterior canines, flanked in front by two tiny teeth; vertebrae 123-129; body pale pinkish grey with numerous interconnected dendritic brown blotches; a very large black spot

87. *Gymnothorax flavimarginatus* (J. Hoover)

88. *Gymnothorax herrei*, 30 cm (J. Randall)

89. *Gymnothorax megaspilus*, about 60 cm (J. Randall)

enclosing gill opening; edge of anal fin and posterior part of dorsal fin white. Largest specimen, 59.5 cm. Known from only three specimens collected in 21 m in the Juzor al Hallaniyat (Kuria Muria Islands) and two specimens from Somalia.

90. *G. nudivomer*, about 80 cm (J. Randall)

YELLOWMOUTH MORAY
Gymnothorax nudivomer (Playfair and Günther, 1867)

Body depth 9-16 in total length; anus before mid-body, the preanal length 2.1-2.3 in total length; head length 9-11 in total length; teeth in jaws uniserial, acutely triangular, compressed, and many finely serrate; a single median intermaxillary canine; no vomerine teeth in adults; vertebrae 126-139; light brown, becoming darker posteriorly, with numerous small white flecks and irregular white spots or short lines anteriorly, and widely separated round dark-edged white spots about pupil size posteriorly; gill opening in a dusky to black blotch; inside of mouth bright yellow. Known from the Hawaiian Islands and western Pacific to East Africa and the Red Sea. Reaches about 100 cm. Common throughout Oman waters.

PHANTOM MORAY
Gymnothorax phasmatodes (Smith, 1962)

Body elongate, the depth 30-33 in total length; anus in about middle of body; head length 10-11 in total length; dorsal fin relatively high; teeth in jaws uniserial, acutely triangular and retrorse; a median row of two or three intermaxillary canines; vertebrae 166-170; light grey to pale yellowish brown, the fins paler, the dorsal with a narrow bluish white margin; each pore on side of jaws in a white spot. Largest specimen, the holotype from Mozambique, 46.5 cm. Known from only a few specimens, the easternmost from the Coral Sea.

HIGHFIN MORAY
Gymnothorax pseudothyrsoideus Bleeker, 1852

Body depth 10-18 in total length; anus in about middle of body; head length 6.5-7.5 in total length; dorsal fin high for a moray; moderately large canine teeth in a single row in jaws; usually with one median row of three intermaxillary canines; pale yellowish, densely spotted with dark brown, the spots clustering to form dark blotches larger than

91. *Gymnothorax phasmatodes*, 42 cm (J. Randall)

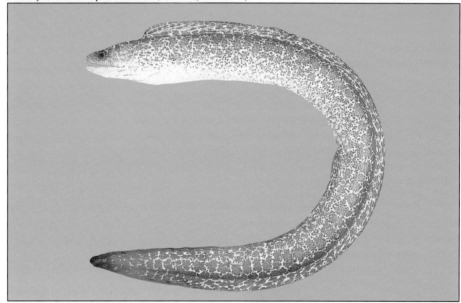

92. *Gymnothorax pseudothyrsoideus*, 33.5 cm (J. Randall)

eye in about four irregular rows on body; juveniles with a white margin on fins. Reaches 80 cm. Western Pacific to India and Oman; specimens mainly from tidepools.

UNDULATED MORAY
Gymnothorax undulatus (Lacepède, 1803)

Body depth 10-19 in total length; anus before mid-body length, the preanal length 2.1-2.3 in total length; head length 6.5-8.5 in total length; teeth in jaws uniserial (except for a few small canines in a medial row on side of upper jaw of young) and compressed, the anterior ones as moderate canines with a small tooth between; three very long intermaxillary canines in a median row; vertebrae 126-138; colour variable, usually pale greenish yellow with large close-set grey-brown blotches and small spots, reducing the ground colour to a very irregular reticu-

93. *Gymnothorax undulatus* (J. Hoover)

lum; dark blotches may merge posteriorly to form irregular bars which are oblique on fins; head finely spotted to eyes; snout and chin light grey-brown, the grooves in throat dark brown; dorsal part of head and nape usually more yellow-green than body. Attains about 100 cm. Broadly distributed in the Indo-Pacific; the most common moray of the genus *Gymnothorax* in Oman. Nocturnal, but will feed opportunistically by day. Prone to bite.

LEOPARD MORAY
Scuticaria tigrina (Lesson, 1829)

Body very elongate, the depth 27-32 in total length; tail short, the preanal length more than two-thirds total length; head length 12-13.5 in total length; gill opening slightly above mid-body; one lateral-line pore anterior to gill opening; dorsal and anal fins rudimentary, confined to posterior end of tail; teeth slender and sharp, in two rows in jaws except posteriorly, the inner series larger and depressible; a few depressible intermaxillary teeth; vertebrae 169-172; pale brown to pale yellowish with well-separated, large and small, irregularly round, dark brown spots (spots anteriorly on head small). Reaches about 120 cm. East Africa to the Society Islands and Hawaii, but with few records. Resembles *Uropterygius polyspilus* (Regan) in colour pattern, but the latter has the anus near the middle of body.

GREY MORAY
Siderea grisea (Lacepède, 1803)

Body slender, the depth 17-22 in total length; anus well in front of middle of length, the preanal length about 2.4 in total length; head 8.5-10.5 in total length; dorsal fin high, its origin about half way between gill opening and eye; conical teeth in jaws (none as long canines) in two rows on side of upper jaw (inner row larger), and a single row in lower jaw and front of upper; two median intermaxillary teeth the largest in mouth; vertebrae 128-136; pale yellowish, the body densely mottled with small light brown spots; head anterior to dorsal fin brownish grey; pores on head in small black spots. Maximum length about 65 cm. Western Indian Ocean and Red Sea; seen more often in Oman waters than any other moray, sometimes in feeding associations with other predaceous fishes (Diamant and Shpigel, 1985). A synchronous hermaphrodite (Fishelson, 1992).

PEPPERED MORAY
Siderea picta (Ahl, 1798)

Body depth 10-20 in total length; anus in about middle of body; head length 6-8 in total length; teeth in jaws uniserial, conical, becoming compressed and retrorse posteriorly; a single median intermaxillary tooth; origin of dorsal fin slightly anterior to gill opening; vertebrae 127-135; white, densely peppered with black dots, these sometimes clumping to form large diffuse blackish blotches (juveniles may have pale centres in the black blotches). Wide-ranging in the Indo-Pacific to islands of the tropical eastern Pacific. A shallow-water species of reef flats and rocky shores. Feeds mainly on crabs, sometimes striking at grapsids above the surface (Chave and H. Randall, 1971). A synchronous hermaphrodite (Fishelson, 1992).

94. *Scuticaria tigrina*, about 60 cm (J. Randall)

95. *Siderea grisea*, about 60 cm (J. Hoover)

96. *Siderea picta* (J. Hoover)

PALENOSE MORAY
Siderea flavocula Böhlke and Randall, 1995

Body depth 18-22 in total length; anus in about middle of body; head length 9-10 in total length; teeth in upper jaw uniserial, conical, compressed, and strongly recurved (juveniles with an inner row of larger teeth about half way back in jaw); two short conical intermaxillary teeth in a median row; lower jaw with slightly compressed conical teeth, uniserial except for a short anterior inner row; vomerine teeth nodular, biserial anteriorly, merging to one row posteriorly; vertebrae 124-131 (four Oman specimens); juveniles pale yellow with large, close-set, round to pentagonal, dark brown spots on body which tend to merge posteriorly; spots progressively smaller anteriorly; front half of head dark grey except snout and tip of chin whitish; adults pale yellowish with the same basic pattern except dark spots more irregular and containing yellowish flecks, and the pale yellowish network with flecks of dark brown; snout and front of chin pink. Largest specimen, 40.7 cm. Known only from the Gulf of Oman to southern Oman; specimens from tidepools to 6 m.

97. Head of *Siderea flavocula* (J. Randall)

98. *Siderea flavocula*, 40 cm (J. Randall)

CONGER EELS
FAMILY CONGRIDAE

In addition to the general charcters of eels, the conger eels have a nearly cylindrical body anteriorly; fused frontal bones; 7-12 branchiostegal rays; moderately large gill opening on lower half of body, the upper end anterior to pectoral-fin base; well-developed flanges on lips; no scales; complete lateral line, usually with one pore per vertebra; and pectoral fins (usually prominent). Most of the species occur in deep water. Following Smith in Böhlke (1989), three subfamilies are recognised. Only one species of the family is recorded from Oman, *Conger cinereus*, of the subfamily Congrinae, but garden eels (Heterocongrinae) might be expected.

MOUSTACHE CONGER
Conger cinereus Rüppell, 1830

Pectoral fin with 16-18 rays; lateral-line pores anterior to anus 37-41; body depth 16-22 in total length; origin of dorsal fin anterior to tip of pectoral fins; teeth in jaws compressed, close-set, forming a shearing edge; vertebrae 139-146; brownish grey with a black margin on median fins; a blackish streak above upper lip. Attains 130 cm. Indo-Pacific; subspecifically different in the Hawaiian Islands. Usually remains hidden in reefs by day, actively foraging for its prey of fishes and crustaceans at night (at which time it assumes a pattern of broad dark grey bars).

99. *Conger cinereus*, 52 cm (J. Randall)

PIKE CONGERS
FAMILY MURAENESOCIDAE

The pike congers have a stout body; well-developed median fins, the dorsal-fin origin over or slightly anterior to pectoral-fin base; large pectoral fins; moderately large crescentic gill opening on lower side; fleshy front of snout extending anterior to lower jaw; no flanges at side of lips; posterior nostril elliptical, in front of middle of eye; no scales; near-complete lateral line; teeth anteriorly in jaws and on vomer enlarged. A small family of four genera (as restricted by Smith in Böhlke, 1989), of which only one representative of the genus *Muraenesox* is known from Oman waters.

DAGGERTOOTH PIKE CONGER
Muraenesox cinereus (Forsskål, 1775)

Pectoral rays 16-17; dorsal rays anterior to anus 66-78; pores anterior to anus 39-47; body depth 15-17 in total length; anus in front of mid-body, the preanal length 2.2-2.3 in total length; head length about 6 in total length; teeth on side of jaws in two to three rows, those at front of jaws enlarged; vomerine teeth in three rows, those of middle row greatly enlarged, triangular, compressed, with a basal cusp at each end; vertebrae 145-159; greyish brown dorsally, pale ventrally, with a black border on median fins. Reports of maximum total length vary from 80 to 220 cm. Ranges in continental waters from the Red Sea and Arabian Gulf to Indonesia and northern Australia, north to Japan. Occurs on mud substrata to depths of 100 m.

SNAKE EELS AND WORM EELS
FAMILY OPHICHTHIDAE

The snake eels are well named for their very long bodies which are cylindrical anteriorly; indeed some have been mistaken for sea snakes. Sea snakes, however, are readily distinguished by having scales on the body, no fins (although the tail is compressed posteriorly for swimming), and no gill opening. The Ophichthidae is the largest and most diverse family of eels; 55 genera and more than 250 species are currently known. Because of the diversity, it is difficult to list characteristics that apply to all; the most useful are the numerous branchiostegal rays which overlap ventrally in the enlarged throat and branchial region; fully fused frontal bones; no palatines; fixed tongue; posterior nostrils which open inside the mouth or through a valve in the upper lip; and lateral line extending onto head, the two sides connected dorsally by frontal and supratemporal canals. There are two subfamilies, the Myrophinae (Echelinae of some authors), characterised by a flexible tail tip with a short caudal fin, and the Ophichthinae with a hard or fleshy tail tip lacking a caudal fin. McCosker (1977) revised the genera. Most species are rarely seen by divers because they are secretive in reefs or buried in sand or mud; those that live in sediment use the tip of their tail for burrowing. Kuronuma and Abe (1986) recorded *Ophichthus celebicus* (Bleeker) and *O. apicalis* (Bennett) from the Arabian Gulf, thus they may be expected from Oman seas.

WORM EELS
SUBFAMILY MYROPHINAE

SLENDER WORM EEL
Muraenichthys gymnotus Bleeker, 1864

Body depth 30-45 in total length; preanal length 2.3-2.4 in total length; head length 9-11 in total length; snout pointed, 5.6-5.8 in head length; rear margin of eye slightly

101. *M. gymnotus*, 18.5 cm (J. Randall)

100. *Muraenesox cinereus*, 76 cm (J. Randall)

anterior to corner of mouth; tubular anterior nostril on ventral side of snout opposite tip of lower jaw; posterior nostril on side of upper lip below front of eye; teeth small and sharp, in two rows on upper jaw and one in lower jaw and on vomer; intermaxillary teeth in a round patch; origin of dorsal fin about half head length posterior to anus; caudal fin very short; no pectoral fins; vertebrae 128-134; pale yellowish, shading to whitish ventrally on head and trunk. Reported to 17 cm. Indo-Pacific.

SCHULTZE'S WORM EEL
Muraenichthys schultzei Bleeker, 1857

Body depth 20-30 in total length; preanal length 2.2-2.3 in total length; head bluntly conical, its length 8-9 in total length; snout 6-7.5 in head length; base of anterior nostril on ventral side of snout above tip of lower jaw; posterior nostril on outside of upper lip ventroanterior to eye; teeth small, sharp, in two or three rows in jaws and on vomer; intermaxillary teeth in a round patch; origin of dorsal fin a short distance behind anus; no pectoral fins; vertebrae about 122; yellowish, finely speckled with black on back and posteriorly. Largest specimen, 14.4 cm. Indo-Pacific; Blegvad (1944) reported three specimens from the stomachs of the sea snake *Microcephalophis gracilis* collected in the Arabian Gulf, Strait of Hormuz, and Gulf of Oman.

SNAKE EELS
SUBFAMILY OPHICHTHINAE

CROCODILE SNAKE EEL
Brachysomophis crocodilinus (Bennett, 1831)

Body cylindrical, the depth 19-22 in total length; anus posterior to middle of body, the preanal length about 1.9 in total length; head length 7-8 in total length; a fleshy flap behind upper part of eye; a narrow deep groove across anterior occiput bearing seven dark pores; upper jaw with an outer row of numerous small close-set recurved teeth well-separated from a medial row of larger teeth; lower jaw with a row of well-separated slender canines; longest teeth a series of about five on vomer; coarse cirri on upper lip beginning below eye; eye over anterior third of gape; snout length 10 in head length; dorsal-fin origin two-fifths head length posterior to gill opening; pectoral fins slightly longer than snout; vertebrae 130 (one Oman specimen); light brown dorsally, sparsely dotted with dark brown, shading to pale yellowish ventrally; each lateral-line pore in a small dark brown spot; head red

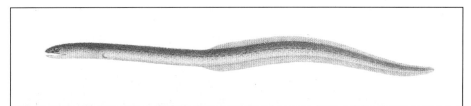

102. *Muraenichthys schultzei* (after Bleeker, 1865)

103A. *Brachysomophis crocodilinus*, 78 cm (J. Randall)

anteriorly with white markings, those on lower jaw as six narrow white bars; dorsal fin blackish with a broad white margin. Attains at least 100 cm. Indo-Pacific, but with few records; type locality, Mauritius. Lives buried beneath sand, except for the anterior upper part of head, usually near reefs; ambushes small fishes that venture near by lunging out of the sand. *B. henshawi* Jordan and Snyder from the Hawaiian Islands is a synonym.

OMAN SNAKE EEL
Ichthyapus omanensis (Norman, 1939)

Body depth about 55 in total length; tail short, the preanal length 1.5 times longer than tail; head length 8 in trunk length; snout pointed and strongly projecting, 9 in head length; eye slightly anterior to middle of cleft of mouth, its diameter about half snout length; anterior nostril below tip of snout and not tubular; posterior nostril a slit in upper lip below eye; gill openings ventral, the interspace narrower than their length; teeth sharp, recurved, in one row in each jaw; four larger depressible intermaxillary teeth, visible when mouth closed; vomerine teeth in two rows anteriorly, one posteriorly;

103B. Head of *B. crocodilinus* (J. Randall)

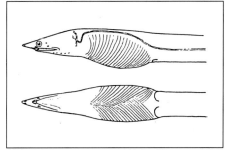

104. *Ichthyapus omanensis* (after Norman, 1939)

origin of dorsal fin a little posterior to anus; greyish brown, paler below; head variegated with dark brown. Known from a single 230-mm specimen taken in 73 m in the Gulf of Oman.

ORIENTAL SNAKE EEL

Lamnastoma orientalis (McClelland, 1844)

Body depth 31-42 in total length; anus in middle of body or slightly posterior to middle; head 8-9 in total length; anterior part of head very narrow, widening abruptly posteriorly; snout moderately pointed; gill opening a longitudinal slit ventrally on throat, with an extra fold of skin to the side; teeth small, sharp, recurved, mostly uniserial in jaws, the intermaxillary and vomerine teeth largest; dorsal and anal fins low, ending before tip of tail; dorsal-fin origin slightly posterior to gill opening; no pectoral fins; vertebrae 136-l41; dark brown dorsally (to below lateral line, the pores of which are white), whitish ventrally. Attains about 30 cm. Western Indian Ocean (Castle in Fischer and Bianchi, 1984). Lives in sand in shallow turbid areas.

RINGED SNAKE EEL

Myrichthys colubrinus (Boddaert, 1781)

Body very elongate, the depth 48-68 in total length; anus at or posterior to midlength, the preanal length 2.0-2.3 in total length; head length 17-20 in total length; snout rounded, 5.5-6.0 in head length; teeth small, molariform, biserial in jaws; dorsal-fin origin on head, the predorsal length 1.7-2.3 in head length; anal fin ending well in advance of posterior end of dorsal fin; pectoral fins very small, 3-5 in snout length; vertebrae 193-202; whitish to yellowish with 25-35 dark brown to black rings that are equal to or narrower than pale interspaces; large specimens may have large dark spots in pale interspaces (usually one and usually round). Largest specimen, 97 cm. Indo-Pacific; occasionally seen entirely exposed by day, moving over sand, rubble, or seagrasses. Reported as a mimic of the banded sea snakes such as *Hydrophis melanocephalus*; McCosker and Rosenblatt (1993) noted that the black circles of *M. colubrinus* are broad like those of the sea snakes where their distributions coincide. In other areas, this snake eel may have much narrower rings.

SPOTTED SNAKE EEL

Myrichthys maculosus Cuvier, 1816

Body elongate, the depth 33-46 in total length; anus in front of mid-length, the preanal length 2.3-2.45 in total length; head length 12.7-15.2 in total length; snout rounded, 4.7-5.7 in head; teeth small, molariform, and biserial in jaws; dorsal-fin origin on head, the predorsal length 1.5-2.0 in head length; pectoral fins shorter than their base; vertebrae 185-199; white with very large, round to elliptical, dark brown to black spots and some lesser round spots. Largest specimen reported, 99 cm. Indo-Pacific except the Hawaiian Islands where the endemic *M. magnificus* (Abbott) occurs (McCosker and Rosenblatt, 1993).

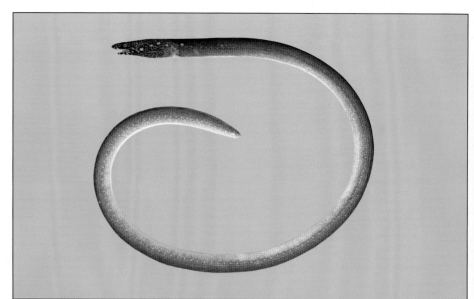

105. *Lamnastoma orientalis*, 21 cm (J. Randall)

106. *Myrichthys colubrinus* (R. Bedford)

107. *Myrichthys maculosus*, about 60 cm (J. Randall)

SPECKLED SNAKE EEL
Ophisurus multiserialis (Norman, 1939)

Body depth about 22 in total length; preanal length a little greater than length of tail; head length a little more than 7 in total length; snout pointed, 7 in head length; eye diameter 2 in snout; mouth large, the upper jaw projecting; teeth sharp, in an outer re-curved series in jaws, the upper jaw with an inner series which consists of a single row anteriorly and broadens to six rows posteriorly, the anterior teeth largest; a row of strong teeth on vomer, decreasing in size posteriorly; six intermaxillary teeth separated from vomerine teeth by a groove which receives tip of lower jaw; dorsal-fin origin a little behind tip of pectoral fins; pectorals about 4 in head length; yellowish brown, the dorsal part of body with numerous small dark brown spots which are smaller and closer together on head. Apparently known only from the 625-mm holotype taken in 220 m in the Gulf of Aden and a 152-mm juvenile collected in 11 m off southern Oman.

HOEVEN'S SNAKE EEL
Pisodonophis hoevenii (Bleeker, 1853).

Body depth 26 in total length; anus in middle of total length; head length 7.5 in total length; snout pointed, 5 in head length; eye about 14 in head length; teeth small, molariform, in about three irregular rows in jaws and on vomer; intermaxillary teeth largest, in an isolated group; dorsal and anal fins well-developed, the dorsal-fin origin above middle of pectoral fins; pectoral fins about 3.5 in head; olivaceous dorsally, yellowish below, the dorsal fin with a blackish margin. Apparently known only from the 217-mm type specimen from Sulawesi and two reported by Blegvad, 1944 (one from the Arabian Gulf and one from the Gulf of Oman, both from the stomach of sea snakes).

HERRINGS, SARDINES, AND SHADS
FAMILY CLUPEIDAE

The fishes of this family are small, silvery, and nearly always encountered in schools. Most are plankton-feeders. They are characterised by a single short dorsal fin near the middle of the body; no spines in fins;

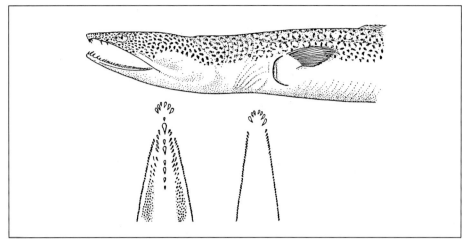

108. *Ophisurus multiserialis* (after Norman, 1939)

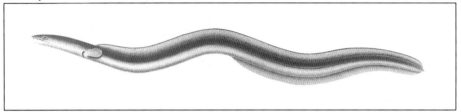

109. *Pisodonophis hoevenii* (after Bleeker, 1865)

pectoral fins low on the body; pelvic fins in a posterior abdominal position; a strongly forked caudal fin; at least one ventral scute (usually a series of these sharp scales from throat to anus); no lateral line on body; teeth usually small or absent; one or two supramaxillae (rarely none); adipose eyelid usually present; and numerous long gill rakers. Scales cycloid, thin, and easily lost (thus making scale counts difficult). The clupeid fishes are grouped in the order Clupeiformes with the anchovies (Engraulidae) and wolf herrings (Chirocentridae). Whitehead (1985)

110. School of *Sardinella longiceps* (J. Randall)

recognised 56 genera and 180 species of clupeid fishes, but he indicated that the true totals will eventually be about 60 genera and 200 species. The Clupeidae is divided into six subfamilies, four of which have representatives in Oman waters. The subfamilies are presented below in alphabetical order.

HERRINGS AND SARDINES
SUBFAMILY CLUPEINAE

SPOTTED SARDINELLA
Amblygaster sirm (Walbaum, 1792)

Dorsal rays 17-18; anal rays 15-19, the last two rays enlarged; pectoral rays 16-17; pelvic rays 8; median predorsal scales in a single well-defined series; abdomen rounded, the scutes not prominent; lower-limb gill rakers 38-42; surface of operculum smooth, i.e. without striae (true of species of *Herklotsichthys* and *Sardinella*); 7-14 striae on each side on top of head (also found on species of *Sardinella*); rear edge of gill opening with two low fleshy lobes (also true of *Herklotsichthys* and *Sardinella*); body depth about 5 in standard length; blue-green on back, silvery on sides and ventrally, with a longitudinal row of 10-20 golden spots on upper side (spots black in preservative). Reported to 27 cm total length. Red Sea (type locality), south to Mozambique and east to the western Pacific (Fiji the most eastern locality). Blegvad (1944) reported the species from the Arabian Gulf and Gulf of Oman.

GULF HERRING
Herklotsichthys lossei Wongratana, 1983

Dorsal rays 16-18; anal rays 16-17; pectoral rays 15-16; longitudinal scale series usually 38-40; ventral scutes 28-31; gill rakers 31-34; 4-7 striae on each side of top of head; lower curved part of second supramaxilla clearly longer than upper curved part (true of other *Herklotsichthys*); body depth 3.6-3.85 in standard length; blue-green on back, silvery on side and ventrally, with a row of faint dark spots on upper side and a brassy spot at upper end of gill opening (often a narrow brassy stripe passing posterior from upper edge of eye, separating blue-green back from silvery side); a blackish area near tip of dorsal fin. Known from the Arabian Gulf and presumed to range into the Gulf of Oman. Attains about 10 cm. Very closely related to *H. punctatus* (Rüppell) from the Red Sea. Wongratana (1983) distinguished *lossei* on the basis of the blackish

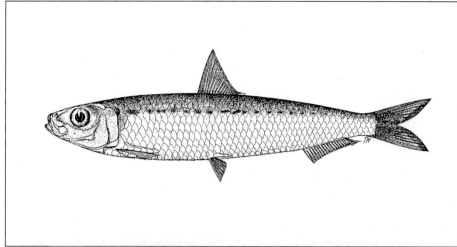

111. *Amblygaster sirm* (after Whitehead, 1985)

112. Feeding school of *Herklotsichthys lossei*, about 7 cm (J. Randall)

113. *Herklotsichthys quadrimaculatus*, 12 cm (J. Randall)

spot on the dorsal fin, supposedly lacking in *punctatus* (however, it is present, though faint); no blackish spots on the back as seen on *punctatus* (they are present on *lossei*); the row of black spots on upper side of *lossei* (not present on all Gulf specimens), higher gill-raker counts of *punctatus* (my counts, 31-34 for *lossei*, 32-36 for *punctatus*), and a lower number of pyloric caeca for *punctatus* (my counts do not confirm this). Further study may show that *lossei* is only subspecifically distinct from *punctatus*.

FOURSPOT SARDINE
Herklotsichthys quadrimaculatus (Rüppell, 1837)

Dorsal rays 17-20; anal rays 17-19; pectoral rays 15-16; longitudinal scale series 38-45; ventral scutes 30-32; transversely elongate scales beneath normal paired predorsal scales; lower-limb gill rakers 30-37; usual body depth 3.1-3.9 in standard length; blue-green on back without dark spots, shading to silvery on sides and ventrally, with an orange-yellow spot just behind upper end of gill opening and another directly below but well-separated from it. Attains 14 cm. Indo-Pacific; accidentally introduced into the Hawaiian Islands. Unlike many clupeids, this species is not apt to be found in brackish environments.

WHITE SARDINELLA
Sardinella albella (Valenciennes, 1847)

Dorsal rays 18-20; anal rays 19-23; pectoral rays 14-17; pelvic rays 8; longitudinal

scale series 40-45; ventral scutes 29-33, sharp and protruding, especially the postpelvic ones; predorsal scales as alternating pairs, not a single straight row of scales (true of other species of *Sardinella*); lower-limb gill rakers 41-68 (the number increasing a little with growth); second supramaxilla symmetrically paddle-shaped (also true of other *Sardinella*); body deep, the depth usually 2.5-3.5 in standard length; back blue-green, silvery below; a black spot at origin of dorsal fin. Attains 18 cm total length. Red Sea south to Natal and Madagascar, east along continental and large

island shores to northern Australia, north to Taiwan. Identified from the Arabian Gulf by Blegvad (1944) and Kuronuma and Abe (1972, 1986) as *S. perforata* Cantor.

GOLDSTRIPE SARDINELLA
Sardinella gibbosa (Bleeker, 1849)

Dorsal rays 17-20; anal rays 17-21; pectoral rays 14-17; pelvic rays 8; longitudinal scale series 42-47; ventral scutes 32-34; lower-limb gill rakers 45-60 (not increasing with growth after 6 cm standard length); body depth 3.2-4.5 in standard length; blue on back, silvery below, sometimes with a narrow golden stripe on side; a black spot at origin of dorsal fin; distal edges of dorsal and caudal fin dusky. Reaches 21 cm. Arabian Gulf and Gulf of Aden to South Africa, east along continental shores to Indonesia and western Australia, north to Taiwan. Abundant in many areas.

INDIAN OIL SARDINE
Sardinella longiceps Valenciennes, 1847

Dorsal rays 16-17; anal rays 14-16; pectoral rays 17; pelvic rays 9 (8 in the other Oman *Sardinella*); longitudinal scale series 45-48; ventral scutes 31-32, not well-developed; gill rakers 150-233 (in fish larger than 6 cm standard length); body depth usually 4.0-4.9 in standard length; body less compressed than other Oman *Sardinella* and more round-bellied; head long, 2.9-3.4 in standard length; greenish on back with iridescence, silvery on side and ventrally; a small black spot at edge of opercle at level of eye; usually a brassy blotch above upper end of gill opening. Reported to 23 cm. East coast of India along continental shelf to Somalia; not known from the Arabian Gulf or Red Sea. Very important commercial fish in India (as much as 30% of the catch of marine fishes in good years); also the dominant clupeid in central and southern Oman.

BLACKTIP SARDINELLA
Sardinella melanura (Cuvier, 1829)

Dorsal rays 15-16; anal rays 18-19; pectoral rays 13-15; pelvic rays 8; longitudinal scale series 38-40; ventral scutes usually 28-30; gill rakers 38-74; body depth 3.0-3.7 in standard length; blue on back, silvery on sides and ventrally; tips of caudal lobes broadly black. Maximum length, 15.5 cm. Northwestern India, along the continental shelf to Mozambique, Madagascar, and Mauritius; also eastern Indonesia and New Guinea east to Tahiti; presence from southwest India to Java and Borneo not confirmed.

114. *Sardinella albella*, 12.5 cm (J. Randall)

115. *Sardinella gibbosa*, 13.5 cm (J. Randall)

116. *Sardinella longiceps*, 12 cm (J. Randall)

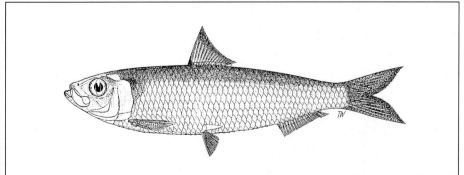

117. *Sardinella melanura* (after Whitehead, 1985)

SIND SARDINELLA
Sardinella sindensis (Day, 1878)

Dorsal rays 16-17; anal rays 18-19; pectoral rays 15; pelvic rays 8; longitudinal scale series 41-44; ventral scutes 31-34; lower-limb gill rakers 38-77; body depth variable, 2.9-4.7 in standard length; back deep blue, silvery to golden on sides; a black spot at origin of dorsal fin; distal margins of dorsal and caudal fins dusky; juveniles with a dark spot on shoulder. Attains 20 cm. Northwestern coast of India along the continental shelf to the Arabian Gulf and Gulf of Aden; also reported from Mauritius.

WHITE SARDINE
Escualosa thoracata (Valenciennes, 1847)

Dorsal rays 16; anal rays 18-19; pectoral rays 12-13; pelvic rays 7; ventral scutes 29-30; body moderately deep, the depth 3.3-3.7 in standard length, and compressed; posterior end of maxilla and second supramaxilla enlarged, the expanded part of the latter more angular than other clupeids; grey on upper third of body with a lateral silvery stripe as broad as eye diameter. Reaches about 13 cm. Gulf of Oman to the Indo-Malayan region. One other species in the genus, *E. elongata* Wongratana, known only from the Gulf of Thailand.

KELEE SHAD
Hilsa kelee (Cuvier, 1829)

Dorsal rays 17-19; anal rays 18-22; pectoral rays 13-16; pelvic rays 8; longitudinal scale series 39-44; scales with small perforations; ventral scutes usually 28-30; gill rakers 75-175, increasing with growth, those on inner arches curling outward; body deep, the depth 2.4-3.0 in standard length; upper jaw with a distinct median notch; two supramaxillae; dorsal surface of head with numer-

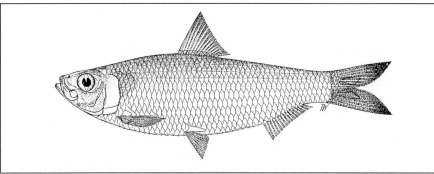

118. *Sardinella sindensis* (after Whitehead, 1985)

119. *Escualosa thoracata*, 10 cm (J. Randall)

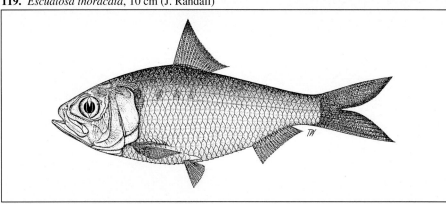

120. *Hilsa kelee* (after Whitehead, 1985)

ous longitudinal striae; greenish on back, silvery on sides and ventrally, with a black spot at upper end of gill opening, followed by three to seven oval blackish spots in a longitudinal row on upper side. Reaches 30 cm. East coast of Africa and Asia to the Indo-Malayan region and China (not record-

ed from the Red Sea, Arabian Gulf, or Australia). Marine but enters estuaries of low salinity.

HILSA SHAD
Tenualosa ilisha (Hamilton, 1822)

Dorsal rays 18-19; anal rays 19-22; pectoral rays 14-15; pelvic rays 8; longitudinal scale series 44-49; scales without perforations; ventral scutes 30-32; lower-limb gill rakers about 100-250, those on inner arches curling outward; body depth 2.8-3.1 in standard length; head length 3.1-3.6 in standard length; upper jaw with a median notch; dorsal surface of head without longitudinal striae; blue-green dorsally, shading to silvery on sides and ventrally; a large dark blotch behind gill opening, followed by a row of dark spots (lost in large adults); caudal fin edged with blackish. Reaches 60 cm. Burma to the Arabian Gulf. A very important commercial fish in west Pakistan and Kuwait. Ascends rivers to spawn.

121. *Tenualosa ilisha*, 27 cm (J. Randall)

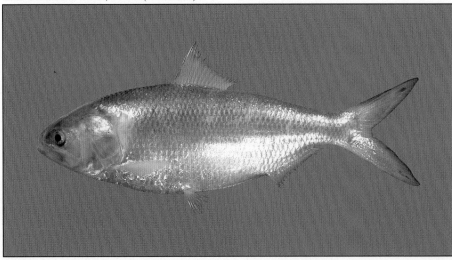

GIZZARD SHADS
SUBFAMILY DOROSOMATINAE

CHACUNDA GIZZARD SHAD
Anodontostoma chacunda (Hamilton, 1822)

Dorsal rays 17-19, the last ray not filamentous; anal rays 19-20; pectoral rays 15; longitudinal scale series 40-42; exposed edge of scales finely serrate; a straight series of median predorsal scales; ventral scutes about 28; lower-limb gill rakers 54-96; body depth increasing with age, usually 2.0-2.5 in standard length; body compressed; snout rounded; mouth inferior; second supramaxilla slender; body silvery, sometimes with golden reflections, with a large black spot behind upper end of gill opening; occiput golden; caudal fin often yellowish. Attains 22 cm. Arabian Gulf to Indo-Malay-an region, northern Australia, and New Caledonia. Feeds on diatoms, radiolarians, molluscs, copepods, and other small crustaceans; ascends rivers to spawn.

ARABIAN GIZZARD SHAD
Nematalosa arabica Regan, 1917

Dorsal rays 17-19, the last greatly prolonged (2.45-2.8 in standard length); anal rays 18-20; pectoral rays 16-17; pelvic rays 8; longitudinal scale series 42-47; scale edges smooth; predorsal scales paired and overlapping; ventral scutes 32-34; gill rakers very numerous but short, about half length of gill filaments on first arch; body depth 2.5-2.8 in standard length; mouth slightly inferior; posterior end of maxilla expanded and curved ventrally; a single supramaxilla; edge of lower jaw flared outward; third suborbital with an oblique anteroventral edge, ending near angle of preopercle; silvery with a faint linear pattern on body from dark centres of scales; a blackish spot about size of pupil behind upper end of gill opening. Reaches 21 cm. Gulf of Oman to the Gulf of Aden. Whitehead (1962b) and Nelson and Rothman (1973) provided additional descriptive data for the species.

BLOCH'S GIZZARD SHAD
Nematalosa nasus (Bloch, 1795)

Dorsal rays 15-18 (modally 17), the last greatly elongate (about 2.5 in standard length); anal rays 18-26 (modally 22 and 23); pectoral rays 15-17; pelvic rays 8; longitudinal scale series 45-49; exposed scale edges finely serrate; predorsal scales paired and overlapping; ventral scutes 29-31; body depth about 2.3-2.7 in standard length; snout rounded; mouth inferior, a single supramaxilla; third suborbital expanded ventroanteriorly almost to lower edge of preopercle, its anterior margin vertical; silvery with a faint linear pattern on dorsal part of body due to dark centres of scales; a black spot the size of pupil or larger behind upper part of gill opening. Reaches 26 cm. Arabian Gulf along the Asian continent to China, with records from Philippines, Taiwan, and southern Japan. Nelson and McCarthy (1995) described two new species of *Nematalosa* from the Arabian Gulf, *N. resticularia* and *N. persara*, which have been confused with *N. nasus*. They are distinguished chiefly by meristic data, especially the number of prepelvic ventral scutes: 18-22 (modally 20) for *N. resticularia* and 18-21 (modally 19) for *N. persara*, compared to 17-20 (modally 18) for *N. nasus*.

122. *Anodontostoma chacunda*, 14 cm (J. Randall)

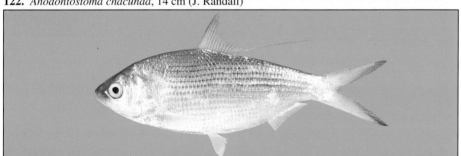
123. *Nematalosa arabica*, 17.5 cm (J. Randall)

124. *Nematalosa nasus*, 20.5 cm (J. Randall)

125. *Dussumieria acuta*, 13.5 cm (J. Randall)

ROUND HERRINGS
SUBFAMILY DUSSUMIERINAE

RAINBOW SARDINE
Dussumieria acuta Valenciennes, 1847

Dorsal rays 18-20; anal rays 15-16; pectoral rays 14; pelvic rays 8; longitudinal scale series 40-44; scales very deciduous; posterior part of scales with fine horizontal striae; ventral scutes absent except for a single W-shaped one surrounding base of pelvic fins; lower-limb gill rakers 19-26; branchiostegal rays 12-15; body depth 3.45-4.55 in standard length; blue on back, silvery on sides and below, with iridescence; in life a narrow brassy stripe on body extending posteriorly from upper end of gill opening. Reaches about 26 cm. Southern Oman and the Arabian Gulf to the western Indo-Malayan region.

SLENDER RAINBOW SARDINE
Dussumieria elopsoides Bleeker, 1849

Dorsal rays 18-20; anal rays 15-16; pectoral rays 14; pelvic rays 8; longitudinal scale series 52-56; no striae on posterior part of scales; a single pelvic scute; lower-limb gill rakers 21-32; branchiostegal rays 13-17; body slender, the depth 4.55-6.25 in standard length; colour as in *D. acuta*. Attains about 26 cm. Kenya, north to the Red Sea, east to the Indo-Malayan region and northern Australia, and north to Taiwan; invaded the eastern Mediterranean via the Suez Canal. Whitehead (1963) and others erred in placing this species in the synonymy of *D. acuta*.

126. *Dussumieria elopsoides*, 16 cm (J. Randall)

RED-EYE ROUND HERRING
Etrumeus teres (De Kay, 1842)

Dorsal rays 17-22; anal rays 10-12; pectoral rays 15-17; pelvic rays 8, the fin entirely posterior to base of dorsal fin; longitudinal scale series 50-56; scales very deciduous; a single W-shaped pelvic scute; lower-limb gill rakers 27-36; branchiostegal rays 14-15; body nearly cylindrical anteriorly, and elongate, the depth about 5-7 in standard length; isthmus with an abrupt narrowing (smoothly pointed in *Dussumieria*); eye completely covered with adipose eyelid; mouth terminal; one supramaxilla; silvery with golden reflections. Reaches 30 cm. Worldwide in isolated populations; Whitehead (1963) studied samples from seven populations; although he found some vari-

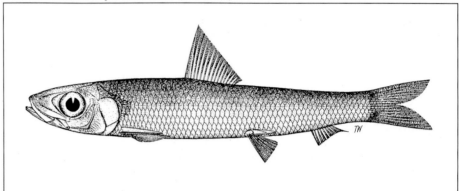

127. *Etrumeus teres* (after Whitehead, 1985)

ation in body depth and number of gill rakers, he concluded all were one species. The population from the most southern part of South Africa was described as *E. whiteheadi* by Wongratana (1983). *E. teres* has colonised the eastern Mediterranean via the Suez Canal. Kuronuma and Abe (1986) recorded the species from the Arabian Gulf.

DELICATE ROUND HERRING
Spratelloides delicatulus (Bennett, 1831)

Dorsal rays 12-13; anal rays 9-11; pectoral rays 11-13; pelvic rays 8; longitudinal scale series 35-41; vertical striae on scales continuous; predorsal scales 8-13; a single W-shaped pelvic scute; lower-limb gill rakers 26-32; branchiostegal rays 6; body depth 4.75-5.6 in standard length; no teeth on maxilla; second supramaxilla nearly symmetrically paddle-shaped; silvery on side and ventrally, but no distinct bright silver lateral stripe; two dark streaks on caudal-fin base. Maximum length, 8.5 cm. Indo-Pacific except the Arabian Gulf and western and southern Australia.

SILVERSTRIPE ROUND HERRING
Spratelloides gracilis (Temminck and Schlegel, 1846)

Dorsal rays 12-13; anal rays 12-13; pectoral rays 13-15; pelvic rays 8; longitudinal scale series 42-48; vertical striae on scales not continuous across middle of scales; a single W-shaped pelvic scute; lower-limb gill rakers 27-37; body elongate, the depth 5.8-7.6 in standard length; small teeth on maxilla; second supramaxilla asymmetrical, the lower curved part much longer than upper; a broad bright silver lateral stripe on body. Attains 10.5 cm. Indo-Pacific except the Arabian Gulf and the Hawaiian Islands.

128. *Spratelloides delicatulus*, 4.5 cm (J. Randall)

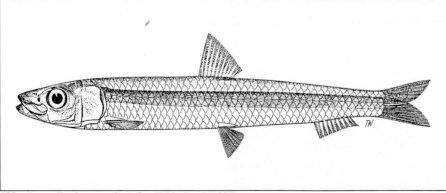

129. *Spratelloides gracilis* (after Whitehead, 1985)

SUBFAMILY PRISTIGASTERINAE

THIN ILISHA
Ilisha compressa Randall, 1994

Dorsal rays 17-18; anal rays 48-52; pectoral rays 18-19; pelvic fins very small, the rays 7; longitudinal scale series 55-56; ventral scutes 32-33; lower-limb gill rakers 18; body depth 3.1-3.2 in standard length; body compressed, the width 3.4-3.5 in depth; swim bladder with a postcoelomic extension on each side; dorsal-fin origin a little anterior to mid-standard length; origin of anal fin below middle of dorsal-fin base; grey dorsally, soon shading to silvery below; edges of jaws blackish dorsoanteriorly; pectoral and caudal fins yellow, the caudal with a blackish margin; dorsal and anal fins whitish. Largest specimen, 34 cm. Described from four specimens from the Arabian Gulf taken by trawl over mud bottom in 8-10 m. Iraq specimens misidentified as *I. filigera* (Valenciennes) by Khalaf (1961) and Kuwait specimens as *I. elongata* (Bennett) by Kuronuma and Abe (1986).

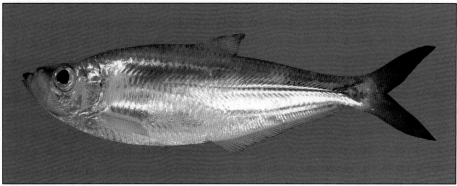

130. *Ilisha compressa*, 28 cm (J. Randall)

INDIAN ILISHA
Ilisha melastoma (Bloch and Schneider, 1801)

Dorsal rays 17-18; anal rays 35-48; pectoral rays 17; pelvic fins very small, the rays 7; longitudinal scale series about 44; ventral scutes 25-30; lower-limb gill rakers 21-25; body moderately deep, the depth 2.4-3.0 in standard length, and moderately compressed, the width 2.9-3.1 in depth; swim bladder with a postcoelomic extension on each side; origin of dorsal fin a little anterior to mid-standard length; origin of anal fin below rear base of dorsal fin; greenish on back, silvery with iridescence on sides and ventrally; dorsal and caudal fins yellowish, the dorsal fin often tipped and the caudal edged with blackish. Reaches 25 cm. Arabian Gulf along Asian coast to China and Taiwan, including Sumatra, Java, and Borneo. Marine, but also into estuaries, from the shallows to 15 m. Blegvad (1944) and Kuronuma and Abe (1972, 1986) recorded this species from the Arabian Gulf as *I. indica* (Swainson), a name based on the drawing of Plate 192 in Russell (1803); however, Whitehead (1973) correctly placed *indica* in the synonymy of *melastoma*.

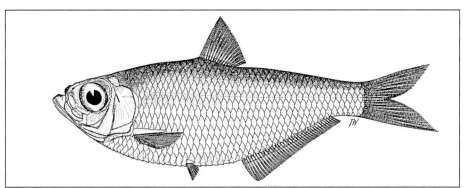

131. *Ilisha melatoma* (after Whitehead, 1985)

132. *Ilisha sirishai*, 28 cm (J. Randall)

LOBEJAW ILISHA
Ilisha sirishai Seshagiri Rao, 1975

Dorsal rays 17-18; anal rays 38-44; pectoral rays 15-17; pelvic rays 7; ventral scutes 27-29; lower-limb gill rakers 22-27; body depth 2.7-3.3 in standard length; swim bladder without a postcoelomic extension; lower jaw strongly projecting; maxilla with a distinct bony flange behind premaxilla; dorsal-fin origin at or before mid-standard length; origin of anal fin slightly behind rear base of dorsal fin; silvery. Largest specimen, 23 cm. Arabian Gulf to India and Thailand. The genus *Ilisha* was reviewed by Seshagiri Rao (1976).

TARDOOR
Opisthopterus tardoore (Cuvier, 1829)

Dorsal rays 15-17; anal rays 56-63; pectoral rays 12-14, the fin length 3.85-4.75 in standard length; no pelvic fins; longitudinal scale series about 50; scales very deciduous; ventral scutes 29-35; lower-limb gill rakers 22-28; body strongly compressed and moderately elongate, the depth 3.0-3.7 in standard length; mouth superior; silvery. Attains 22.5 cm. Gulf of Oman to coast of India; also from Andaman coast of Thailand and western Indonesia; marine and estuarine.

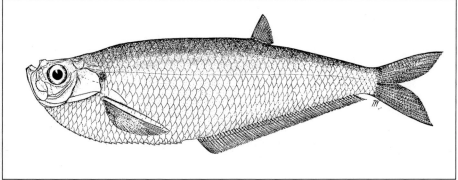

133. *Opisthopterus tardoore* (after Whitehead, 1985)

INDIAN PELLONA
Pellona ditchela Valenciennes, 1847

Dorsal rays 17-19; anal rays 36-40; pectoral rays 14-18; pelvic rays 7; longitudinal scale series 37-44; scales with vertical striae discontinuous, but slightly overlapping in scale centre; ventral scutes 26-28; lower-limb gill rakers 22-27; body moderately deep, the depth 2.6-3.0 in standard length; toothed hypomaxillary bone at edge of upper jaw between premaxilla and maxilla (only a ligament present at this site on the species of *Ilisha*); brown on back, silvery on sides. Maximum length about 21 cm. Continental shores of the Indian Ocean (Red Sea and Arabian Gulf excepted) to Indonesia, New Guinea, Philippines, and Queensland. Marine, brackish, and will enter freshwater.

ANCHOVIES
FAMILY ENGRAULIDAE

The anchovies, like the related clupeids, are small, silvery, schooling, plankton-feeding fishes with a single short dorsal fin usually near the middle of the body, no spines in fins, pectorals low on body, pelvic fins in abdominal postition (those in Oman with 7 rays), and a strongly forked caudal fin. The teeth are usually very small; typically there are two supramaxillae. All the Indo-Pacific species except those of the genus *Engraulis* have sharp ventral scutes. Anchovies are easily recognised by their distinctive head (with unique osteological characters as well). With few exceptions, the snout is rounded and overhanging, hence the mouth is ventral; the lower jaw is slender. Scales are deciduous; usually many are missing on specimens (therefore, scale counts are difficult to make; the longitudinal scale series of Oman species vary within the range of 38-46). At the present time 16 genera and 139 species of anchovies are recognized (Whitehead et al., 1988). In need of confirmation is the Oman record (as indicated by the distribution map of Whitehead in Fischer and Bianchi, 1984) of *Encra-*

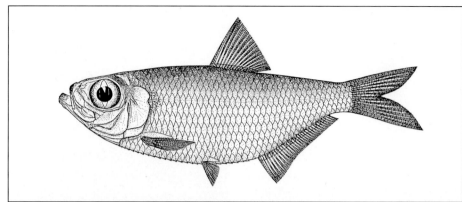

134. *Pellona ditchela* (after Whitehead, 1985)

135. *Encrasicholina devisi*, 6.5 cm (J. Randall)

136. *Encrasicholina punctifer*, 7.5 cm (J. Randall)

sicholina heteroloba (Rüppell). *Thryssa mystax* (Bloch and Schneider) was erroneously recorded by Kuronuma and Abe (1986) from the Arabian Gulf (see account of *T. whiteheadi* below).

DE VIS' ANCHOVY
Encrasicholina devisi (Whitley, 1940)

Dorsal rays 15 (initial three rays unbranched, the first very small); anal rays 18-20 (initial three unbranched, the first very small); pectoral rays 15; needle-like prepelvic scutes 3-6 (usually 5); no postpelvic scutes (true of all species of *Encrasicholina* and *Stolephorus*); body elongate with slightly rounded abdomen (applies to other *Encrasicholina* and the Oman species of *Stolephorus*); body width about half body

depth; lower-limb gill rakers 20-27; tip of maxilla pointed, extending beyond anterior border of preopercle; isthmus short, a small bony plate on urohyal exposed; origin of anal fin below rear base of dorsal fin; a broad bright silver to gold stripe on side of body bordered above by a blue line, the back blue-grey. Maximum length 9.5 cm. From the Gulf of Aden along the Asian continent to the Indo-Malayan region and northern Australia; also recorded from Fiji, Tonga, and Caroline Islands. This and other species of *Encrasicholina* often classified in *Stolephorus*.

BUCCANEER ANCHOVY
Encrasicholina punctifer Fowler, 1938

Dorsal rays 14-15 (first two rays unbranched); anal rays 14-16 (first two rays unbranched); pectoral rays 16-18; needle-like prepelvic scutes 2-7 (usually 4 or 5); lower-limb gill rakers 23-26; tip of maxilla blunt, not reaching anterior border of pre-operculum; isthmus short, preceded by a fleshy thickening on urohyal; origin of anal fin distinctly posterior to rear base of dorsal fin; pinkish grey with a broad bright silver stripe on side. Reported to 13 cm, but average adult size much smaller. Indo-Pacific from East Africa and Red Sea to Hawaii and Tahiti. Although often taken close inshore, this species has been reported hundreds of miles from land. *Stolephorus buccaneeri* Strasburg is a synonym.

COMMERSON'S ANCHOVY
Stolephorus commersonnii Lacepède, 1803

Dorsal rays usually 16; anal rays usually 21-22 (dorsal and anal counts include three initial unbranched rays, the first very small; true of other species of *Stolephorus*); pectoral rays 14-15; needle-like prepelvic scutes usually 1-4 (most often 2-3); lower-limb gill rakers 23-28; body width 1.8-2 in body depth; tip of maxilla pointed, reaching posterior border of preopercle; isthmus long, the urohyal not exposed; origin of anal fin

below posterior third of dorsal-fin base; pelvic tips extending posterior to origin of dorsal fin; translucent grey with a narrow bright silver stripe on side of body; a pair of blackish blotches on top of head behind occiput, followed by two dark lines to dorsal-fin origin. Attains about 12 cm. Mauritius (type locality) and Madagascar, north on African coast to Gulf of Aden, east to the Indo-Malayan region, north to Hong Kong. Coastal; reported to enter estuaries. Usually misspelled *S. commersonii*.

INDIAN ANCHOVY
Stolephorus indicus (van Hasselt, 1823)

Dorsal rays 15-17; anal rays 19-21; pectoral rays 15-17; needle-like prepelvic scutes 2-6 (most often 4); lower-limb gill rakers 20-28; body width about 1.5-2 in body depth; tip of maxilla pointed, reaching to or slightly beyond anterior border of preopercle; isthmus long, the urohyal not exposed; origin of anal fin below or a little posterior to middle of dorsal-fin base; pelvic tips not reaching posterior to a vertical at dorsal-fin origin; translucent grey with a narrow bright silver stripe on side of body; a pair of dusky blotches dorsally on head behind occiput. The largest (to 18 cm) and most widespread (Red Sea and entire East African coast to the Caroline Islands and Tahiti) of the 19 species of the genus. Coastal marine; tolerant of brackish water.

BAELAMA THRYSSA
Thyrssa baelama (Forsskål, 1775)

Dorsal rays 15-16; anal rays 29-32 (counts include initial three unbranched dorsal and anal rays, the first very small; true of other Oman *Thryssa*); pectoral rays 13-14; abdomen anterior to pelvic fins with 4-9 sharply pointed ventral scutes, none anterior to base of pectoral fins (other species of *Thryssa* with prepelvic scutes extending to isthmus); postpelvic scutes 12-18; lower-limb gill rakers 18-26 (usually 20-24); body depth about 4-5 in standard length; body width about 3 in body depth; tip of snout in front of centre of eye; maxilla pointed and short, reaching slightly posterior to anterior border of preopercle; silvery, the back bluish grey; about ten short orange venules extending posteriorly from upper part of gill opening; snout and interorbital orangish. Reaches 13.5 cm. Red Sea (type locality) south to Mozambique, Madagascar, and Mauritius, east to Pakistan, but without records from the Arabian Gulf or coast of India; definite from Sri Lanka, Indo-Malayan region, and northern Australia, east to Tonga and the Marianas. Usually found in bays or mangrove sloughs; often caught by seines and throw nets.

137. *Stolephorus commersonnii*, 11.5 cm (J. Randall)

138. *Stolephorus indicus*, 15 cm (J. Randall)

139. *Thryssa baelama*, 12 cm (J. Randall)

HAMILTON'S THRYSSA
Thryssa hamiltonii (Gray, 1835)

Dorsal rays 14-15; anal rays 32-40; pectoral rays 12-13; ventral scutes 23-26, the first 16-19 prepelvic; lower-limb gill rakers 11-15 (usually 12-14); body moderately deep, the depth about 3.5 in standard length, and compressed, the width 3.5-4 in depth; front of snout distinctly above centre of eye; tip of maxilla pointed, extending slightly posterior to edge of operculum; dorsal part of body grey, shading to silvery on sides and ventrally; a blackish blotch posterior to upper part of gill opening consisting of irregular horizontal black venules. Attains 25 cm. Arabian Gulf east to Indo-Malayan region and northern and western Australia, north to Taiwan and Marianas.

140. *Thryssa hamiltoni*, 18 cm (J. Randall)

LONGJAW THRYSSA
Thryssa setirostris (Broussonet, 1782)

Dorsal rays 14-15; anal rays 32-39; pectoral rays 12-14; ventral scutes 25-28, the anterior 16-18 prepelvic; lower-limb gill rakers 10-12; body depth about 4 in standard length, and width about 2.5 in depth; snout very short, its tip in front of centre of eye; unique among anchovies in the extreme prolongation of the maxilla, reaching at least to tip of pectoral fins, in some individuals beyond pelvic tips; greenish grey on back, silvery below, with a blackish blotch behind upper part of gill opening (from horizontal black venules); caudal fin yellowish. Reported to 18.5 cm. South Africa to Gulf of Aden, east along continental shores to Indo-Malayan region and tropical coast of Australia, north to China and Taiwan; easternmost record, Vanuatu (type locality). Found mostly inshore in bays and estuaries.

141. *Thryssa setirostris*, 11 cm (J. Randall)

ORANGEMOUTH THRYSSA
Thryssa vitrirostris (Gilchrist and Thompson, 1908)

Dorsal rays 13-15; anal rays 34-43; pectoral rays 13-14; ventral scutes 24-30, the first 16-19 prepelvic; lower-limb gill rakers 18-24; body depth 3.5-4 in standard length; body width about 3 in depth; tip of snout slightly above level of centre of eye; maxilla long, extending beyond base of first pectoral ray; back yellowish grey, soon shading to silvery; a blackish blotch from horizontal black venules behind upper part of gill opening; caudal fin yellowish (at least on upper and lower part of lobes), the posterior margin blackish; inside of mouth and gill chamber orange. Largest, 21.5 cm. South Africa and Madagascar to India, including the Arabian Gulf but not the Red Sea.

142. *Thryssa vitrirostris*, 13 cm (J. Randall)

72

WHITEHEAD'S THRYSSA
Thryssa whiteheadi Wongratana, 1983

Dorsal rays 13; anal rays 42-46; pectoral rays 14; ventral scutes 25-28, the anterior 15-17 prepelvic; lower-limb gill rakers 18-21; body depth about 3.8 in standard length; body compressed, the width nearly 4 in depth; snout short, its tip above centre of eye; mouth terminal or with lower jaw slightly projecting; teeth in jaws large for the genus; tip of maxilla varying from nearly reaching to extending slightly beyond edge of operculum; bluish grey on back, silvery on sides and ventrally; blackish blotch at upper end of gill opening faint or absent; fins whitish. Largest specimen, the one illustrated herein, 25.8 cm. Presently known only from the Arabian Gulf, but might range into the Gulf of Oman. Kuronuma and Abe (1986) recorded *Thyrssa mystax* (Bloch and Schneider) from the Arabian Gulf; however their meristic data do not match those of *mystax*, and their illustration (Plate 4) is *T. whiteheadi*.

WOLF HERRINGS
FAMILY CHIROCENTRIDAE

This family consists of a single genus and two species of clupeiform fishes. They share a number of characters with the clupeid fishes such as an elongate compressed body; no lateral line on body; two supramaxillae; scales cycloid and very deciduous; adipose eyelid; a single short dorsal fin; no spines in fins; pectoral fins low on body; pelvic fins small, with 7 rays, abdominal in position; and a strongly forked caudal fin. They differ in lacking scutes ventrally on the body, having very small scales, branchiostegal rays 8 (usually 6 or 7 in Clupeidae); the dorsal fin distinctly posterior in position, and long canine teeth in the jaws (two forward-projecting canines at front of upper jaw and a series of compressed canines on lower jaw, the largest on midside of jaw). Both species attain large size (over a meter in total length), and both are wide-ranging in the Indian Ocean and

143. *Thryssa whiteheadi*, 26 cm (J. Randall)

western Pacific. Fossil from the Cretaceous. Dorsal and anal fin-ray counts below include small initial unbranched rays.

BLACKFIN WOLF HERRING
Chirocentrus dorab (Forsskål, 1775)

Dorsal rays 16-18; anal rays 29-36; pectoral rays 14-16; gill rakers 3 + 13-15; depth of head at centre of eye 10.5-11.9 in standard length; tip of maxilla not extending posterior to a vertical through centre of eye; pectoral-fin length 7.6-8.6 in standard length; a narrow dark blue-green zone on back; head and rest of body silvery; dorsal fin broadly tipped with blackish; some blackish pigment often present anteriorly on anal fin. Reported to 120 cm, but rarely exceeds 80 cm. Continental subtropical-tropical shores of Indian Ocean including South Africa, Madagascar, Mauritius (where it is called Sabre), and Sri Lanka, to the Indo-Malayan region and northern Australia, north to southern Japan and east to Solomon Islands. A voracious predator on small fishes and shrimps.

WHITEFIN WOLF HERRING
Chirocentrus nudus (Swainson, 1839)

Dorsal rays 16-18; anal rays 31-33; pectoral rays 14-15; gill rakers 4-5 + 16-17; depth of head at centre of eye 8.4-9.7 in standard length; tip of maxilla extending posterior to centre of eye; pectoral-fin length 5.6-6.7 in standard length; a narrow dark blue zone on back, the head and rest of body silvery; dorsal fin not tipped with blackish. Reported to 120 cm, but rarely exceeding 80 cm. Distribution similar to the preceding but not reaching South Africa, Japan, or the Solomons.

144. *Chirocentrus dorab*, 41.5 cm (J. Randall)

145. *Chirocentrus nudus*, 44.5 cm (J. Randall)

MILKFISH
FAMILY CHANIDAE

This family consists of a single wide-ranging species with primitive teleost characters of no spines in fins, a single short dorsal fin near middle of body; pectoral fins low on body; pelvic fins abdominal, a deeply forked caudal fin, and a leptocephalus larva. See the following account for the diagnosis and remarks of the species.

MILKFISH
Chanos chanos Forsskål, 1775

Dorsal rays 13-17; anal rays 8-11; pectoral rays 15-17; pelvic rays 10-12; scales ctenoid, none on head; lateral-line scales 78-90; more than 250 slender gill rakers; branchiostegal rays 4; mouth small, without teeth; body depth 3.5-4.5 in standard length; silvery blue-green on back, silvery on sides and ventrally. Reported to 180 cm. Tropical and subtropical Indo-Pacific and eastern Pacific. Solitary or in small schools. Feeds primarily on algae; sometimes seen with mouth open at the surface feeding on algal scums. Spawns in the sea, but metamorphosis of the larvae is said to take place in brackish water. A valuable food fish of southeast Asia, Indonesia, and the Philippines; the young are caught in fine-mesh nets along the shore and reared in ponds.

SEA CATFISHES
FAMILY ARIIDAE

Catfishes are represented by 34 families, 412 genera, and about 2400 species of the order Siluriformes. Most are confined to freshwater. The sea catfishes are mainly marine and are generally found in muddy coastal waters; they occur in all tropical to warm temperate seas. Many freely enter freshwater, and a few are confined to freshwater. Fourteen genera and about 124 species of the Ariidae are recognised (Jayaram and Dhanze, 1986). *Arius* is much the largest genus and the only one with species in Oman. The sea catfishes are readily identified by having three pair of barbels around the mouth (reduced to two in a few species): one pair on the chin (termed mental), one farther back below the lower jaw (mandibular), and one from the side of the upper jaw (maxillary); there are no nasal barbels. The anterior and posterior nostrils are close together, the posterior partly covered by a flap. All species have a strong serrate spine at the front of the dorsal fin and each pectoral fin; these spines are venomous, and wounds from them are extremely painful (immersion of the wounded member in water as hot as can be tolerated greatly helps to alleviate the pain). There is a ray-free adipose fin (dorsally on body above anal fin) and a large forked caudal fin; pelvic fins have 6 rays, the fins abdominal in position. Scales are absent, but a distinct lateral line is present. The anterior 5-7 vertebrae are fused (7 in *Arius*). There is a complex bony shield dorsally on the head and nape just under the skin; it extends posteriorly to end just before a small predorsal plate (the shape of the head shield and predorsal plate may be useful in classification). Teeth in the jaws are in villiform bands; the small teeth in patches on the roof of the mouth vary from conical to granular. Males incubate the large eggs and newly hatched young in the mouth (eggs generally about pea size, but may be as large as 2 cm). These fishes are well known for sound production from vibration of thin bones on the dorsal surface of the swim bladder which acts as a resonating chamber. Some species form schools. The name Tachysuridae is sometimes erroneously used for this family (*Tachysurus*, however, is not a sea catfish).

146. *Chanos chanos*, about 90 cm (J. Randall)

ROUNDSNOUT SEA CATFISH
Arius bilineatus (Valenciennes, 1840)

Dorsal rays I,7; anal rays 17-21 (mean ray count 18.1); pectoral rays I,11; free vertebrae 46-52; snout broadly rounded and short; villiform teeth in two large subtriangular patches on palate (one on each side a short distance behind premaxillary teeth), each patch composed of two small anterior parts and a single large posterior part (the three parts separate in juveniles, merging with growth); head shield granules relatively coarse; color described as dark grey, reddish or bluish brown, often with a bronze lustre, the sides silvery to bronze. Attains about 80 cm. Arabian Gulf to the Indo-Malayan region, northern Australia, Queensland, and north to southern Japan. *Arius bilineatus* was regarded as a junior synonym of *A. thalassinus* until Kailola (1986) showed that it is a valid species.

SPOTTED SEA CATFISH
Arius maculatus (Thunberg, 1792)

Dorsal rays I,7, the first ray often prolonged as a filament; anal rays 19-22; pectoral rays I,11; teeth on palate granular and close-set, in a large elliptical patch on each side a short distance behind premaxillary teeth; head shield coarsely granular and stellate in shape; predorsal plate C-shaped; median longitudinal groove on head short, not extending onto supraoccipital process; maxillary barbel nearly or just reaching pectoral-fin base; dorsal and pectoral spines strong, the pectoral spines shorter than dorsal spine; grey to brown dorsally, shading to silvery grey on sides and whitish ventrally with dusky spots; maxillary barbel black; adipose fin with a blackish blotch; dorsal filament black. Reaches about 80 cm. Gulf of Oman to Indonesia, north to Japan (type locality); commercially important on the west coast of India.

THINSPINE SEA CATFISH
Arius tenuispinis Day, 1877

Dorsal rays I,7; anal rays 17-18; pectoral rays I,10-11; a single subtriangular patch of well-separated granular teeth on each side of palate far back on roof of mouth; granular nodules on head shield small; predorsal plate small and V-shaped; median longitudinal groove on head long, extending anterior to interorbital space; maxillary barbel nearly or just reaching pectoral-fin base; dorsal spine slender, equal to or slightly longer than pectoral spines; grey dorsally, shading to silvery grey on sides, and whitish ventrally. Attains at least 36 cm. Mozambique and Arabian Gulf to Sri Lanka.

147. *Arius bilineatus*, 59 cm (J. Randall)

148. *Arius maculatus*, 23 cm (J. Randall)

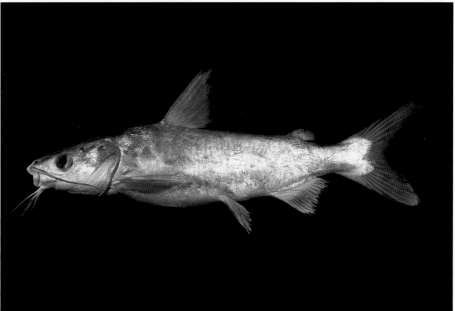

149. *Arius tenuispinis*, 20 cm (J. Randall)

GIANT SEA CATFISH
Arius thalassinus (Rüppell, 1837)

Dorsal rays I,7; anal rays 14-17 (mean ray count 15.8); pectoral rays I,11; free vertebrae 38-44; snout bluntly wedge-shaped when viewed from above (relatively longer in adults than young), and longer than that of *A. bilineatus* of comparable size; dentition as in *A. bilineatus*; head shield with a narrowing anterior projection on each side extending to above eye; head shield granular nodules relatively fine; predorsal plate small and V-shaped; median longitudinal groove on head short; colour variable but often blue on back, shading to silvery grey on side and silvery white ventrally. Reported to 185 cm, but any length over 100 cm should be verified. Known from Mozambique, Tanzania, Red Sea, Arabian Gulf east to the Indo-Malayan region, Australia south to Sydney, and Asia north to China. Feeds mainly on crabs, shrimps, and stomatopods, occasionally on fishes and molluscs.

EEL CATFISHES
FAMILY PLOTOSIDAE

This Indo-Pacific family of catfishes is relatively small, consisting of about nine genera and 32 species. Approximately half are found only in freshwater (these in Australia and New Guinea). Only two species, both in the genus *Plotosus*, occur in Oman. The eel catfishes are named for their somewhat elongate bodies and the confluence of the dorsal and anal fins with the caudal fin; there is no adipose fin. Usually there are four pairs of barbels (a nasal pair in addition to the usual three pairs seen in

150. *Arius thalassinus*, 24 cm (J. Randall)

ariid catfishes). The anterior nostrils are in a short tube, well-separated from the slit-like posterior nostrils; teeth are small, those in upper jaw conical; teeth in lower jaw and on palate granular, the latter in a crescentic or triangular patch. No scales and no bony shield on head; lateral line complete. A dendritic organ consisting of vascular epithelial folds present just behind anus. First dorsal fin short with a stout spine bearing retrorse barbs along the anterior and posterior edges (barbs larger anteriorly) and 4-6 rays; soft dorsal and anal fins very long. Pectoral fins with a stout initial barbed spine and 9-16 rays; pelvic fins abdominal with 10-16 rays. The dorsal and pectoral spines are highly venomous, and a few deaths have been reported. The venom glands lie on each side along the length of the spine (but thickest on the distal third), covered with delicate integumentary tissue which is easily damaged when the spine enters the flesh

of the victim. The author has been stung once by each of the species which occur in Oman and can testify to the virulence of the venom. The *Plotosus limbatus* sting was from a 23-cm fish collected from a tidepool near Duqm that had been on ice for more than three hours. As the mucus was being washed off in preparation for a photograph, the fish slipped in his grasp, and one pectoral spine stuck deeply into a thumb. Three tugs, each more forceful, were needed to extricate the spine. The pain was agonizing. Only when the thumb was placed in very hot water was it barely tolerable. Four hours of soaking in water (that was continuously maintained as hot as could be withstood) were needed before the thumb could be removed from the water; even then, pethidine was administered to alleviate the pain. The thumb remained too sore to use in any way for two days.

BROWN EEL CATFISH
Plotosus limbatus Valenciennes, 1840

Dorsal rays I,4-6 – 106-133; anal rays 87-126; caudal rays 9-11; pectoral rays I,13-16; gill rakers 20-25; free vertebrae 69-77; nasal barbels short, extending only a short distance posterior to rear edge of eye; body depth 5.3-7.7 in standard length; brown, the edges of the median fins narrowly blackish. Largest specimen collected, 58.5 cm. Coasts of India and Sri Lanka to Kenya, including southern and central Oman; not known from the Arabian Gulf or Red Sea. Marine and estuarine; may be seen in surprisingly shallow water along rocky coasts; probably nocturnal. Gomon and Taylor (1982) described

151. *Plotosus limbatus*, about 43 cm (J. Randall)

the closely related *P. nkunga* from South Africa, differentiating it from *P. limbatus* principally by its fewer gill rakers (16-21). It will be of interest to determine if the ranges of these two species overlap on the east coast of Africa.

STRIPED EEL CATFISH
Plotosus lineatus (Thunberg, 1787)

Dorsal rays I,4 – 69-115; anal rays 58-82; caudal rays 9-11; pectoral rays I,9-13; free vertebrae 49-58; nasal barbels short, reaching only slightly posterior to rear edge of eye; body depth 5.8-8.0 in standard length; dark brown with two narrow pale yellow to white stripes (stripes may be obscure in large adults); abdomen and ventral part of head white; edge of median fins black. Reaches 32 cm. Indo-Pacific from Red Sea and east coast of Africa east to Samoa, north to Japan and south to New South Wales. Occurs in a variety of inshore habitats, including coral reefs, estuaries, sand flats, and seagrass beds. Adults observed actively foraging for food at night; reported to feed on small crustaceans, molluscs, and fishes. Juveniles form dense aggregations which swarm over the substratum.

152. *Plotosus lineatus*, night, about 11 cm (J. Randall)

LIZARDFISHES
FAMILY SYNODONTIDAE

Lizardfishes are aptly named for their reptile-like head. They have a large mouth and numerous needle-like teeth; even the tongue has teeth. The body is cylindrical and moderately elongate. There are no spines in the fins; there is a single, relatively high dorsal fin of 10-14 rays and an adipose fin; the pelvic fins are large, with 8-9 rays; the caudal fin is forked. The family, one of several of the order Aulopiformes, is divisible into three subfamilies: the Synodontinae with two genera, *Synodus* (25 Indo-Pacific species; revised by Cressey, 1981; supplemented by Waples and Randall, 1988), and the monotypic *Trachinocephalus*; the Harpadontinae, also with two genera, *Saurida* (with 11 Indo-Pacific species – see Shindo and Yamada, 1972; and Waples, 1982) and *Harpadon* (with four species – see Klausewitz, 1983); and the Bathysaurinae with one genus containing two deep-water species. Lizardfishes generally live on sedimentary substrata; they are able to bury themselves quickly in sand or mud with only their eyes showing. All are voracious carni-vores, darting upward with great rapidity to seize small fishes, shrimps, or squids that venture near. The late larval stage, which may reach more than 5 cm in length, is slender and transparent with a row of prominent internal black spots ventrally on each side of the body; the number of these spots is useful in the identification of some of the species.

SLENDER LIZARDFISH
Saurida gracilis (Quoy and Gaimard, 1824)

Dorsal rays 11-12 (rarely 12); anal rays 9-10; pectoral rays 12-14 (usually 13); pelvic rays 9 (true of all species of *Saurida*), the outer rays longer than inner; lateral-line scales 49-52; scale rows above lateral line to dorsal fin 3.5; numerous small teeth exposed on side of jaws when mouth closed (true of other species of *Saurida*); palatine teeth in two rows on each side of roof of mouth (also characteristic of the genus); small teeth on vomer (no vomer in *Synodus*); origin of dorsal fin posterior to midpoint of distance from snout to adipose fin; tip of pectoral fin reaches to within two or three predorsal scales of dorsal fin origin; mottled brown and white dorsally, white ventrally, with a row of blackish blotches on side of body and a second smaller row below, some of which are connected to those above; three diffuse blackish blotches dorsally on posterior half of body, the largest behind dorsal fin; fins with rows of dark spots forming transverse bands. Reaches 28 cm. Wide-ranging throughout the Indo-Pacific region; usually found on sand or silty sand near protected reefs.

153. *Saurida gracilis* (J. Randall)

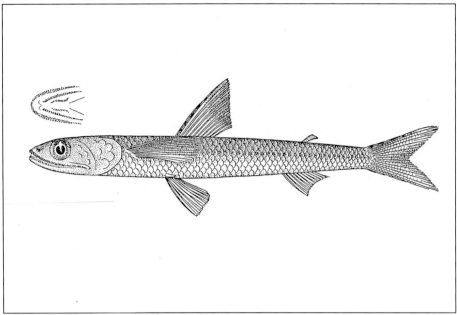

154. *Saurida longimanus* (after Norman, 1939)

LONGFIN LIZARDFISH
Saurida longimanus Norman, 1939

Dorsal rays 11-12; anal rays 10-11; pectoral rays 14; lateral-line scales 45-49; body elongate, the depth about 8 in standard length; head large, its length about 3.5 in standard length; outer band of palatine teeth with two rows of teeth anteriorly; no teeth on vomer; longest dorsal ray nearly four times longer than last ray; pectoral fins long, reaching well beyond base of pelvic fins to about midbase of dorsal fin; brownish above, silvery white below, the distal part of dorsal, caudal, and pectoral fins blackish; sometimes traces of dark spots along upper edge of caudal fin. Attains at least 25 cm. Described from six specimens trawled in 106-201 m in the Gulf of Oman; also recorded from Indonesia and northern Australia.

155. *Saurida nebulosa* (P. Woodhead)

NEBULOUS LIZARDFISH
Saurida nebulosa Valenciennes, 1849

Dorsal rays 10-11; anal rays 9-10; pectoral rays 12 (rarely 11 or 13); lateral-line scales 50-52; scale rows above lateral line to dorsal fin 3.5; no teeth on vomer; tip of pectoral fins short, extending to within four to six predorsal scales of origin of dorsal fin; similar in colour pattern to *S. gracilis* (*nebulosa* is best distinguished by its usual pectoral count of 12 and shorter pectoral fins). Largest specimen, 20 cm. Indo-Pacific, usually in shallow turbid areas.

156. *Saurida tumbil*, 34 cm (J. Randall)

GREATER LIZARDFISH
Saurida tumbil (Bloch, 1795)

Dorsal rays 11-13 (usually 12); anal rays 11-12; pectoral rays 14 or 15; lateral-line scales 50-56; 4.5-5.5 rows of scales above lateral line to dorsal fin; lateral series of palatine teeth in three rows anteriorly; a small patch of teeth on vomer; longest dorsal ray about four times longer than last ray; pectoral fins short, just reaching origin of pelvic fins; light brown on back (often in a linear pattern), silvery white below, sometimes with a series of small elongate brown spots along lateral line; no series of dark spots on leading edge of dorsal fin and upper lobe of caudal fin; lower lobe of caudal fin dusky to blackish (distinctly darker than upper lobe); paired fins often with a large dusky area on membranes. Attains at least 40 cm. Red Sea and coast of East Africa and Madagascar, east along the continental shelf to the Indo-Malayan region and Australia. Usually taken by trawling over mud bottoms in 10-60 m.

BRUSHTOOTH LIZARDFISH
Saurida undosquamis (Richardson, 1848)

Dorsal rays 11-12 (usually 12); anal rays usually 10-11; pectoral rays 14-15; lateral-line scales 45-52; rows of scales above lateral line to dorsal fin 3.5-4.5; lateral series of palatine teeth in two rows; no teeth on vomer; longest dorsal ray about three times longer than last ray; pectoral fins not extending beyond base of pelvic fins and not reaching origin of dorsal fin; brown dorsally (the edges of scales darker), silvery white ventrally, with a series of about nine elongate dark spots along lateral line; fins unmarked except for a series of small blackish spots along leading edge of dorsal fin and upper lobe of caudal fin. Reported to 50 cm. Red Sea and coast of Africa, east to the Indo-Malayan region, south to Australia and north to southern Japan, principally in continental shelf waters, but also reported from the Maldives and Seychelles; has invaded the eastern Mediterranean via the Suez Canal. Generally found on muddy bottoms in the depth range of 20 to at least 200 m, but the illustrated specimen was collected on sand in 18 m off Karan Island, Arabian Gulf.

157. *Saurida undosquamis*, 22.5 cm (J. Randall)

158. *Synodus dermatogenys*, 12 cm (J. Randall)

159. *Synodus variegatus*, 24 cm (J. Randall)

CLEARFIN LIZARDFISH
Synodus dermatogenys Fowler, 1912

Dorsal rays 11-13 (rarely 13); anal rays 8-10; pectoral rays 11-13; pelvic rays 8 (true of all *Synodus*); lateral-line scales 59-62; scale rows above lateral line 5.5; cheek usually not scaled as far posterior as preopercular margin; rows of small teeth not exposed on side of jaws when mouth closed (as in *Saurida*); palatine teeth in a single series on each side of roof of mouth (also characteristic of *Synodus*); an anterior group of palatine teeth distinctly longer than remaining teeth; membranous flap on anterior nostril long and slender; pectoral fins not reaching a line connecting origin of pelvic and dorsal fins; a series of eight or nine dark blotches (often with pale centres) along lateral line, the blotches smaller than pale interspaces, linked with another series along back and a series of bars (twice as numerous) on lower side; six black dots dorsally on tip of snout; pelvic and anal fins without dark markings; black peritoneal spots 10-12. Attains 23 cm. Wide-ranging throughout the Indo-Pacific region; usually found on sand or sand-rubble substrata, often near coral reefs. Frequently misidentified as *S. variegatus*.

REEF LIZARDFISH
Synodus variegatus (Lacepède, 1803)

Dorsal rays 12-14; anal rays 8-10; pectoral rays 12-13; lateral-line scales 61-63; scales above lateral line to base of dorsal fin 3.5; cheek behind mouth fully scaled to preopercular margin; a discrete group of anterior palatine teeth longer than remaining teeth; nasal flap short and triangular; pectoral fins not reaching a line connecting origins of pelvic and dorsal fins; a midlateral stripe (the lateral line forming its upper edge) nearly as broad as eye containing a series of nine rectangular blotches which may be dark brown, reddish, or greenish; every other blotch of lateral series linked with a diffuse dark blotch on back; a series of short dark bars, twice as numerous as lateral blotches, extending below lateral stripe; black peritoneal spots 7-10. Largest specimen, 28.3 cm. Indo-Pacific; more reef-oriented than any other lizardfish; often seen at rest on coral or other hard substrata of reefs. *S. englemani* Schultz is a synonym.

SNAKEFISH
Trachinocephalus myops (Forster, 1801)

Dorsal rays 11-14; anal rays 13-18; pectoral rays 11-13; pelvic rays 8, the inner rays longer than outer; lateral-line scales 51-61; scales above lateral line 3.5; snout very short, equal to or shorter than eye diameter; mouth strongly oblique; interorbital space deeply concave; body with alternating dark-edged pale blue and yellow stripes; an oblique black spot at upper end of gill opening. Reported to 33 cm. Indo-Pacific and Atlantic in tropical to warm temperate seas; occurs from the shallows to depths as great as 400 m; found on sand in which it is usually nearly completely buried.

160. *Trachinocephalus myops*, 15 cm (J. Randall)

VELIFERS
FAMILY VELIFERIDAE

The Veliferidae is one of seven bizarre families of fishes of the order Lampridiformes which contain only about 21 species, most of which are pelagic. It consists of two monotypic genera, *Velifer* and *Metavelifer* (Walters, 1960). These fishes have a deep compressed body, small highly protractile mouth with no teeth, 6 branchiostegal rays, very deciduous cycloid scales, pelvic fin with 7-9 rays (no spine), and a swim bladder which bifurcates posteriorly, each part extending well beyond the anus.

SAILFIN VELIFER
Velifer hypselopterus Bleeker, 1879

Dorsal rays I-II,30-34; anal rays I,24-27, the spine very small; pectoral rays 15-16; pelvic rays 7-8; lateral-line scales about 70-72; body depth 2.1-2.2 in standard length; dorsal and anal fins very elevated anteriorly, the first dorsal soft ray about equal to body depth, the remaining rays progressively shorter posteriorly; caudal fin forked; silvery grey with six dark bars on body; dorsal fin with curved yellow bands. Reported to reach 40 cm. Recorded only from Japan, Vietnam, India, Madagascar, and a trawl catch in the Gulf of Oman; observed by J.P. Hoover and J.L. Earle while diving off southern Oman.

161. *Velifer hypselopterus*, 20 cm (after Smith and Heemstra, 1986)

BROTULAS AND CUSK EELS
FAMILY OPHIDIIDAE

The order Ophidiiformes includes five families, of which the best known are the Ophidiidae, Carapidae, and Bythitidae. Only one ophidiid is reported herein and none of the other two families, but surely other species will eventually be found in Oman waters. Many of the pearlfishes (Carapidae) live commensally or parasitically in sea cucumbers, bivalves, and starfishes; a number of sea cucumbers from Oman were examined by the author for carapids, but none was found. The ophidiids are moderately elongate with the long-based dorsal and anal fins confluent with the caudal fin; no spines in fins; pelvic fins, if present, consist of only one or two slender rays, anterior to pectoral-fin base; barbels on head present or absent; scales small and cycloid. Unlike the viviparous bythitids, the ophidiids are oviparous.

BEARDED BROTULA
Brotula multibarbata Temminck and Schlegel, 1846

Dorsal rays 109-139; anal rays 80-106; caudal rays 9; pectoral rays 22-26; pelvic rays 2 (about outer half free from membrane); lateral-line scales 144-181; three pairs of barbels on snout and three pairs on chin; body depth 4.4-7.0 in standard length; grey-brown, shading to whitish on abdomen and ventrally on head; edge of median fins narrowly white, usually with a diffuse dark submarginal band; small juveniles translucent with dark grey spots. Reaches about 60 cm. Widespread in the Indo-Pacific. Usually found in shallow reef areas, but has been recorded to 650 m. Nocturnal; hides in reefs by day. Quickly retreats to shelter when illuminated at night. Hubbs (1944) revised the genus *Brotula*.

162. *Brotula multibarbata*, 37.5 cm (J. Randall)

TOADFISHES
FAMILY BATRACHOIDIDAE

The toadfish family is the sole family of the order Batrachoidiformes. These fishes are characterised by a large depressed head with the eyes oriented as much dorsally as laterally; the body of most is cylindrical anteriorly, becoming compressed posteriorly; the mouth is large, the teeth small and conical; the gill opening is restricted to the side of the body just in front of the pectoral-fin base; the skin is thick, generally without scales, and loosely attached to body; three or four stout spines on operculum, usually hidden by skin; short fleshy tentacles often present on head. The spinous dorsal fin consists of two or three short spines; the soft dorsal and anal fins are long-based, without spines; the pelvic fins are anterior to the pectorals and gill opening, with one spine and two or three soft rays; the caudal fin is rounded. The family consists of 24 genera (some as yet undescribed) and 71 species (David W. Greenfield, pers. comm.) which are divided into three subfamilies, the large cosmopolitan Batrachoidinae with three dorsal spines and no canine teeth; the New World Porichthyinae with two dorsal spines, canine teeth, most species with photophores; and the New World Thalassophryninae with two hollow dorsal spines and a hollow opercular spine associated with venom glands. Toadfishes are benthic and sluggish; they are generally found in shallow water; some occur on coral reefs or rocky substrata, others on seagrass, sand, or mud. They are carnivorous, feeding principally on crustaceans, molluscs, and fishes. A few are well known for sound production.

FLAT TOADFISH
Austrobatrachus dussumieri (Valenciennes, 1837).

Dorsal rays III + 18-20; anal rays 14-16; pectoral rays 22-24; pelvic rays I,2; two lateral lines, the upper with 33-41 pores; head and anterior part of body depressed; body depth 3.6-4.2 in SL; three sharp spines on opercle; three irregular rows of sharp conical teeth anteriorly in jaws, narrowing posteriorly to a single row; a broad arc of larger conical teeth in two rows on palate; short tentacles and dermal flaps on chin, snout, and one above eye; a foramen in upper part of pectoral axil; light brown, shading to white ventrally, with four, irregular, branching, dark brown bars on body and dark bands and blotches on head and fins. Attains 27 cm. Arabian Gulf to India (Malabar, the type locality) and Sri Lanka. May occur in coral reefs or in seagrass or weedy bottoms; has been collected in tidepools. Often misidentified as *Batrachus grunniens* (Linnaeus). A new genus will be proposed for this species (David W. Greenfield, pers. comm.).

163. *Austrabatrachus dussumieri* (J. Randall)

TWO-FACED TOADFISH
Bifax lacinia Greenfield, Randall, and Mee, 1994

Dorsal rays III + 23-24; anal rays 15-18; pectoral rays 20-21; two lateral lines, the upper one with 47-56 pores; body depth 6.2-7.6 in standard length; head greatly depressed; a large fleshy flap extending laterally on each side at front of head, with an eye spot on outer part of anterior side; a row of tentacles of variable size on chin, and a single nasal tentacle; three opercular and two subopercular spines; a double row of sharp conical teeth at front of jaws, narrowing to a single row posteriorly; vomer and palatines with a single row of conical teeth; a shallow pit at top of pectoral-fin axil, and glandular tissue present in axil; dark purplish brown, abruptly white on abdomen and ventrally on head; front of upper lip, nasal tentacles, and outer part of cephalic flaps yellow; eye spot within yellow part of each cephalic flap black with a rim of brown; fins yellow and purplish brown, the caudal, pectoral, and especially the second dorsal fins largely yellow. Largest specimen, 33 cm. Known only from the coast of southern and central Oman; all specimens came from crevices in steep rocky bottom in the depth range of 6-8 m. When one was placed in an aquarium with other fishes and starfishes, the fishes soon showed distress. Although they were transferred to another tank, they died within 10 minutes. The starfishes were also removed but were dead the following morning. The author tasted the mucus of this toadfish and found it most unpleasant. The glandular tissue of the pectoral axil may be responsible for the production of the skin toxin which probably serves as a deterent to predators such as moray eels. The generic name *Bifax* is from the Latin for two-faced, in reference to the cephalic flaps with eye spots and the apparent purpose to deceive predators by making the fish seem larger than it is.

FROGFISHES
FAMILY ANTENNARIIDAE

The frogfish family is one of 16 of the order Lophiiformes, all of which have the first ray of the spinous dorsal fin, if present, on the head and modified into an illicium (from the Latin for attraction or enticement) which is tipped with the esca (bait) for luring their prey to the vicinity of

164. *Bifax lacinia*, 31.5 cm (J. Randall)

the mouth. Whereas most of the lophiiform fishes are residents of the deep sea, the frogfish family is mainly a shallow-water group. All the species are benthic except the widespread epipelagic *Histrio histrio*. Frogfishes are laterally compressed (in contrast to the depressed goosefishes, batfishes, and anglerfishes); the skin, which is loose on the body, is naked or with denticles; wart-like protuberances or small tentacles or cirri may be present. The mouth is very large and highly oblique to vertical; the teeth are villiform. The first dorsal fin consists of three separate cephalic spines, the most anterior at the front of the snout modified to the illicium, the third curved and usually broadly connected by membrane posteriorly to the nape; the second dorsal and anal fins are without spines; the prehensile pectoral fins are limb-like with an "elbow" joint; the small jugular pelvic fins have a spine and 5 soft rays; the gill opening is small and round, located on the posterior basal part of the pectoral appendage or just behind it. The colour of many of the frogfishes is extremely variable; generally they match their surroundings remarkably well; the same species may be yellow near yellow coral, red near red sponge, or black near black tunicates. Although these fishes are able to slowly stalk their prey of small fishes or crustaceans, they usually remain stationary and lure by enticingly wriggling the illicium with its esca above the mouth. The prey may be longer than the frogfish predator and still end up in the capacious stomach of the latter. The eggs form a floating raft-like mass on the surface. The wide-ranging Indo-Pacific

165. *Antennarius pictus* (K. Fiedler)

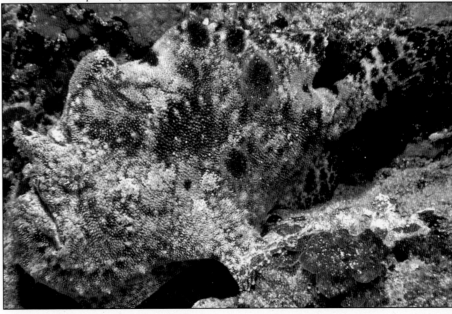

and eastern Pacific *A. commersoni* (Latreille) should be expected from Oman. Pietsch and Grobecker (1987) revised the family.

FRECKLED FROGFISH
Antennarius coccineus (Cuvier, 1831)

Dorsal soft rays 12 (rarely 13), the last two or three branched; anal rays 7, all branched; pectoral rays 10 (rarely 11 in the western Indian Ocean), all simple; last pelvic ray branched; illicium about as long as second dorsal spine, the esca usually a small sphere of folded tissue plus a few short tentacles; second dorsal spine strongly curved, without membrane linking it to head; no caudal peduncle; usual ground colour mottled yellowish grey, brownish yellow, or dull red, often with small, irregular, dark grey or reddish spots, especially on abdomen; esca usually white; a round dark spot at base of second dorsal fin may be present. Largest specimen, 12 cm. A common, shallow-water, wide-ranging, Indo-Pacific and eastern Pacific species; one specimen from southern Oman was collected in 10 m.

INDIAN FROGFISH
Antennarius indicus Schultz, 1964

Dorsal soft rays 12, the posterior two or three branched; anal rays 7; pectoral rays 12 or 13 (usually 13), none branched; fifth pelvic ray branched; illicium equal in length or slightly longer than second dorsal spine; esca large, consisting of a cluster of leaf-like appendages; usual colour yellow to yellowish brown with two or three dark ocelli (one at base of second dorsal fin and the other one or two beneath pectoral fins); dark brown bars or rows of spots on fins; illicium darkbanded. Attains 25 cm. A rare species known only from the western Indian Ocean, including the Gulf of Aden and Gulf of Oman.

FINANCIER FROGFISH
Antennarius nummifer (Cuvier, 1817)

Dorsal soft rays 12 (rarely 13), the last two branched; anal rays 7 (rarely 8), all but the first branched; pectoral rays 10-11 (rarely 12), all simple; fifth pelvic soft ray branched; caudal peduncle present (i.e. rear base of anal fin ending before caudal-fin base); illicium about equal in length to second dorsal spine; esca large and variable, but often resembling a small shrimp; a shallow naked depression between second

and third dorsal spines; ground colour may be yellow, orange, pink, red, olive, brown, or brown mixed with another colour; a prominent ocellated black spot usually present at base of soft dorsal fin. Largest specimen, 12 cm. Indo-Pacific (including the Arabian Gulf) and islands of the tropical and subtropical eastern Atlantic; known from the shallows to depths as great as 176 m (average depth for Indo-Pacific captures, 19 m). The specific part of the scientific name means "bearer of coins".

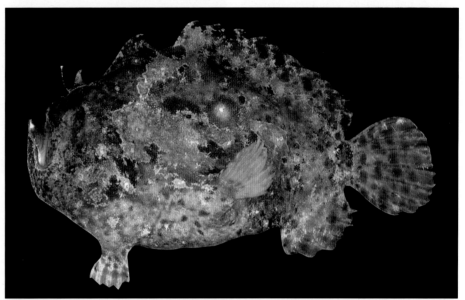

166. *Antennarius coccineus*, 9.5 cm (J. Randall)

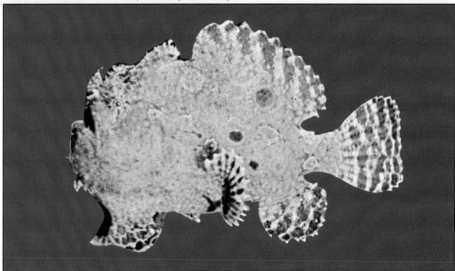

167. *Antennarius indicus*, about 11 cm (K. Paysan; courtesy of T.F.H. Publications)

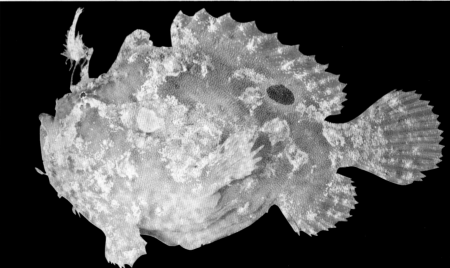

168. *Antennarius nummifer*, 6 cm (J. Randall)

83

PAINTED FROGFISH
Antennarius pictus (Shaw and Nodder, 1794)

Dorsal soft rays 12 (rarely 11 or 13), the last two or three branched; anal rays 7 (rarely 6), all branched; pectoral rays 10 (rarely 9 or 11), all simple; last pelvic ray branched; illicium about twice as long as second dorsal spine; esca usually long and ribbon-like with filaments; second dorsal spine attached by membrane to head, the membrane with small spinules except along outer margin; skin sometimes with low wart-like protuberances; colour highly variable; may be black (sometimes with small yellow spots), yellowish, orange, rust red, or brown, usually with numerous ocellated dark spots of variable size on head, body, and fins; dark phases with pectoral ray tips white. Largest, 21 cm. Widespread in the Indo-Pacific from East Africa and the Red Sea to Hawaii and the Society Islands (type locality, Tahiti); a shallow-water species, in general, but reported to depths as great as 75 m. *A. chironectes* Lacepède is a synonym.

CALICO FROGFISH
Antennarius sarasa Tanaka, 1916

Dorsal soft rays 13, the posterior three to nine branched; anal rays 8, all branched; pectoral rays 13, all branched; all soft rays of pelvic fins branched; illicium about equal in length to second dorsal spine; esca a small oval-shaped mass of vertical folds or short filaments; caudal peduncle present; a single dark ocellus basally in soft dorsal fin. Largest specimen, 38 cm. Known from only six specimens (Japan, Philippines in 173-185 m, New Zealand in 73 m, Réunion, and the illustrated specimen collected by J.P. Hoover from southern Oman in 6 m).

SARGASSUMFISH
Histrio histrio (Linnaeus, 1758)

Dorsal soft rays 12 (rarely 11 or 13), the last two or three branched; anal rays 7 (rarely 6 or 8), the last two to six branched; pectoral rays 10 (rarely 9 or 11), all simple; pelvic rays simple; illicium short, less than half length of, and very close to, second dorsal spine; esca a cluster of short filaments; second dorsal spine straight to slightly curved, with small tentacles and no membrane linking it to head; head, body, and fins with scattered small cutaneous flaps; pelvic fins unusually long, less than 4.0 in standard length; usual colour pale yellowish with a coarse reticulum of dark yellowish brown on body and scattered small white spots; large pale spots formed by reticulum edged in

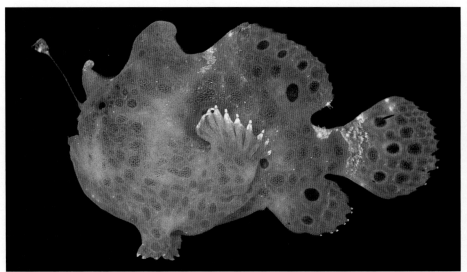

169. *Antennarius pictus*, 3.3 cm (J. Randall)

170. *Antennarius sarasa*, 23 cm (J. Hoover)

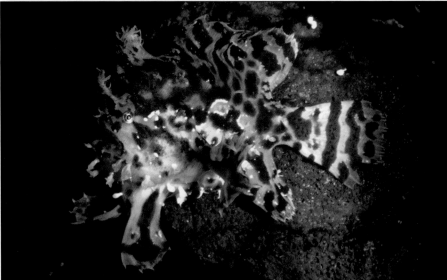

171. *Histrio histrio*, about 10 cm (J. Randall)

white; irregular dark yellowish bands radiating from eye; fins with irregular dark yellowish brown bands and large spots; small cutaneous flaps on body mainly white, those on head light yellowish; some individuals dark brown with the reticulum and fin markings black; juveniles may be entirely black with white-tipped pectorals. Maximum length 19 cm. Widespread in the tropical to temperate Indo-Pacific and Atlantic; usually found in masses of floating *Sargassum*.

SILVERSIDES
FAMILY ATHERINIDAE

This family, one of seven families of the order Atheriniformes, consists of small, slender, zooplankton-feeding fishes which usually form schools in inshore waters; most are marine or estuarine, but some are confined to freshwater. They have two well-separated dorsal fins, the first with three to eight flexible spines; the second dorsal and anal fins are preceded by a single spine; the pectoral fins are high on the side of the body; the pelvic fins, with I,5 rays, are distinctly posterior to the base of the pectoral fins; scales are cycloid; there is no lateral line; the mouth is small, the premaxilla often protractile, the teeth usually very small. Typically they have a broad silvery stripe on the side of the body, hence the common name. Silversides

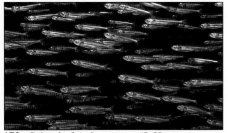

172. School of *A. lacunosus* (J. Hoover)

are often caught by dipnet at the surface at night when attracted to a light. They are heavily preyed upon by jacks and other roving predaceous fishes. The eggs are large, demersal, with adhesive threads. The family contains about 25 genera and 165 species; only two species are known from Oman seas.

HARDYHEAD SILVERSIDE
Atherinomorus lacunosus (Forster, 1801)

Dorsal rays IV-VII + I,8-11; anal rays I,12-16; pectoral rays 15-19; longitudinal scale series 39-44; predorsal scales 17-22; lower-limb gill rakers 18-25; body robust, the depth 4.1-5.6 in standard length; eye large, 2.4-3.1 in head length; rear of upper jaw extending to or a little posterior to a vertical at front edge of pupil; ascending process of premaxilla short and blunt; origin of first dorsal fin posterior to middle of standard length; caudal fin forked; anus at or a little anterior to tips of pelvic fins; greenish grey on back, the scale edges dusky; a broad silvery stripe on side, the upper edge with an iridescent blue line. Reaches 13 cm. Indo-Pacific. Often classified in *Pranesus*; *Atherina pinguis* Lacepède and *A. forskalii* Rüppell are synonyms (Whitehead and Ivantsoff, 1983).

SAMOAN SILVERSIDE
Hypoatherina temminckii (Bleeker, 1855)

Dorsal rays V-VII + I,8-10; anal rays I,11-14; pectoral rays 14-18; longitudinal scale series 38-44; predorsal scales 16-18; lower-limb gill rakers 21-25; body slender, the depth 5.6-6.9 in standard length; upper jaw extending to below front edge of orbit; ascending process of premaxilla moderately long and narrow (longer than twice the width); origin of dorsal fin posterior to mid-point of standard length; caudal fin forked; anus posterior to pelvic tips; blue-green on back with a lateral silvery stripe that is about one-fourth as wide as body depth. Attains about 6 cm. Indo-Pacific from the Red Sea and coast of East Africa to Samoa.

NEEDLEFISHES
FAMILY BELONIDAE

The needlefishes are grouped with the sauries, halfbeaks, and flying-fishes in the order Beloniformes. They are very elongate with extremely long, pointed jaws bearing numerous needle-like teeth; the nasal organ in a cavity on the side of the snout, with a protruding lobe; the fins lack spines; the dorsal and anal fins are posterior in position; the pelvics of 6 rays are abdominal; the scales are small, cycloid, and decidu-ous; the lateral line commences on the throat and passes along the lower side of the body, with an upward branch to the pectoral-fin origin. These fishes are surface-dwelling and protectively coloured for this mode of life, green or blue on the back, and silvery below; some species have green bones. Needlefishes feed mainly on small fishes. When frightened, as by the approach of a predator or boat, or confused, as by a light at night, they skitter and leap

173. *Atherinomorus lacunosus*, 12.5 cm (J. Randall)

174. *Hypoatherina temminckii*, 8 cm (J. Randall)

at the surface. They may injure people who lie in their path at this time, and fatalities have resulted (Randall, 1960). The eggs are large and attached with adhesive filaments to floating objects. The family includes ten genera and 32 species, 11 of which are restricted to freshwater. Parin (1967) reviewed the Indo-Pacific marine species of the family.

FLAT NEEDLEFISH
Ablennes hians (Valenciennes, 1846)

Dorsal rays 23-26; anal rays 24-28; pectoral rays 13-15; no gill rakers; vertebrae 87-93; body elongate, the depth 9-10.5 in standard length, and greatly compressed; caudal peduncle without a lateral keel; caudal fin emarginate, the lower lobe longer than upper; dorsal and anal fins strongly elevated anteriorly to form distinct lobes, the dorsal with a large elevated posterior lobe in juveniles and subadults; pectoral fins falcate (distal margin of pectoral fins of other needle-fishes not concave); blue-green dorsally, silvery white on side and ventrally, with a series of vertically elongate blackish spots on side of body. Attains about 120 cm. Cosmopolitan in tropical to warm temperate seas; tends to occur farther offshore than the other species of needlefishes, but occasionally seen in coastal waters.

KEELTAIL NEEDLEFISH
Platybelone argalus platura (Rüppell, 1837)

Dorsal rays 12-15; anal rays 15-20; pectoral rays 10-12; gill rakers 4-5 + 6-7; vertebrae 62-75; body extremely elongate, its depth 20-25 in standard length; width slightly greater than depth; jaws exceedingly long; caudal peduncle depressed, with a scaly keel on side; lateral line passing along lower side of keel (received by edge of keel in species of *Tylosurus*); caudal fin slightly emarginate, the lobes of about equal size; origin of dorsal fin slightly posterior to anal-fin origin; dorsal and anal fins elevated anteriorly, but not forming prominent lobes; blue or blue-green on back, silvery on sides and ventrally. Reaches 45 cm. Divisible into three subspecies, *P. argalus platura* from the Red Sea to the Arabian Gulf; *P. a. platyura* (Bennett) in the rest of the Indo-Pacific; and *P. a. argalus* (Lesueur) in the tropical Atlantic. An inshore species; often observed in small aggregations.

BANDED NEEDLEFISH
Strongylura leiura leiura (Bleeker, 1850)

Dorsal rays 17-21; anal rays 23-25; pectoral rays 10-11; predorsal scales 130-160; no gill rakers; vertebrae 80-83; body elongate, the depth 17-21 in standard length; body laterally compressed, almost rectangular in cross section; no keel on side of caudal peduncle; caudal fin slightly emarginate, the lower lobe longer; origin of dorsal fin above seventh to tenth anal ray; anterior part of dorsal and anal fins forming a distinct lobe; greenish grey dorsally with a silver stripe along side which broadens posteriorly; lower part of body white; outer part of pectoral fins blackish except tip yellowish; tips of soft dorsal and anal fin lobes yellowish; distal margins of dorsal and caudal fins often blackish. Maximum length about 80 cm. Natal, Seychelles, and Arabian Gulf to western Pacific where it ranges from Queensland to Taiwan; a coastal species which may be found in brackish environments. Parin (1967) recognised the subspecies *S. leiura ferox* (Günther) from southeastern and southwestern Australia based on higher dorsal-ray, anal-ray, and predorsal-scale counts.

SPOTTAIL NEEDLEFISH
Strongylura strongylura (van Hasselt, 1823)

Dorsal rays 12-15; anal rays 15-18; pectoral rays 10-12; predorsal scales 100-130; no gill rakers; vertebrae 59-65; body moderately elongate, the depth 15-17.5 in standard length, and somewhat compressed, the width 1.1-1.4 in depth; caudal peduncle more compressed, without a lateral keel; caudal fin truncate to rounded; origin of dorsal fin above fourth to seventh anal ray; base of dorsal and anal fins scaled; greenish grey dorsally, silvery on side, and white ventrally; a prominent round black spot on caudal fin near the base; caudal and dorsal fins yellow distally. Reaches about 45 cm. Arabian Gulf east to Indo-Malayan region and northern Australia, north to China and Taiwan. An inshore species often occurring in shallow mangrove or estuarine areas; known to penetrate freshwater; has been found buried (and surviving) in mud at low tide.

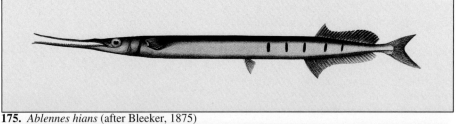

175. *Ablennes hians* (after Bleeker, 1875)

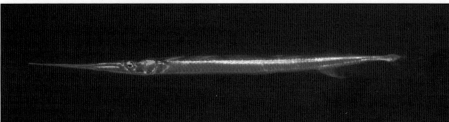

176. *Platybelone argalus platura* (J. Randall)

177. *Strongylura leiura leiura*, 62 cm (J. Randall)

178. *Strongylura strongylura*, 38 cm (J. Randall)

AGUJON
Tylosurus acus melanotus (Bleeker, 1850)

Dorsal rays 24-27; anal rays 22-24; pectoral rays 13-14; predorsal scales very small, 270-340; no gill rakers; vertebrae 90-95; head length 3.1-3.3 in standard length; upper jaw curved, hence a gap readily apparent when jaws closed; teeth more-or-less perpendicular in jaws; body moderately elongate, the depth in adults 14.5-16 in standard length (in juveniles of 16.7 to 21 cm, the depth 23-24 in standard length), and somewhat compressed, the width 1.3-1.5 in depth; a small black keel on side of caudal peduncle; caudal fin deeply forked, the lower lobe much longer than upper; origin of dorsal fin above origin of anal fin; anterior part of dorsal and anal fins elevated; juveniles with an elevated black posterior part of dorsal fin which is lost with growth (true of other *Tylosurus*); pectoral fins 8.0-12.4 in standard length; back blue, shading to silvery on sides and ventrally; outer part of posterior half of dorsal fin blackish; margin of caudal fin blackish. Reported to reach 100 cm. This subspecies is wide-ranging in the tropical and subtropical Indo-Pacific region; occurs more offshore, in general, than the other species of the genus. Also known by the common name Blackfin Houndfish. Two other subspecies are recognized, *T. acus pacificus* (Steindachner) in the eastern Pacific, and *T. acus acus* (Lacepède) in the Atlantic (Parin, 1967). *T. appendiculatus* (Klunzinger) from the Red Sea is a synonym based on a specimen with a keel-like bony outgrowth extending ventrally from tip of lower jaw; occasional individuals larger than 50 cm may have this unusual appendage (one specimen from Muscat in the Natural History Museum, London).

RED SEA HOUNDFISH
Tylosurus choram (Rüppell, 1837)

Dorsal rays 19-24 (usually 21); anal rays 19-22; pectoral rays 12-14; predorsal scales 280-310; no gill rakers; vertebrae 75-80; head 2.6-3.1 in standard length; jaws straight, without an obvious gap when closed; teeth perpendicular in jaws; body depth (of specimens more than 40 cm) 14.0-14.8 in standard length (in juveniles 16-26 cm long, the depth is 16.5-18.5 in standard length); body width 1.1-1.3 in depth; caudal peduncle depth slightly greater than width; keel posteriorly on side of caudal peduncle and base of fin not well-developed; caudal fin emarginate, the lower lobe longer; origin of dorsal fin slightly posterior to anal-fin origin; anterior part of dorsal and anal fins elevated; green on back, silvery on sides and ventrally. Reported to 120 cm. Red Sea to

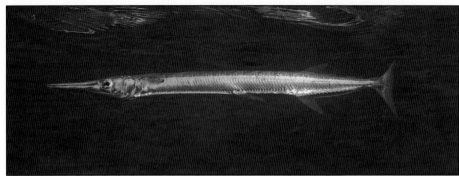

179. *Tylosurus acus melanotus* (J. Randall)

180. *Tylosurus choram*, 66.5 cm (J. Randall)

181. *Tylosurus crocodilus crocodilus*, 48 cm (J. Randall)

Gulf of Oman (and the eastern Mediterranean via the Suez Canal); a coastal species. Parin (1967) recognised a form of *T. choram* from several Indian Ocean and western Pacific localities which he suspects is a different subspecies from the Red Sea-Oman form; however, pending further study, he left this unnamed.

HOUNDFISH
Tylosurus crocodilus crocodilus (Peron and Lesueur, 1821)

Dorsal rays 21-24 (usually 22 or 23); anal rays 19-22; pectoral rays 13-15; predorsal scales 270-360; no gill rakers; vertebrae 80-86; head length 3.0-3.6 in standard length; jaws nearly straight with no obvious gap when closed (jaws shorten in relative length with growth in this and other species of *Tylosurus*); teeth in jaws usually inclined slightly forward; body depth variable with growth, 19-23 in juveniles of 12-21 cm in length, 15-19 in specimens 22.5-37 cm, and 8.8-14.1 in larger adults; a black keel on side of caudal peduncle and base of caudal fin,

receiving end of lateral line; caudal fin deeply emarginate, the lower lobe much longer than upper; origin of dorsal fin over or slightly posterior to anal-fin origin; anterior part of dorsal and anal fins strongly elevated (higher at any given length than lobes of *T. acus*); pectoral fins relatively long, 6.6-8.3 in standard length; green dorsally, silvery below; outer posterior part of dorsal fin blackish, this pigmentation lost in large adults. Reaches 135 cm (reports to 150 cm need verification). Wide-ranging in tropical to warm temperate seas of the Indo-Pacific and Atlantic; replaced in the eastern Pacific by *T. crocodilus fodiator* Jordan and Gilbert. Usually found in coastal waters, but has been taken offshore. *Esox belone* var. *maris rubri* Bloch and Schneider, 1801 (after *Esox belone* non Linnaeus, Forsskål) was used as a senior synonym of *Tylosurus crocodilus* by Mees (1962); however, Forsskål's specimen of *Esox belone* is not extant, and it is not possible to know what species he had without a specimen. *Belone marisrubri marisrubri* Mees was named from a mixture of *T. choram* and *T. crocodilus crocodilus* (Parin, 1967).

HALFBEAKS
FAMILY HEMIRAMPHIDAE

The halfbeaks share many of the characters of the needlefishes, such as the elongate body, no spines in fins, posterior position of dorsal and anal fins, abdominal pelvic fins with 6 rays, nasal organ in a cavity in front of eye, easily detached cycloid scales, the lateral line along the lower side of the body with an anterior part extending upward to pectoral-fin base, and a colouration adapted to surface-dwelling, blue or green on the back, silvery below. They differ most obviously in having a short triangular upper jaw and a prolonged lower jaw (species of four genera lack the long lower jaw as adults, but juveniles of all have a distinct beak); they differ also in having larger scales, well-developed gill rakers (few in number or absent in belonids), small teeth (tricuspid in many species) in several rows, and 37-73 vertebrae (hence usually fewer than those of needlefishes). These fishes leap and skitter at the surface like needlefishes; the ventral part of the body tends to be flat, so they can skip on the surface as one can skip a flat stone. Two offshore species, *Euleptorhamphus viridis* (van Hasselt) and *Oxyporhamphus micropterus* Valenciennes, are able to glide on outstretched pectoral fins like flying-fishes. Some species of halfbeaks feed primarily on zooplankton and small fishes, while others eat mainly floating plant material, especially seagrasses. Twelve genera and about 85 species are known in the family, of which four genera and about 24 species occur in freshwater. Species of three of the four genera are viviparous. The eggs of oviparous species have adhesive filaments and are generally attached to floating or benthic plants. Parin et al. (1980) reviewed the marine halfbeaks of the Indo-Pacific region.

SPOTTED HALFBEAK
Hemiramphus far (Forsskål, 1775)

Dorsal rays 12-14; anal rays 10-12; pectoral rays 11-12; predorsal scales 36-41; gill rakers 24-36; vertebrae 50-55; body depth 5.7-7.3 in standard length; body width 1.3-1.8 in depth; triangular upper jaw without scales; lower jaw (measured from below tip of upper jaw) longer than head length; caudal fin forked, the lower lobe longer than upper (true of other Oman halfbeaks, though less strongly forked in species of *Hyporhamphus*); origin of anal fin below fifth to seventh rays of dorsal fin; green dorsally, shading to silvery on sides and ventrally, with a series of three to nine (usually four to six) blackish spots on upper side (spots may be vertically elongate); upper lobe of caudal fin and front of dorsal fin suffused with orange-yellow; tip of lower jaw light red. Attains 45 cm. Red Sea and east coast of Africa to Samoa. Appears to feed principally on floating pieces of seagrass.

182. *Hemiramphus far*, about 25 cm (J. Randall)

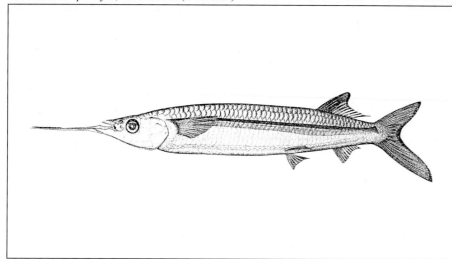

183. *Hemiramphus marginatus*, 33.5 cm (after Parin et al, 1980)

BLACKEDGE HALFBEAK
Hemiramphus marginatus (Forsskål, 1775)

Dorsal rays 12-14; anal rays 11-13; pectoral rays 11-13; predorsal scales 33-36; gill rakers 30-37; vertebrae 50-53; body depth about 5.5-6.3 in standard length; body width 1.55-1.75 in depth; triangular upper jaw without scales; lower jaw equal to or shorter than head length; origin of anal fin below fifth to seventh dorsal rays; blue-green on back with a midlateral silvery stripe edged dorsally in dark green; margin of caudal fin blackish; anterior part of dorsal fin (to about the sixth ray) blackish. Largest specimen, 38 cm. Red Sea to Arabian Gulf.

SIND HALFBEAK
Hyporhamphus sindensis (Regan, 1905)

Dorsal rays 13-15; anal rays 14-17; pectoral rays 12-13; predorsal scales 31-36; gill rakers 24-33; vertebrae 47-50; body depth 7.4-9.7 in standard length; triangular upper jaw scaled, its width usually shorter than its length; lower jaw length (measured from below tip of upper jaw) 0.9-1.7 in head length; teeth in jaws tricuspid; a bony ridge between eye and nasal cavity; preorbital distance short, 2.05-2.65 in orbit diameter; origin of anal fin below dorsal-fin origin or slightly anterior or slightly posterior to it; distance from origin of pelvic fins to caudal-fin base equal to distance from origin of pelvic fins to edge of preopercle; grey with a narrow lateral silvery stripe that broadens somewhat posteriorly; upper edge of silvery stripe green; the upper edge of which is green; tip of lower jaw red. A small species, the maximum length about 25 cm. Arabian Gulf to coast of Pakistan.

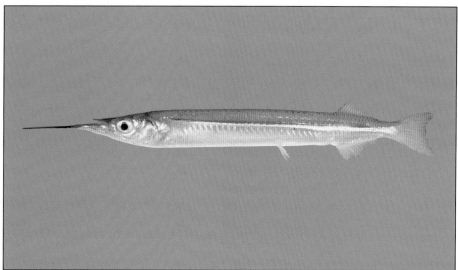

184. *Hyporhamphus sindensis*, 20.5 cm (J. Randall)

SIMPLETOOTH HALFBEAK
Hyporhamphus unicuspis Collette and Parin, 1978

Dorsal rays 14-16; anal rays 16-18; pectoral rays 10-12; predorsal scales 33-40; gill rakers 30-34; vertebrae 49-51; body depth 7.3-12.1 in standard length; triangular upper jaw scaled, its width about equal to its length; lower jaw length (measured from below tip of upper jaw) 0.8-0.95 in head length; teeth nearly all unicuspid; preorbital distance 1.4-1.6 in orbit diameter; origin of anal fin approximately below origin of dorsal fin; distance from origin of pelvic fins to caudal-fin base equal to or less than distance from origin of pelvic fins to edge of preopercle; greenish grey on back, the edges of the scales dusky, with a silver stripe along side of body; margin of caudal fin blackish; anterior lobe of dorsal fin broadly blackish. Largest specimen, 31.5 cm, from off Muscat. Arabian Gulf to Andaman Sea.

185. *Hyporhamphus unicuspis*, 15 cm (J. Randall)

GEORGE'S HALFBEAK
Rhynchorhamphus georgii (Valenciennes, 1846)

Dorsal rays 13-16; anal rays 13-16; pectoral rays 10-12; predorsal scales 36-45; gill rakers 47-67; vertebrae 55-57; nasal papilla fringed (characteristic of the genus; not fringed in species of *Hemiramphus* and *Hyporhamphus*); upper jaw scaled, and longer than wide; lower jaw much longer than head (head length 1.35-2.65 in lower jaw length); origin of anal fin below fourth or fifth ray of dorsal fin; origin of pelvic fins

186. *Rynchoramphus georgii*, 29 cm (J. Randall)

much closer to caudal-fin base than base of pectoral fins; Oman specimens silvery on back with purple and blue iridescence, the scales edged in black; side and ventral part of body silvery with lavender iridescence; fins lavender-grey, the dorsal rays dark purple, the caudal with a blackish margin; tip of lower jaw red. Reaches 35 cm. Arabi-an Gulf along the continental shelf of southern Asian to Malaysia, East Indies, and northern Australia. *R. arabicus* Parin and Scherbachev is known from 11 specimens from the Yemen coast of the Gulf of Aden; it differs from *R. georgii* notably in having 68-78 gill rakers. Collette (1976) revised the species of *Rhynchorhamphus*.

FLYINGFISHES
FAMILY EXOCOETIDAE

Like the related needlefishes and halfbeaks, the flyingfishes have no spines in the fins, the dorsal and anal fins posterior in position, the pectorals high on the side of the body, the pelvics abdominal with 6 rays, the lateral line passing along the ventral side of the body, and the nasal organ in a cavity with a protruding lobe. The caudal fin is deeply forked with a much longer lower than upper lobe. The scales are cycloid, large, and deciduous; the gill rakers are well-developed. Adults are blue or blue-green on the back and silvery white below; juveniles are often coloured differently from adults. Unlike nearly all belonids and hemiramphids, the exocoetids have short jaws, less elongate bodies, and enormous pectoral fins (many with extremely large pelvics as well). Flyingfishes are well known for their ability to rapidly swim free of the surface and glide on outstretched pectoral fins (those with long pelvics hold these fins to the side too). Juveniles of some species have one or two pairs of long chin barbels. The eggs are large with adhesive filaments; they are usually attached to floating plants. The close relationship of the flyingfishes to the halfbeaks is evident from several lines of evidence, one being that some of the primitive exocoetids pass through a developmental stage with a prolonged lower jaw. The genus *Oxyporhamphus* has usually been classified as a flyingfish because of its relatively long pectoral fins (or as a separate family), but it is now placed in the Hemiramphidae. Six (sometimes seven) genera of exocoetids are recognised, with a total of about 60 species (species-level taxonomy still not definitive). Most flyingfishes are found in offshore waters well away from land; only those that enter the coastal waters of Oman are treated here.

187. *Cypselurus oligolepis*, 28 cm (J. Randall)

188. *Hirundichthys oxycephalus* (after Bleeker, 1875)

LARGESCALE FLYINGFISH
Cypselurus oligolepis (Bleeker, 1866)

Dorsal rays 10-12; anal rays 7-9; pectoral rays 14-15, only the first ray unbranched; predorsal scales 23-27; head short, 3.9-4.8 in standard length; lower jaw a little shorter than upper; palatine teeth present; pectoral fins very long, reaching posterior to midbase of dorsal fin, 1.35-1.55 in standard length; pelvic fins large, reaching well beyond origin of anal fin; anal fin origin below fourth to seventh dorsal ray; no barbels on chin of juveniles; pectoral fins black except tip and about lower fifth which are hyaline; pelvic membranes clear or blackish distally; dorsal and anal fins clear with whitish rays. Largest specimen, 27.7 cm, from Gulf of Oman. Described from Indonesia; scattered records from tropical western Indian Ocean, including Arabian Gulf.

BONY FLYINGFISH
Hirundichthys oxycephalus (Bleeker, 1852)

Dorsal rays 10-12; anal rays 10-12; pectoral rays 15-17, only the first ray unbranched; predorsal scales 32-35; head length 4.0-4.3 in standard length; mouth terminal; palatine teeth not present; pectoral fins very long, reaching posterior to midbase of dorsal fin, 1.45-1.6 in standard length; pelvic fins long, reaching well beyond origin of anal fin; origin of anal fin below or slightly anterior to origin of dorsal fin; no barbels on chin of juveniles; pectoral fins dark except for a pale distal margin and a small pale triangle near lower base. Reaches 23 cm. Arabian Sea to Western Pacific; pelagic in continental shelf waters.

AFRICAN SAILFIN FLYINGFISH
Parexocoetus mento (Valenciennes, 1846)

Dorsal rays 9-12 (usually 10 or 11); anal rays 10-12; pectoral rays 13-14, the first unbranched; predorsal scales 16-20; head 3.7-4.0 in standard length; upper jaw protrusible (unique among exocoetid genera); branch of lateral line to pectoral base present (absent in other genera); pectoral fins not very long, 1.8-2.1 in standard length; pelvic fins of medium size, just reaching or extending slightly beyond anal-fin origin; dorsal fin very elevated, the longest ray just reaching caudal-fin base when depressed; juveniles without barbels on chin; pectoral fin membranes transparent; dorsal fin largely black. Maximum length about 12 cm. Tropical western Pacific and Indian Oceans, including the Red Sea (also an immigrant via the Suez Canal to the eastern Mediterranean) and Arabian Gulf; a near-shore pelagic species. Often confused with *P. brachypterus* (Richardson) which differs in having 12-14 dorsal and anal rays, 20-24 predorsal scales, and a higher dorsal fin (reaches well past caudal-fin base when depressed).

SHORTFIN FLYINGFISH
Prognichthys brevipinnis (Valenciennes, 1846)

Dorsal rays 10-11; anal rays 8-10; pectoral rays 16-18, the first three unbranched; predorsal scales 25-28; head 4.0-4.3 in standard length; lower jaw a little shorter than upper; palatine teeth absent; pectoral fins very long, 1.45-1.55 in standard length; pelvic fins also long, reaching well beyond origin of anal fin; origin of anal fin below third to fifth ray of dorsal fin; anterior dorsal and anal rays longest; juveniles without chin barbels; pectoral fins grey (black in juveniles); pelvic fins pale (black in juveniles). Reaches about 25 cm. Western Pacific, as far north as southern Japan, and tropical Indian Ocean; common in Arabian Sea; neritic.

189. *Parexocoetus mento* (after Bleeker, 1875)

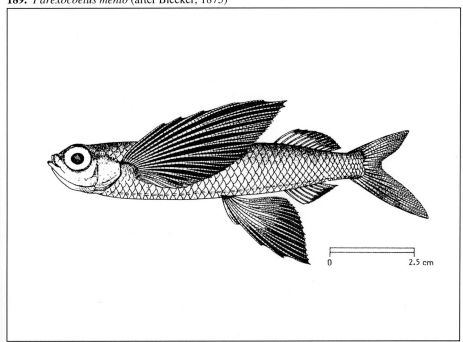

190. *Prognichthys brevipinnis* (after Fischer and Bianchi, 1984)

KILLIFISHES AND PUPFISHES
FAMILY CYPRINODONTIDAE

This family is one of several of the order Cyprinodontiformes (the number of families not agreed upon by all who study the group). In the most restricted sense, the family consists of nine genera and about 100 species. These are small fishes which occur in shallow water of variable salinity (the cyprinodontids are well known for being euryhaline and eurythermal). They have no spines in the fins, a single dorsal fin posterior in position and opposite the anal fin, pectoral fins low on the body, pelvic fins (when present) abdominal, caudal fin usually truncate or rounded, and scales (when present) cycloid and usually large; the lateral line system is best developed on the head, with only pitted scales on the body; the top of the head is nearly flat; the mouth is superior; the upper jaw is bordered only by the premaxilla which is protrusible; the teeth are conical or tricuspid; the dorsal processes of the maxillae are expanded medially, nearly meeting in the midline. Unlike some related viviparous families, the cyprinodontids are oviparous. Most species are sexually dimorphic; the females are larger and have smaller fins, and the males are often more colourful.

ARABIAN PUPFISH
Aphanius dispar dispar (Rüppell, 1828)

Dorsal rays 8-11 (usually 9); anal rays 9-11; scales in longitudinal series 24-28; scales above lateral line to origin of dorsal fin 3.5; gill rakers 11-17 (usually 13-16); teeth tricuspid, 12-20 in each jaw; dorsal fin of adult males elevated (may reach base of caudal fin when depressed); females with narrow dark bars on body; males with small irregular pale blotches on body and two or three dark bars in caudal fin. Males reported to 8 cm, females to 6 cm. Eastern Mediterranean and Red Sea to Arabian Gulf and Pakistan. Usually found in estuaries, but has been taken in shallow reef areas; it is able to live and reproduce in freshwater, and it survives high salinities and temperatures.

191. *Aphanius dispar dispar*, male above (5 cm), female below (J. Randall)

LIVEBEARERS
FAMILY POECILIIDAE

This family has often been included with the Cyprinodontidae; it differs principally in the male having the anterior anal rays modified to a gonopodium for internal fertilization of the ova. The family includes many popular aquarium fishes such as the guppies, mollies, platies, and swordtails; also the mosquitofishes (*Gambusia*). Many of these fishes have been widely introduced (as for mosquito control) or released by aquarists. The single species discussed below is an introduction; it is included because it may be found in the sea.

SAILFIN MOLLY
Poecilia latipinna (Lesueur, 1821)

Dorsal rays 15-16; anal rays 8; scales in longitudinal series 26; body depth 2.5-3.0 in standard length; head small, flattened dorsally, 3.5-4 in standard length; mouth small; dorsal fin low on female, greatly elevated in male (higher than body depth), the distal margin nearly straight (damaged in illustrated specimen from Bahrain); caudal fin slightly rounded; females olivaceous dorsally, silvery grey on side and ventrally, with dark dots in dorsal fin; males with a small black spot on each scale of body, orange-

192. *Poecilia latipinna*, female above (7 cm), male below (J. Randall)

yellow over lower head and on chest, and small pale spots on dorsal and caudal fins. Attains 7.5 cm. Native to low coastal areas from South Carolina to northern Mexico; could be expected, as a result of introduction, in estuaries of the Arabian Gulf and Gulf of Oman.

FLASHLIGHT FISHES
FAMILY ANOMALOPIDAE

The flashlight fish family is one of seven families of the order Beryciformes. It consists of six species classified in five genera (*Anomalops*, *Photoblepharon*, and *Parmops* in the Indo-Pacific region and *Kryptophanaron* and *Phthanophaneron* in the New World). The family name is derived from the Greek meaning "abnormal eye", in reference to the unique light organ located just below and partly covering the lower part of the eye; the light is produced by a symbiotic bacterium. The fish provides the medium in its light organ for the bacterium to grow, and the bacterium produces the light as a by-product of its metabolism. Flashlight fishes have a moderately deep, compressed body and bluntly rounded head; there is either a single dorsal fin preceded by two spines (*Photoblepharon*) or two dorsal fins, the first with four or five spines (remaining genera); the anal fin is preceded by two spines; the pelvic fins have 6-7 rays; the caudal fin is forked. These fishes are nocturnal, hiding deep in recesses in reefs by day and emerging only on moonless nights. Their light organs can be turned off and on by raising and lowering an eyelid-like black curtain (*Photoblepharon*) or rotating the entire light organ downward and internally, or both (other genera). The light enables these fishes to see small planktonic animals on which they feed, to confuse predators (after turning the light off, the fish rapidly change direction), and for communication (McCosker and Rosenblatt, 1987; Johnson and Rosenblatt, 1988).

RED SEA FLASHLIGHT FISH
Photoblepharon steinitzi Abe and Haneda, 1973

Dorsal rays II,18-20; anal rays II,14-15; pectoral rays 16-17; pelvic rays 6; light organ below eye covered at will by an eyelid-like structure raised from below; mouth moderately large and oblique; small conical teeth in bands in jaws; blackish, the opercular membrane and lateral-line light blue; fin rays blackish, the membranes transparent. Attains about 11 cm. Presently known only from the Red Sea, southern Oman (Debelius, 1993), Comoro Islands (McCosker and Rosenblatt, 1987), and the Maldives (Randall and Anderson, 1993). Described first from the Red Sea as a subspecies of *P. palbebratus*; raised to a species by McCosker and Rosenblatt (1987) on the basis of *palbebratus* having an additional pelvic ray, a more conspicuous white spot at the upper corner of the opercle, and differences in the sculpuring of the head bones. In the northern Red Sea on dark nights, this fish may be seen in water as shallow as a metre or two, whereas *palpebratus* is generally found at depths greater than 30 m.

PINEAPPLE FISHES
FAMILY MONOCENTRIDAE

The curious fishes of this small Indo-Pacific family are also known as pinecone fishes. They are characterised as follows: body covered with large, rigidly united, plate-like scales, each bearing a sharp, posteriorly-directed spine; head with mucous cavities rimmed by rugose ridges; two dorsal fins, the first with four to seven spines, without connecting membranes, and not in alignment but alternating to each side; second dorsal fin with 9-12 soft rays; pelvic fins with a long stout spine, which can be locked in erect position, and 2-4 small soft rays; anal fin with 10-12 soft rays; a light organ on the side or near the tip of the lower jaw, the light produced by luminous bacteria. There are two genera, the monotypic *Cleidopus* from Australia and *Monocentris* with two species. Kotlyar (1985) reviewed the family; he recognised three species of *Monocentris*, but he questioned the validity of *M. neozelanicus* (Powell), described from a single specimen. Paxton in Paxton et al. (1989) examined the specimen and concluded that it is *M. japonicus*.

193. *Photoblepharon steinitzi*, 9 cm (J. Randall)

PINEAPPLE FISH
Monocentris japonicus (Houttuyn, 1782)

Dorsal rays V-VII+10-12; anal rays 9-11; pectoral rays 13-15; lateral-line scales 13-16; body moderately deep, the depth about 1.7 in standard length, and compressed, the width about 2.3 in depth; snout broadly rounded and overhanging the ventral mouth; teeth in jaws finely villiform; a small light organ ventrally on each side of lower jaw near tip; yellow, the edges of the scales blackish. Reported to 17 cm. Western Pacific from Japan to Australia and New Zealand, west to South Africa and the northern Red Sea; also reported from Mauritius and Sri Lanka; observed in Oman waters only off the south coast. Occurs from shallow water to 200 m; nocturnal, but may occasionally be seen in small caves or beneath ledges during the day.

194. *Monocentris japonicus*, about 8.5 cm (J. Randall)

SQUIRRELFISHES AND SOLDIERFISHES
FAMILY HOLOCENTRIDAE

The fishes of this family are distinctive in having very large eyes, XI or XII dorsal spines, IV anal spines, and pelvic fins with I,7 rays; the caudal fin is forked; the scales are coarsely ctenoid, the lateral line complete; the bones of the head have ridges and grooves, and some have spines; the margins of the bones of the operculum and the suborbitals have a series of spinules; the nasal organ is in a subtriangular cavity (fossa) in front of the eye; mouth of moderate size, the teeth small; most of the species are red or partly red.

The family is divisible into two subfamilies: the Holocentrinae (squirrelfishes) with three genera (*Neoniphon*, *Sargocentron*, and the Atlantic *Holocentrus*), characterised by having a long sharp spine (which may be venomous) at the corner of the preopercle, 7-10 anal soft rays, and a moderately pointed snout; and the Myripristinae (soldierfishes) with four genera (*Myrpristis*, *Plectrypops*, *Pristilepis*, and the Atlantic *Corniger*), characterised by lacking a spine at the preopercular angle or having only a short, broad-based one (except *Corniger*), having 10-16 anal soft rays, some teeth outside the mouth, and a blunt snout. Unlike most of their beryciform relatives, the holocentrids are mostly shallow-water fishes. They are nocturnal, as their large eyes would suggest, generally hiding in caves or beneath ledges by day and emerging at night to forage for food; the squirrelfishes feed mainly on benthic crustaceans, and the soldierfishes on the larger animals of the zooplankton. The record of *Myripristis xanthacrus* Randall and Guézé from Oman by Debelius (1993) is an error. *Myripristis* was revised by Greenfield (1974), and supplemented by Randall and Guézé (1981). The Holocentrinae of the western Indian Ocean was reviewed by Randall and Heemstra (1985).

BLOTCHEYE SOLDIERFISH
Myripristis murdjan (Forsskål, 1775)

Dorsal rays XI,13-15; anal rays IV,11-13; pectoral rays 14-16; lateral-line scales 27-32; gill rakers 36-43; body depth 2.3-2.5 in standard length; snout short, 4.9-5.3 in head; interorbital space relatively broad, 3.8-4.4 in head; lower jaw slightly projecting when mouth closed; a pair of tooth patches at front of lower jaw outside mouth; vomerine teeth in a triangular patch with rounded corners; lower part of pectoral axil with small scales; light red, the edges of scales brown; opercular membrane dark brown to about level of middle of eye; axil of pectoral fins dark brown; spinous dorsal fin light red on basal two-thirds, darker red on outer third; leading edges of soft dorsal, anal, caudal, and pelvic fins white, sometimes with blackish pigment submarginal to the white on soft dorsal and anal fins. Maximum length, 23 cm. Indian Ocean to the western Pacific; known from Oman only off the southern coast.

195. *Myripristis murdjan*, about 23 cm (J. Hoover)

94

SPOTFIN SQUIRRELFISH
Neoniphon sammara (Forsskål, 1775)

Dorsal rays XI,11-12 (usually 12), the last spine longer than penultimate spine and close to first soft ray; anal rays IV,7-8 (usually 8); pectoral rays 13-14; lateral-line scales 38-43; body moderately elongate, the depth 3.0-3.6 in standard length; lower jaw projecting when mouth closed; preopercular spine short, about one-third eye diameter; silvery, each scale with an elongate dark reddish brown spot, thus forming longitudinal dark lines on body; a reddish stripe following lateral line; snout and top of head light red; spinous portion of dorsal fin with a large black spot tinged with red on first four membranes; caudal fin yellowish with a broad red band on upper and lower margins. Attains 28 cm. Indo-Pacific; from Oman only in the south.

196. *Neoniphon sammara*, about 18.5 cm (J. Randall)

TAILSPOT SQUIRRELFISH
Sargocentron caudimaculatum (Rüppell, 1838)

Dorsal rays XI,13-15, the last spine shortest (true of other species of the genus); anal rays IV,9; pectoral rays 13-14 (usually 14); lateral-line scales 38-43; body depth 2.5-2.9 in standard length; premaxillary groove dorsally on snout not reaching beyond a vertical at front edge of eye; nasal fossa with one or two spinules on posterior edge; preopercular spine long, about equal to eye diameter; head and body red, the scales edged in silvery white; posterior third of body often white; a bright silvery white spot anterodorsally on caudal peduncle (may disappear after death). Reaches about 25 cm. Indo-Pacific where coral reefs are well-developed; not known from the Arabian Gulf and Gulf of Oman, but occasional off the southern coast. *S. andamanensis* (Day) is a synonym.

197. *Sargocentron caudimaculatum*, about 15.5 cm (J. Randall)

CROWN SQUIRRELFISH
Sargocentron diadema (Lacepède, 1801)

Dorsal rays XI,12-14; anal rays IV,8-9 (usually 9); pectoral rays 13-15; lateral-line scales 46-50; body depth 2.7-3.2 in standard length; nasal fossa small, without spinules; preopercular spine small, 2-3 in eye diameter; body with alternating stripes of red and silvery white, the red stripes more than twice as broad as the white; caudal peduncle often whitish; spinous portion of dorsal fin dark red, the membrane tips white, with a longitudinal white to light red stripe (often disjunct in middle). Attains 17 cm. An abundant species throughout the Indo-Pacific region, but rare in Oman waters where it is known only from the south coast.

198. *Sargocentron diadema*, about 19 cm (J. Randall)

REDCOAT
Sargocentron rubrum (Forsskål, 1775)

Dorsal rays XI,12-14; anal rays IV,8-10; pectoral rays 13-15; lateral-line scales 34-38; oblique rows of scales on cheek 5; body depth 2.4-2.8 in standard length; upper edge of first suborbital bone with a short, blunt, lateral spine a little behind a vertical at front edge of eye; nasal fossa usually without spinules; preopercular spine about three-fourths eye diameter; body with alternating stripes of brownish red and silvery white of about equal width, the third and fourth and the fifth and sixth reddish stripes merging posteriorly on body; an elongate dark spot beneath posterior soft portion of dorsal fin and a smaller one above rear base of anal fin; a dark spot at midbase of caudal fin at end of merged third and fourth reddish stripes; distal part of second to fourth soft pelvic rays blackish. Reaches 27 cm. Red Sea (and as an immigrant to the eastern Mediterranean) to the Gulf of Oman, east to the western Pacific. Occurs in reef or rocky areas of protected inshore waters. Often confused with *S. praslin* (Lacepède) which has four oblique rows of scales on the cheek and dark pigment of the pelvic fins mainly on the first soft ray.

YELLOWTIPPED SQUIRRELFISH
Sargocentron seychellense (Smith and Smith, 1963)

Dorsal rays XI,12-13 (rarely 12); anal rays IV,8-10; pectoral rays 13-15; lateral-line scales 35-39; body depth 2.4-2.65 in standard length; upper edge of first suborbital bone with a row of short, blunt, postero-lateral spines, the most anterior largest; nasal fossa without spinules on edge; head and body colour much like *S. rubrum*, but tips of spinous dorsal membranes, pelvic fins, and rays of median fins yellow. Reaches 25 cm. Known previously only from islands of the western Indian Ocean; the Oman record is based on the photograph by the author presented here; it was taken at Al Hallanniyaat (Kuria Muria Islands).

SABRE SQUIRRELFISH
Sargocentron spiniferum (Forsskål, 1775)

Dorsal rays XI,14-16; anal rays IV,9-10 (usually 10); pectoral rays 14-16; lateral-line scales 41-46; scales above lateral line to midbase of spinous dorsal fin 3.5 (2.5 on other Oman species of the genus); body deep and compressed, the depth 2.4-2.6 in standard length; dorsal profile of head nearly straight; lower jaw projecting when mouth closed; nasal fossa without spinules;

199. *Sargocentron rubrum*, about 22 cm (J. Hoover)

200. *Sargocentron seychellense*, about 20 cm (J. Randall)

201. *Sargocentron spiniferum*, about 35 cm (J. Randall)

anterior end of nasal bones usually with one or two short spines; preopercular spine of adults usually longer than eye diameter; spinous membranes of dorsal fin not incised; head and body red, the scale edges silvery white; a vertically elongate crimson spot on preopercle behind eye, the edges of which are silvery white and continue ventrally to outline scale patch on preopercle; spinous portion of dorsal fin solid deep red. The largest of the squirrelfishes; reaches about 45 cm. Wide-ranging on coral reefs and rocky bottom throughout the tropical and subtropical Indo-Pacific region. Wounds from the long venomous preopercular spine very painful. Known in Oman only in the south, and rare there.

202. *Fistularia commersonii* (J. Hoover)

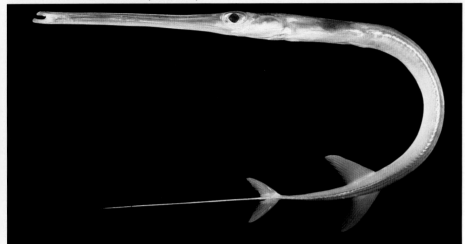

203. *Fistularia petimba*, 52 cm (J. Randall)

CORNETFISHES
FAMILY FISTULARIIDAE

This distinctive family of a single genus, *Fistularia*, and four species is represented by two species in Oman seas. These fishes have an extremely elongate, somewhat depressed body; a very long tubular snout; small mouth with minute teeth; no spines in fins; dorsal and anal fins short-based and opposite; pelvic fins with 6 soft rays; and caudal fin forked, but the middle two rays prolonged to a long filament. Juveniles with rows of small hooked spinules which may persist in adults. Cornetfishes feed on small fishes and crustaceans by using their snout like a giant pipette to suck in the prey. The fistulariids are usually grouped with the Aulostomidae (trumpetfishes), Pegasidae (seamoths), Syngnathidae (pipefishes and seahorses), Solenostomidae (ghost pipefishes), Macrorhamphosidae (snipefishes), and Centriscidae (shrimpfishes) in the order Syngnathiformes, but some recent authors prefer to group them into the Gasterosteiformes (which includes the sticklebacks). The genus *Fistu-*

laria was reviewed by Fritzsche (1976). The trumpetfish *Aulostomus chinensis* (Linnaeus) remains unknown from Arabian waters.

SMOOTH CORNETFISH
Fistularia commersonii Rüppell, 1835

Dorsal rays 15-17; anal rays 14-16; pectoral rays 13-15; interorbital space flat with longitudinal ridges; ridges of snout serrate in adults; skin of adults naked; no elongate median bony plates on body; posterior lateral-line ossifications without a retrorse spine; olive dorsally, shading to silvery white ventrally, with two pale blue stripes or rows of pale blue spots on back. Reported to 150 cm. Indo-Pacific and tropical eastern Pacific. An active, free-swimming, but bottom-oriented fish generally seen over reefs, seagrass beds, or sand, usually in the vicinity of reefs. When near the substratum and motionless, it may take on a dark-barred pattern.

SERRATE CORNETFISH
Fistularia petimba Lacepède, 1803

Dorsal rays 14-16; anal rays 14-15; pectoral rays 15-17; interorbital space concave, without ridges; ridges on snout serrate, the serrae on lateral ridge with antrorse spines; spinules on skin persisting in adults; a row of narrow bony plates middorsally anterior

and posterior to dorsal fin and midventrally anterior to anal fin; posterior lateral-line ossifications with a retrorse spine; orangish brown dorsally, shading to silvery below. Although reported to 150 cm, none over 100 cm is known to the author. Indo-Pacific and tropical Atlantic; a continental shelf species of moderate to deep water not found at oceanic islands except Hawaii. *F. serrata* Cuvier and *F. villosa* Klunzinger are synonyms.

SEAMOTHS
FAMILY PEGASIDAE

The bizarre little fishes of this family are encased in bony plates formed from highly modified, fused scales, those on the tail as rings, hence this part of the body is flexible; the head and body are depressed; there is a long rostrum (from fused nasal bones) extending well anterior to the small, ventral, toothless mouth; the dorsal and anal fins are on the second to fourth tail rings, each with 5 unbranched soft rays; pectoral fins horizontally-inserted, large, and wing-like; pelvic fins thoracic in position, with one spine and 2 or 3 unbranched rays; there are two lateral lines, one along the dorsolateral bony ridge and the other along the ventrolateral bony ridge. The family consists of two genera and five species (Palsson and Pietsch, 1989). Seamoths are benthic and usually found in shallow water, though there is a depth record of 152 m. The wide-ranging *Eurypegasus draconis* (Linnaeus) is recorded from southern Yemen, hence might be expected from Oman waters; it is distinctive in having 8 (rarely 9) tail rings and modally 10 pectoral rays.

LONGTAIL SEAMOTH
Pegasus volitans Linnaeus, 1758

Pectoral rays 9-12 (usually 10 or 11); tail rings 12, the posterior three fused; last tail rings each with a lateral pair of posteriorly-directed spines; body slender, the depth 9.5-14.0 in standard length, the width 4.8-6.5 in standard length; rostrum 3.1-5.8 in standard length, narrow, and of nearly equal width throughout its length; colour variable, ranging from nearly black to pale with blackish bars. Attains at least 11 cm. East Africa and Arabian Gulf to the Indo-Malayan region, all of the south coast of Australia except the south, and north to southern Japan; not recorded from any oceanic islands. Known from the depth range of 1-73 m; usually collected by seine, dredge, or trawl from mud or sand bottoms.

204. *Pegasus volitans*, 9 cm (J. Randall)

PIPEFISHES AND SEAHORSES
FAMILY SYNGNATHIDAE

This large, well-known family is characterised by an elongate body encased in a series of bony rings; there is one dorsal fin (absent in adults of three genera), a small anal fin of 2-6 rays (rarely absent), pectoral fins usually present, no pelvic fins, a small caudal fin with 8-11 rays (most often 10) present or absent (caudal peduncle may be prehensile in those species without a caudal fin), and a very small gill opening; some species have dermal flaps, tentacles, or cirri. Most syngnathid fishes are small, and most are marine from depths less than 50 m. Unique to the family is parental care of the ova by the male; the female attaches the eggs to the ventral surface of the male, often in a special pouch. The family includes 52 genera and over 200 species; it is divisible into two subfamilies, the Syngnathinae (pipefishes) and the Hippocampinae (sea-horses). The Indo-Pacific pipefishes were ably revised by Dawson (1985), and the diagnoses below are largely from his monograph; the Hippocampinae, however, is in great need of revision. The number of trunk rings (the first trunk ring is the ring bearing the pectoral-fin base and the last is the ring bearing the anus) and the number of tail rings are important in the classification. The identification of species of pipefishes often involves the configuration of ridges on the body. The body is generally quadrangular in cross-section, so there are ridges dorsally and ventrally (termed superior and inferior) on both the trunk and the tail; in addition there is a ridge along the side, termed lateral.

205. *Corythoichthys flavofasciatus*, about 12 cm (J. Randall)

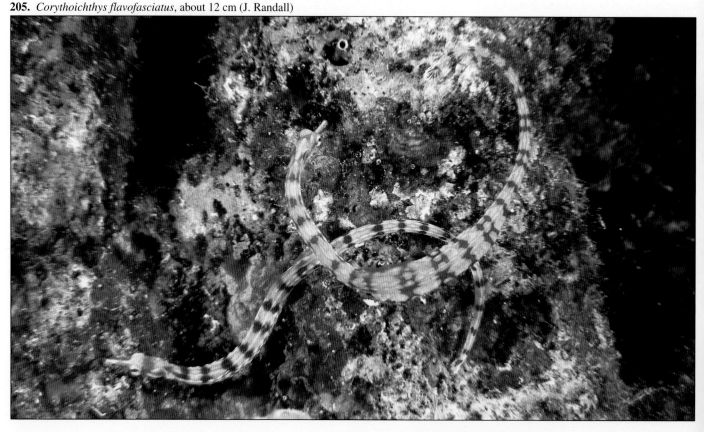

PIPEFISHES
SUBFAMILY SYNGNATHINAE

PIPEHORSE
Acentronura tentaculata Günther, 1870

Dorsal rays 14-16; pectoral rays 14-16; trunk rings 12; tail rings 39-44; no caudal fin; tail prehensile like a seahorse, but the head in line with the body rather than flexed sharply downward as in the seahorses; stout-bodied, the trunk depth about 14 in total length; head length 5.9-6.8 in total length; snout length 2.8-3.6 in head length; least snout depth 2.0-3.0 in snout length; dermal flaps and tentacles usually long and numerous in adults. Reaches at least 6.3 cm. Reported from the Red Sea, Gulf of Aden, Arabian Sea, Arabian Gulf, Mozambique, Madagascar, and the Torres Strait.

PINK PIPEFISH
Bryx analicarens (Duncker, 1915)

Dorsal rays 27-33; no anal fin; pectoral rays 13-14; trunk rings 16-18; tail rings 35-39; superior trunk and tail ridges discontinuous; lateral trunk ridge straight, ending near anal ring; no dermal flaps; about 15 broad dark bars alternating with narrow pale bars; one record of life colour as pink. Reaches about 13 cm. Western Indian Ocean, including the Red Sea, Gulf of Oman, and Arabian Gulf, from the depth range of less than 1 m to 45 m.

SHORTBODIED PIPEFISH
Choeroichthys brachysoma (Bleeker, 1855)

Dorsal rays 18-26; pectoral rays 18-23 (usually 19-20); trunk rings 14-18; tail rings 17-20; superior and trunk ridges continuous; inferior trunk ridge ends on anal ring; lateral trunk ridge confluent with inferior tail ridge; head length 4.1-5.9 in standard length; snout length 1.8-2.4 in head length; least snout depth 3.8-5.8 in snout length; two rows of small dark spots usually on side of trunk (the upper row incomplete on males); a lateral stripe on side of snout passing through eye onto opercle. Attains about 6.5 cm. Indo-Pacific; most common in sea-grass and coral-reef habitats from depths of less than 5 to 25 m.

DARKBARRED PIPEFISH
Corythoichthys amplexus Dawson and Randall, 1975

Dorsal rays 23-30; pectoral rays 12-15 (modally 14); trunk rings 14-16; tail rings

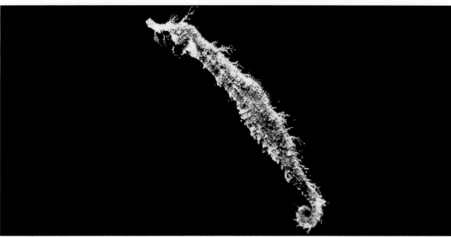

206. *Ancentronura tentaculata* (T. Paulus/Ikan, after Debelius, 1993)

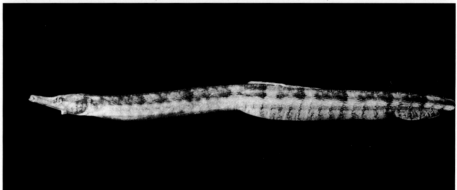

207. *Bryx analicarens*, 12.7 cm (after Dawson, 1985)

208. *Choeroichthys brachysoma*, 4 cm (J. Randall)

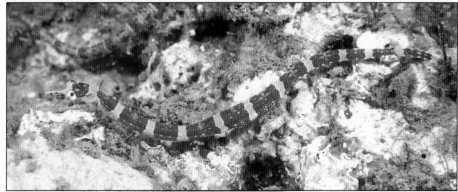

209. *Chorythoichthys amplexus*, about 8 cm (J. Randall)

35-39; superior trunk and tail ridges discontinuous; lateral trunk ridge straight, ending near anal ring; inferior trunk and tail ridges continuous; head length 8.4-12.0 in standard length; snout length 2.1-2.8 in head length; least snout depth 3.7-5.4 in snout length; body with dark brown bars of three to four rings in width; no dark stripes on postorbital head. Reaches 9 cm. Gulf of Oman and Seychelles to Samoa; depth range 0.2-30.5 m.

YELLOWBANDED PIPEFISH
Corythoichthys flavofasciatus (Rüppell, 1838)

Dorsal rays 26-36; pectoral rays 13-17; trunk rings 15-17; tail rings 32-39; ridges as in the preceding species; head length 6.8-10.9 in standard length; snout length 1.9-2.6 in head length; least snout depth 3.5-6.3 in snout length; pale with reticulate dark reddish bars and narrow, irregular, longitudinal yellow bands or elongate spots; prominent narrow dark stripes on head; snout largely red; a large bright blue spot (black in preservative) ventrally on anal ring of males. Reaches about 11.5 cm. Red Sea and Madagascar to the Tuamotu Archipelago, but not yet recorded from Indonesia or the Philippines. Found mainly on coral reefs.

210. *Corythoichthys flavofasciatus*, about 12 cm (J. Randall)

MESSMATE PIPEFISH
Corythoichthys haematopterus (Bleeker, 1851)

Dorsal rays 23-33; pectoral rays 13-18 (modally 16); trunk rings 16-18; tail rings 32-37; ridges on body as above; head length 6.3-9.4 in standard length; snout length 1.9-2.4 in head length; least snout depth 3.8-8.0 in snout length; trunk and anterior tail usually with poorly defined dark blotches or concentrations of reticulate horizontal black lines; head usually with dark stripes. Reaches 12 cm. East Africa and Madagascar to the western Pacific. Kuronuma and Abe (1986) recorded a 19-cm specimen from the southern Arabian Gulf taken by dredge in 21 m; usually found in shallow water.

211. *Corythoichthys haematopterus*, about 10 cm (J. Randall)

BANNER'S PIPEFISH
Cosmocampus banneri Herald and Randall, 1972

Dorsal rays 16-20; pectoral rays 11-14; trunk rings 15; tail rings 27-30; superior trunk and tail ridges discontinuous; lateral trunk ridge straight, ending near anal ring; inferior trunk and tail ridges continuous; head length 7.1-8.3 in standard length; snout length 2.2-2.7 in head length; least snout depth 2.8-3.6 in snout length; median dorsal ridge on snout with two to four triangular projections; dermal flaps present on head, including eye; pale, often with two rows of small dark spots anteriorly on lower half of trunk. Maximum length about 6.5 cm. Red Sea to South Africa, east to the Marshall Islands and Fiji. Occurs on coral reefs to depths of at least 30 m.

212. *Cosmocampus banneri*, 6 cm (J. Randall)

INVESTIGATOR PIPEFISH
Cosmocampus investigatoris (Hora, 1925)

Dorsal rays 22-24; pectoral rays 12-15; trunk rings 15; tail rings 31-33; ridges as in preceding species; head length 7.9-10.4 in standard length; snout length 2.5-3.1 in head; least snout depth 2.1-3.0 in snout length; median snout ridge without projections; dermal flaps usually present on head, including eye; pale with numerous faint dark bars. Reaches about 8.5 cm. Known from the Arabian Gulf, Sri Lanka, Burma, and Gulf of Thailand. Small individuals (to 5.5 cm standard length) taken with surface tow nets and at nightlights; others (3.4-7.2 cm standard length) in dredges or with SCUBA in 2-15.2 m.

ORANGESTRIPE PIPEFISH
Doryrhamphus aurolineatus Randall and Earle, 1994

Dorsal rays 21; pectoral rays 22-23; trunk rings 18-19; tail rings 11-12; superior trunk and tail ridges discontinuous; lateral trunk ridge confluent with inferior tail ridge on second tail ring; principal ridges of trunk and tail with a spine on each ring; a blade-like ridge dorsally on snout with about six pointed elevations; stout-bodied for a pipefish, the trunk depth 9.4-10.2 in standard length; head length 4.0 in standard length; snout short, 2.65-2.7 in head length; male with a pair of fleshy flaps on each ventrolateral ridge of snout; dark grey with a middorsal bright orange stripe; caudal fin black with an irregular orange spot in centre. Largest specimen, 3.5 cm. Known from only two specimens collected in 11 m on the east side of Masirah Island, Oman.

BLUESTRIPE PIPEFISH
Doryrhamphus excisus excisus Kaup, 1856

Dorsal rays 21-29; pectoral rays 19-23; trunk rings 17-19; tail rings 13-17; ridges as in the preceding species; males with a ventrolateral projection on snout; stout-bodied, the depth 13-17.5 in standard length; head length 3.9-4.9 in standard length; snout length 2.0-2.4 in head length; least snout depth 3.9-7.1 in snout length; orange with a broad blue stripe on upper side of trunk, tail, and postorbital head; a black stripe from front of snout, through eye, and narrowing to end on opercle; caudal fin orange with large black spots and a blue margin. Maximum length, 7.5 cm. Indo-Pacific, including the Arabian Gulf; a different subspecies in the Red Sea, *D. excisus abbreviatus* Dawson. A cryptic reef species rarely seen

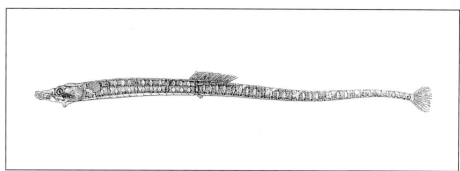

213. *Cosmocampus investigatoris* (after Hora, 1926)

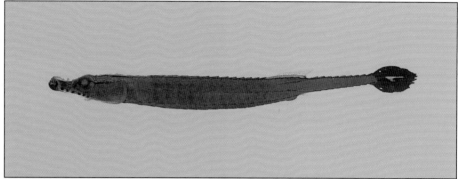

214. *Doryrhamphus aurolineatus*, 3.4 cm (J. Randall)

215. *Doryrhamphus excisus excisus*, 6.4 cm (J. Randall)

216. *Halicampus mataafae*, 11.5 cm (J. Randall)

in the open; often found as pairs. *D. melanopleura* (Bleeker) is a synonym.

SAMOAN PIPEFISH
Halicampus mataafae (Jordan and Seale, 1906)

Dorsal rays 21-26 (usually 21-24); pectoral rays 12-14; trunk rings 15; trail rings 33-36 (rarely 33); superior trunk and tail ridges discontinuous; inferior trunk ridge ends at anal ring; lateral trunk ridge conflu-ent with inferior tail ridge; a series of spinous ridges dorsally on snout; small tentacles often present dorsally on head; head length 10.2-13.0 in standard length; snout length 2.5-4.0 in head; least snout depth 1.2-2.7 in snout length; caudal fin about as long as eye or a little shorter; mottled brown often with two series of faint dark-edged vertically elongate spots and one on tail. Attains about 13 cm. Red Sea to Natal and east to Marshall Islands and Samoa (type locality); a shallow-water species sometimes found in tidepools.

ZAVORA PIPEFISH
Halicampus zavorensis Dawson, 1984

Dorsal rays 22-23; pectoral rays 13; trunk rings 14; tail rings 36-37; head length 8.8-10.9 in standard length; snout length 2.6-2.9 in head length; least snout depth 2.3-3.2 in snout length; main body ridges as in previous species; median dorsal ridge on snout continuous and low; body pale with about 14 diffuse dark bars 0.5 to 1.0 ring in width; lower side of head and body with irregular dark brown bars, one per ring on trunk and tail. Attains about 9.5 mm. Known only from one specimen from Zavora, Mozambique and two from Sur, Oman.

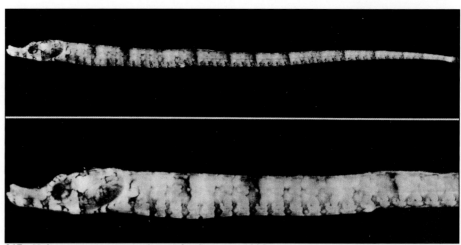

217. *Halicampus zavorensis*, 6 cm (after Dawson, 1985)

BLUESPECKLED PIPEFISH
Hippichthys cyanospilus (Bleeker, 1854)

Dorsal rays 20-28, the fin origin on last or penultimate trunk ring; pectoral rays 13-16; trunk rings 12-14; tail rings 32-35; superior trunk and tail ridges discontinuous; posterior end of lateral trunk ridge deflected downward; inferior trunk and tail ridges continuous; head length 7.5-9.8 in standard length; snout length 1.3-2.6 in head length; least snout depth 3.0-5.4 in snout length; body plain or mottled; often finely flecked with pale blue; lower part of snout often pale; three or four dark dots on each dorsal ray. Reaches 16 cm. Red Sea and coast of East Africa to the western Pacific where it ranges from the Ryukyu Islands to Queensland, east to Caroline Islands and Fiji. Occurs in coastal and brackish habitats; the illustrated specimen came from silty sand in 2 m.

218. *Hippichthys cyanospilus*, 8.7 cm (J. Randall)

BEADY PIPEFISH
Hippichthys penicillus (Cantor, 1849)

Dorsal rays 23-31, the fin origin on tail; pectoral rays 14-18; trunk rings 15-17; tail rings 35-41; superior trunk and tail ridges discontinuous; posterior end of lateral trunk ridge not deflected downward; inferior trunk and tail ridges continuous; head length 5.6-8.0 in standard length; snout long, 1.5 -2.2 in head length; least snout depth 3.3-7.8 in snout length; yellowish brown with numerous, very small, dark-edged, white spots; lower side of tail with a series of larger dark-edged white spots; a dark brown stripe on side of snout; two dark brown stripes diverging posteriorly from eye. Attains 19 cm. Arabian Gulf and northwest India to the Indo-Malayan region, north to Japan and south to New South Wales; not known from oceanic islands. Usually found in shallow brackish habitats.

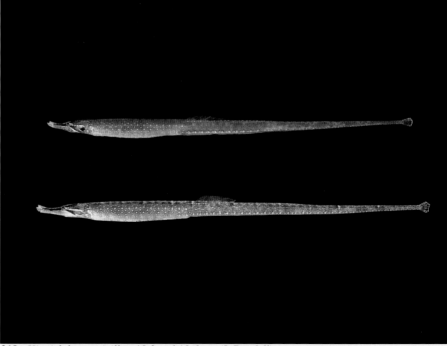

219. *Hippichthys penicillus*, 10.3 and 10.6 cm (J. Randall)

SHORTNOSE PIPEFISH
Micrognathus andersonii (Bleeker, 1858)

Dorsal rays 17-24; pectoral rays 11-13; trunk rings 15-17; tail rings 28-32; superior trunk and tail ridges discontinuous; inferior trunk ridge ends on anal ring; lateral trunk ridge continuous with inferior tail ridge; dorsal profile of snout concave; median dorsal ridge on snout low; head without spines or serrations; no spines on rings; head length 8.1-10.4 in standard length; snout short, its length 2.7-3.4 in head length; least snout depth 1.6-2.8 in snout length; brown, often with nine to 13, dark-edged white spots or short white bars dorsally on body and two longitudinal series of small pale spots. Attains about 8.5 cm. Known from the Red Sea and coast of East Africa to Samoa; photographed specimen from Bahrain.

220. *Micrognathus andersonii*, 7.3 cm (J. Randall)

221. *Trachyrhamphus bicoarctatus*, about 40 cm (J. Randall)

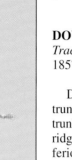

222. *Hippocampus hystrix* (J. Randall)

DOUBLE-ENDED PIPEFISH
Trachyrhamphus bicoarctatus (Bleeker, 1857)

Dorsal rays 24-32; pectoral rays 15-19; trunk rings 21-24; tail rings 55-63; superior trunk and tail ridges discontinuous, the trunk ridge arched dorsally below dorsal fin; inferior trunk ridge ends at tail ring; lateral trunk ridge confluent with inferior tail ridge; body very slender, the depth at mid-trunk 36-58 in standard length; head length 9.9-13.0 in standard length; snout long, 1.5-2.0 in head length; least snout depth 5.2-11.1 in snout length; caudal fin well-developed in young but usually missing or vestigial in adults; colour highly variable, from nearly black to brown or whitish, with or without dark bars, and often with very small pale and/or black spots. Attains about 40 cm. Red Sea to South Africa, east to the western Pacific where it ranges from Japan to New South Wales; also known from Guam and New Caledonia. Generally found on sand, rubble, or seagrass substrata; it is believed the caudal fin is lost due to their anchoring themselves with the end of the tail when current is strong.

SEAHORSES
SUBFAMILY HIPPOCAMPINAE

THORNY SEAHORSE
Hippocampus histrix Kaup, 1853

Dorsal rays 17-19; anal rays 4; pectoral rays 17-18; trunk rings 11; tail rings 33-34; ridges between rings of body with prominent sharp spines, those on superior ridge longest; coronet of five short spines; a long median spine anterior to coronet with one equally long to either side, preceded by a smaller one at posterior edge of eye; supraorbital spine also long; a smaller median spine on snout just before eye; snout as long or longer than rest of head; two spines on superior ridge below dorsal-fin base; colour variable; spines dorsally on body may be black-tipped. Reported to reach 17 cm when fully outstreched. Indo-Pacific; usually found on seagrass or weedy bottoms. *H. jayakarai* Boulenger, described from an 8.5-cm specimen collected off Muscat, appears to be a synonym.

YELLOW SEAHORSE
Hippocampus kuda Bleeker, 1852

Dorsal rays 15-18; anal rays 4; pectoral rays 15-17; trunk rings 11; tail rings 34-37; short spines or tubercles on ridges of body; coronet of five small tubercles projecting obliquely backward; a small median tubercle or bump in front of coronet flanked on each side by a small spine; a short supraorbital spine preceded by a small tubercle; a small median tubercle or bump on snout just before eye; snout as long or a little longer than postorbital head; three tubercles on superior ridge below base of dorsal fin; colour variable; may be yellow, yellowish brown, black, or black irregularly barred with white. Reported to 30 cm in total length when outstretched. Indo-Pacific.

SHRIMPFISHES
FAMILY CENTRISCIDAE

This small Indo-Pacific family consists of only two genera, *Aeoliscus* and *Centriscus*, with two species each. These strange fishes are encased in thin, transparent, bony plates that are expansions of the vertebral column; the body is extremely compressed, the ventral edge sharp; the snout is long and tubular, the mouth small and without teeth; the caudal fin and soft dorsal fin are displaced ventrally, so the spinous dorsal fin is in the usual position of the caudal fin, the long first dorsal spine in alignment with the dorsal edge of the body; there is no lateral line. The species of *Aeoliscus* differ in having a movable posterior part of the first dorsal spine. These fishes are usually encountered in aggregations swimming vertically with the head down. They feed mainly on small crustaceans. Mohr (1937) revised the family; she treated *Aeoliscus* as a subgenus of *Centriscus*, but most authors regard it as a genus.

223. *Hippocampus kuda* (J. Randall)

GROOVED SHRIMPFISH
Centriscus scutatus Linnaeus, 1758

Dorsal rays IV (including long, terminal, immovable spine) + 10-12; anal rays 11-12; caudal rays 9; pectoral rays 10; pelvic fins small, with 4 rays; body depth 6.5-7.5 in total length; interorbital space nearly flat with a median groove that extends onto occiput; silvery to silvery pink, becoming transparent along sharp ventral part of body; abdomen dark grey with vertical silver lines. Reaches 15 cm. Red Sea and Arabian Gulf to the Indo-Malayan region, south to Queensland and north to Japan. Occurs over mud or silty sand substrata from less than 5 to 80 m.

224. *Centriscus scutatus*, 9.2 cm (J. Randall)

SCORPIONFISHES
FAMILY SCORPAENIDAE

The scorpionfishes are named for the venomous fin spines possessed by many of the species. They are grouped, along with 24 other families, in the order Scorpaeniformes. The Scorpaenidae is characterised by an external bony reinforcing plate passing from the second suborbital bone across the cheek below the eye to the preopercle; it is apparent as a ridge, usually bearing posteriorly-directed spines; other ridges and spines on the head, including three to five spines on the preopercle and usually two on the opercle; there is a large mouth with small villiform teeth; a single dorsal fin, often strongly notched between spinous and soft portions; caudal fin usually rounded; pelvic fins with one spine and 2-5 (usually 5) soft rays; lateral line present; scales present or absent. There are often fleshy flaps or cirri on the head and body, frequently one above the eye; there is much varia-tion within species in the develop-ment of these cutaneous appendages. There is also much variation in colour. Scorpionfishes are benthic or at least bottom-oriented; most tend to match their surroundings in colour, and many are camouflaged further by having flaps and small tentacles on the skin. The turkey-fishes (*Pterois* spp.) and lionfishes (*Dendrochirus* spp.) of the subfamily Pteroinae are exceptions in having rather distinct colour patterns. These fishes, along with those of the Choridactylinae (stingfishes, includ-ing *Inimicus*), the Tetraroginae (waspfishes), and Synanceiinae (stonefishes), have the most virulent venoms of any fishes; deaths have resulted from wounds from the spines (especially the species of the genus *Synanceia*). The dorsal, anal, and pelvic spines are venomous. The spines are generally T-shaped or anchor-shaped in cross-section; the glandular tissue producing the venom lies in the longitudinal space on either side of the spines (or in the case of the stonefishes as a large pyriform gland in the groove, but bulging laterally); the apical end of the gland narrows to a venom duct which passes in the groove to the spine tip. When the spine enters the flesh of the victim, pressure on the gland forces the venom into the duct. Placing the wounded member in water as hot as can be tolerated lessens the excruciating pain. Anti-venin has been developed for *Synan-ceia* venom. Most of these fishes are lie-and-wait predators, ambush-ing small fishes and crustaceans that venture near. The turkeyfishes and lionfishes often slowly stalk their prey. The Synanceinae was reviewed by Eschmeyer and Rama Rao (1975) and the Choridactylinae by Eschmeyer et al. (1979b).

225. *Scorpaenopsis barbatus* (J. Hoover)

BEARDED WASPFISH

Apistus carinatus (Bloch, 1801)

Dorsal rays XIV-XVI,8-10; anal rays III-IV,6-8; pectoral rays 11-13, the lowermost ray free from membrane; longitudinal scale series 65-85; three barbels at front of lower jaw (one at symphysis, and one on either side); lacrymal bone with two short antero-ventral spines and a long posterior one; body depth 3.0-4.0 in standard length; pectoral fins long, often reaching beyond rear base of anal fin; grey, becoming white ventrally; a large ocellated black spot posteriorly in spinous portion of dorsal fin; pectoral fins black except for white uppermost ray and free lower ray. Reaches about 17 cm. A continental and large insular shelf species from the Red Sea and southern Africa east to the Indo-Malayan region, north to Japan, and south to Queensland. Found on mud or silty sand bottoms to depths of at least 60 m; generally caught in trawls, occasionally by seines from shore.

226. *Apistus carinatus*, 11 cm, Japan (Y. Kobayashi)

SERRATE LIONFISH

Brachypterois serrulata (Richardson, 1846)

Dorsal rays XIII,10-11; anal rays III,5-6; pectoral rays 15-16, the third to eighth or ninth rays branched; pelvic rays I,5; fin spines T-shaped in cross-section (true of other Pteroinae); scales ctenoid, about 45 in longitudinal series; gill rakers 4-6 + 10-12; numerous serrate ridges on head; body depth 2.7-3.0 in standard length; dorsal spines short, the longest 4.3 in standard length, linked by membranes only basally; pectoral fins long, reaching to or beyond rear base of anal fin, the rays fully joined by membranes; caudal fin long, its length 2.5-2.9 in standard length; reddish with five blackish bars on body; a black spot larger than eye on opercle; pectoral-fin membranes black; soft dorsal, anal, caudal, and pelvic fins with orange-red spots. Largest specimen, 11.5 cm. Known only from China (type locality), southern Japan (Kanayama and Amaoka, 1981), Philippines (Fowler, 1938, as *B. serrulifer*), India off Madras (two Bishop Museum specimens), the Red Sea off Massaua (William N. Eschmeyer, pers. comm.), and the Gulf of Oman. Taken by trawls in 23-79 m.

227. *Brachypterois serrulata*, 10.5 cm (J. Randall)

LINED STINGFISH

Choridactylus lineatus Poss and Mee, 1995

Dorsal rays XIV,8-9; anal rays II,8; pectoral rays 12, the lower three rays free of membrane and thickened; no filamentous upper pectoral ray; no scales; lateral-line pores 13-14; body depth 3.1-3.45 in standard length; head blunt, the dorsal profile of snout nearly vertical, and short, 3.3-3.45 in standard length; fleshy cirri on chin; origin of dorsal fin on head a short distance posterior to eye; spinous membranes of dorsal fin deeply incised; caudal fin rounded, longer than head; dark brown with wavy longitudinal white lines on body and fins except pelvics, those on dorsal fin progressively steeper anteriorly; white lines on head vermiculate and broken into dots; inner surface of pectoral fins without white markings. Largest specimen, 25 cm. Known from only two specimens taken by trawl off Salalah, southern Oman in 41 m.

228. *Choridactylus lineatus*, 25.5 cm (J. Randall)

229. *C. multibarbus*, warning display (G.Michie)

ORANGEBANDED STINGFISH
Choridactylus multibarbus Richardson, 1848

Dorsal rays XII-XIV,8-9 (usually 9); anal rays II,8-9 (usually 8); pectoral rays 12, the lower three detached and free of membrane; no filamentous upper pectoral ray; no scales; two pairs of barbels on lower jaw, the more posterior pair small; posterior of two lacrymal spines and uppermost of two preopercular spines very long; body depth 2.7-2.9 in standard length; head blunt, the dorsal profile of snout nearly vertical; head length 2.9-3.0 in standard length; mottled reddish brown; a diagonal white band between fourth and sixth dorsal spines, extending onto back; pelvic fins and outer and posterior part of anal fin dark brown to black with basal pale dots; caudal fin white with broad submarginal and basal dark bars; inner surface of pectoral fins black with longitudinal bright orange bands that do not extend to fin margins (when the fish is alarmed it may spread these fins to display the warning colouration). Maximum length about 12 cm. Red Sea and Arabian Gulf to Thailand, north to the Philippines and China. Occurs on soft bottoms to depths of about 50 m.

OBLIQUEBANDED STINGFISH
Minous dempsterae Eschmeyer, Hallacher, and Rama-Rao, 1979

Dorsal rays X-XI (usually XI),11-13, the first spine less than half length of second and close to its base; anal rays II,9-11 (rarely 11); pectoral rays 12, the lowermost slightly enlarged and completely free from rest of fin (true of all species of the genus); scales absent; gill rakers 11-15; lacrymal bone with two strong spines which extend over maxilla, the anteroventral one about half length of posteroventral one; swim bladder absent; pectoral fins reaching at most to above middle of anal fin; grey dorsally, usually with oblique pale bands in dorsal fin which extend onto upper two-thirds of body, the lower third of body pale; pectoral fins black, becoming pale on base; inner surface of pectoral fins grey with dark-edged white spots. Largest specimen, 11.3 cm. Gulf of Oman, Pakistan, and northwestern India in 5-117 m on mud or clay substrata.

230. *Choridactylus multibarbus*, 10.8 cm (J. Randall)

231. *Minous dempsterae*, 10.8 cm, western India (after Eschmeyer et al., 1979)

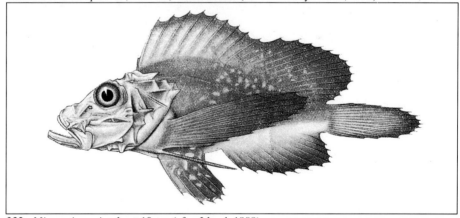

232. *Minous inermis*, about 10 cm (after Lloyd, 1909)

LONGFIN STINGFISH
Minous inermis Alcock, 1889

Dorsal rays IX-X,12-14, the first spine much shorter than second spine and close to its base; anal rays II,10-14; scales absent; gill rakers 14-18; lacrymal bone with two strong spines of about equal length extending over maxilla, the posterior one projecting backward as well as downward; upper preopercular spine not extending beyond margin of opercle; swim bladder absent; pectoral fins very long (third or fourth rays longest), reaching beyond base of last anal ray; dark grey, the young with pale spots, shading to white ventrally; outer part of median fins dark grey; pectoral fins increasingly dark distally; inside of pectoral fins light grey; pelvic fins dark grey with pale spots. Reaches about 14 cm. Known from Somalia, Gulf of Oman, India, Burma, and western Thailand in the depth range of 35-420 m. Eschmeyer et al. (1979a) reviewed the Indo-Pacific subfamily Minoinae; it consists of the single genus *Minous*, of which they recognised nine species; Amaoka and Kanayama (1981) added a tenth by recovering *M. longimanus* Regan from the synonymy of *M. inermis*.

GREY STINGFISH
Minous monodactylus (Bloch and Schneider, 1801)

Dorsal rays IX-XI,10-12, the first spine equal to or longer than second spine and well-separated from it; anal rays II,7-10 (usually 9); scales absent; gill rakers 11-16; lacrymal bone with two spines extending over maxilla, the ventroposterior spine at least twice the length of the ventroanterior one; swim bladder present; pectoral fins reaching at most to above middle of anal fin; mottled light grey, pale ventrally; a large black spot distally on anterior part of soft portion of dorsal fin; anal and paired fins dark brown distally; inner surface of pectorals pale; caudal fin with two broad dark bars. Attains about 12 cm. Red Sea, Mauritius, Maldives, and Arabian Gulf to Indo-Malayan region, north to Japan. Found on mud or silty sand from near shore to at least 55 m. The most common and widespread species of the genus.

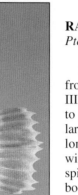

233. *Minous monodactylus*, 7 cm (J. Randall)

234. *Pterois antennata*, about 19 cm (J. Randall)

235. *Pterois miles*, about 27 cm (J. Hoover)

RAGGEDFIN TURKEYFISH
Pterois antennata (Bloch, 1787)

Dorsal rays XII,11-12, the spines free from membrane except basally; anal rays III,6; pectoral rays 16-17, the outer fourth to half of rays free of membranes; scales largely ctenoid; supraocular tentacle usually long with dark cross bands that coincide with extensions in width of tentacle; dorsal spines long, the longest clearly longer than body depth; numerous, white-edged, red to dark reddish brown bars of variable width on body; an oblique dark reddish band from eye across cheek, ending in a dark spot at edge of operculum; soft portion of median fins with small black spots on rays; spines of dorsal fin with reddish bands; pectoral fin membranes with large red-edged brown spots, the filamentous rays white. Reaches about 20 cm. Indo-Pacific except Red Sea, Arabian Gulf, and Hawaii; the most common species of the genus in the Gulf of Oman. Found mainly on coral reefs, often in caves or upside down under ledges; divers should be alert to their presence in unusual places.

MILITARY TURKEYFISH
Pterois miles (Bennett, 1828)

Dorsal rays XIII,9-11 (strongly modal on 10); anal rays III,6; pectoral rays 13-15 (usually 14); scales cycloid and small, 90-120 in longitudinal series; suborbital and preopercular bones of adults with spinous points; supraocular tentacle of variable length, rarely with faint bands; dorsal spines long, the longest clearly longer than body depth, each with membrane to tip but isolated from other spines except basally; pectoral membranes of adults broad and plume-like; numerous dark red to black bars of variable width on head and body (bars increasing in number with growth); small dark spots on soft rays of median fins; dorsal spines and membranes with dark red cross bands. Reaches at least 31 cm. Red Sea and Arabian Gulf south to South Africa and east to Sumatra. Usually found on coral reefs or rocky bottom or sand or seagrass in the vicinity of hard substrata from the shallows to at least 50 m. The closely related *P. volitans* (Linnaeus) is found in western

Australia and Viet Nam east to the Pitcairn Group. Schultz (1986) distinguished the two species on the basis of *volitans* having modally 11 dorsal soft rays, 7 anal rays, and usually longer pectoral fins. At present there is no overlap in their distributions. It will be of interest to see if they coexist in the present gap in their distribution in Indonesia between Sumatra and Sulawesi. The venom of this species is virulent, and people stuck by the spines all report agonising pain (Ray and Coates, 1958; Steinitz, 1959). If a diver approaches this turkeyfish and *volitans* closely, the fish tend to point their dorsal spines in the direction of the intruder; if alarmed further as by close approach, they can make an overt movement toward the diver and strike with their dorsal spines very rapidly, moving the head downward and thrusting the spines forward.

MOMBASA TURKEYFISH
Pterois mombasae (Smith, 1957)

Dorsal rays XIII,10; anal rays III,6-7; pectoral rays 18-20; scales mostly ctenoid; supraorbital tentacle tiny to moderate, sometimes banded; length of longest dorsal spines slightly less than body depth, each with membrane to spine tip (broader on anterior spines), isolated except basally; pectoral fins long, the longest rays extending to or posterior to caudal-fin base; outer fourth to more than half of rays of upper half of pectoral fins free of membrane (upper free rays progressively longer); body with reddish brown bars of variable width, the

236. *Pterois mombasae*, about 18 cm (J. Hoover)

pale interspaces with a dark line; head with diagonal dark red bands, broader than pale interspaces; a large oval dark brown spot on subopercle, one of the pale diagonal bands of head bifurcating to pass around it; dorsal spines and adjacent membranes with dark cross bands, the distal part of membranes broadly white to pink; small black spots on

rays of soft dorsal, anal, and caudal fins; pelvic fin membranes dark basally, becoming paler distally, without spots, the rays whitish. Largest specimen, 18.6 cm. Known from Natal to Kenya, south coast of Oman, Gulf of Oman, Sri Lanka, and New Guinea; generally found on hard substratum in more than 20 m.

CLEARFIN TURKEYFISH
Pterois radiata Cuvier, 1829

Dorsal rays XII-XIII,11; anal rays III,5-6; pectoral rays 16; scales mostly ctenoid; supraorbital tentacle long and not banded; longest dorsal spines greater than body depth, without membranes except basally; pectoral rays long, the longest reaching well beyond base of caudal fin, connected by membranes on only about basal third; body with broad, white-edged, dark reddish brown bars, the first and second separated dorsally by a reddish triangle and the third and fourth separated above and below by a reddish triangle; side of caudal peduncle with a broad reddish stripe; head with a white-edged, dark reddish brown bar from nape across operculum and a diagonal one from eye across cheek; fin spines and rays red, the pectorals becoming white distally; fin membranes clear, without spots. Reaches 20 cm. Indo-Pacific, on coral reefs or rocky bottom.

237. *Pterois radiata*, about 17 cm (J. Randall)

LARGETAIL TURKEYFISH
Pterois russelli Bennett, 1831

Dorsal rays XIII,10-11; anal rays III,6-7; pectoral rays 13; scales cycloid; supraorbital tentacle small or absent; longest dorsal spines usually a little less than body depth, with membranes nearly to spine tips but not broad, the spines linked only basally by membrane; pectoral fins not reaching base of caudal fin (except in young), the rays with membranes to ray tips but upper rays curved and not linked by membrane to adjacent rays for about half their length; caudal fin long, about 2.5 in standard length (compared to about 3.0 in other species of the genus); body with alternating dark reddish brown and whitish bars, the white bisected by a dark reddish brown line; a prominent black spot above pectoral-fin base; postorbital head with two narrow dark brown bars, the pale interspaces with reddish brown lines; reddish brown lines extending ventrally from eye; dorsal spines and membranes with blackish cross bands; paired fins with black spots on rays (basally on pectorals); remaining fins without spots, the rays largely red. Attains 30 cm. Mauritius (type locality), east coast of Africa, and Arabian Gulf east to Indo-Malayan region, Australia, and north to China. Generally taken by trawls over mud bottoms to depths at least as great as 60 m.

BLACKFIN STONEFISH
Pseudosynanceia melanostigma Day, 1875

Dorsal rays XV-XVII,4-6; anal rays III,7-8; pectoral rays 14-15; pelvic rays I,3; no scales; body without wart-like protuberances; eyes small, dorsally on head, well-separated, and oriented mainly upward; mouth superior; head with low ridges; spines on head not well-developed; dorsal spines with venom glands; pectoral fins long, reaching to above anal spines; finely mottled grey, pale yellowish to white ventrally; a whitish area anteriorly on soft portion of dorsal fin, the fin abruptly black posteriorly; outer and posterior part of anal fin black; caudal fin white with a broad submarginal black bar; pectoral fins broadly edged in black. Reported to 18 cm. Arabian Gulf to west coast of India; lives in mud; marine and estuarine.

SHORE SCORPIONFISH
Scorpaenodes littoralis (Tanaka, 1917)

Dorsal rays XIII,9; anal rays III,5 (last dorsal and anal rays branched to base, hence might be counted as 10 and 6, respectively);

pectoral rays 17-19; scales ctenoid, about 45 in longitudinal series; a pair of interorbital spines present (small to absent in juveniles); suborbital ridge with three posteriorly-directed spines; preopercle with three spines; red to dark reddish brown, densely mottled with pale, with a conspicuous dark red to dark brown spot larger than pupil on subopercle; obscure broad dark bands radiating from eye; a double red to reddish brown bar posteriorly on caudal peduncle and base of caudal fin, the two parts separated by an irregular or broken pale vertical line; usually a pale spot on back below juncture of spinous and soft portions of dorsal fin. Attains 11 cm. Indo-Pacific; common on coast of southern and central Oman, but cryptic; occurs on reef or rocky bottom in from 2 to 30 m.

238. *Pterois russelli*, 34 cm (J. Randall)

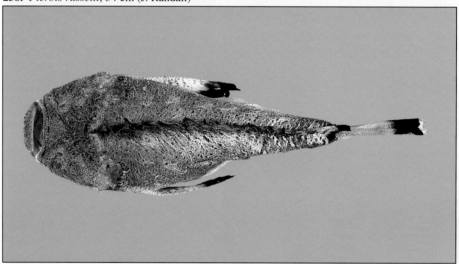

239. *Pseudosynanceia melanostigma*, dorsal view, 18.3 cm (J. Randall)

240. *Scorpaenodes littoralis*, 5.3 cm (J. Randall)

BEARDED SCORPIONFISH
Scorpaenopsis barbatus (Rüppell, 1838)

Dorsal rays XII,9; anal rays III,5; pectoral rays 17-19; scales ctenoid, about 50-55 in longitudinal series; palatine teeth absent (a character of the genus); suborbital ridge with three or four posteriorly-directed spines, leading to uppermost double spine of preopercle; upper opercular spine single; an indentation in dorsal profile of snout before eye, preceded on each side by nasal spine (true of other species of *Scorpaenopsis*); interorbital space narrower than eye diameter; longitudinal ridges in interorbital space prominent, diverging posteriorly to join ridge at front of occipital depression; no coronal spines (at posterior end of each interorbital ridge); a prominent suborbital depression, deepest below front of eye; fleshy flaps and cirri present on head, body, and fins (also applies to a variable degree to others of the genus); body depth 2.7-3.2 in standard length; second anal spine equal to or slightly longer than third spine; last dorsal ray divided to base and broadly joined by membrane to caudal peduncle (characteristic of other *Scorpaenopsis* herein); dark brown to reddish brown, densely mottled with pale; caudal fin dark with a broad whitish posterior margin and an irregular whitish bar near base of fin. Reaches about 25 cm. Long known only from the Red Sea and Gulf of Aden, but reported by Al-Baharna (1986) from the Arabian Gulf. Common in Oman seas, but easily overlooked due to its camouflage.

DEVIL SCORPIONFISH
Scorpaenopsis diabolus (Cuvier, 1829)

Dorsal rays XII,9; anal rays III,5; pectoral rays 17-19; scales ctenoid, 43-48 in longitudinal series; suborbital ridge with four to ten small spines of variable size, not in a

241. *Scorpaenopsis barbatus*, about 23 cm (J. Randall)

242. *Scorpaenopsis diabolus*, about 28 cm (J. Randall)

row; upper opercular spine divided to two or more points; a middorsal depression behind eyes; depression below front of eye very deep; back highly arched below anterior part of dorsal fin; body depth 2.3-2.7 in standard length; interorbital space broad and deeply concave, its least width greater than orbit diameter; colour highly variable, but diagnostic are the white outer border of pelvic fins and the inner surface of the pectoral fins which is bright orange-yellow with a black spot or spots in upper part (when the

fish is disturbed, this colour may be flashed by moving the pectorals forward, thus serving as warning colouration). Reaches 30 cm. Indo-Pacific; occurs on coral reefs and on rocky substrata.

WHITEBLOTCHED SCORPIONFISH
Scorpaenopsis lactomaculata (Herre, 1945)

Dorsal rays XII,9; anal rays III,5; pectoral rays 18-19 (usually 18); scales ctenoid, 60-67 in longitudinal series; suborbital ridge with four posteriorly-directed spines leading to uppermost of three preopercular spines; upper opercular spine single; interorbital space deeply concave, slightly narrower than eye diameter; interorbital ridges poorly developed, wide apart, with a deep channel between; middorsal depression behind eyes very shallow; a well-developed depression below front of eye; no coronal spines; body depth about 2.7 in standard length; second anal spine equal to or slightly longer than third spine; reddish brown, mottled with white, the most conspicuous white markings a spot below front of eye, one below ninth dorsal spine, and a large one on caudal peduncle. Largest specimen, 28 cm. West coast of India (type locality, Bombay) to Arabian Gulf; taken by trawls in moderate depths.

243. *Scorpaenopsis lactomaculata*, 28 cm (J. Randall)

111

RAGGY SCORPIONFISH
Scorpaenopsis venosa (Cuvier, 1829)

Dorsal rays XII,9; anal rays III,5; pectoral rays 16-18 (usually 17); scales ctenoid, about 50 in longitudinal series; interorbital space narrower than orbit diameter; interorbital ridges moderate, nearly straight, ending at front of middorsal depression behind eyes; no coronal spines; tympanic spines at anterior corners of occipital depression nearly joined by a strong ridge which forms front of depression; body depth about 3.0 in standard length; second anal spine longer than third; strongly mottled brown to reddish brown; dark spots in fins tend to be in rows, the darkest usually posteriorly in spinous portion of dorsal fin. Largest specimen, 22 cm. East coast of Africa and Arabian Gulf (record from Friedhelm Krupp) to Indo-Malayan region and Australia, north to Taiwan. *S. novaguineae* (Cuvier) and *S. rosea* Day are synonyms.

GÜNTHER'S WASPFISH
Snyderina guentheri (Boulenger, 1889)

Dorsal rays XIII,10-11; anal rays III,5-6 (usually 6); pectoral rays 13-14 (rarely 14); body with very small, nonimbricate, partially embedded scales; head naked; lateral-line scales 21-26 (including one at caudal-fin base); gill rakers short, 3-4 + 9-13; lacrymal bone with a short downward-pointing spine and a long posterior one (reaches beyond middle of eye); a single preopercular spine nearly as long as posterior lacrymal spine; villiform teeth in bands on jaws and vomer, none on palatines; body depth 2.5-2.9 in standard length; caudal peduncle slender; origin of dorsal fin anterior to middle of eye; caudal fin long and broadly rounded; dark reddish brown with small pale spots; three dark bars radiating downward from eye and one above to origin of dorsal fin; the illustrated fish, photographed off Muscat in 24 m, seems to be a subadult; although the colour is different from that described for the holotype and specimens reported from India by Talwar (1977), another specimen from the Gulf of Oman with similar colour was identified as *S. guentheri* by W.N. Eschmeyer and S.G. Poss. Largest reported, 21.5 cm. Known only from the Gulf of Aden, Gulf of Oman, and southwest India from the depth range of 24-300 m.

DWARF SCORPIONFISH
Synanceia nana Eschmeyer and Rama-Rao, 1973

Dorsal rays XIV (rarely XV),5; anal rays III,4-6; pectoral rays 14-16 (rarely 16); pelvic rays I,5; no scales; body with wart-like protuberances; no palatine teeth; dorsal surface of head flat; eyes dorsally on head, elevated, and directed upward as much as laterally; mouth superior; posterior interorbital space with a deep depression, bordered behind by a ridge which is the anterior edge of a shallow rectangular occipital depression; no deep pit below eye; dorsal spines short, subequal, the thick skin covering venom glands; grey dorsally, the ridges on head and protuberances on skin whitish, soon shading to pale yellowish grey on side and ventrally; spinous portion of dorsal fin whitish; anal and paired fins black distally; caudal fin coloured like body on basal third, followed by a broad white bar and a broad black bar flecked with white, the ray tips white. Largest specimen, 13.5 cm. Northern Red Sea to Arabian Gulf; depth of capture, 3.5-18 m.

244. *Scorpaenopsis venosa*, about 21 cm (J. Randall)

245. *Snyderina guentheri* (B.L. Simpson)

246. *Synanceia nana*, 11.2 cm (J. Randall)

STONEFISH
Synanceia verrucosa Bloch and
Schneider, 1801

Dorsal rays XII-XIV (usually XIII),5-7; anal rays III,5-6; pectoral rays 17-19 (usually 18); pelvic rays I,4-5 (rarely 4); no scales; skin thick, with wart-like protuberances; head broad and dorsally flattened; eyes broadly separated, directed mainly upward; a deep depression behind each eye and one below front of eye; mouth superior with a fringe of cirri at edge; no teeth on vomer or palatines; dorsal spines subequal; a venom gland in groove on each side of dorsal spines, covered by thick skin; pectoral fins large; colour highly variable, closely matching surroundings. Largest specimen, 37.2 cm, 2.4 kg, from the northern Red Sea (Arik Diamant, pers. comm.). Indo-Pacific. Usually seen on coral reefs, often in caves or under ledges, but able to bury in sand with only the eyes and mouth showing. This and *S. horrida* (Linnaeus) are the most feared venomous fishes in the sea; wounds from the spines are excruciatingly painful, and deaths have resulted (Smith, 1957; Halstead, 1970).

247. *Synanceia verrucosa*, 23 cm (J. Randall)

DRACO WASPFISH
Vespicula dracaene (Cuvier, 1829)

Dorsal rays XII,7; anal rays III,5-6; last dorsal and anal rays fully connected by membrane to caudal peduncle; pectoral rays 12-13 (usually 12); pelvic rays I,5; no scales; lateral-line pores about 18-20; gill rakers 4-5 + 13-14; body depth 2.45-3.1 in standard length; lacrymal with two spines, a short ventral one and a large posterior one that extends to below centre of eye; a large spine on preopercle in line with suborbital ridge; a second, lower, very small, blunt spine on preopercle; origin of dorsal fin above rear edge of eye; a broad space between third and fourth dorsal spines, the associated membrane deeply incised, nearly dividing the dorsal into two fins; caudal fin truncate, slightly rounded when spread; light brown, irregularly blotched with darker brown; a broad dark band across interorbital,

248. *Vespicula dracaene*, 4.1 cm (J. Randall)

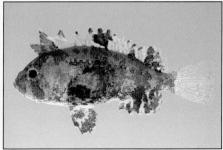

continuing as a bar below eye and another band from origin of dorsal fin to eye; dorsal fin pale with a large dark brown blotch in middle of fin (usually between sixth and ninth spines) and other irregular brown blotches, especially posteriorly; caudal fin whitish with faint small dark spots. Reported to 7.5 cm. Arabian Gulf to west coast of India (type locality, Malabar coast) and Sri Lanka.

GURNARDS AND SEAROBINS
FAMILY TRIGLIDAE

This family, also in the order Scorpaeniformes, is distinctive in having the head encased in bony plates bearing ridges and spines; no barbels on chin; scales small to moderate, mainly ctenoid; front of snout usually with a rostral projection on each side, often bearing a spine or spines (hence snout bilobed when viewed from above); mouth usually slightly inferior; maxilla largely covered by preorbital bone when mouth closed; villiform teeth in jaws; dorsal fin divided into spinous and soft portions, the spinous with seven to eleven spines; lower three pectoral rays enlarged, free of membranes, used for "walking" on the bottom and to probe in the sediment for food (which consists mainly of crustaceans and molluscs); pelvic fins broadly separated, with one spine and five soft rays; swim bladder bilobed in most species and used in sound production. The common name searobin is derived from the chirping sound some species make when boated. These fishes are benthic, usually found on sand or mud of continental shelves in tropical to warm temperate seas; they are most often caught in trawls. The dominant genus of the family in the Indian Ocean is *Lepidotrigla*, all of which have a deep transverse groove in the occiput just behind the eyes. The Indian Ocean species of the genus were revised by Richards and Saksena (1977).

249. *Lepidotrigla bispinosa*, 8.5 cm (after Steindachner, 1898)

BULLHORN GURNARD
Lepidotrigla bispinosa (Steindachner, 1898)

Dorsal rays VIII-X + 14-15; anal rays 14-16; pectoral rays 13, the lower three free of membrane and thickened; lateral-line scales about 58; rows of scales below lateral line 15-19 (usually 18), those on lower side cycloid; a row of posteriorly-directed spines on back at base of dorsal fins (true of other species of *Lepidotrigla*); nape and abdomen fully scaled; chest and interpelvic area naked; rostral process of preorbital bone ending in a single sharp spine; head length 2.4-3.15 in standard length; interorbital width 4.8-8.2% standard length; front of anterior dorsal spines serrate (also applies to other *Lepidotrigla*); caudal fin slightly emarginate; red dorsally, shading to white on lower side and ventrally. Reaches 16 cm. Red Sea and Arabian Gulf to western India; recorded from depths of 9-115 m.

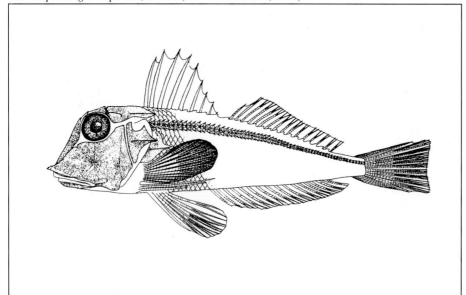

250. *Lepidotrigla faueri* (after Fischer and Bianchi, 1984)

PRICKLY GURNARD
Lepidotrigla faueri Gilchrist and Thompson, 1914

Dorsal rays VIII-IX + 15-17; anal rays 15-16; pectoral rays 14, the lower three free and thickened; lateral-line scales 57-64; rows of scales below lateral line 14-15; abdomen fully scaled; scales deciduous; rostral process of preorbital bone ending in 4-6 small spines; head length 2.6-3.4 in standard length; interorbital width 4.7-7.1% standard length; caudal fin slightly emarginate; colour primarily red. Attains about 16 cm. Natal to the Gulf of Oman and India; recorded from depths of 50-175 m.

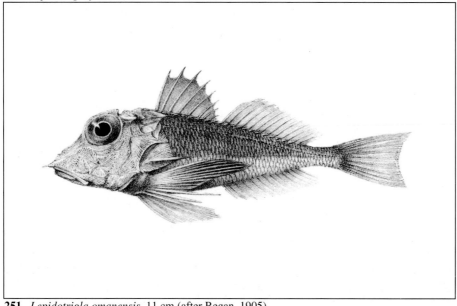

251. *Lepidotrigla omanensis*, 11 cm (after Regan, 1905)

OMAN GURNARD
Lepidotrigla omanensis Regan, 1905

Dorsal rays VIII-IX (usually IX) + 13-15; anal rays 13-15; pectoral rays 14, the lower three free and thickened; lateral-line scales 53-58; scale rows below lateral line 12-14; scales on lower side ctenoid; nape and abdomen fully scaled; chest and interpelvic area naked; rostral process of preorbital bone ending in a single sharp spine; head length 2.3-2.6 in standard length; interorbital width 7.3-8.9% standard length; inner surface of pectoral fins black with a white margin that is broadest ventrally; spinous dorsal fin dusky posteriorly. Gulf of Aden and Gulf of Oman to south India; reported from depths of 56-275 m.

SPOTTEDWING GURNARD
Lepidotrigla spiloptera Günther, 1880

Dorsal rays VIII-IX (usually IX) + 15-16; anal rays 16; pectoral rays 14-16, the lower three free and thickened; scales ctenoid, deciduous except for lateral-line scales; lateral-line scales 60-65; rows of scales below lateral line 19-21; abdomen fully scaled; chest and interpelvic area naked; rostral process of preorbital bone ending in series of about 7 spines, one clearly larger than the rest; head length 2.5-3.0 in standard length; interorbital width 6.0-7.7% standard length; caudal fin slightly emarginate; red dorsally, white below; pectoral membranes and rays between second and ninth rays black. A small species, reaching only about 10 cm. Known from scattered records from Zanzibar, Somalia, southern Red Sea, Bay of Bengal, Indonesia, and Philippines; two Bishop Museum specimens from Arabian Gulf identified as *L. spiloptera* by William J. Richards. Depth range 54-256 m.

252. *Lepidotrigla spiloptera*, 10.7 cm (J. Randall)

BLACKSPOTTED GURNARD
Pterygotrigla hemisticta (Temminck and Schlegel, 1842)

Dorsal rays VIII-IX (usually VIII) + 10-12; anal rays 10-12; pectoral rays 15; scales small and cycloid, the lateral-line scales 62-72; nape scaleless; no transverse groove across top of head behind eyes (as in *Lepidotrigla*); no small bony plates along base of soft dorsal fin; rostral process of preorbital bone ending in a long spine which angles slightly outward; opercular spine also long; caudal fin forked; head and upper half of body light orange-red with small dark spots on back and postorbital head; lower half of body silvery white; a black spot in outer posterior part of spinous dorsal fin; pectoral membranes blackish. Reaches 30 cm. Known from Japan to the Indian Ocean; depth for one collection off Cochin, India, 138-210 m. *Trigla arabica* Boulenger, described from one 23-cm specimen taken off Muscat, is a synonym (Richards and Saksena, 1974). Baranes and Golani (1993) recorded specimens from the Gulf of Aqaba as *Pterygotrigla* sp. for which they listed slight differences from Japanese specimens of *P. hemisticta*.

253. *Pterygotrigla hemisticta* (J. Randall)

FLATHEADS
FAMILY PLATYCEPHALIDAE

These scorpaeniform fishes are elongate with a depressed body; head more depressed and broader than body, with bony ridges usually bearing spines or serrations; eyes oriented more dorsally than laterally; a lappet on iris of eye; mouth large, the lower jaw projecting; villiform teeth in jaws, on vomer, and usually on palatines (a few species with canine teeth); two dorsal fins, the first of VII to X (usually IX) spines, the first spine short and barely connected by membrane to the second spine; soft dorsal and anal fins with 10-15 rays; pelvic fins broadly separated, with one spine and 5 soft rays; scales small, ctenoid; lateral-line complete, the first few scales often with a backward-directed spine (a few species with a spine on all or nearly all lateral-line scales). Most of these fishes are found on sand or mud substrata in which they are usually buried except for their eyes (at least by day); a few of the larger species may be seen on reefs or rocky bottom, but they are often overlooked because they are protectively coloured and rarely move. Flatheads feed mainly on crustaceans and small fishes. The family consists of 19 genera and about 60 species, all from tropical to temperate waters of the Indo-Pacific region except one eastern Atlantic species.

CROCODILE FLATHEAD
Cociella crocodila (Tilesius, 1812)

Dorsal rays VIII-IX (usually VIII)+11; anal rays 11; pectoral rays 19-22; lateral-line scales 52-55, the anterior two to 16 bearing a small spine; longitudinal scale series 59-76; gill rakers 1 + 4-5; head length 2.6-3.0 in standard length; suborbital ridge with three spines; preopercular spines usually 2, the upper about three times longer than lower; light brown, shading to silvery white ventrally, with five short dark bars and scattered small dark brown spots on back; spinous dorsal, caudal, and pelvic fins with a large distal dark area; small dark brown spots in soft dorsal, caudal, and pectoral fins. Attains about 50 cm. Continental shelf of East Africa, Red Sea, and Gulf of Oman to western Pacific; reported on sand and mud substrata from near shore to about 100 m.

254. *Cociella crocodila*, 17.2 cm (J. Randall)

ROUGH FLATHEAD
Grammoplites scaber (Linnaeus, 1758)

Dorsal rays VIII-IX+12; anal rays 12; pectoral rays 19-21; lateral-line scales 49-54, all with a backward-directed spine; longitudinal scale series about 90; scales on head with a rough ridge; gill rakers 1 + 5-6; head length 3.0-3.2 in standard length; two suborbital ridges, the upper with three to five spines; three preopercular spines, the upper much longer, but not reaching edge of opercular membrane, a small spine at its base; brown, often with faint dark bars on body; chest blotched with yellow; outer part of spinous dorsal fin broadly blackish; rays of soft dorsal fin with two rows of small black spots; a large blackish spot covering most of outer half of caudal fin; broad middle part of pectoral fins blackish. Attains about 27 cm. Arabian Gulf to Indo-Malayan region, north to Hong Kong.

255. *Grammoplites scaber*, 20 cm (J. Randall)

SPOTFIN FLATHEAD
Grammoplites suppositus (Troschel, 1840)

Dorsal rays IX+12; anal rays 13; pectoral rays 21-23; lateral-line scales 51-55, all with a posteriorly-directed spine (occasionally a few posterior scales lack the spine); longitudinal scale series about twice as numerous as lateral-line scales; gill rakers 1 + 8; head length 3.0-3.2 in standard length; bones dorsally on head rugose; uppermost of three preopercular spines very long, usually extending posterior to opercular membrane, with a small spine on its base; brown, sometimes faintly mottled with darker brown, shading to light brown ventrally; a large black spot posteriorly in spinous dorsal fin; soft dorsal and pectoral fins with small dusky spots; caudal fin light grey; pelvic fins dark grey. Reaches about 25 cm. Red Sea and Arabian Gulf along the continental shelf to Sri Lanka, usually on mud bottoms from 45-94 m. *Platycephalus maculipinna* Regan is a synonym.

256. *Grammoplites suppositus*, 21 cm (J. Randall)

SPINY FLATHEAD
Kumococius rodericensis (Cuvier, 1829)

Dorsal rays IX+1; anal rays 12; pectoral rays 18-20 (usually 19 or 20); lateral-line scales 52-54, the anterior 3-16 with a small spine; gill rakers 2 + 7-9; head length 2.9-3.0 in standard length; bony ridges on head with stout spines, the suborbital ridge with four or more spines; usually three preopercular spines, the uppermost much the largest, reaching to or beyond edge of opercle; interopercular membrane with a pointed flap; pectoral fins slightly falcate (posterior margin concave); brown with four or five faint dark bars on back; fins dusky, the outer part of caudal fin and edges of pectoral fins darker; a submarginal black spot may be present on second and fourth spinous dorsal membranes. Attains about 20 cm. Arabian Gulf to western Pacific where it ranges from northern Australia to Japan.

257. *Kumococius rodericensis*, 17 cm (J. Randall)

TENTACLED FLATHEAD
Papilloculiceps longiceps (Cuvier, 1829)

Dorsal rays IX+11; anal rays 11; pectoral rays 20-22; lateral-line scales 51-56;

258A. Head of *P. longiceps* (J. Hoover)

longitudinal scale series 54-64; gill rakers 1 + 4-5; head length 2.6-3.0 in standard length; snout long, the orbit diameter 2.5-3.0 in snout length; a short tentacle dorsally on eye; suborbital ridge with a single spine below posterior edge of eye; two preopercular spines of about equal length, the lower broader; interopercular membrane with a prominent lobe; mottled grey-brown, shading to white ventrally where irregularly spotted with dark brown or black; a dark brown bar below eye; two irregular dark brown bars below each dorsal fin; paired fins densely spotted with dark brown to black spots of variable size. Reaches 70 cm. Natal to the Red Sea and southern Oman (Oman record from a photographs by Philip Woodhead and John Hoover). Usually found on rock, coral reefs, or on sand near reefs.

INDIAN FLATHEAD
Platycephalus indicus (Linnaeus, 1758)

Dorsal rays VIII-X (the first and last often separated from rest of fin)+13; anal rays 13; pectoral rays 17-20 (usually 19); lateral-line scales 67-84; longitudinal scale series 85-106; gill rakers 1-2 + 6-9; head length 2.9-3.2 in standard length; ridges on head smooth; a single small preocular spine; two preopercular spine, the upper a little shorter than lower and angling dorsally; vomerine teeth in a single transverse patch (in two patches in other genera); dorsal half of body olivaceous to light brown with numerous small blackish spots, the lower half white; caudal fin distinctly coloured white and yellow with two or three black stripes; spines and rays of dorsal fins with faint dark spots; paired fins whitish with small dark spots, those on pelvics larger. Reported to reach 100 cm, but few exceed 70 cm. Red Sea (and into eastern Mediterranean) and coast of East Africa and Madagascar east along the continental shelf to the Indo-Malayan region, south to New South Wales and north to Japan. May be found in very shallow water on sandy shores, or in estuaries, to a maximum depth of about 25 m.

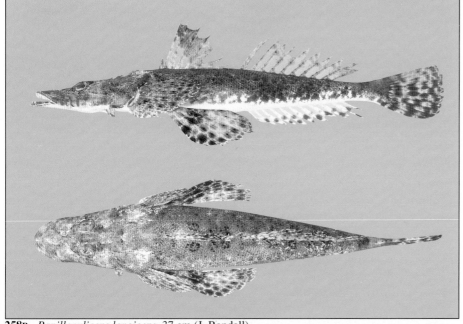

258B. *Papilloculiceps longiceps*, 37 cm (J. Randall)

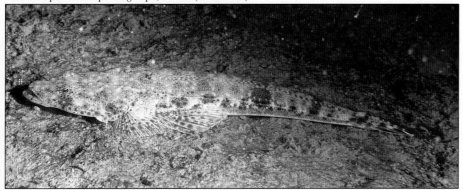

259. *Platycephalus indicus*, about 25 cm (J. Randall)

THORNY FLATHEAD
Rogadius pristiger (Cuvier, 1829)

Dorsal rays IX+10-12; anal rays 10-12; pectoral rays 21-23; lateral-line scales 49-54, the anterior 5-12 with a small spine; longitudinal scale series about the same number as lateral-line scales; gill rakers 1 + 6-7; ridges of head with fine serrations; a single preocular spine; preopercular spines usually four (the uppermost largest), plus a fifth antrorse spine anteriorly; teeth on vomer and palatines somewhat enlarged, those on palatines in two rows; brown dorsally, shading to paler ventrally, with four or five dark bars on upper half of body; caudal fin with dark bars; large dark blotches on paired fins. Attains about 17 cm. Mozambique to Red Sea and Gulf of Oman, east to the western Pacific; recorded from the depth range of 15-95 m.

260. *Rogadius pristiger*, 16 cm (J. Randall)

OBSCURE FLATHEAD
Sorsogona melanoptera Knapp and Wongratana, 1987

Dorsal rays IX+12-13; anal rays 12; pectoral rays 20-22; lateral-line scales 52-55, the anterior 13-34 with a weak spine; anterior two-thirds of each lateral-line scale covered by the adjacent upper and lower scales; scales above lateral line to origin of second dorsal fin 6-8 (usually 7); gill rakers 2-3 + 8-10; head length 2.6-2.8 in standard length; suborbital bone with two ridges bearing serrae and small spines, both ending at base of the large uppermost of three pre-opercular spines; preocular region with a modest spine, flanked anteroventrally by three to six progressively smaller spines; brown, shading to paler ventrally, sometimes with indistinct bars; dorsal fins with prominent blackish spots along spines and rays; pelvic fins dusky. Largest specimen, 14.5 cm. Gulf of Oman to Andaman Sea off southern Thailand. Specimens were caught by trawling on sand or mud bottoms from 15-117 m.

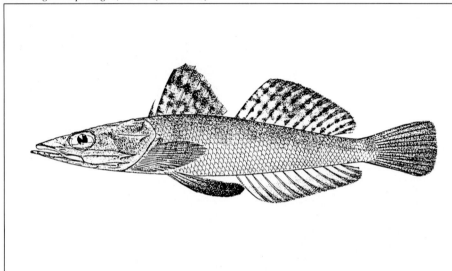

261. *Sorsogona melanoptera*, 10.8 cm (after Knapp and Wongratana, 1987)

BLACKFIN FLATHEAD
Sorsogona nigripinna (Regan, 1905)

Dorsal rays IX+12; anal rays 12; pectoral rays 19-22; lateral-line scales about 52-55, the first 14-30 with a backward-directed spine; more than two-thirds of each lateral-line scale covered by adjacent scales of upper and lower series; scales above lateral line to origin of second dorsal fin 8-9; gill rakers 3-5 + 11-13; head length about 3.0 in standard length; interorbital width about 4.5 in head length; bones dorsally on head rugose, but cranial ridges relatively smooth;

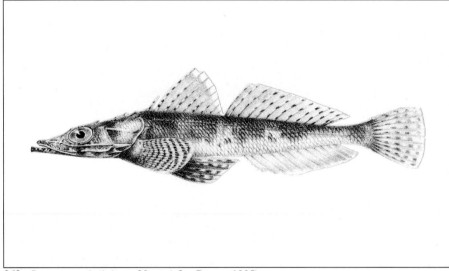

262. *Sorsogona nigripinna*, 20 cm (after Regan, 1905)

a moderate preocular spine with about six lesser adjacent spines; three preopercular spines, the uppermost longest, reaching edge of operculum; six dark bars on upper part of body; fins blackish except base and margin of anal fin which are pale. Reaches at least 20 cm. Described from a single specimen taken in about 30 m off Muscat; known otherwise only from off Somalia (Leslie W. Knapp, pers. comm.); taken by trawling at depths of 27-80 m.

HALFSPINED FLATHEAD
Sorsogona prionota (Sauvage, 1873)

Dorsal rays IX+12; anal rays 12-13; pectoral rays 19-22; lateral-line scales 50-54, the first 15-20 with a small spine; scales above lateral line to origin of second dorsal fin 4-6 (usually 5); gill rakers 2-4 + 7-10; head length 2.6-2.9 in standard length; two small preocular spines; ridges on head serrate; three preopercular spines; light brown, shading to whitish ventrally, with about five, poorly defined, dark bars on back; a dark purplish area with irregular white lines on naked humeral area covered by opercular flap; spinous dorsal fin with a large dusky area covering more than half of fin, the spines white with small blackish spots; soft dorsal, caudal, and pelvic fins with clear membranes, the rays white with small blackish spots, those on pelvics and outer half of caudal fin larger; anal fin pale with whitish rays; pectoral fins light brown with small brown spots on rays. Attains 22 cm. Occurs from Red Sea (type locality) south to Mozambique and east to the Arabian Gulf, Gulf of Oman and coast of Pakistan; reported from depths of 1-61 m. *Platycephalus townsendi* Regan is a synonym.

263. *Sorsogona prionota*, 20.7 cm (J. Randall)

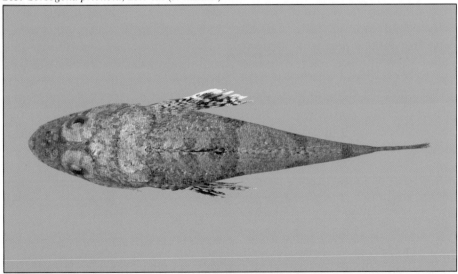

264. *Sorsogona tuberculata*, 10.2 cm (J. Randall)

265. *Thysanophrys celebica*, 9.1 cm (J. Randall)

TUBERCULATE FLATHEAD
Sorsogona tuberculata (Cuvier, 1829)

Dorsal rays IX+11; anal rays 11; pectoral rays 19-22 (usually 21); lateral-line scales 49-53 (usually 51 or 52), the anterior 19-33 with a small spine; scales above lateral line to origin of second dorsal fin 5-6; gill rakers 1 + 6-8; head length about 2.8 in standard length; two small preocular spines (sometimes a smaller third spine); top of head with bony tubercles and ridges bearing small spines or serrations; lower opercular spine serrate on base; usually four or more preopercular spines, the uppermost largest; brown, shading to pale ventrally, with four dark bars on back; humeral area under opercular flap dusky; dorsal and paired fins with small dark spots; caudal fin dusky. Reaches about 14 cm. Arabian Gulf to Indo-Malayan region and Australia; one record from the Maldives. Reported from depths of 9-61 m.

SULAWESI FLATHEAD
Thysanophrys celebica (Bleeker, 1854)

Dorsal rays VIII+12; anal rays 13; pectoral rays 18-20; lateral-line scales 50-54, the first two to six with a small spine; gill rakers 1 + 4-5; head length about 2.8 in standard length; bony interorbital width 3.9-4.5 in orbit diameter; a small tentacle on eye; no papillae on lips; suborbital ridge with eight or nine backward-directed spines, ending in the upper largest of three preopercular spines; one preocular spine; supraorbital ridge with nine small spines; body light grey-brown, flecked with dark brown, shading ventrally to whitish, with an irregular dark brown bar dorsally on body below rear base of each dorsal fin and a small saddle-like dark brown spot on caudal peduncle; all fins except anal with small black spots of variable size mainly on rays, those in caudal fin tending to form three or four dark bars. Reaches about 17 cm. Known from Natal to Zanzibar, the Arabian Gulf, the Indo-Malayan region, and Queensland; generally found on sand or silty sand in the vicinity of reefs.

LONGSNOUT FLATHEAD
Thysanophrys chiltonae Schultz, 1966

Dorsal rays VIII-IX+11-12; anal rays 11-12 (usually 12); pectoral rays 19-22 (usually 21); lateral-line scales 50-57 (about same number for longitudinal scale series); gill rakers 1 + 5-6; head length 2.5-2.85 in standard length; snout long, 2.9-3.0 in head length; bony interorbital width 5.5-6.0 in orbit diameter; ridges dorsally on head with well-developed spines; suborbital ridge with four or more spines, ending in upper largest of two or three preopercular spines; one preocular spine; iris lappet with slender lobes; interopercular membrane with a notch in margin behind preopercular spines; light grey-brown with four or five indistinct dark bars dorsally on body and scattered small dark blotches; usually a dark bar across interorbital and extending ventrally from eye; dorsal and caudal fins with dark spots on rays, those on caudal larger and forming about three dark bars in fin; a blackish blotch in outer part of spinous dorsal fin; posterior part of dorsal and anal fins white; paired fins with prominent black spots of variable size. Attains about 20 cm. Indo-Pacific; found in sand near coral reefs; collected in the depth range of 1-54 m, the latter depth by the author in Kiritimati, Line Islands.

HELMET GURNARDS
FAMILY DACTYLOPTERIDAE

These fishes are usually called flying gurnards, an inappropriate name, as they are bottom-dwelling (except when larval) and sluggish. They have extremely long pectoral fins which can be extended broadly and wing-like to the side of the body, but this is done when the fish is alarmed, suddenly making it appear much larger. The bones of the head are united to form a heavy external armour; there is a very long, stout spine extending posteriorly from corner of preopercle, and the shoulder girdle on each side is expanded shield-like posteriorly, ending in a sharp spine. The dorsal profile of the snout is very steep; mouth inferior, with small granular teeth in jaws, none on palate; body covered with scute-like

266. *Thysanophrys chiltonae*, about 13.5 cm (J. Randall)

scales; lateral line absent or obscured by scales; dorsal fin with one or two anterior isolated spines, the first just behind head, the second (when present, as in *Dactyloptena*) between the first spine and the origin of the rest of the dorsal fin which is divided into separate spinous and soft portions, with a short spinous point between; base of pectoral fins horizontal, with 30 or more rays, including an anterior part of 5 rays partly free of membranes that is used in searching for food; pelvic fins with I,4 rays, used for "walking" along the bottom. The late postlarval stage has a more massive helmet-like cover on the head and dorsal body and even larger preopercular and scapular spines; it is attracted to a light at night. These fishes live on rubble, sand, or mud substrata; they are reported to feed mainly on benthic crustaceans and molluscs, occasionally on small fishes. The family consists of two genera, the monotypic *Dactylopterus* of the Atlantic and the Indo-Pacific *Dactyloptena* with six species.

267. *Dactyloptena orientalis* with pectoral fins spread, about 23 cm (J. Randall)

HELMET GURNARD
Dactyloptena orientalis (Cuvier, 1829)

Dorsal rays I + I + V + 9; anal rays 6-7; pectoral rays 32-35; longitudinal scale series 45-47; side of abdomen with three or four enlarged keeled scales, the first above anus; body moderately elongate, the depth 5.1-6.6 in standard length; isolated first dorsal spine about equal to or longer than head length taken to end of preopercular spine; second isolated dorsal spine about equal to or a little longer than eye diameter; pectoral fins reaching to or beyond base of caudal fin; caudal fin slightly emarginate; brown dorsally, sometimes blotched with dark brown, shading to nearly white on abdomen; pectoral fins with dark orangish spots, the outer part with irregular bright blue markings. Reported to reach 38 cm, but any over 28 cm would be regarded as unusually large. Red Sea and East Africa to the Hawaiian Islands and French Polynesia. Lives on open sand or rubble substrata, usually at depths greater than 20 m.

268. *Dactyloptena orientalis*, 18 cm (J. Randall)

GLASSFISHES
FAMILY AMBASSIDAE

This is the first of the many families of the order Perciformes to be treated in this book. The common name is derived from the semitransparent body of many of these fishes. The family name Chandidae has been used by many authors, but Eschmeyer and Bailey in Eschmeyer (1990) are followed here in the use of Ambassidae. These are small fishes (most 10 cm or less in total length) with moderately compressed bodies, a somewhat pointed head with projecting lower jaw, small teeth in jaws and on vomer and palatines; no opercular spines, but various other bones of the head often serrate. There is a single dorsal fin, usually deeply notched before the last dorsal spine, the spinous part with VII or VIII spines, the soft with 8-11 rays; anal fin III,8-11; caudal fin forked with 15 branched rays; scales thin, cycloid, and easily detached; branchiostegal rays 6; gill rakers well-developed. The family is found only in the Indian Ocean and western Pacific. There are eight genera, of which the largest is *Ambassis* with over half of the 41 known species. These fishes generally occur in fresh or brackish water, though they may be found in shallow marine habitats; 21 species are confined to fresh water.

269. *Ambassis gymnocephalus*, 10.8 cm (J. Randall)

BALD GLASSFISH
Ambassis gymnocephalus (Lacepède, 1801)

Dorsal rays VIII,8-10; anal rays III,8-10; pectoral rays 14-15; lateral line interrupted, the pored scales 12-13 + 12-13; predorsal scales 14-16; gill rakers 8-10 + 22-25; supraorbital spines 1-5 (Oman specimens with 2 or 3); serrae present on lower margin of preopercle, lower margin of preopercular ridge, edge of preorbital, and preorbital ridge; body depth 2.6-3.0 in standard length; translucent with a thin, partly broken, midlateral black line commencing below third dorsal spine, a blackish line at base of dorsal and anal fins, and membrane between second and third dorsal spines blackish. Maximum length about 10 cm. The most widespread species of the family, occurring from the Red Sea to South Africa, east to the Indo-Malayan region and Australia. Allen and Burgess (1990) reported the typical habitat as brackish inlets and estuaries. Oman specimens from Qurm Creek, Muscat were examined from the collection of the Museum of Comparative Zoology, Harvard University.

GROUPERS AND SEA BASSES
FAMILY SERRANIDAE

The Serranidae is a large family in the largest order of fishes, the Perciformes. It is among the least specialised, hence it is difficult to present a diagnosis that will apply to all species. In general, these fishes share the following characters: pelvic fins I,5 (rays reduced in a few species), the fins below or nearly below the base of the pectoral fins; caudal fin with 17 or fewer principal rays (those that extend to the posterior margin of the fin); mouth large, the maxilla not forming part of the gape, its posterior end fully exposed on the cheek; lower jaw usually projecting anterior to the upper; jaws with bands of slender sharp teeth, the medial rows inwardly depressible; usually a pair of stout canines at front of jaws; preopercular margin nearly always serrate, and opercle with three flat spines; scales small and ctenoid (or secondarily cycloid). The Oman species of the family fall into three subfamilies, the Anthiinae (dominated by the colourful species of anthias), the Epinephelinae (groupers; general Arabic name, hamour), and the Grammistinae (soapfishes). The presentation below will be alphabetical by subfamily in order to keep similar species together. The fishes of these three subfamilies are protogynous hermaphrodites – they begin mature life as female and change sex later to males. The fishes of the genus *Pseudanthias* are haremic; that is, a single male, which has a different colour than the females and is generally larger, maintains a harem of females. If he dies, the ranking female soon changes sex and takes over the harem. Some of the groupers are known to form large aggregations at spawning time. Unfortunately, fishermen often learn of the sites of these aggregations and catch many of these fishes at this time. When spawning sites are discovered, an effort should be made to set these aside as reserves. The larger groupers may take many years to reach full adult size; their populations are thus very vulnerable to depletion from overfishing. All of the serranids are predaceous; the anthiines feed mainly on zooplankton, whereas the groupers and soapfishes take larger prey, generally fishes and crustaceans. The soapfishes are named for their copious quantity of mucus. When under stress, these fishes exude a powerful skin toxin, grammistin, which is a very effective deterrent to predation (Randall et al., 1971). Randall and Heemstra (1990) reviewed the 110 species of Epinephelinae of the Indo-Pacific region.

270A. *Epinephelus lanceolatus*, about 2 m (J. Randall)

270B. *Pseudanthias marcia* and *P. townsendi* (J. Hoover)

SUBFAMILY ANTHIINAE

BANNER ANTHIAS
Plectranthias vexillarius Randall, 1980.

Dorsal rays X,17; anal rays III,7; pectoral rays 13, all unbranched; branched caudal rays 15; lateral line complete, the pored scales 29; diagonal rows of scales on cheek 7; dorsal part of head scaled anteriorly almost to nostrils; gill rakers 6 + 13; no spines on ventral margin of preopercle; body depth 2.7 in standard length; third dorsal spine longest, 2.05 in head, with a long cirrus extending from its tip (and lesser cirri from other spine tips); caudal fin emarginate, the upper and lower lobes prolonged; pale in preservative with large, irregular, brown blotches on body (probably red in life). Known from only one 11.8-cm specimen taken by trawl in 49-63 m in the Gulf of Oman.

MARCIA'S ANTHIAS
Pseudanthias marcia Randall and Hoover, 1993

Dorsal rays X,16; anal rays III,7; pectoral rays 19-21; lateral-line scales 47-50; no auxiliary scales on body; gill rakers 11-12 + 27-30; no papillae on posterior edge of orbit; vomerine teeth in a triangular patch (characteristic of the genus); body depth 2.5-2.9 in standard length; dorsal spines progressively longer, the last 2.5-2.9 in head length; caudal fin of females deeply emarginate; lower half of caudal fin of males slightly rounded to truncate, the upper half with a prolonged filamentous lobe (total caudal fin length as much as 59% of standard length); females orange-red, the scale centres on lower side yellow, becoming whitish or pale yellow on lower head and abdomen; caudal lobe tips bright red; males similar in body colour but with a red bar on upper side below eighth and ninth dorsal spines and a pale zone dorsally on caudal peduncle; caudal fin yellow, shading to red posteriorly, the filament red or yellow. Males reach 16 cm (including caudal filament). Known only from the Gulf of Oman to southern Oman on rugged rocky bottom in the depth range of 14-30 m. Like other species of *Pseudanthias*, usually encountered in aggregations.

271. *Plectranthias vexillarius*, 8.2 cm (J. Randall)

272. *Pseudanthias marcia*, female, 7.6 cm (J. Randall)

273. *Pseudanthias marcia*, males (J. Hoover)

123

TOWNSEND'S ANTHIAS
Pseudanthias townsendi (Boulenger, 1897)

Dorsal rays X,16-17 (rarely 17); anal rays III,7-8 (rarely 8); pectoral rays 16-18; lateral-line scales 38-42; no auxiliary scales on body; gill rakers 10-12 + 25-28; no papillae on posterior edge of orbit; body depth 2.9-3.2 in standard length; head length 2.8-3.1 in standard length; third dorsal spine longest, 2.0-2.3 in head of females, longer in males, 1.65-1.95 in head; caudal fin emarginate, the caudal concavity 2.6-3.8 in head; females with scales of body partly pink and partly yellow, the yellow dominating dorsally and the pink ventrally; head orange-red to a narrow lavender band from below eye to pectoral base, pale yellow below; tips of caudal lobes yellow; males with two broad deep red stripes, one from eye to lower part of caudal fin and the other from nape to upper part of fin, the two linked with a curved band in middle of fin; rest of body pink (stripes and intervening zones may vary greatly in colour, sometimes with yellow predominating); a semicircular deep red band in outer part of caudal fin preceded and followed by curved blue bands; caudal lobe tips broadly yellow. Males reach 9 cm. Arabian Gulf to southern Oman and southern Iran; more common in the Gulf of Oman than the Arabian Sea; generally found on rocky bottom at depths greater than 15 m; deepest recorded, 63 m.

BOULENGER'S ANTHIAS
Sacura boulengeri (Heemstra, 1973)

Dorsal rays X,14; anal rays III,7; pectoral rays 16-17; lateral-line scales 28-31; maxilla scaled; no scales on lower jaw; basal third of soft dorsal and anal fins scaled; gill rakers 14-16 + 30-33; head large, subequal to body depth, 2.3-2.4 in standard length; vomerine teeth in a triangular patch; third dorsal spine greatly prolonged, especially in males, 2-5 times longer than fourth spine; third to fifth dorsal soft rays and second soft anal ray filamentous; caudal fin lunate; yellowish brown with irregular lavender-pink stripes or series of irregular blotches; bands and blotches on head violet; dorsal fin lavender basally, dusky yellow distally except ray tips and filaments which are lavender; cirrus at tip of filamentous third spine black. Reaches 19 cm. Known from only five male specimens taken off Muscat; one depth record, 49 m. Boulenger (1889) described *Anthias formosus* from the Muscat specimens. On noting that the name was preoccupied by *Anthias formosus* Bloch, Heemstra (1973) provided the new name, *Anthias boulengeri*, for this fish which was later reclassified in *Sacura* (Heemstra and Randall, 1979).

274. *Pseudanthias townsendi*, female (J. Randall)

275. *Pseudanthias townsendi*, male (J. Hoover)

276. *Sacura boulengeri* (after Boulenger, 1895)

THREADTAIL ANTHIAS
Tosana niwae (Smith and Pope, 1906)

Dorsal rays X,13-14 (usally 14); anal rays III,7; pectoral rays 15-16 (usually 16); lateral-line scales 34-37; two rows of scales between lateral line and middle of dorsal fin; gill rakers 10-12 + 23-25; body depth 3.0-3.6 in standard length; head length 3.25-3.55 in standard length; vomerine teeth in a triangular patch; third dorsal spine longest, 1.8-2.7 in head length; caudal fin extremely lunate with filamentous lobes (the upper longer), the caudal concavity as much as 1.6 in standard length; pelvic fins in females 2.5-5.5 in standard length, much longer in males, 1.7-2.2 in standard length; pink with a midlateral yellow stripe from side of snout through eye onto anterior body, and a second fainter stripe from upper lip under eye and across operculum. Attains 20 cm. Katayama in Masuda et al., 1984 gave the distribution as Japan to South China Sea "in fairly deep water". Al-Baharna (1986) recorded the species in her *Fishes of Bahrain*, without any locality or depth information.

SUBFAMILY EPINEPHELINAE

REDMOUTH GROUPER
Aethaloperca rogaa (Forsskål, 1775)

Dorsal rays IX,16-18 (rarely 16); anal rays III,8-9 (rarely 8); pectoral rays 17-18

277. *Tosana niwae* (after Katayama, 1960)

(usually 18); lateral-line scales 48-54; longitudinal scale series 94-104; scales ctenoid; body deep, the depth 2.1-2.4 in standard length; a distinct notch in lower margin of subopercle; fifth or sixth pectoral ray longest (middle rays longest in other species of Epinephelinae); caudal fin truncate; dark brown, often with a whitish bar centred on

278. *A. rogaa*, juvenile, 11 cm (J. Randall)

abdomen; inside of mouth largely orange-red. Reported to 60 cm. Western Pacific to Arabian Gulf, Red Sea, and coast of East Africa; not observed in southern Oman, but occasional in the Gulf of Oman and Arabian Gulf; a coral-reef species usually found within or in the vicinity of caves. The only species of the genus. Feeds mainly on small fishes.

SLENDER GROUPER
Anyperodon leucogrammicus
(Valenciennes, 1828)

Dorsal rays XI,14-16; anal rays III,8-9 (usually 9); pectoral rays 15-17 (rarely 17); lateral-line scales 63-72; longitudinal scale series 110-125; scales largely ctenoid; body elongate, the depth 3.15-3.7 in standard length, and compressed, the width 2.3-2.8 in depth; lower jaw strongly projecting; no palatine teeth (present in other groupers); caudal fin rounded; adults greenish to brownish grey with numerous small orange-red spots; four longitudinal whitish stripes usually present on head and body, frequently broken into series of bands or elongate spots (stripes tend to be lost in large adults); juveniles with alternating stripes of orange-yellow and blue, a blue-edged black spot at base of caudal fin, and one in dorsal fin. Largest adult specimen reported, 65 cm. Red Sea and East Africa to the Marshall Islands and Samoa; rare in Oman waters. Only this species in the genus. The young mimic the wrasse *Halichoeres purpurescens*, probably to get closer to their prey in the guise of the wrasse (Randall and Kuiter, 1989). Adults appear to feed mainly on fishes.

281. *A. leucogrammicus*, juvenile (J. Randall)

279. *Aethaloperca rogaa*, adult (J. Randall)

280. *Anyperodon leucogrammicus*, about 34 cm (J. Randall)

PEACOCK GROUPER

Cephalopholis argus Bloch and Schneider, 1801

Dorsal rays IX,15-17 (usually 16, rarely 15); anal rays III,9; pectoral rays 16-18; lateral-line scales 46-51; longitudinal scale series 95-110; scales ctenoid except ventrally on abdomen; auxiliary scales present on body (not found on remaining species of *Cephalopholis*); snout scaled; lower-limb gill rakers 17-19 (13-18 on remaining species of the genus); caudal fin rounded; dark brown with numerous, small, black-edged blue spots on head, body, and fins; a large pale area on chest and five or six pale bars often present on posterior half of body; tips of spinous membranes of dorsal fin orange.

Largest examined, 55 cm; reported to 60 cm. Indo-Pacific, but not known from the Arabian Gulf or Gulf of Oman; occasional in southern Oman; introduced to the Hawaiian Islands from French Polynesia. About 80% of the diet is fish; most of the rest crustacean.

282. *Cephalopholis argus*, about 40 cm (J. Randall)

283. *Cephalopholis hemistiktos*, about 26 cm (J. Randall)

284. *Cephalopholis miniata*, about 40 cm (J. Randall)

HALFSPOTTED HIND

Cephalopholis hemistiktos (Rüppell, 1830)

Dorsal rays IX,14-15 (rarely 15); anal rays III,8-9 (rarely 8); pectoral rays 16-19; lateral-line scales 47-52; longitudinal scale series 94-121; scales ctenoid, including abdomen; no scales on snout; pectoral fins pointed; caudal rounded; dark brown to red with small dark-edged blue spots on head (more numerous on lower half) and body (mainly on lower half, those on chest largest); small blue spots also on soft portion of dorsal and anal fins and on caudal fin; outer fourth of pectoral fins yellow; one colour phase with a large pale yellowish area dorsally on body posterior to pectoral fins. Reaches at least 35 cm. Northern Red Sea to Arabian Gulf and coast of Pakistan; none observed in southern Oman but should be expected there. The population in the Gulf of Oman and Arabian Gulf differs from Red Sea fish in having modally 18 pectoral rays (17 in Red Sea), 108-121 scales in longitudinal series (94-104 in Red Sea), and larger size. Known from the depth range of 4-55 m; in the deeper water the ground colour is red. Shpigel and Fishelson (1989) reported fishes in 64% of the stomachs and crustaceans the rest.

CORAL HIND

Cephalopholis miniata (Forsskål, 1775)

Dorsal rays IX,14-16; anal rays III,8-9 (rarely 8); pectoral rays 17-18 (usually 18); lateral-line scales 47-55; longitudinal scale series 94-114; scales ctenoid, becoming cycloid on abdomen; snout scaled to nostrils; head length 2.45-2.65 in standard length; caudal fin rounded; orange-red to reddish brown, with numerous blue spots (smaller than pupil and usually faintly dark-edged) on head, body, and median fins; pectoral fins orange-yellow (or brown with outer part orange-yellow); juveniles often yellow with scattered faint pale blue spots. Reported to 41 cm. Red Sea and coast of East Africa to the Line Islands in the central Pacific; not known from the Arabian Gulf or Gulf of Oman, but occasional in southern Oman. A clear-water, coral-reef species occurring from the shallows to at least 80 m. Shpigel and Fishelson (1989) reported 86% of the prey as fishes.

SIXSPOT GROUPER
Cephalopholis sexmaculata (Rüppell, 1830)

Dorsal rays IX,14-16; anal rays III,9; pectoral rays 16-18; lateral-line scales 49-54; longitudinal scale series 95-108; scales ctenoid; snout scaled; head length 2.35-2.5 in standard length; caudal fin rounded; orange-red with numerous small blue spots on head, body, and median fins, and six large quadrangular blackish blotches on back, the first four extending basally onto dorsal fin and continuing faintly onto lower body where they birfurcate. Largest specimen, 50 cm. Indo-Pacific; rare in Oman. Usually found in caves.

285. *Cephalopholis sexmaculata*, about 40 cm (J. Randall)

TOMATO GROUPER
Cephalopholis sonnerati (Valenciennes, 1828)

Dorsal rays IX,14-16; anal rays III,9; pectoral rays 18-20; lateral-line scales 66-80; longitudinal scale series 115-134; scales ctenoid, cycloid on abdomen; snout scaled; nape of adults prominently convex; lower margin of preopercle serrate or irregular with spinules (smooth on above species of *Cephalopholis*); median fins fleshy basally; caudal fin rounded; orange-red to reddish brown, often with scattered small whitish blotches; head purplish to reddish brown with numerous close-set orange-red spots (pale in preservative); fins usually darker than body; juveniles dark reddish brown to nearly black with a broad whitish posterior border on caudal fin and sometimes on pectorals. Reported to 57 cm. East Africa to the Line Islands in the central Pacific (densely spotted with brownish red in Pacific localities); not known from the Red Sea or Arabian Gulf. Usually found at depths greater than 30 m. Harmelin-Vivien and Bouchon (1976) reported that crustaceans are the principal prey, especially galatheids and brachyuran crabs.

286. *C. sonnerati*, juv., about 15 cm (J. Randall)

SMOOTH GROUPER
Dermatolepis striolata (Playfair and Günther, 1867)

Dorsal rays XI,17-19; anal rays III,9-10 (usually 9); pectoral rays 17-19; lateral-line scales 70-76; longitudinal scale series 115-126; scales on body cycloid; auxiliary scales present on body; body deep, the depth 2.4-2.8 in standard length, and compressed, the width 2.3-2.85 in depth; a broad concavity in dorsal profile above eye; only two opercular spines apparent (the lower third spine covered by skin; may be absent in large individuals); fins fleshy; caudal fin slightly rounded to truncate; yellowish to reddish brown with numerous small dark brown spots (may be horizontally elongate) on head and body (fewer on fins); large irregular pale blotches often present on head and body. Maximum length reported, 85 cm. Known only from the Gulf of Oman (where rare) and southern Oman (where common) to South Africa; also listed from the Comoro Islands and Aldabra. Occurs on coral reefs or rocky bottom, often lurking in or near caves.

287. *Cephalopholis sonnerati* (J. Hoover)

288. *Dermatolepis striolata*, about 45 cm (J. Randall)

289. *E. areolatus*, juvenile, 8 cm (J. Randall)

AREOLATE GROUPER
Epinephelus areolatus (Forsskål, 1775)

Dorsal rays XI,15-17; anal rays III,7-8 (rarely 7); pectoral rays 17-19 (rarely 19); lateral-line scales 49-53; longitudinal scale series 97-116; scales on body largely ctenoid; auxiliary scales present on body; gill rakers 8-10 + 14-16; margin of soft portion of anal fin rounded to slightly angular; caudal fin slightly emarginate to truncate; pectoral fins 1.5-1.85 in head; whitish with numerous, close-set, round to polygonal, brown to yellowish brown spots on head, body, and fins, the largest spots on adults about size of pupil; caudal fin with a distinct posterior white margin. Maximum length about 40 cm. Red Sea to South Africa, east to the western Pacific; present in Gulf of Oman and Arabian Gulf. Generally found in somewhat turbid water on silty sand or seagrass bottom around isolated small rock outcrops or coral heads; depth range, 6-200 m.

BLEEKER'S GROUPER
Epinephelus bleekeri (Vaillant, 1877)

Dorsal rays XI,16-18; anal rays III,8-9 (rarely 9); pectoral rays 17-19 (rarely 17); lateral-line scales 49-53; longitudinal scale series 99-116; scales largely ctenoid; body moderately elongate, the depth 3.0-3.5 in standard length; rounded corner of preopercle with two to nine enlarged serrae; caudal fin truncate to very slightly rounded; brownish to purplish grey with numerous orange-yellow spots (about half pupil diameter in

290. *Epinephelus areolatus*, 33 cm (J. Randall)

291. *Epinephelus bleekeri*, 37 cm (J. Randall)

adults) on head, body, dorsal fin, and upper third of caudal fin; lower two-thirds of caudal fin dark purplish grey. Reported to 76 cm. Arabian Gulf to Indo-Malayan region and northern Australia, north to China and Taiwan. Generally taken by trawling in 30-45 m or by handlining from rocky banks; not known from coral reefs.

WHITESPOTTED GROUPER
Epinephelus caeruleopunctatus (Bloch, 1790)

Dorsal rays XI,15-17; anal rays III,8; pectoral rays 17-19; lateral-line scales 51-61; longitudinal scale series 86-109; scales of adults cycloid except for a broad ctenoid

zone along side of body; numerous auxiliary scales on body; gill rakers 7-10 + 14-17; body moderately elongate, the depth 3.0-3.4 in standard length; head pointed, the lower jaw strongly projecting, the dorsal profile nearly straight; snout length 4.1-5.3 in head; teeth on side of jaws small, those on midside of lower jaw of adults in three to five rows; posterior nostril of adults vertically elongate and enlarged; caudal fin rounded; brownish grey, the body, posterior head, and dorsal fin with scattered large whitish blotches (some larger than eye) and numerous small pale spots; remaining fins dark brownish grey, the soft dorsal, caudal and pectorals with a narrow white margin; a series of indistinct dark spots along back at base of dorsal fin and one dorsally on caudal peduncle; juveniles darker with small white spots. Reported to 76 cm. Arabian Gulf and east coast of Africa to Fiji and the Gilbert Islands (Kiribati). Generally found on coral reefs or rocky bottom, often in or near caves; juveniles may occur in tidepools.

293. *E. caeruleopunctatus*, 21 cm (J. Randall)

292. *Epinephelus caeruleopunctatus*, about 50 cm (J. Randall)

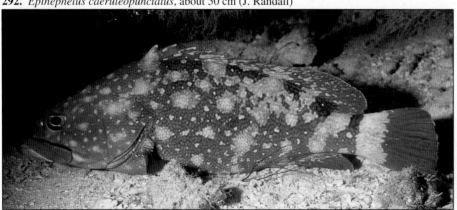

ORANGESPOTTED GROUPER
Epinephelus coioides (Hamilton, 1822)

Dorsal rays XI,13-16 (rarely 13, usually 16); anal rays III,8; pectoral rays 18-20 (rarely 18); lateral-line scales 55-65; tubes of anterior lateral-line scales of adults branched; longitudinal scale series 58-65; scales on body largely ctenoid; auxiliary scales present on body; gill rakers 8-10 + 14-17; small bony platelets on side of first gill arch at base of rakers; body moderately elongate, the depth 2.9-3.7 in standard length, but little compressed; teeth on midside of lower jaw in two rows (three on large adults); caudal fin rounded; light greyish brown, shading to whitish ventrally, with numerous brownish orange or brownish yellow spots the size of pupil or smaller on head, body, and fins (only basally on pectorals) and five slightly diagonal greyish brown bars on body which bifurcate ventrally, the first four extending basally into dorsal fin (dorsal part of bars more darkly pigmented). Largest examined by author, 94.5 cm; probably exceeds 100 cm, but reports to 200 cm are undoubtedly misidentifications of *E. lanceolatus*. Red Sea to Natal and east to the western Pacific; has invaded the eastern Mediterranean via the Suez Canal. The dominant grouper and most important commercial fish in the Arabian Gulf (where it has usually been misidentified as *E. tauvina* (Forsskål), a valid species not known from the Gulf). Found along continental and large island shores, not oceanic islands; often occurs in brackish areas. Deepest record, 100 m. Doi et al. (1991) documented the successful artificial propagation of this species (as *E. suillus*) in Malaysia.

294. *E. coioides*, juv., about 7.5 cm (J. Randall)

295. *Epinephelus coioides*, about 85 cm (J. Randall)

296. *Epinephelus diacanthus*, 48 cm (J. Randall)

SPINYCHEEK GROUPER
Epinephelus diacanthus (Valenciennes, 1828)

Dorsal rays XI,15-17; anal rays III,8-9 (rarely 9); pectoral rays 18-20; lateral-line scales 52-59; longitudinal scale series 102-121; scales ctenoid in a broad zone along size of body and posteriorly, cycloid elsewhere; auxiliary scales present on body of adults; gill rakers 8-10 + 15-18; head large, 2.15-2.4 in standard length; corner of preopercle with one to five prominent large serrae; light greyish brown with five dark brown bars on body broader than pale interspaces; a dark brown streak along upper edge of maxillary groove and continuing diffusely across lower cheek; no small dark spots on fins. Attains 52 cm. Gulf of Aden and Gulf of Oman to Madras, India. Usually caught over mud or muddy sand substrata; known from the depth range of 10-120 m; probably occurs even deeper.

SPOTTEDBACK GROUPER
Epinephelus epistictus (Temminck and Schlegel, 1842)

Dorsal rays XI,14-15 (usually 14); anal rays III,7-8 (rarely 7); pectoral rays 16-19 (usually 17 or 18); lateral-line scales 55-70; longitudinal scale series 105-127; scales on body ctenoid; gill rakers 8-10 + 15-18; head large, 2.25-2.45 in standard length; posterior nostril of adults larger than anterior; corner of preopercle with three to five enlarged serrae; caudal fin slightly to moderately rounded; light brown to yellowish brown, shading to pale lavender-brown ventrally, with very small dark brown spots along side or upper part of body; two narrow oblique dark brown bands on cheek, one from eye and the other a continuation of dark streak at upper edge of maxillary groove; corners of caudal fin and sometimes soft portions of dorsal and anal fins with a white margin. Reported to 80 cm. Red Sea and coast of Africa to Indo-Malayan region, north to Japan; not known from oceanic islands. Depth records vary from 71-291 m. *Serranus praeopercularis* Boulenger from Muscat is a synonym.

297. *Epinephelus epistictus*, 27 cm (J. Randall)

BLACKTIP GROUPER
Epinephelus fasciatus (Forsskål, 1775)

Dorsal rays XI,15-17 (rarely 15); anal rays III,7-8 (rarely 7); pectoral rays 18-20 (rarely 20); lateral-line scales 49-56; longitudinal scale series 92-124; scales on body largely ctenoid; gill rakers 6-8 + 14-18; midside of lower jaw with three to four rows of teeth (two in juveniles); caudal fin slightly to moderately rounded; light greenish grey to pale yellowish red, with or without five dark bars of about equal width or broader than pale interspaces; outer triangular part of spinous dorsal membranes black or deep red. Reaches 36 cm. Indo-Pacific; the most wide-ranging of the groupers, but not yet recorded from the Arabian Gulf or Gulf of Oman. Population differentiation in the Pacific (see Randall and Heemstra, 1991). Feeds on crustaceans, especially crabs, fishes, and octopus. *Epinephelus marginalis* Bloch is a synonym.

298. *Epinephelus fasciatus*, about 30 cm (J. Hoover)

BLUE-AND-YELLOW GROUPER
Epinephelus flavocaeruleus (Lacepède, 1801)

Dorsal rays XI,16-17 (usually 17); anal rays III,8; pectoral rays 18-19 (usually 19); lateral-line scales 61-74; longitudinal scale series 129-148; scales on body largely ctenoid; auxiliary scales present on body of adults (but not numerous); gill rakers 9-10

299. *Epinephelus flavocaeruleus*, about 35 cm (J. Hoover)

+ 15-17; body moderately deep, the depth 2.45-2.8 in standard length, and compressed, the width 2.0-2.8 in depth; posterior nostril of adults larger than anterior; membranes of spinous portion of dorsal fin not incised; caudal fin truncate to slightly emarginate; small adults blue, sometimes flecked with light blue, becoming yellow on caudal peduncle and fin (except posterior margin or the corners black); remaining fins yellow or yellow with blue at base; some individuals with yellow anteriorly on head; large adults lose the yellow colouration and become nearly black. Reported to 90 cm. Southern Oman to South Africa, islands of the Indian Ocean, and Indonesia (one record for western Sumatra and one for western Java). Adults tend to occur on deep reefs (to 150 m).

GABRIELLA'S GROUPER
Epinephelus gabriellae Randall and Heemstra, 1991

Dorsal rays XI,14-15; anal rays III,8; pectoral rays 17-18; lateral-line scales 52-54; longitudinal scale series 106-126; most scales on body strongly ctenoid; numerous auxiliary scales on body; gill rakers 10-12 + 17-19; body moderately elongate, the depth 3.2-3.6 in standard length; margin of soft portion of anal fin distinctly angular; caudal fin emarginate, the caudal concavity of adults 4.5-14.0 in head; pale brownish grey to whitish with numerous, small, close-set, dark orange to orangish brown spots on head, body, and fins (only basally on pectorals); caudal fin and soft portions of dorsal and anal fins with a narrow white margin; a disruptive pattern of five dark bars dorsally on body may be exhibited at will. Largest specimen, 52 cm. Known only from the south coast of Oman, where it is common, and Somalia; occurs on reefs and rocky bottom from near shore to at least 40 m.

301. *Epinephelus gabriellae*, about 35 cm (J. Hoover)

300. *E. gabriellae*, juvenile (J. Randall)

SOMALI GROUPER
Epinephelus indistinctus Randall and Heemstra, 1991

Dorsal rays XI,14; anal rays III,8; pectoral rays 18; lateral-line scales about 64; longitudinal scale series about 114; scales cycloid except beneath pectoral fins where ctenoid; numerous auxiliary scales dorsally on body; gill rakers 9 + 14; small bony platelets on side of gill arches; body depth about 3.1 in standard length; body width about 1.4 in body depth; head large, about 2.4 in standard length; snout moderately long, about 3.2 in head; teeth on side of lower jaw in two rows; membranes of spinous portion of dorsal fin deeply incised; caudal fin slightly rounded; brownish grey without distinct markings. Described from a single 81-cm specimen obtained by trawling in 70-80 m off Somalia. Occasionally landed at the Salalah market, always with stomach everted from the mouth from expansion of the swim bladder, thus indicating capture in relatively deep water.

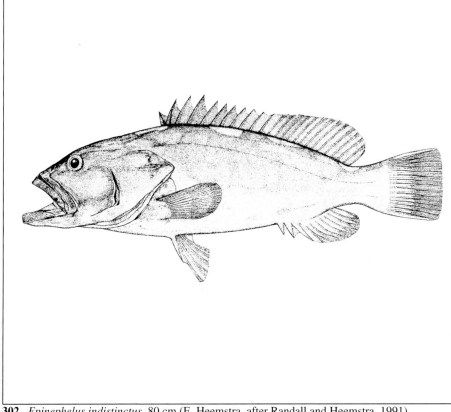

302. *Epinephelus indistinctus*, 80 cm (E. Heemstra, after Randall and Heemstra, 1991)

303. *Epinephelus lanceolatus*, about 1.8 m (J. Randall)

GIANT GROUPER
Epinephelus lanceolatus (Bloch, 1790)

Dorsal rays XI,14-16; anal rays III,8; pectoral rays 18-19 (usually 19); lateral-line scales 54-62, the anterior scales with branched tubes (except juveniles); longitudinal scale series 95-105; scales cycloid; auxiliary scales present on body; gill rakers 8-10 + 14-17, short in adults; small bony platelets on side of gill arches; body of adults thick, the width 1.5-1.75 in depth; eye proportionately smaller with growth, varying from 5.8 in head of a specimen 12.2 cm standard length to 13.7 in head of a 177-cm specimen; interorbital space relatively broader with growth, the width 6.2 in head of 12.2 cm specimen and 3.3 in head of 177-cm fish; teeth on midside of lower jaw varying from two rows in juveniles to 15-16 rows in large adults; third to fifth dorsal spines longest in juveniles, about 3 in head; last dorsal spine longest in adults, 5.7 in head of 177-cm specimen; caudal fin rounded; adults mottled dark grey-brown with numerous small black spots in fins; juveniles yellow with broad irregular black bars. Reaches a length of at least 250 cm and a weight of at least 300 kg; reports of larger fish need confirmation. Indo-Pacific, but rare at all localities. Not known from the Arabian Gulf or Gulf of Oman, but reported from the coast of Pakistan near the entrance to the Gulf of Oman and observed by John P. Hoover and other divers off Raysut, southern Oman. The young are often found in estuaries. Adults feed on a wide variety of prey, including spiny lobsters, crabs, bony fishes, small sharks, and skates.

304. *Epinephelus latifasciatus*, 34 cm (J. Randall)

BANDED GROUPER
Epinephelus latifasciatus (Temminck and Schlegel, 1842)

Dorsal rays XI,12-14 (usually 12, rarely 14); anal rays III,7-8 (rarely 7); pectoral rays 17-19 (rarely 17); lateral-line scales 56-65; longitudinal scale series 91-106; scales of adults cycloid; gill rakers 8-11 + 15-18; body moderately elongate, the depth 2.9-3.45 in standard length; two rows of teeth on midside of lower jaw; corner of preopercle with three to seven greatly enlarged serrae; caudal fin slightly to moderately rounded; juveniles and subadults lavender-grey, shading to whitish ventrally, with two broad, black-edged, white stripes, the first from below eye to lower half of caudal peduncle, the second from above eye to anterior

305. *E. latifasciatus*, subadult, 21 cm (J. Randall)

soft portion of dorsal fin; dorsal and caudal fins with black spots; with growth the white stripes disappear and the black edges break into dashes and spots; with further growth the black markings may vanish. Largest specimen, 157 cm, 58.55 kg. A continental shelf species reported from the Red Sea, Gulf of Oman, Pakistan, India, northwest Australia, Sabah, China, Korea, and Japan; known from depths of 20 to at least 230 m.

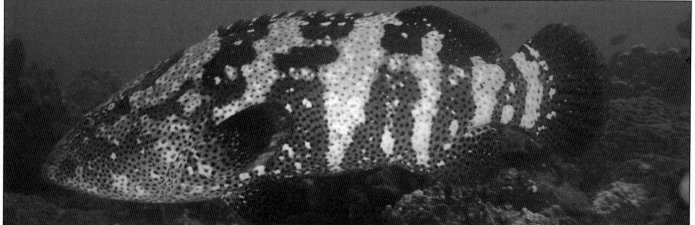

306. *Epinephelus malabaricus*, about 120 cm (J. Hoover)

MALABAR GROUPER
Epinephelus malabaricus (Bloch and Schneider, 1801)

Dorsal rays XI,14-16 (rarely 16); anal rays III,8; pectoral rays 18-20 (usually 19); lateral-line scales 54-64, the anterior scales of adults with two to four branched tubes; longitudinal scale series 101-117; scales on body ctenoid except anterodorsally, on chest, and abdomen; auxiliary scales on body; gill rakers 8-11 + 15-18; numerous small bony platelets on outer face of gill arch at base of gill rakers; body moderately elongate, the depth 3.0-3.6 in standard length; body width 1.4-1.9 in depth; two rows of teeth on midside of lower jaw in juveniles and subadults, increasing to 4 or 5 rows in large adults; caudal fin rounded; light greyish to yellowish brown with five slightly oblique, broad, dark brown bars on body which bifurcate ventrally, and numerous, small, well-separated black spots and scattered larger pale spots and blotches; fins with scattered small black spots. Largest reliably reported in the literature, 88.5 cm, but reaches at least 120 cm. Red Sea and Gulf of Oman, south to South Africa, Seychelles, and Comoros, to western Pacific from Ryukyu Islands to New South Wales, east to Tonga. A highly esteemed food fish regarded as most desirable for aquaculture (Kohno et al., 1988).

YELLOWBELLY GROUPER
Epinephelus marginatus (Lowe, 1834)

Dorsal rays XI,15-16 (usually 16); anal rays III,8-9 (rarely 9); pectoral rays 17-19; lateral-line scales 62-72; longitudinal scale series 102-120; scales cycloid except for a broad zone of ctenoid scales on side of body; auxiliary scales on body; gill rakers 8-11 + 14-16; head large, 2.3-2.5 in standard length; fourth or fifth dorsal spines longest, 2.3-2.65 in head; caudal fin rounded in young, truncate with rounded corners in adults;

307. *Epinephelus marginatus*, about 70 cm (J. Hoover)

308. *Epinephelus marginatus*, same fish to show colour change (J. Hoover)

309. *E. marginatus*, juvenile, 6.6 cm (J. Randall)

reddish to greyish brown dorsally, brownish yellow or orange-yellow ventrally, usually with irregular pale grey to yellowish blotches of variable size on head and body; a blackish streak usually present at upper edge of maxillary groove; outer triangular part of spinous membranes of dorsal fin usually orange or yellow; caudal fin and soft portions of dorsal and anal fins dark greyish brown with a narrow white margin. Reported to attain 150 cm, but 120 cm is the more likely maximum length. The distribution is unusual: Mediterranean Sea, Azores, Madeira, Cape Verde Islands, southern Brazil, Angola, and South Africa to southern Mozambique; it is here reported from southern Oman. As indicated by the above distribu-

tion, the species is subtropical to warm temperate, so its occurrence off southern Oman is probably related to the cooler sea there from upwelling. It is found on rocky bottom in the depth range of 8 to 200 m. Most authors have identified this species as *E. guaza* (Linnaeus); however, the description of Linnaeus referred to an unidentified species of *Mycteroperca* (no type specimen extant).

WHITEBLOTCHED GROUPER
Epinephelus multinotatus (Peters, 1876)

Dorsal rays XI,15-17; anal rays III,8-9 (rarely 9); pectoral rays 18-20; lateral-line scales 64-81; longitudinal scale series 130-162; scales on body largely ctenoid; numerous auxiliary scales on body; gill rakers 9-

310. *E. multinotatus*, juvenile, 9 cm (J. Randall)

311. *Epinephelus multinotatus*, about 50 cm (J. Hoover)

312. *Epinephelus poecilonotus*, 63 cm (J. Randall)

11 + 15 -18; body deep, the depth 2.55-2.95 in standard length, and compressed, the width 1.95-2.67 in depth; individuals above about 500 mm standard length with a step-like discontinuity on lower edge of maxilla; 2 rows of teeth on midside of lower jaw; posterior nostrils of adults larger than anterior; membranes of spinous portion of dorsal fin not incised; caudal fin slightly emarginate to truncate; dark brownish to purplish grey, paler ventrally, with scattered irregular whitish blotches of variable size on body and small ones on head; median fins as dark or darker than body, sometimes with small pale blotches; juveniles in the Arabian Gulf and Gulf of Oman coloured much like the young of *E. flavocaeruleus*, blue with yel-

low caudal peduncle and fin; posterior dorsal and anal fins yellow; pelvic fins blackish. This pattern is remarkably similar to that of the damselfish *Neopomacentrus sindensis* (Day), and it has been suggested that the juvenile grouper is a mimic of the damselfish (Nigel Downing, pers. comm.). Reported to 100 cm. Known only from the Indian Ocean where it appears to have differentiated into three populations: Arabian Gulf and Gulf of Oman; western Indian Ocean (Maldives, Chagos Archipelago and Mauritius to East Africa); and Western Australia (Randall and Heemstra, 1991). Known from the depth range of 1-100 m. *Serranus jayakari* Boulenger and *Epinephelus leprosus* Smith are synonyms.

DOT-DASH GROUPER
Epinephelus poecilonotus (Temminck and Schlegel, 1842)

Dorsal rays XI,14-15; anal rays III,8; pectoral rays 17-19 (rarely 19); lateral-line scales 54-63; longitudinal scale series 110-121; scales on body largely ctenoid; no auxiliary scales on body; gill rakers 8-10 + 15-18; two rows of teeth on midside of lower jaw; two to five large serrae at corner of preopercle; anterior interspinous membranes of dorsal fin deeply incised; caudal fin rounded; pectoral fins not fleshy; juveniles yellowish grey with a very large black spot on back and basal part of spinous portion of dorsal fin; a semicircular dark brown band from nape, paralleling large black spot, bifurcating below it, with each part ending in soft portion of dorsal fin; two parallel dark brown bands below this; with growth the dark bands break into series of small spots, and the large black spot into a group of small dark brown spots; large adults show only traces of dark markings; outer part of spinous membranes of dorsal fin orange. Reported to reach 65 cm. Known from southern Oman, East Africa, islands of the western Indian Ocean, Sri Lanka, India, Viet Nam, Taiwan, Korea, and Japan. The depth of capture has ranged from 45-375 m.

313. *E. poecilonotus*, juvenile, 14 cm (J. Randall)

SMALLSCALE GROUPER
Epinephelus polylepis Randall and Heemstra, 1991

Dorsal rays XI,16-17 (usually 17); anal rays III,8; pectoral rays 18-19 (usually 18); lateral-line scales 65-72; longitudinal scale series 126-137; most scales of body coarsely ctenoid; auxiliary scales present on body; body depth 2.6-3.25 in standard length; head pointed; dorsal profile of head straight; maxilla not extending posterior to eye; two rows of teeth on midside of lower jaw; margin of anal fin rounded to slightly angular, the longest ray 2.1-2.5 in head; caudal fin truncate to slightly emarginate; whitish with numerous, small, very close-set, round to polygonal, dark brown spots on head, body and fins; a narrow dark brown streak at upper edged of maxillary groove; caudal fin with a narrow white posterior margin. Attains at least 55 cm (a 54.7-cm specimen is a female; with sex change and further growth, a significantly larger size is expected). Known from the Gulf of Aden, Gulf of Oman, Arabian Gulf, Pakistan, and western India. Most specimens from trawling in 33 to 55 m. Previously misidentified as the wide-ranging *E. chlorostigma* (Valenciennes) which is not known from the Oman or the Arabian Gulf. *E. polylepis* differs in its more numerous lateral-line scales (48-53 for *chlorostigma*), less angular anal fin (longest anal ray of *chlorostigma* 1.85-2.3 in head), and in its dark spots being closer together and more often polygonal.

OBLIQUEBANDED GROUPER
Epinephelus radiatus (Day, 1867)

Dorsal rays XI,13-15 (rarely 13); anal rays III,8; pectoral rays 17-18; lateral-line scales 52-66; longitudinal scale series 102-120; scales on body largely ctenoid; no auxiliary scales on body; gill rakers 8-9 + 16-18; head large, 2.15-2.35 in standard length; maxilla extending slightly posterior to eye; two rows of teeth on midside of lower jaw; posterior nostril of adults larger than anterior; two to five greatly enlarged serrae at corner of preopercle; interspinous mem-

314. *Epinephelus polylepis* (P. Woodhead)

315. *Epinephelus radiatus*, 36 cm (J. Randall)

316. *E. radiatus*, juvenile, 5 cm (J. Randall)

branes of dorsal fin deeply incised; caudal fin slightly to moderately rounded; pectoral fins not fleshy; pale greyish to yellowish brown with five, irregular, oblique, dark-edged, brown bands which bifurcate ventrally, the first on nape and extending onto head, the second to fourth extending into dorsal fin, and the last on caudal peduncle. Attains about 70 cm. Known from scattered localities in the Indian Ocean, including the Red Sea, Gulf of Oman, Mauritius, India, Western Australia, and the western Pacific. Adults occur at depths of about 80 to 370 m, but juveniles have been collected as shallow as 18 m.

RED-TIPPED GROUPER
Epinephelus retouti Bleeker, 1868

Dorsal rays XI,16-17 (usually 16); anal rays III,8; pectoral rays 19-20 (rarely 20); lateral-line scales 64-76; longitudinal scale series 120-141; scales on body mainly ctenoid; numerous auxiliary scales on body; gill rakers 6-8 + 15-17; dorsal profile of head to nape straight; snout long, 3.5-4.1 in head; maxilla not reaching a vertical at rear edge of eye; adults with three-four rows of teeth on midside of lower jaw; interspinous membranes of dorsal fin deeply incised; caudal fin truncate to very slightly rounded; dull yellowish orange to brownish red (scales red with greenish grey centres), usually with five faint dark bars on body; orbit edged with deep red and surrounded with a light blue line; a red line at base of dorsal fin, and distal part of spinous membranes deep red; caudal fin orange-red except for about upper fifth which is olivaceous brown. Reaches about 47 cm. Mozambique Channel to the Society Island, but with few records; Oman specimens obtained from the Salallah fish market. Adults have been caught from depths of about 70-220 m, but juveniles may be seen in SCUBA-diving depths. *E. truncatus* Katayama is a synonym.

318. *E. retouti*, juvenile, 14 cm (J. Randall)

317. *Epinephelus retouti*, 35 cm (J. Randall)

HALFMOON GROUPER

Epinephelus rivulatus (Valenciennes, 1830)

Dorsal rays XI,16-18; anal rays III,8; pectoral rays 17-19 (rarely 19); lateral-line scales 48-53; longitudinal scale series 86-98; scales on body ctenoid except for chest and abdomen; a zone of very small cycloid scales with numerous pores on nape and anterodorsally on body; gill rakers 6-8 + 14-16; two close-set rows of teeth on midside of lower jaw; serrae at corner of preopercle enlarged; caudal fin rounded; reddish to greenish brown with a small white or pale blue spot on each body scale; five, broad, irregular, dark brown bars usually present on body and one on nape; third and fourth bars close together (and may be partly joined); a large semicircular dark red to reddish brown spot at base of pectoral fins; head with scattered irregular bluish lines and spots; a median dark brown spot anteriorly on isthmus; dorsal fin often with a dark brown line at base. Reaches about 39 cm. Southern shore of the Arabian Peninsula, east coast of Africa, Mauritius, Western Australia, and western Pacific from New South Wales and New Caledonia to Japan. In Australia and the western Pacific the head has irregular dark brown bands instead of bluish lines and spots. Occurs in a variety of habitats from coral reefs to algal and seagrass beds, and from less than 1 to 150 m. *Serranus rhyncholepis* Bleeker and *Epinephelus grammatophorus* Boulenger are synonyms.

EPAULET GROUPER

Epinephelus stoliczkae (Day, 1875)

Dorsal rays XI,16-18; anal rays III,8; pectoral rays 17-19; lateral-line scales 48-53; longitudinal scale series 93-106; scales on body cycloid except beneath and slightly posterior to pectoral fins; auxiliary scales on body; gill rakers 6-7 + 13-15; two rows of teeth on midside of lower jaw; caudal fin rounded; yellowish grey with a broad dark greyish brown bar on body below posterior spinous portion of dorsal fin, two more dark bars close together beneath soft portion of dorsal fin, and one on caudal peduncle; numerous dark reddish brown spots on head (where closely spaced) and anterior half to two-thirds of body; a dark blotch behind

321. *E. stoliczkae*, juvenile, 6.3 cm (J. Randall)

eye. Largest reported, 38 cm. Ranges from the Suez Canal to the Gulf of Oman (where common) and Pakistan; also known from the Horn of Africa just outside the Gulf of Aden. A shallow-water species generally found on sand around small coral heads; not often seen on well-developed coral reefs.

POTATO GROUPER

Epinephelus tukula Morgans,1959
(Photograph on page 137)

Dorsal rays XI,14-15 (usually 15); anal rays III,7-8 (rarely 7); pectoral rays 18-20; lateral-line scales 62-70; longitudinal scale series 113-130; scales on body largely ctenoid; auxiliary scales present on body of adults; gill rakers 9-10 + 15-17; body depth 2.95-3.5 in standard length; head pointed, its length 2.35-2.55 in standard length; three to six rows of teeth on midside of lower jaw; posterior nostril at most 1.5 times larger than anterior; membranes of spinous portion of dorsal fin incised; caudal fin rounded in young, slightly rounded in adults; light grey to light brown, the body with dark brown to black spots, mostly larger than eye, which vary from round to horizontally elongate (most spots separated by spaces less than their diameter); head with small dark spots and irregular narrow bands, many of which radiate from eye; dark brown to black spots of variable size on fins, tending to become smaller distally. Largest specimen, 139 cm, but reported to attain 200 cm. Known from the Red Sea and East Africa, Gulf of Aden, southern Oman, Pakistan, southwest India, Australia, Tawian, and southern Japan; curiously, not yet reported from the Indo-Malayan region. Unusual for a large grouper in allowing close approach by a diver.

319. *Epinephelus rivulatus*, 30 cm (J. Randall)

320. *Epinephelus stoliczkae*, about 25 cm (J. Hoover)

322. *Epinephelus tukula*, about 100 cm; description on p. 136 (J. Hoover)

WAVY-LINED GROUPER

Epinephelus undulosus (Quoy and
Gaimard, 1824)

Dorsal rays IX,17-19; anal rays III,7-9
(usually 8); pectoral rays 18-19 (more often
19); lateral-line scales 63-76; longitudinal
scale series 124-150; scales on body largely
ctenoid; body with numerous auxiliary
scales; gill rakers 12-16 + 20-23; a distinct
step-like discontinuity on ventral margin of
maxilla about one-fourth distance from
posterior end (which may develop into a
hook-like process on large adults); two rows
of teeth on midside of lower jaw; membranes of spinous portion of dorsal fin not
incised; caudal fin truncate to slightly emarginate; purplish to brownish grey with yellow to yellowish brown dots on head and
slightly wavy longitudinal lines on about
upper three-fourths of body. Reported to
attain 75 cm. Occurs along continental
shores from Kenya north to the Gulf of Aden
and Gulf of Oman, east to the Indo-Malayan

323. *Epinephelus undulosus*, 36 cm (J. Randall)

region, and north to Taiwan. Morgans
(1982) reported on 111 specimens taken
from the North Kenya Banks in 24-94 m;
they had fed mainly on small fishes, but in
some localities on pelagic invertebrates such
as the tunicate *Thalia democatica*.

137

MARBLED CORALGROUPER
Plectropomus punctatus (Quoy and Gaimard, 1824)

Dorsal rays VIII,11; anal rays III,8; pectoral rays 16-18 (usually 17); lateral-line scales 88-95; longitudinal scale series 123-130; no embedded scales in interorbital space; developed gill rakers (higher than their base) 1-2 + 6-9; posterior nostril of adults notably larger than anterior; a pair of large canine teeth anteriorly in jaws and one to four on side of lower jaw (true of other species of the genus); longest dorsal soft ray 2.25-2.6 in head; outer margin of anal fin convex from fourth to eighth ray; caudal fin slightly emarginate to truncate (usually truncate); brown to reddish brown, often irregularly marbled with pale; no small blue spots or dark bars on body; orbit edged with blue; pectoral fins dark brown, the posterior margin abruptly pale yellowish; juveniles with numerous small horizontally elongate white spots. Largest reported, 96 cm. Western Indian Ocean (but not the Red Sea, Gulf of Oman, Arabian Gulf, or coast of India). Observed in Oman waters only at Juzor al Hallaniyat (Kuria Muria Islands). Usually found on coral reefs or rocky substrata; like others of the genus, it is more of a roving predator than the species of *Epinephelus* or *Cephalopholis*. Feeds mainly on fishes. *Plectropomus marmoratus* Talbot is a synonym.

324. *P. punctatus*, juv., about 25 cm (J. Randall)

325. *Plectropomus punctatus*, about 100 cm (J. Hoover)

327. *Variola louti*, about 45 cm (J. Randall)

326. *Variola louti*, juvenile, 18 cm (J. Randall)

CORONATION GROUPER
Variola louti (Forsskål, 1775)

Dorsal rays IX,13-14 (rarely 13); anal rays III,8; pectoral rays 16-19 (usually 17 or 18); lateral-line scales 66-77; longitudinal scale series 113-135; scales on body largely ctenoid; no auxiliary scales on body; gill rakers 7-10 + 15-18; a pair of large canines at front of jaws and one or two large canines on side of lower jaw; membranes of spinous portion of dorsal fin little incised; tenth and eleventh dorsal soft rays and fourth and fifth anal soft rays prolonged; caudal fin lunate, the caudal concavity 1.3-2.15 in head; yellowish brown to orange-red (fish from deeper water more red) with numerous small irregular spots or dashes which vary from blue to lavender or pink; median fins coloured like body except for a broad yellow crescent at posterior margin of caudal fin, and a broad yellow zone posteriorly on dorsal and anal fins; outer third to fourth of pectoral fins abruptly yellow; juveniles with a broad irregular black stripe on upper side of body. Largest examined, 81 cm. Indo-Pacific; known from Oman only from the south where rare. Feeds mainly on fishes (Randall, 1980).

SUBFAMILY GRAMMISTINAE

SIXLINE SOAPFISH
Grammistes sexlineatus (Thunberg, 1792)

Dorsal rays VII,13-14, the fin nearly completely divided into spinous and soft portions; anal rays II,9; pectoral rays 16-18; lateral-line scales 60-72; scales cycloid and embedded; body depth 2.3-2.8 in standard length; a small fleshy flap at tip of chin; posterior preopercular margin with two to four short spines; caudal fin rounded; adults black with six to eight yellow stripes (in addition to one middorsal on head and nape), the stripes breaking into series of dashes in very large adults; juveniles with fewer stripes, and small juveniles with two rows of large pale yellow spots. Reaches 27 cm. Indo-Pacific; a shallow-water coral-reef fish that tends to be cryptic. Well known for producing a strong skin toxin which is extremely bitter to the taste.

328. *Grammistes sexlineatus*, about 17 cm (J. Randall)

CAVE BASS
FAMILY DINOPERCIDAE

This small family of perciform fishes consists of two species, *Dinoperca petersi* (Day) from continental shores of the western Indian Ocean and *Centrarchops chapin* Fowler from northern Angola. These two fishes have usually been classified in the family Serranidae, but Heemstra and Hecht (1986) established the family Dinopercidae for them, differentiating it from the Serranidae primarily in having a high median crest on the frontal bones which is fused with the higher supraocciptial crest and a large swim bladder with three pairs of intrinsic muscles.

CAVE BASS
Dinoperca petersi (Day, 1875)

Dorsal rays IX-XI,18-20; anal rays III,12-14; pectoral rays 17-18; lateral-line scales 53-63; head, body, and fins with small ctenoid scales; body depth 2.3-2.5 in standard length; head pointed, the lower jaw strongly projecting; dorsal profile of head nearly straight; opercle with two flat spines; preopercle serrate; soft portions of dorsal and anal fins elevated, the longest soft ray twice or more the length of longest spine; caudal fin truncate; dark brown with scattered small white spots on body; a broad, slightly diagonal, dark brown band on cheek broadly bordered above and below by a pale band. Attains 62 cm. Known from Pakistan (type locality), southern Oman, Kenya, Mozambique, and South Africa (south to Algoa Bay). Found on rocky bottom, usually beneath ledges or in caves by day. Capable of making a loud drumming noise. *Dinoperca queketti* Boulenger is a synonym.

329. *Dinoperca petersi*, about 32 cm (J. Hoover)

DOTTYBACKS AND SNAKELETS

FAMILY PSEUDOCHROMIDAE

This Indo-Pacific family is characterised by having a moderately to extremely elongate body; a long dorsal fin with only one to three spines (none in one snakelet species); anal fin with one to three spines (except the snakelets with none); pelvic fins of one spine and three to five soft rays (may be absent in snakelets), inserted below or slightly anterior to the pectoral fins; 6 branchiostegal rays; scales moderate to small, ctenoid to cycloid; the eggs with filaments. The family is divisible into four subfamilies: the Pseudochrominae (presented first below) with I,5 pelvic rays, scaled head, interrupted lateral line, and palatine teeth; the Pseudoplesiopinae with I,3 to I,4 pelvic rays, scaled head, one tubed anterior lateral-line scale, and palatine teeth; Anisochrominae (one genus with two species; Springer et al., 1977), with I,4 pelvic rays, one dorsal spine, naked head, and no palatine teeth; and the Congrogadinae (snakelets; Winterbottom, 1985) with a very elongate body, pelvic fins with I,2-I,4 rays or absent, 0-2 dorsal spines, no anal spines, small cycloid scales, no palatine teeth, and eggs with tiny cruciform hooks. The Congrogadinae was previously regarded as a blennioid or trachinoid family; Godkin and Winterbottom (1985) reclassified it as a subfamily of the Pseudochromidae. The species of the first three subfamilies are small, generally less than 12 cm in length (maximum 22 cm); most of the congrogadines are also small, but one species is reported to 50 cm. The pseudochromid fishes are cryptic and quick to take shelter. The male of some species of *Pseudochromis* have been observed to aggressively guard a ball of eggs within his shelter until hatching (Lubbock, 1975).

330A. *Pseudochromis omanensis* (J. Randall)

330B. *Haliophis diademus* (J. Hoover)

SUBFAMILY PSEUDOCHROMINAE

ARABIAN BLUESTRIPED DOTTYBACK
Pseudochromis aldabraensis Bauchot-Boutin, 1958

Dorsal rays III,27-31 (usually 28-30); anal rays III,16-19 (usually 18-19); pectoral rays 16-19 (usually 17-18); anterior lateral-line scales 24-33; posterior lateral-line scales 4-10; predorsal scales 17-27 (usually 20-24); gill rakers 3-6 + 11-13; body depth 4.1-5.1 in standard length; caudal fin truncate; bright orange to orange-brown with three blue stripes on head, the uppermost continuing to caudal peduncle, the middle one ending at yellow-rimmed dark spot on opercular flap; postorbital head between upper two blue stripes blackish; dorsal fin blackish with two blue stripes; upper and lower edges of caudal fin blue, the upper with a black streak within the blue. Attains about 10 cm. Reported from Aldabra (only from the holotype), Arabian Gulf, Gulf of Oman, southern Oman, Pakistan, and Sri Lanka. Common in the Arabian Gulf and

331. *Pseudochromis aldabraensis*, about 9 cm (J. Hoover)

Gulf of Oman. Has been confused with *P. dutoiti* Smith from the East African coast which is very similar in colour; the latter differs in the second blue stripe passing below the spot on the opercular flap and modally more dorsal and anal rays and anterior lateral-line scales.

BANDTAIL DOTTYBACK
Pseudochromis caudalis Boulenger, 1898.

Dorsal rays III,28-30 (rarely 30); anal rays III,17-19 (rarely 19); anterior lateral-line scales 36-44; posterior lateral-line scales 7-16; longitudinal scale series 45-52; predorsal scales 18-26; gill rakers 4-6 + 10-13; body depth 3.8-4.6 in standard length; caudal fin truncate to emarginate; brownish yellow with a dark bluish spot in centre of scales on upper part of body; a black-edged bright blue spot behind eye at upper end of preopercular margin; two converging submarginal black bands in caudal fin of large adults. Attains 11 cm. Sri Lanka and southern India to the Gulf of Oman and Strait of Hormuz; occurs on rocky substrata in the depth range of about 12 to at least 30 m.

332. *Pseudochromis caudalis*, about 5.5 cm (J. Randall)

333. *Pseudochromis leucorhynchus* (J. Hoover)

WHITELIP DOTTYBACK
Pseudochromis leucorhynchus Lubbock, 1977.

Dorsal rays III,28-32 (usually 30-31); anal rays III,17-20; pectoral rays 17-18 (usually 18); anterior lateral-line scales 30-34; posterior lateral-line scales 5-8; predorsal scales 17-22; gill rakers 4-7 + 10-12; body depth 3.7-4.5 in standard length; caudal fin rounded; dark olive-brown to yellow, the scale centres orange-red; a black stripe on side of snout bordered above with white, the white broadening and ending medially on upper lip (a conspicuous marking underwater); a black spot on opercular flap, edged posteriorly with yellow. Reaches about 9 cm. Known from northern Kenya (type locality), Somalia, and southern Oman; a shallow-water species of coral reefs and rocky bottom; depths of capture range from 1-8 m. The species in Kenya has lower scale counts than in Oman (Gill and Mee, 1993).

334. *Pseudochromis leucorhynchus*, dark phase, about 6 cm (J. Randall)

141

LINDA'S DOTTYBACK

Pseudochromis linda Randall and Stanaland, 1989

Dorsal rays III,26-29 (usually 27-28); anal rays III,14-16 (usually 15-16); anterior lateral-line scales 31-38; posterior lateral-line scales 0-18; predorsal scales 26-35; gill rakers 4-7 + 10-14; body depth 2.9-3.4 in standard length; caudal fin rounded; dark olive-brown, shading to yellow posteriorly on caudal peduncle and caudal fin; a black-edged dark blue spot, rimmed with yellow posteriorly, on opercular flap; a few dark spots usually present on body, mainly anteriorly; a second colour phase almost entirely black. Largest specimen, 8.1 cm. Occurs from Pakistan to the Arabian Gulf and the Somali coast of the Gulf of Aden; common in the Gulf of Oman, but not in southern Oman; collected from depths of 1-6 m; unusually cryptic, so not often seen. Similar to the Red Sea endemic *P. olivaceus* Rüppell which differs in having an emarginate caudal fin that is not primarily yellow, and numerous, curved, vertically elongate, dark blue spots on the body.

BLACKSTRIPE DOTTYBACK

Pseudochromis nigrovittatus Boulenger, 1897

Dorsal rays III,26-28 (usually 27); anal rays III,15-17 (usually 16-17); pectoral rays 16-19 (usually 18); anterior lateral-line scales 32-40; posterior lateral-line scales 5-13; predorsal scales 12-27; gill rakers 4-5 +

335. *Pseudochromis linda*, about 6 cm (J. Randall)

336. *Pseudochromis nigrovittatus* (J. Hoover)

10-11; body depth 4.1-4.8 in standard length; caudal fin truncate; greenish grey dorsally, shading to whitish ventrally, usually with a dark stripe which commences on side of upper lip, passes through eye, broadens along side of body, narrows on caudal fin, ending at posterior margin; stripe apparently labile, varying from nearly black to faintly dusky, to entirely absent; scattered small bright blue spots on body, mainly on upper half; a semicircular black-edged bright blue spot on opercular flap, rimmed posteriorly with yellow; caudal fin some-

times yellow. Maximum length about 9 cm. Known from Makran coast of Iran (type locality), Gulf of Oman, Arabian Gulf, south coast of Oman, and Djibouti; occurs from tidepools to depths of at least 12 m.

OMAN DOTTYBACK

Pseudochromis omanensis Gill and Mee, 1993

Dorsal rays III,29-31 (usually 30); anal rays III,19-20; pectoral rays 18-20 (usually19); anterior lateral-line scales 49-60; posterior lateral-line scales 5-15; scale rows between anterior and posterior lateral lines 3; predorsal scales 22-27; circumpeduncular scales 20-21 (rarely 21); gill rakers 4-5 + 10-11; body depth 4.0-4.7 in standard length; caudal fin slightly rounded to slightly emarginate; orangish brown, the scale centres dark bluish dorsally (the scale-centre spots extending half way down body anteriorly, progressively lower posteriorly until none on caudal peduncle) and orange-red ventrally, sometimes with a dark stripe from side of upper lip through eye, along upper side, and ending dorsally in basal part of caudal fin; a black-edged dark blue spot on head at upper end of preopercular margin; irregular, oblique, light blue lines on cheek; one colour phase very dark brown with scattered blue dots posteriorly on body and basally on caudal fin; pectoral fins red; caudal fin often yellowish. Largest collected, 12 cm; estimated to reach 15 cm. Known from the central and southern coast of Oman from the shallows to at least 15 m on hard substratum. Appears to be a close relative of *P. persicus*.

337. *Pseudochromis omanensis*, striped phase, about 9 cm (J. Randall)

338. *Pseudochromis omanensis*, dark phase (J. Hoover)

142

PERSIAN DOTTYBACK
Pseudochromis persicus Murray, 1887

Dorsal rays III,28-31 (usually 30); anal rays III,18-21 (usually 19-20); pectoral rays 18-20 (usually 18-19); anterior lateral-line scales 42-56; posterior lateral-line scales 7-17; scale rows between anterior and posterior lateral lines usually 4 (rarely 3 or 5); predorsal scales 21-29; circumpeduncular scales 20-24 (rarely 20); gill rakers 4-7 + 10-13; body depth 3.7-4.5 in standard length; caudal fin slightly rounded to slightly emarginate; variable in colour, one phase light yellowish brown on back, shading to white on side and ventrally; another dark grey on back, abruptly white below a demarcation from snout to upper caudal-fin base; another orangish brown, becoming whitish on lower head and abdomen; and another very dark brown – all phases with numerous but scattered small bright blue spots on body and a few posteriorly on head, small bright blue spots on dorsal and caudal fins, those on dorsal fin in regular rows, and a black spot edged anteriorly with bright blue on head at upper end of preopercular margin. Largest specimen 15.4 cm. Known from the Arabian Gulf to Karachi, Pakistan; Oman record from Musandam at the Strait of Hormuz.

339. *Pseudochromis persicus*, light phase, 9.5 cm (J. Randall)

340. *P. persicus*, dark phase, 10 cm (J. Randall)

341. *Pseudochromis punctatus*, about 9 cm (J. Randall)

342. *Pseudochromis punctatus* (J. Hoover)

BLACKBACK DOTTYBACK
Pseudochromis punctatus Kotthaus, 1970

Dorsal rays III,26; anal rays III,15; pectoral rays 17-19 (usually 18); anterior lateral-line scales 32-35; posterior lateral-line scales 5-11; predorsal scales 16-20; body depth 4.0-4.35 in standard length; caudal fin rounded; head and body dark grey to black dorsally, brownish yellow to pale pink or whitish ventrally, the two areas separated by a yellow stripe; dorsal fin with numerous black dots; dark dots also in anal fin of large individuals. Largest specimen, 10.4 cm. Known only from the holotype collected from Somalia in 55-65 m and four specimens from Juzor al Hallaniyat (Kuria Muria Islands) taken by John L. Earle in 17-21 m. Closely related to *P. pesi* Lubbock from the Red Sea and *P. melas* Lubbock from Kenya to South Africa (Gill and Randall, 1994).

143

SUBFAMILY PSEUDOPLESIOPINAE

COCKATOO DOTTYBACK
Chlidichthys cacatuoides Gill and
Randall, 1994

Dorsal rays II,23, the last seven rays
branched; anal rays III,14 (last five rays
branched); pectoral rays 17; pelvic rays I,4
(soft rays unbranched); a single anterior
tubed lateral-line scale (a character of the
subfamily), followed by pitted scales to
below the 20th to 22nd dorsal soft ray; a
second series of pitted scales posteriorly on
midside of body commencing above anteri-
or part of anal fin; longitudinal scale series
39-40; predorsal scales 8-9; gill rakers 3 +
9-10; body depth 3.85-4.05 in standard
length; lower lip not forming a free fold
across front of lower jaw (a character of the
genus); first four or five dorsal soft rays
elongate with deeply incised membranes;
caudal fin truncate; female reddish brown
dorsally, shading to pale greyish brown
below, the scales with a pinkish brown basal
spot; an orange-yellow area behind eye,
dorsal fin pale grey on basal third, dark grey
on outer two-thirds, the two zones separated
by a narrow pale blue stripe and a narrow
reddish brown stripe, the rays orangish
brown; basal third of caudal fin coloured
like body, the outer two-thirds dark grey;
pectoral fins pinkish hyaline; pelvic fins pale
blue; male similar to female except head,
chest, and body anterior to pectoral-fin base
bright orange-yellow. Known from only
three specimens collected at Juzor al Hallaniyat (Kuria Muria Islands) in 21 m, the
largest 4.6 cm.

343. *Chlidichthys cacatuoides*, male above (4.6 cm), female below (J. Randall)

SUBFAMILY CONGROGADINAE

ROOSTER SNAKELET
Halidesmus coccus Winterbottom and
Randall, 1994

Dorsal rays I,64-68; anal rays 52-55; pectoral rays 9-12; no pelvic fins; three lateral
lines, each with a single series of pores;
body with very small cycloid scales; no
scales on head, and none above upper lateral
line; gill rakers 2-3 + 5-6; vertebrae 69-73;
head length 7.7-8.3 in standard length; body
elongate, the depth 1.4-1.65 in head; a convex median fleshy crest on head from tip of
snout to posterior interorbital space; dorsal
and anal fins fully confluent with caudal fin;
dark brown with scattered small pale flecks
and a large ocellated black spot above gill
opening; crest pale with dark flecks; lips and
lower half of head pale with vertical dark
brown lines on lips and below eye. Largest
specimen, 8.9 cm. Described from 13 specimens from large tidepools on the south coast
of Oman.

THOMASEN'S SNAKELET
Halidesmus thomaseni Nielsen, 1960

Dorsal rays I,58-64; anal rays 45-50; pectoral rays 7-9; no pelvic fins; three lateral
lines, each with a single series of pores;
body with very small cycloid scales; scales
present on nape and cheek; gill rakers 2-3 +
6-7; vertebrae 64-68; head length 7.3-7.4 in
standard length; body elongate, the depth
1.6-1.7 in head; a median fleshy crest on
snout elevated to a short fleshy tentacle in
interorbital space; dorsal and anal fins fully
confluent with caudal fin; dark brown with
numerous, irregular, small, pale blotches on
body; a large, pale-edged, black spot above
gill opening; lower part of head light brown
with a narrow dark brown stripe extending
posteriorly from eye and a dark brown bar
extending ventrally from eye. Attains about
14 cm. Known from both coasts of India,
Pakistan (type specimens from rock pools
near Karachi), and Masirah Island off the
central coast of Oman (also from tidepools).

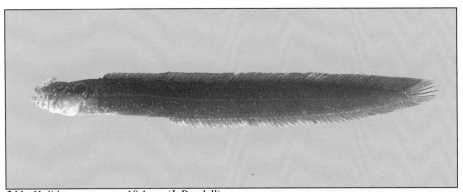

344. *Halidesmus coccus*, 10.1 cm (J. Randall)

345. *Halidesmus thomaseni*, 10 cm (J. Randall)

144

STARS-AND-STRIPES SNAKELET
Haliophis diademus Winterbottom and Randall, 1994

Dorsal rays II,47, the second spine minute; anal rays 39; pectoral rays 11; no pelvic fins; a single short lateral line of 20-22 pores; cheek and body with small cycloid scales, the rest of head naked; gill rakers 2 + 8-9; gill membranes fused to isthmus; head length 5.95 in standard length; body elongate, the depth 1.85 in head; last dorsal and anal rays joined by membrane to caudal fin about two thirds their length; caudal fin rounded; white with five rows of dark reddish brown to black spots on body, reduced to three rows posteriorly, the spots larger than interspaces; head with a dark brown to black stripe on side of snout, continuing behind eye, bifurcating posteriorly on head, each branch leading to a row of spots on body; a third postorbital stripe from upper part of eye ending in uppermost series of spots on body; a black spot nearly as large as eye above gill opening; a dark stripe basally in dorsal and anal fins. Described from a single 8.3-cm specimen collected in 8 m at Mahallah, south Oman. Named for its hiding among the spines of the sea urchin *Diadema* when first observed. A 10-cm specimen was collected in 11 m at the same locality; the species was also observed at Masirah Island.

SPOTTED SNAKELET
Haliophis guttatus (Forsskål, 1775)

Dorsal rays II,41-47, the second spine minute; anal rays 33-39; pectoral rays 10-11; no pelvic fins; a single complete lateral line, the anterior part arched to below about sixth dorsal soft ray; small embedded cycloid scales present on body, cheek, and opercle; gill rakers 3 + 8-9; head length 5.5-6.8 in standard length; body elongate, the depth 1.5-1.8 in head length; last dorsal and anal rays joined by membrane to caudal fin for about two-thirds their length; caudal fin rounded; brown, shading to dark brown posteriorly, with narrow black bars (some incomplete) or five or six series of small dark brown spots (Oman specimens the barred form); an ocellated black spot as large as eye above gill opening; irregular dark brown spots on snout and postorbital head (smaller spots over all of head in form with spotted body). Largest specimen examined, 15.5 cm. Known from the Red Sea (type locality) and coast of Africa south to Mozambique and Madagascar; depth of capture 1-15 m; here recorded from south Oman.

ORANGESTRIPED SNAKELET
Rusichthys sp.

Dorsal rays II,46-48, the second spine minute; anal rays 36-38; pectoral rays 14-15; pelvic rays I,4; no lateral line; small embedded cycloid scales present on cheek, opercle, and body; gill rakers 4-5 + 10; body elongate, the depth 1.9-2.1 in head length; head length 4.1-4.6 in standard length; last dorsal and anal rays joined by membrane to caudal peduncle for one-quarter to one-third their length; body tan, shading to grey on head; an orange stripe dorsolaterally on head continuing to below middle of dorsal fin; a second orange stripe from rear margin of orbit across cheek and opercle; basal fourth of dorsal and anal fins blackish; distal margin of posterior third of dorsal fin dusky; base of caudal fin blackish, continuing as a central band to end of fin; paired fins hyaline. Largest specimen, 5.2 cm. Known from only three specimens collected in 27 m off southern Oman.

346. *Haliophis diademus*, 8.7 cm (J. Randall)

347. *Haliophis guttatus*, 6.9 cm (J. Randall)

348. *Rusichthys* sp. (J. Hoover)

LONGFINS AND SPINY BASSLETS
FAMILY PLESIOPIDAE

This perciform family consists of small fishes known only from the Indo-Pacific region. They have 6 branchiostegal rays, the third longer than adjacent rays, resulting in a projection on the branchiostegal membrane (except in *Calloplesiops*); no opercular spine (or a secondary spine in *Acanthoplesiops*); the margin of the preopercle is smooth; the pelvic fins have one spine and two or four rays, their insertion anterior to the base of the pectoral fins; the pelvic fins of most species are long, the elongate first soft ray often thickened and bifurcate; the dorsal fin is long and unnotched; the posterior part of the dorsal and anal fins is often prolonged well posterior to caudal-fin base; the caudal fin is rounded to pointed; there are one to three lateral lines; when one, it may be incomplete or disjunct. The family is divisible into two subfamilies, the Plesiopinae with seven genera (Mooi, 1995), and the Acanthoclininae with four (Smith-Vaniz and Johnson, 1990). The plesiopines have a disjunct lateral line, 4 soft pelvic rays, a dorsal fin of XI to XV spines, an anal fin of III spines, and scales on the operculum (also often dorsally on head). The acanthoclinines have one to three lateral lines, 2 soft pelvic rays, a dorsal fin of XVII to XXVI spines, an anal fin of VII to XVI spines, and no scales or only a few on the head. Many of the plesiopid fishes, including those of the largest genus, *Plesiops*, are very cryptic and rarely seen by divers.

SUBFAMILY PLESIOPINAE

MOUSTACHE LONGFIN
Plesiops mystaxus Mooi, 1995

Dorsal XII,7, the spinous membranes deeply incised; anal rays III,8; pectoral rays 19-23, the lower 7-10 free of membrane; anterior lateral-line scales 18-19; posterior lateral-line scales 11-15; predorsal scales 5-7; cheek scale rows 3-4; longitudinal scale series 26-27; gill rakers 3-5 + 8-12; body depth 3.1-3.7 in standard length; pelvic fins very long, 1.95-2.45 in standard length; caudal fin rounded, its length 2.85-3.3 in standard length; dark brown, the base of scales paler than the broad edges, with or without faint dark bars on body; head with two broad dark bars radiating posteriorly from eye, with a whitish spot at edges; other scattered whitish spots on head, including five along posterior margin of preopercle and three on maxilla; dorsal margin of maxilla black; fins brown, the membranes of spinous portion of dorsal fin broadly tipped with bright orange, with a submarginal dark brown line, and below this a whitish line. Largest specimen, 9 cm. Known to date only from the Comoro Islands (type locality), Madagascar, Red Sea, and southern Oman; collections have come from rocky or rubble substrata at depths of 0.3-8 m. The common, wide-ranging *P. coeruleolineatus* Rüppell is not recorded from Oman but might be expected. It is similar in colour to *P. mystaxus*, differing in having XI dorsal spines and no long black streak on the maxilla.

WHITESPOTTED LONGFIN
Plesiops nigricans (Rüppell, 1828)

Dorsal rays XI-XIII,7-8 (usually 7), the spinous membranes deeply incised; anal rays III,7-9 (usually 8); pectoral rays 19-22, the lower 5-8 free of membrane; anterior lateral-line scales 19-23; posterior lateral-line scales 12-15; longitudinal scale series

349. *Plesiops mystaxus*, 9.2 cm (J. Randall)

350. *Plesiops nigricans*, 17 cm (J. Randall)

27-29; predorsal scales 7-10 (usually 9-10); cheek scale rows 5-7 (rarely 5); gill rakers 4-7 + 11-14; body depth 2.8-3.2 in standard length; pelvic fins long, reaching posterior to third anal spine; caudal fin rounded, its length 3.1-3.45 in standard length; black with a vertical blue line on scales of body (the lines curved dorsally), except on head, chest, abdomen, and median and pelvic fins where very small blue spots predominate (blue markings may fade to pale yellowish); no ocellus on opercle. Largest specimen examined, 17 cm. Red Sea to southern Oman where found in large tidepools along rocky shores.

SUBFAMILY ACANTHOCLININAE

SCOTTIE
Acanthoplesiops indicus (Day, 1888)

Dorsal rays XIX-XX,3-4; anal rays VIII-X,3-4; pectoral rays 14-17; tubed lateral-line scales 8-12; longitudinal scale series about 33; scales cycloid, those on about posterior third of body secondarily cycloid, pyriform, often bilobed or trilobed; abdomen fully scaled; gill rakers 1 + 4; last dorsal and anal rays joined by membrane to caudal fin for two-thirds or more their length; caudal fin rounded; black with a broad white bar posteriorly on body and base of caudal fin, including posterior ends of dorsal and anal fins, this bar bisected by a red line; a broad white middorsal band from tip of snout to and including the first two or three spines of dorsal fin; front of anal fin white; distal end of caudal and pelvic fins white. Largest specimen, 2.9 cm. Known previously from Madras, India (type locality), Seychelles, and coast of Africa from Natal to Kenya; here recorded from Masirah Island off the coast of central Oman in 7 m.

351. *A. indicus*, 2.1 cm (J. Randall)

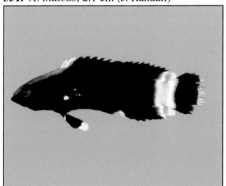

BIGEYES
FAMILY PRIACANTHIDAE

This family is characterised by having extremely large eyes which have a unique tapetum lucidum (a reflective layer at the back of the eye); opercle with two flat spines; preopercle serrate with a broad spine variously developed at corner; mouth moderately large and very strongly oblique with projecting lower jaw; villiform teeth in jaws and on vomer and palatines; small rough scales (but not ctenoid) on body and head; a moderately deep, compressed body; fin rays with tiny spinules; continuous dorsal fin with X spines; anal fin with III spines; caudal fin with 16 principal rays; and pelvic fins I,5, the last ray broadly joined to abdomen by membrane. The colour is usually red or dominantly red; some species are able to quickly change from solid red to silvery or to barred or mottled red and silver. There are four genera: the monotypic and circumtropical *Cookeolus* and *Heteropriacanthus*, *Pristigenys* (four species), and *Priacanthus* (12 species) Starnes (1988). These fishes are known from a depth

352. *Cookeolus japonicus*, 37.4 cm (J. Randall)

range of 2 to about 400 m; they are generally found by day hiding in caves or beneath ledges, but some are taken by trawls on sedimentary substrata. They are primarily nocturnal; those for which there are data on food habits have fed mainly on the larger animals of the zooplankton, such as larval fishes, crab megalops, and so on.

BULLEYE
Cookeolus japonicus (Cuvier, 1829)

Dorsal rays X,12-14; anal rays III,12-14; pectoral rays 17-19; lateral-line scales 60-73; gill rakers 5-8 + 17-20; body depth 1.8-2.95 in standard length (body becoming more elongate with growth); swim bladder without anterior or posterior extensions; preorbital (lacrymal) bone with large serrations anteriorly; pelvic fins very long, 1.4 times longer than head in young, 1.1 times longer in large adults; soft portions of dorsal and anal fins strongly elevated; caudal fin slightly rounded to slightly rhomboid; red, the fins except the pectorals sometimes yellowish. Maximum length recorded, 68 cm. Found in all tropical to warm temperate seas, but most common off islands; reported from depths of 60 to at least 400 m. Often misidentified as *C. boops* (Bloch and Schneider), but this is a junior synonym of *Heteropriacanthus cruentatus* (Lacepède) (Starnes, 1988).

PEONY BIGEYE
Priacanthus blochii Bleeker, 1853

Dorsal rays X,12-14; anal rays III,13-15; pectoral rays 17-19; lateral-line scales 69-74; gill rakers 3-5 + 14-17; body depth 2.6-2.95 in standard length; swim bladder with paired anterior and posterior projections (true of other species of the genus); preorbital bone and second suborbital finely serrate; preopercular spine of adults not reaching tip of interopercle; pelvic fins equal to or a little longer than head length (1.0-1.2 times head length); soft portions of dorsal and anal fins not greatly elevated, the margin rounded; caudal fin slightly rounded; red or silvery blotched with red; about 14 small dark red spots along lateral line; a black spot at base of second and third pelvic rays. Maximum length about 35 cm. Known from the southern Red Sea, Gulf of Aden, southern Oman, Seychelles, Indo-Malayan region, Australia, and Samoa; depth range 15-30 m.

GOGGLE-EYE
Priacanthus hamrur (Forsskål, 1775)

Dorsal rays X,13-15; anal rays III,13-16 (usually 14 or 15); pectoral rays 17-20; lateral-line scales 70-90; gill rakers 4-6 + 18-21; body depth 2.35-3.0 in standard length; preorbital bone and second suborbital finely serrate; spine at corner of preopercle short in adults; pelvic fins not long, 1.2-1.3 in head; soft portions of dorsal and anal fins not elevated, their distal margin rounded; caudal fin usually emarginate (more crescentic with age); red or red blotched with silver; about 14 or 15 small dark red spots along lateral line; a dark spot at base of second and third pelvic soft rays. Reported to attain 40 cm. Indo-Pacific (except Hawaii where replaced by the closely related *P. meeki*). Common in southern Oman (shoals of subadults seen in October and November), but rare in the Gulf of Oman.

354. *P. hamrur*, juveniles (J. Hoover)

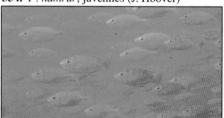

353. *Priacanthus blochii*, about 21 cm (J. Randall)

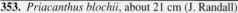

PURPLESPOTTED BIGEYE
Priacanthus tayenus Richardson, 1846

Dorsal rays X,11-13; anal rays III,12-14; pectoral rays 17-19; lateral-line scales 51-67; gill rakers 3-6 + 17-19; body depth 2.5-3.15 in standard length; preorbital and second suborbital bones with large serrations; preopercular spine very long in juveniles, remaining moderately long in adults (usually reaching beyond end of subopercle); pelvic fins usually longer than head (1.0-1.3 times head length); soft portions of dorsal and anal fins somewhat elevated, the dorsal outline distinctly angular; caudal fin slightly rounded in young, truncate in adults, the upper and lower rays of large adults greatly prolonged (apparently only in males, but not all males have the long caudal filaments); light red or orange-red dorsally, shading to silvery pink on sides and ventrally; deep purple to black spots on pelvic fins, the largest on membrane linking fin to body. Attains 35 cm. Arabian Gulf, India, Andaman Sea, Indo-Malayan region, China and off both western and eastern coasts of Australia. Known from the depth range of 20-200 m; usually caught by trawling.

355. *Priacanthus hamrur*, about 26 cm (J. Randall)

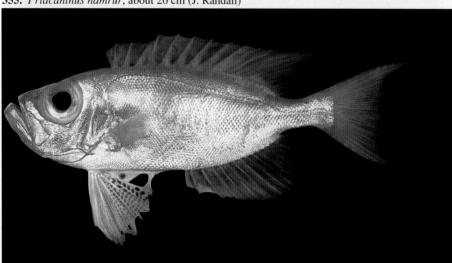

356. *Priacanthus tayenus*, 22.3 cm (J. Randall)

148

HAWKFISHES
FAMILY CIRRHITIDAE

The most distinctive feature of this family is all having 14 pectoral rays, the lower 5 to 7 of which are unbranched and enlarged; there is a single dorsal fin of X spines which is notched between spinous and soft portions; anal rays III,6 or 7 (usually 6); one or more cirri project from the tips of the dorsal spines; a fringe of small cirri on the posterior edge of the anterior nostril; two indistinct flat spines on opercle; scales cycloid; no swim bladder. The family consists of nine genera (an Easter Island-Pitcairn species may require placement in a new genus) and 35 species, of which only three occur in the Atlantic and four in the eastern Pacific. These fishes sit on rock or coral (though *Cyprinocirrhites polyactis* frequently leaves the bottom to feed on zooplankton), using their thickened lower pectoral rays to wedge themselves in place. All are carnivorous, darting out rapidly to prey on small fishes and crustaceans. Some species, at least, are protogynous (begin mature life as females and change sex later to males). Randall (1963) revised the family.

357. *Cirrhitichthys calliurus*, about 11 cm (J. Randall)

SPOTTEDTAIL HAWKFISH
Cirrhitichthys calliurus Regan, 1905

Dorsal rays X,12; anal rays III,6; pectoral rays 14, the lower seven unbranched; lateral-line scales 42; three rows of scales above lateral line in middle of body; four rows of scales on cheek (applies to other species of the genus); gill rakers 3-4 + 10-12; palatine teeth present (true of the genus); preopercular margin coarsely serrate (also generic); body depth about 2.4 in standard length; longest dorsal spine about 2.3 in body depth; tips of interspinous membranes of dorsal fin with a tuft of cirri (generic); first dorsal soft ray prolonged; caudal fin slightly emargi-nate to truncate; orange with dusky blotches, becoming blackish posteriorly; caudal fin white with small blackish spots and a black posterior border. Reaches about 12 cm. Known from the Gulf of Oman (type locality, Muscat) to the Gulf of Aden; usually observed in the depth range of 15 to 30 m. Closely related to *C. bleekeri* Day from the east coast of India and *C. aureus* (Temminck and Schlegel) from southern Japan to Hong Kong.

PIXIE HAWKFISH
Cirrhitichthys oxycephalus (Bleeker, 1855)

Dorsal rays X,12-13 (rarely 13); anal rays III,6; pectoral rays 14, the lower six unbranched; lateral-line scales 40-44; scale rows above lateral line in middle of body 3; gill rakers 4-6 + 10; body depth 2.8-3.0 in standard length; maxilla extending posterior to a vertical at front edge of eye; fifth dorsal spine longest, 1.7-2.2 in body depth; first dorsal soft ray prolonged (at standard lengths of about 35 mm or greater); caudal slightly emarginate to slightly rounded; body whitish with three rows of large, red-edged, dark brown spots and scattered small red spots; small dark spots on head, those on lower part mostly in alignment to form two bands extending downward from eye. Reaches 8.5 cm. A wide-ranging, coral-reef species occurring from the Red Sea and coast of East Africa to the eastern Pacific; known from Oman only from the author's photograph taken at Juzor al Hallaniyat (Kuria Muria Islands) and John Hoover's photograph from Hino near Marbat.

358. *Cirrhitichthys oxycephalus*, about 6 cm (J. Randall)

STOCKY HAWKFISH
Cirrhitus pinnulatus (Bloch and Schneider, 1801)

Dorsal rays X,11; anal rays III,6; pectoral rays 14, the lower seven unbranched and thickened; lateral-line scales 39-44; rows of scales above lateral line in middle of body 4; scales on cheek much smaller than those of body; gill rakers 5-7 + 12-14; body robust, the depth 2.7-3.0 in standard length; snout short and blunt; posterior margin of preopercle finely serrate; a tuft of cirri from membrane near tip of each dorsal spine; caudal fin slightly rounded; ground colour of body white, but so heavily overlaid with dark brown blotches and small reddish brown to black spots that the white remains only as three rows of irregular white spots except ventrally on chest and abdomen where unmarked; head white, densely spotted with dark reddish brown and black. Attains 30 cm. Indo-Pacific; lives inshore on reefs or rocky bottom exposed to surge; feeds mainly on crabs, but also takes shrimps, other crustaceans, fishes, small sea urchins, and brittle stars.

BLACKSIDE HAWKFISH
Paracirrhites forsteri (Bloch and Schneider, 1801)

Dorsal rays X,11; anal rays III,6; pectoral rays 14, the lower seven unbranched and thickened; lateral-line scales 45-49; scales above lateral line in middle of body 5; rows of large scales on cheek 5 or 6; body depth 2.6-2.8 in standard length; margin of preopercle finely serrate; a single cirrus from membrane near tip of each dorsal spine; caudal fin slightly rounded; yellowish with

359. *Cirrhitus pinnulatus*, about 27 cm (J. Randall)

360. *Paracirrhites forsteri*, largest about 13 cm (J. Randall)

a faint longitudinal banding following scale rows; a broad blackish stripe usually present on upper side of posterior two-thirds of body extending nearly to centre of caudal fin (stripe sometimes broken into large blotches); head and anterior body with small brownish red spots; fins varying from yellowish to pink. Maximum length 22 cm. Indo-Pacific, but not known from the Arabian Gulf or Gulf of Oman; a common coral-reef species often seen at rest on live coral. Feeds mainly on small fishes.

FLAGTAILS
FAMILY KUHLIIDAE

As now understood, the Kuhliidae consists of a single genus, *Kuhlia*, with about six species. The genus is characterised by a moderately deep, compressed body; a pointed head with a straight to slightly concave dorsal profile; eye large; strongly oblique mouth with lower jaw projecting; no canine teeth, the jaws, vomer, and palatines with a band of villiform teeth; two flat spines on opercle; preopercular and preorbital bones serrate; ctenoid scales; a continuous, deeply notched dorsal fin with ten spines and nine to twelve rays; a scaly sheath at base of dorsal and anal fins; pelvic rays I,5; no pelvic axillary process; caudal fin slightly to deeply forked. The usual colour is silvery; the caudal fin is variously marked with black. The species are marine, but at least one (*K. rupestris*) is able to live in freshwater. Most occur in shallow water; they are nocturnal, feeding mainly on planktonic crustaceans.

361. School of *Kuhlia mugil* (J. Randall)

FIVEBAND FLAGTAIL
Kuhlia mugil (Forster and Schneider, 1801)

Dorsal rays X,9-11; anal rays 10-11; pectoral rays 14-15 (usually 14); lateral-line scales 48-51; no scales in interorbital space; gill rakers 9-11 + 23-27; body depth 2.6-3.1 in standard length; maxilla not reaching to below middle of eye; dorsal fin deeply notched between spinous and soft portions; caudal fin deeply forked; silvery, the front of snout and chin blackish; caudal fin white with five black bands (one median and two across each lobe); a dusky band in outer part of soft portion of dorsal fin. Attains at least 20 cm. Indo-Pacific and eastern Pacific; known from Oman only in the south. Occurs in shallow water along rocky shores exposed to surge; the young often found in tidepools. Adults frequently seen in large aggregations by day. *Kuhlia sterneckii* Steindachner from the Gulf of Aqaba is a synonym.

362. *Kuhlia mugil*, 13.2 cm (J. Randall)

TERAPONS
FAMILY TERAPONIDAE

The fishes of this Indo-Pacific family are also called tigerperches, grunters, and trumpeters, the last two names alluding to the sound produced by their unique swim bladders equipped with extrinsic muscles. Vari (1978) revised the family; he is followed here in using the common name terapon. These fishes have oblong, moderately compressed bodies; a relatively small, usually oblique mouth (maxilla not reaching to below centre of eye); teeth in villiform bands in jaws with the outer row enlarged (but not as canines; the teeth vary in shape from conical to flattened to tricuspidate); teeth usually present on vomer and palatines of juveniles but lost in most species as adults; opercle with two spines, the lower one larger; preopercular margin serrate; scales ctenoid, moderate to small; lateral line complete, continuing onto caudal fin; dorsal fin with eleven to fourteen spines, the spinous portion folding into a basal scaly sheath; fourth to seventh dorsal spines longest, decreasing in length to penultimate spine (rarely to the last), the fin distinctly notched as a result of elevation of the soft portion; anal fin with three spines; caudal fin emarginate (except a few freshwater species where truncate or rounded); pelvic fins I,5, inserted posterior to base of pectoral fins. About 45 species are known, classified in nine genera; 35 of the species are confined to freshwater of Australia and New Guinea. The marine species usually have three or more dark stripes on the body.

FOURLINE TERAPON
Pelates quadrilineatus (Bloch, 1790)

Dorsal rays XII-XIII,9-11; anal rays III,9-10; pectoral rays 13-16; lateral-line scales 66-75; gill rakers 16-18 + 23-28; body depth 2.6-3.2 in standard length; posttemporal bone covered by skin, not serrate, and not expanded posteriorly; lower opercular spine large, but not extending beyond edge of opercular membrane; last two dorsal spines subequal; second and third anal spines subequal and shorter than longest anal soft ray; silvery grey dorsally, silvery white ventrally, with four (sometimes five or six) very narrow dark brown stripes on body, the third from front of snout through eye to upper third of caudal-fin base; a large dusky blotch usually present above gill opening, its lower part on second dark stripe; mouth and gill cavity red; juveniles with six or seven dusky bars. Reaches about 20 cm. Red Sea to South Africa, east to the western Pacific where it ranges from Japan to New South Wales; not recorded from oceanic islands; an immigrant to the eastern Mediterranean via the Suez Canal. A coastal marine species; often enters estuaries.

363. *Pelates quadrilineatus*, about 11 cm (J. Randall)

151

JARBUA
Terapon jarbua (Forsskål, 1775)

Dorsal rays XI-XII,9-11; anal rays III,7-10; pectoral rays 13-14; lateral-line scales 70-100; gill rakers 6-8 + 13-16; body depth 2.5-3.2 in standard length; posttemporal bone exposed (above gill opening), expanded posteriorly, the edge serrate (true of other species of *Terapon*); lower opercular spine very large, extending posterior to opercular membrane; penultimate dorsal spine about half length of last spine; second and third anal spines subequal, shorter than longest anal soft ray; silvery grey dorsally, silvery white ventrally, with three, down-curved, broad, dark brown to black stripes on body (sometimes a faint fourth stripe present ventrally), the first commencing at origin of dorsal fin, the second on nape, and the third on occiput, continuing to end of middle of caudal fin; each caudal lobe with a broad black crossband and a black tip (or lower lobe with a blackish spot or short band submarginal to tip); a large black spot distally in dorsal fin between third and sixth spines, and two or three blackish spots at margin of soft portion of fin. Reported to 33 cm. Wide-ranging in the Indo-Pacific from the Red Sea and east coast of Africa to Samoa; insular localities in the Indian Ocean include the Seychelles, Mauritius, and Maldives. An inshore species often seen over sand flats where the curved dark stripes serve the fish well as camouflage because of the ever-changing curved shadows cast upon the pale sand bottom from the ripples at the surface; also enters brackish habitats. Feeds mainly on benthic invertebrates and small fishes; also known to bite scales from other fishes (hence not a good candidate for an aquarium). Known for adopting a defensive posture with body bent in a C-shape, the spines erect and the operculum (with the long opercular spine) flared.

364. *Terapon jarbua*, about 12 cm (J. Randall)

365. *Terapon puta*, 10.5 cm (J. Randall)

366. *Terapon puta*, about 9 cm, night (J. Randall)

SPINYCHEEK TERAPON
Terapon puta (Cuvier, 1829)

Dorsal rays XI-XII,9-11; anal rays III,8-9; pectoral rays 13-15; lateral-line scales 70-85; gill rakers 7-9 + 19-25; body elongate for the genus, the depth 3.0-4.0 in standard length; lower opercular spine large, extending posterior to opercular membrane; preopercle strongly serrate; penultimate dorsal spine about half length of last spine; second and third anal spines subequal, shorter than longest anal soft ray; light brown dorsally, shading to silvery white ventrally, with four very narrow dark brown stripes on body (the lowermost stripe may be primarily yellow), the third stripe beginning at front of snout and continuing midlaterally to end of caudal fin; a large black spot on outer part of dorsal fin between the fourth and seventh or eighth spines; each caudal lobe with two narrow dark crossbands; one colour phase with a longitudinal row of large white blotches between stripes; juveniles with six or seven dusky bars. Reaches 15 cm. Red Sea (and into Mediterranean via the Suez Canal) to Zanzibar, east to Indo-Malayan region and northern Queensland; well known from Arabian Gulf and Oman waters; marine but known to enter estuaries or even fresh water. The specific name is derived from the native name "Keel-puta" at Vizagapatam, India.

LARGESCALE TERAPON
Terapon theraps (Cuvier, 1829)

Dorsal rays XI-XII,9-11; anal rays III,7-9; pectoral rays 14-15; lateral-line scales 46-56; gill rakers 6-8 + 15-18; body depth 2.4-3.5 in standard length; lower opercular spine large, extending posterior to edge of opercular membrane; penultimate dorsal spine about half length of last spine; third anal spine longest, but shorter than longest anal ray; silvery grey dorsally, shading to silvery white ventrally, with four broad blackish stripes, the third beginning at front of snout and extending midlaterally along body to end of caudal fin; each lobe of caudal fin with a broad blackish crossband; tip of upper lobe broadly blackish; a large black spot on outer part of dorsal fin between third and sixth or seventh spines; two or three blackish spots at margin of soft portion of fin; juveniles with six or seven dusky bars. Reported to 30 cm. Arabian Gulf and Red Sea, south to South Africa and east to the western Pacific where it ranges from the Ryukyu Islands to southern Queensland; an inshore species sometimes found in brackish habitats.

367. *Terapon theraps*, 9.1 cm (J. Randall)

CARDINALFISHES
FAMILY APOGONIDAE

Although named cardinalfishes, most of the species of this large family are not red. They are distinct in having two separate dorsal fins, the first of VI to VIII spines (the first spine may be very short), the second dorsal fin of one spine and 8 to 14 soft rays; an anal fin of two spines and 8 to 18 rays; 7 branchiostegal rays; large eyes; a large oblique mouth with variable dentition (canines present or absent); a single flat opercular spine (often poorly developed); a ridge on preopercle preceding the margin, the edge of both varying from smooth to serrate; scales usually finely ctenoid, but cycloid in some, and absent in the species of *Gymnapogon*; lateral line continuous. The body depth varies considerably, but all are laterally compressed. These fishes are nocturnal (though some of the larger species may feed opportunistically by day); most eat zooplankton, but some concentrate their feeding on prey on or near the bottom. Many species are known to incubate the eggs in the mouth; the male has long been believed to assume this role, but there are reports of female apogonids as mouth brooders. The family is represented in all tropical to warm temperate seas and in a variety of habitats. Most of these fishes are marine but several such as the species of *Glossamia* are found only in freshwater. Most apogonids are small, generally less than 12 cm, but a few such as *Cheilodipterus macrodon* and *Holapogon maximus* often exceed 20 cm. Fraser (1972) recognised three subfamilies, Apogoninae, Pseudaminae, and Epigoninae, but the last-mentioned is now given family status. Twenty-two genera and an estimated 250 species are known worldwide. New species continue to be discovered. Gon (1993) revised the genus *Cheilodipterus*, describing five species as new. Gon (1995) also revised the species of *Apogon* of the subgenus *Lepidamia*, describing one of the four species as new.

368. *Apogon aureus*, about 11 cm (J. Hoover)

GOLDEN CARDINALFISH
Apogon aureus (Lacepède, 1802)

Dorsal rays VII + I,9; anal rays II,8; pectoral rays 13-15 (usually 14); lateral-line scales 24 (plus four more posterior to caudal-fin base); median predorsal scales 5; gill rakers 6-8 + 16-20; posterior margin of preopercle serrate, and most of the ventral margin as well; preopercular ridge smooth; body depth 2.25-2.85 in standard length; caudal fin slightly emarginate; golden to bronze with iridescence; a broad black bar encircling posterior caudal peduncle, usually broader dorsally and ventrally; a blackish stripe edged in bright blue from front of snout through eye, continuing a short distance posterior to eye, the blue lines breaking into dashes and spots; a bright blue line on upper lip, extending across maxilla, and continuing a short distance posteriorly; tip of lower jaw blackish. Largest specimen, 14.5 cm. Gulf of Oman to Natal, east to Tonga; in the western Pacific from Japan to New South Wales; known from depths of 1-40 m on coral reefs or rocky substrata where caves and crevices provide for diurnal shelter; those found in depths of only a few metres occur in protected bays and lagoons; often seen in small aggregations.

RUBY CARDINALFISH
Apogon coccineus Rüppell, 1838

Dorsal rays VI + I,9; anal rays II,8; pectoral rays 13; lateral-line scales 24; median predorsal scales 6; gill rakers 3-5 + 13-15; upper preopercular edge serrate (the dorsal third to half often smooth), the ventral margin membranous and crenate; preopercular ridge smooth; body depth 2.8-3.2 in standard length; caudal peduncle long and slender its length about twice its depth, 3.6-4.0 in standard length; second dorsal spine short, 1.9-2.3 in head length; caudal fin emarginate with rounded lobes; translucent red with a broad blackish streak midlaterally on caudal peduncle. Red Sea to Arabian Gulf; observed only at night (and then never far from cover).

COOK'S CARDINALFISH
Apogon cookii Macleay, 1881

Dorsal rays VII + I,9; anal rays II,8; pectoral rays 15; lateral-line scales 24; predorsal scales 3-4; gill rakers 4-5 + 12-15 (total count, 17-20); posterior edge and corner of preopercle serrate; preopercular ridge smooth; least bony width of interorbital space 4.15-5.1 in head length; body depth 2.5-2.8 in standard length; last dorsal and anal rays not longer than penultimate rays;

369. *Apogon aureus*, about 12 cm (J. Hoover)

370. *Apogon coccineus*, about 4 cm, night (J. Randall)

371. *Apogon cookii*, about 9 cm (J. Hoover)

caudal fin forked with rounded lobes; whitish with six dark brown stripes broader than pale interspaces, the first middorsal, the second from snout to upper caudal-fin base, the third narrow and not extending beyond second dorsal fin, the fourth from snout through eye, ending in a round spot at caudal-fin base, the fifth and sixth on lower part of body; black bands basally in second dorsal and anal fins, the one in the dorsal with a narrow pale band below it. Reaches 10 cm. Red Sea and Gulf of Oman south to Natal and east to the western Pacific where it ranges from Japan to the Great Barrier Reef and New Caledonia; an inshore species generally found at depths less than 2 m.

YELLOWSTRIPED CARDINALFISH
Apogon cyanosoma Bleeker, 1853

Dorsal rays VII + I,9; anal rays II,8; pectoral rys 14; lateral-line scales 24; predorsal scales 3; gill rakers 6-7 + 15-16; preopercular edge nearly fully serrate, the ridge smooth; body depth 2.7-3.0 in standard length; body bluish silver with seven orange-yellow stripes that are narrower than silver interspaces, the first middorsal and very narrow, passing from interorbital space to origin of dorsal fin, the second passing to the side of dorsal fins and ending dorsally at base of caudal fin, the third, fifth, and sixth extending a short distance into base of caudal fin, the narrow fourth from upper edge of eye but not reaching beyond second dorsal fin, the seventh ventrally on head and body, ending on base of anal fin. Attains about 8 cm. Arabian Gulf and Red Sea south to Mozambique and east to the western Pacific. Occurs in a variety of habitats from 1 to 50 m; gathers in aggregations in caves and beneath ledges by day, sometimes sheltering among the long spines of *Diadema*.

EYESHADOW CARDINALFISH
Apogon exostigma (Jordan and Seale, 1906)

Dorsal rays VII + I,9; anal rays II,8; pectoral rays 12-14 (usually 13); lateral-line scales 23-25 ; predorsal scales 5; circum-

372. *Apogon cyanosoma*, about 7 cm (J. Randall)

373. *Apogon cyanosoma*, about 5.5 cm, night (J. Randall)

peduncular scales 12; gill rakers 4-5 + 13-15; preopercular edge and ridge serrate; body depth 2.9-3.6 in standard length; caudal fin emarginate with slightly rounded lobes; grey to tan dorsally, shading on side to silvery with iridescence, with a dark stripe from front of snout through eye, narrowing as it passes to midbase of caudal fin; a black spot smaller than pupil above and adjacent

to end of lateral dark stripe; leading edge of first dorsal fin broadly blackish; upper and lower edges of caudal fin narrowly blackish. Largest specimen, 12 cm. Appears to have a disjunct east-west distribution: Red Sea to Oman and Cocos-Keeling Islands to the Tuamotu Archipelago (see Fraser and Lachner, 1985, who revised the subgenus *Pristiapogon* which includes this species, *A. fraenatus*, and *A. kallopterus*).

TWOSTRIPE CARDINALFISH
Apogon fasciatus (Shaw, 1790)

Dorsal rays VII + I,9; anal rays II,8; pectoral rays 15-16; lateral-line scales 24; predorsal scales 4-5; gill rakers 5-6 + 13-14; preopercular edge fully serrate; preopercular ridge of adults usually irregular, often with a few serrae on corner; body depth 2.7-3.0 in standard length; caudal fin slightly emarginate; grey dorsally, shading to silvery white on sides and ventrally, with two blackish stripes, the narrow first from interorbital along back to upper edge of caudal peduncle, the second from front of snout through eye along side a little above middle of body to end at posterior end of caudal fin (stripe darkest on opercle and caudal fin). Largest specimen, 10.3 cm. Red Sea and Arabian Gulf to Mozambique, east to the western Pacific where it ranges from Japan to Sydney (type locality); generally found around small isolated coral or rock on silty sand or mud substrata in the depth range of 15 to at least 74 m, but one collection came from a beach seine. Lachner in Schultz and collaborators (1958) restricted the name *fasciatus* to this species by designation of a neotype;

374. *Apogon exostigma*, about 10 cm, night (J. Randall)

375. *Apogon fasciatus*, 6.4 cm (J. Randall)

155

A. quadrifasciatus Cuvier then became a synonym. *A. kiensis* Jordan and Snyder is similar in colour but has VI spines in the first dorsal fin, 14 pectoral rays, and 22-25 gill rakers. Hayashi in Masuda et al. (1984) misidentified *A. fasciatus* as *A. kiensis*.

FLOWER CARDINALFISH
Apogon fleurieu (Lacepède, 1801)

Dorsal rays VII + I,9; anal rays II,8; pectoral rays 13-15 (usually 14); lateral-line scales 24 (not including four on caudal-fin base); median predorsal scales 5; gill rakers 5-7 (rarely 7) + 14-17 (rarely 14 or 17); posterior edge and most of ventral edge of preopercle serrate; preopercular ridge smooth; body depth 2.4-2.85 in standard length; caudal fin slightly forked; golden to coppery with iridescence; a broad black bar posteriorly on caudal peduncle, not expanded dorsally and ventrally (in juveniles this marking begins as a circular spot on side of peduncle); head colouration similar to *A. aureus*. Attains about 11 cm. Occurs in the Red Sea and Arabian Gulf (*A. aureus* not recorded from either), Gulf of Oman and scattered localities in East Africa, Seychelles, India, Sri Lanka, the Indo-Malayan region, and Hong Kong. The validity of this species and *aureus* was demonstrated by Randall et al. (1990). The two are best separated on gill-raker counts (19-23 for *fleurieu* and 22-27 for *aureus*) and the shape of the dark peduncular bar.

SPURCHEEK CARDINALFISH
Apogon fraenatus Valenciennes, 1832

Dorsal rays VII + I,9; anal rays II,8; pectoral rays 13-15 (usually 14); lateral-line scales 23-25; predorsal scales 5; circumpeduncular scales 12; gill rakers 4-5 (usually 4) + 12-14; preopercular edge and ridge serrate; body depth 2.4-3.1 in standard length; caudal fin emarginate with slightly rounded lobes; grey to tan dorsally, shading on sides to silvery with iridescence, with a midlateral tapering black stripe ending in a black spot nearly the size of pupil at base of caudal fin; leading edge of first dorsal fin broadly black; upper and lower edges of caudal fin black. Largest specimen, 10.5 cm. Indo-Pacific but not ranging north of Philippines; occurs in the Gulf of Oman and Musandam.

COPPERSTRIPED CARDINALFISH
Apogon holotaenia (Regan, 1905)

Dorsal rays VII + I,9; anal rays II,8; pectoral rays 13-15 (usually 14); lateral-line scales 24; predorsal scales 3-4; gill rakers 5-6 + 15-16; posterior preopercular edge

376. *Apogon fleurieu*, subadults (P. Woodhead)

377. *Apogon fraenatus*, about 7.5 cm, night (J. Randall)

378. *Apogon holotaenia*, about 5 cm (J. Randall)

serrate, the ventral edge about half serrate; preopercular ridge smooth; some slightly enlarged incurved teeth at front of lower jaw; body depth 2.8-3.0 in standard length; caudal fin slightly emarginate, the lobes rounded posteriorly; bluish silver with seven coppery stripes similar to pattern of *A. cyanosoma* except lowermost stripe poorly developed, the bluish silver stripe above it replaced with a series of bluish silvery spots, and the midlateral stripe becoming dark brown on caudal peduncle and continuing to end of caudal fin. Attains 8 cm. Known from Oman (type locality, Muscat), India (misidentified as *A. endekataenia* Bleeker by Day, 1875), and Mozambique [*A. nitidus* (Smith) is a synonym] (J.K.L. Mee, pers. comm.). Collected by the author in Seychelles, Réunion, and Malaysia; photographed at Musandam, Oman.

ODDSCALE CARDINALFISH
Apogon evermanni Jordan and Snyder, 1904

Dorsal rays VI + I,9; anal rays II,8; pectoral rays 12; lateral-line scales 24; longitudinal scale series 45-48; predorsal scales 10-12; circumpeduncular scales 28-31; gill rakers 4-6 + 15-17; preopercular edge finely serrate; preopercular ridge smooth; body depth 2.7-3.7 in standard length; dorsal profile of head straight; caudal fin forked, the lobes strongly rounded; red with a large black spot at rear base of second dorsal fin and adjacent back, and a small white spot immediately behind; a dark brown streak from snout through eye to end of operculum. Largest specimen, 12.2 cm. Indo-Pacific (except Red Sea) and western Atlantic; Oman record based on the photograph by Philip Woodhead, reproduced herein; it was taken off southern Oman. Nearly identical in colour to *A. isus* Randall and Böhlke from the Red Sea, which differs in having the lateral-line scales equal in size to those of the rest of the body.

379. *Apogon evermanni*, about 5 cm (J. Randall)

380. *Apogon evermanni* (P. Woodhead)

TEN-BAR CARDINALFISH
Apogon lineatus Temminck and Schlegel, 1842

Dorsal rays VII + I,9; anal rays I,8; pectoral rays 14-16 (usually 15); lateral-line scales 24; predorsal scales 4; gill rakers 3-5 + 11-13 (developed gill rakers 2 + 11-12); rounded corner of preopercle and most of ventral edge serrate; posterior edge largely smooth; preopercular ridge smooth; mouth strongly oblique; body depth 2.7-2.9 in standard length; head length 2.3-2.5 in standard length; snout length 5.4-6.1 in head length; caudal fin slightly rounded; light grey dorsally, the edges of the scales dusky, shading to silvery on sides and ventrally, with ten dusky bars on body narrower than pale interspaces; a dusky bar from below posterior part of eye and another longer bar from behind upper part of eye to corner of preopercle; front of snout and chin dusky; outer half of first dorsal fin blackish; second dorsal and caudal fins slightly dusky. Attains at least 9 cm. Occurs on sand or mud substrates to depths as great as 100 m; the illustrated specimen was taken by trawl in the Gulf of Oman in 46 m. *Apogon striatus* Smith and Radcliffe is a synonym.

381. *Apogon lineatus*, 6.4 cm (J. Randall)

MANYLINE CARDINALFISH
Apogon natalensis Gilchrist and
Thompson, 1908

Dorsal rays VIII + I,9 (the eighth spine
small, generally hidden by scales); anal rays
II,8; pectoral rays 14-16 (usually 15); lateral-line scales 40-47 (usually 41-44); predorsal scales 2-5; gill rakers 5-6 + 14-16;
preopercular edge very finely serrate; preopercular ridge smooth; body depth 2.5-2.9
in standard length; caudal fin emarginate
with rounded lobes; light red, the body with
longitudinal dark brown lines along the
upper and lower edges of scales, those above
lateral line following its curvature, those
below straight; fins light red, the first dorsal
with a black spot on third membrane near
base; a semicircular dark brown spot across
pectoral-fin base; margin of caudal fin narrowly blackish. Largest specimen, 19 cm.
Southern Oman to Natal; the illustrated
specimen was collected in 7 m in Rahah
Bay, Oman.

382. *Apogon natalensis*, adult, 16.1 cm (J. Randall)

383. *A. natalensis*, subadult, about 12 cm (J. Hoover)

BULLS-EYE CARDINALFISH
Apogon nigripinnis Cuvier, 1828

Dorsal rays VII + I,9; anal rays II,8; pectoral rays 15-16 (usually 16); lateral-line
scales 24; median predorsal scales 2; gill
rakers 3-5 + 12-13; preopercular edge serrate, the ridge smooth; body depth 2.3-2.7
in standard length; caudal fin truncate; grey-
brown dorsally, shading to silvery on side
and ventrally, with three dark brown bars,
the first containing a yellow-edged black
spot clearly larger than pupil on midside and
continuing broadly at front of first dorsal fin;
second bar with its ends in the second dorsal
and anal fins; third bar across caudal-fin
base; lesser, incomplete, dark bars on nape,
below interdorsal space, and on caudal
peduncle; an oblique dark brown line from
lower edge of eye to corner of preopercle.
Attains 10 cm. Red Sea and Arabian Gulf
to Mozambique, east to the Indo-Malayan
region and Australia.

384. *Apogon nigripinnis*, 7.5 cm (J. Randall)

OMAN CARDINALFISH
Apogon omanensis Gon and Mee , 1995

Dorsal rays VIII + I,9 (eighth dorsal spine usually concealed by scales in adults); anal

385. *A. omanensis*, juv., about 4 cm (J. Randall)

rays II,8; pectoral rays 16-17; lateral-line scales 43-48; predorsal scales 3-5; gill rakers 5-6 + 14-16; preopercular edge weakly serrate, the ridge smooth; body depth 2.5 -3.1 in standard length; caudal fin slightly emarginate with broadly rounded lobes; adults pale reddish brown dorsally, shading to whitish ventrally, with longitudinal dark brown lines following upper and lower edges of scales, those above lateral line paralleling it and those below straight; juveniles translucent with three blackish stripes and

a large black spot at base of each of the median fins. Largest specimen, 15.5 cm. Known only from central to southern Oman (type locality, Masirah Island); a shallow-water species; greatest depth, 8 m (most specimens have come from tidepools). One of four species of the subgenus *Lepidamia* (revised by Gon, 1995).

DOUBLEBAR CARDINALFISH
Apogon pseudotaeniatus Gon, 1986

Dorsal rays VII + I,9; anal rays II,8; pectoral rays 15; lateral-line scales 24; predorsal scales 3; gill rakers 4-5 + 13-14; preopercular edge serrate; preopercular ridge smooth; body depth 2.3-2.5 in standard length; caudal fin slightly emarginate with rounded lobes; light reddish brown to grey dorsally, shading to light silvery grey with iridescence on side, with two narrow dark brown bars on body, the first continuous with a band at front of first dorsal fin, the second originating below anterior part of second dorsal fin; a small dark brown spot on lateral line posteriorly on caudal peduncle. Reported to 14 cm. Red Sea and Arabian Gulf to the Indo-Malayan region, north to Japan. Identified as *A. bifasciatus* Rüppell by authors until Gon (1986) determined that *bifasciatus* is a junior synonym of *A. taeniatus* Cuvier.

SIGNAL CARDINALFISH
Apogon queketti Gilchrist, 1903

Dorsal rays VII + I,9; anal rays II,8; pectoral rays 16; predorsal scales 3; gill rakers 5 + 12 (developed rakers 2 + 11-12); lateral-line scales 24; predorsal scales 3; upper preopercular edge smooth but lower edge not well-ossified and crenulate; preopercular ridge smooth; mouth large and strongly oblique, the maxilla reaching or nearly reaching a vertical at rear edge of eye; body depth 2.9-3.0 in standard length; head length 2.3-2.5 in standard length; snout length 5.8-6.1 in head; caudal fin slightly to moderately rounded; light pinkish grey dorsally, the edges of the scales dark brown, shading to silvery on sides and ventrally, with a dark brown spot on scales on side of body below lateral line forming longitudinal rows (spots poorly developed or absent on caudal peduncle); a diagonal dusky streak usually present on cheek; first dorsal fin with a large black spot in outer posterior part of fin; anal and caudal fins (and to a lesser extent the second dorsal) with a blackish outer margin. Occurs from the Arabian Gulf to South Africa and east to India; generally taken by trawling, the illustrated specimen from 73 m.

386. *Apogon omanensis*, 10.5 cm (J. Randall)

387. *Apogon pseudotaeniatus*, about 7.5 cm (J. Randall)

388. *Apogon queketti*, 9.1 cm (J. Randall)

OBLIQUEBANDED CARDINALFISH
Apogon semiornatus Peters, 1876

Dorsal rays VI + I,9; anal rays II,8; pectoral rays 12; lateral-line scales 24; predorsal scales 6; gill rakers 4-5 + 12-13; posterior preopercular edge serrate, the ventral edge membranous and crenulate; preopercular ridge smooth; body depth 2.6-2.8 in standard length; caudal fin emarginate with broadly rounded lobes; transparent light red with a broad, oblique, blackish band from eye to base of anal fin, and another following lateral line and continuing to end of caudal fin; a narrow blackish band from nape to rear base of second dorsal fin. Reaches 5 cm. Red Sea and Gulf of Oman south to Natal and east to the western Pacific; a very secretive species generally seen only at night (and then only briefly, because it quickly takes shelter when illuminated).

ELONGATE CARDINALFISH
Apogon smithvanizi Allen and Randall, 1995

Dorsal rays VI + I,9; anal rays II,8; pectoral rays 14-15 (rarely 15); lateral-line scales 24; gill rakers 5-7 + 17-18; preopercular edge finely serrate, the preopercular ridge smooth or weakly crenulate; body elongate for the genus, 3.0-4.0 in standard length; dorsal profile of head straight to slightly concave except for rounded front of snout; caudal fin forked; body translucent whitish, partly silvery ventrally; head silvery except dorsally; a blackish streak on side of snout; a small amount of black pigment directly behind eye. Largest specimen, 6.6 cm. Known from six specimens taken by trawl off Bahrain and the Gulf of Oman in 33-40 m. Because of their elongate body and colouration, they were believed at first to be a species of *Rhabdamia*.

389. *Apogon semiornatus*, 4.5 cm, night (J. Hoover)

390. *Apogon smithvanizi*, 6.6 cm (J. Randall)

STRIPED CARDINALFISH
Apogon taeniatus Cuvier, 1828

Dorsal rays VII + I,9; anal rays II,8; pectoral rays 14-15; lateral-line scales 24; predorsal scales 3; gill rakers 4-5 + 12-15 (usually 4 + 13-14); posterior preopercular edge and corner finely serrate, the ventral edge smooth; preopercular ridge smooth; body depth 2.4-2.6 in standard length; caudal fin slightly emarginate with the posterior margin of each lobe rounded; grey, shading to silvery grey with iridescence on side and ventrally, with brown stripes following scale rows, the upper three parallel with curve of lateral line and the lower seven or eight horizontal; four blackish bands radiating from posterior and lower edge of eye, the most prominent across cheek to corner of preopercle; three faint dark bars on body, one below each dorsal fin and one at base of caudal fin, the first with a large ocellated black spot above pectoral fin within first dark bar. Largest specimen, 10.5 cm. Red Sea and Arabian Gulf (where abundant) south to Mozambique, Aldabra, and Madagascar; a shallow-water species often found in seagrass or substrata with heavy algal growth. Often confused with *A. nigripinnis* which also has an ocellus above the pectoral fin, but it lacks stripes on the body and has more sharply defined dark bars, 2 predorsal scales, and 15 or 16 pectoral rays.

391. *Apogon taeniatus*, about 7 cm, night (J. Randall)

TIMOR CARDINALFISH
Apogon timorensis Bleeker, 1854

Dorsal rays VII + I,9; anal ras II,8; pectoral rays 15-16; lateral-line scales 24; predorsal scales 3; gill rakers 3-4 + 11-12; posterior preopercular edge serrate, the ventral edge about half serrate; preopercular ridge smooth; body depth 2.5-2.8 in standard length; dorsal profile of head nearly straight except for bluntly rounded front of snout; caudal fin slightly emarginate, the lobes rounded; brown dorsally, shading to silvery or bronze with iridescence on lower side, with two broad dark bars (often indistinct) on body, one beneath each dorsal fin, and sometimes a third narrower bar at base of caudal fin; a faint dark bar on nape; a strongly oblique dark brown line from lower edge of eye to corner of preopercle; first dorsal fin and pelvic fins blackish distally. Reaches 9 cm. Red Sea and southern Oman to Natal, east to the western Pacific; known from coral reefs or rocky bottom from less than 0.5 to about 12 m.

FLAGFIN CARDINALFISH
Apogon truncatus Bleeker, 1854

Dorsal rays VII + I,9; anal rays I,8; pectoral rays 16-17 (usually 17); lateral-line scales 24; predorsal scales 4; gill rakers 3-5 + 11-12 (developed gill rakers 1 + 10); preopercular edge with a few serrae at corner, the ridge smooth; mouth strongly oblique and large, the maxilla nearly or just reaching a vertical at rear edge of eye; body depth 2.9-3.0 in standard length; head length 2.5-2.6 in standard length; snout length 4.7-5.1 in head length; caudal fin slightly rounded; light grey dorsally, the scale edges dusky, shading to silvery on side and ventrally, with five or six large dusky spots in a longitudinal row above lateral line; front of snout and chin blackish; outer half of first dorsal fin black; second dorsal and anal fins with a middle blackish band, the second dorsal and caudal with a distal blackish margin. Reported to 15 cm. Occurs from the Red Sea and Arabian Gulf along the southern Asian shore to the Indo-Malayan region, north to Japan and south to Queensland; usually taken by trawls at depths greater than 20 m. *A. ellioti* Day is a synonym (O. Gon, pers. comm.).

DHOFAR CARDINALFISH
Apogon dhofar Mee, 1995

Dorsal rays VII + I,9; anal rays II,8; pectoral rays 14-16 (usually 15); lateral-line scales 24; predorsal scales 3; gill rakers 5 + 14-16; preopercular margin nearly fully ser-

392. *Apogon timorensis*, 7.2 cm (J. Randall)

393. *Apogon truncatus*, 5.8 cm (J. Randall)

394. *Apogon dhofar*, about 12 cm (J. Randall)

rate, the ridge smooth; body depth 2.5-2.7 in standard length; first dorsal spine about half length of second; second spine about one-fourth length of third; third spine 2.0-2.4 in head length; caudal fin emarginate; body brown, shading to silvery brown with iridescence ventrally, the edges of scales dark brown; two narrow dark brown bars on body, each continuing onto front of a dorsal fin (bars may be faint or absent in large adults); head brown without any obvious dark markings; juveniles and subadults with a small blackish spot posteriorly on lateral line. Attains about 14 cm. Known only from the southern and central coast of Oman where it is common on rocky bottom from less than 1 to at least 10 m. Under study by J.K.L. Mee.

ORANGELINED CARDINALFISH
Archamia fucata (Cantor, 1850)

Dorsal rays VI + I,9; anal rays II,15-18; pectoral rays 13-15 (usually 14); lateral-line scales 24; predorsal scales 5-6; gill rakers 5-6 + 14-16; posterior preopercular edge serrate only at corner, the ventral margin about half serrate; preopercular ridge angular (often a small flat spine at corner), without serration; body moderately deep, the depth 2.3-2.5 in standard length, and compressed, the width nearly 3 in depth; caudal fin slightly forked; iridescent silvery to coppery with vertical orange lines following posterior edges of scales, curving forward as they pass ventrally; a diffuse blackish spot larger than pupil posteriorly on side of caudal peduncle; an orange stripe on side of snout; lower jaw mainly orange-yellow. Reaches 8 cm. Coast of East Africa, Red Sea, and Arabian Gulf east to Samoa. Usually seen in aggregations in the shelter of coral reefs (sometimes among branches of coral) or rocky bottom by day; feeds on zooplankton as solitary individuals well above the substratum at night.

PALE CARDINALFISH
Archamia pallida Gon and Randall, 1995

Dorsal rays VI + I,9; anal rays I,13-14; pectoral rays 14-15; lateral-line scales 24; predorsal scales 5-6; gill rakers 5-6 + 13-15 (developed gill rakers 2-3 + 13-14); preopercular edge serrate except dorsal half of posterior margin, the largest serrae at corner; preopercular ridge smooth; body depth 2.95-3.1 in standard length; body width 2.2-2.4 in body depth; caudal peduncle length 4.1-4.0 in standard length; translucent with a round black spot nearly as large as pupil at midbase of caudal fin, a narrow midlateral black stripe from front of snout through eye, across opercle, and along side of body to end

395. *Archamia fucata*, about 5.5 cm (J. Hoover)

396. *Archamia pallida*, about 3.5 cm (J. Randall)

in the black spot (the part of stripe on body consists of a single row of black dots); upper fifth of body with about five longitudinal rows of black dots; a narrow blackish streak above eye; front of lips blackish; front of both dorsal fins slightly blackish (all black markings mixed with traces of yellow pigment). Attains about 4 cm. Known only from the east side of Masirah Island off the central coast of Oman in 12 m. The specimens appear to be subadults; adults may be more heavily pigmented.

ARABIAN CARDINALFISH
Cheilodipterus arabicus (Gmelin, 1788)

Dorsal rays VI + I,9; anal rays II,8; pectoral rays 13-14 (usually 14); lateral-line scales 24; developed gill rakers (those higher than their base) 2 + 8-11; preopercular edge serrate; preopercular ridge smooth (true of all species of *Cheilodipterus*); large canine teeth in jaws, including front of lower jaw; body depth 2.8-3.7 in standard length; caudal fin of adults slightly to moderately forked (also generic); grey-brown dorsally, shading to silvery with iridescence on side and ventrally, with 13-17 brassy brown stripes equal to or narrower than pale interspaces (in fish larger than 6.5 cm standard length); large adults (i.e. fish over about 10 cm standard length) with a broad blackish bar across caudal-fin base; juveniles with a pupil-size or smaller black spot at caudal-fin base, its diameter 3.4-4.6 in peduncle depth. Largest specimen, 15.3 cm. Red Sea (type locality) south to Natal and east to Pakistan and Seychelles; occurs in southern Oman and the Gulf of Oman, but not the Arabian Gulf. *Perca lineata* Forsskål is a primary homonym of *P. lineata* Linnaeus, hence unavailable for this species. Gmelin provided the new name *P. arabica* (= *Cheilodipterus arabicus*).

397. *Cheilodipterus arabicus*, about 15 cm (J. Randall)

LARGETOOTH CARDINALFISH
Cheilodipterus macrodon (Lacepède, 1802)

Dorsal rays VI + I,9; anal rays II,8; pectoral rays 12-14 (usually 13); lateral-line scales 23-24; developed gill rakers (higher than their base) 1-2 + 6-9; posterior preopercular edge serrate, the serrae relatively smaller with growth and may be absent in large individuals; ventral edge of preopercle smooth or with a few small serrae; canine teeth in jaws large, including a pair at front of lower jaw; body depth 3.1-3.8 in standard length; adults silvery white with seven to ten dark brown stripes broader than pale interspaces on body (fewer as they converge on head), usually ending on caudal peduncle anterior to a large black spot or blackish bar centred on base of caudal fin (thus often a whitish area between stripes and black spot or bar); first dorsal fin dusky with a large blackish area distally; upper and lower edges of caudal fin blackish. This and *Holapogon maximus* are the largest of the cardinalfishes; reaches at least 25 cm. Indo-Pacific, including the Arabian Gulf (record from underwater photograph by Rodney V. Salm). A coral-reef species usually seen by day in caves or beneath ledges, generally in less than 30 m.

398. *Cheilodipterus macrodon*, about 22 cm (J. Randall)

399. *Cheilodipterus novemstriatus*, about 7 cm (J. Randall)

TWOSPOT CARDINALFISH
Cheilodipterus novemstriatus (Rüppell, 1838)

Dorsal rays VI + I,9; anal rays II,8; pectoral rays 11-13 (usually 12); lateral-line scales 23-24; developed gill rakers (higher than their base) 2-3 + 9-12; posterior edge of preopercle finely serrate, the ventral edge smooth; no canine teeth at front of lower jaw; body depth 3.2-3.7 in standard length; grey, shading to silvery with iridescence on side of body and ventrally, with five narrow black stripes, the first middorsal and along base of dorsal fins, the fifth mainly ventral but arching upward from pelvic-fin origin onto chest; a black spot of about pupil size, broadly edged in bright yellow, posteriorly on side of caudal peduncle and base of caudal fin, with a small black spot middorsally above it (often a midventral small black spot on peduncle as well). A small species, the largest 8 cm. Occurs from the Red Sea to the Arabian Gulf; generally found in protected areas at depths of about 1-10 m; often hides among the spines of sea urchins of the genus *Diadema*. *C. bipunctatus* (Lachner) is a synonym.

PERSIAN CARDINALFISH
Cheilodipterus persicus Gon, 1993

Dorsal rays VI + I,9; anal rays II,8; pectoral rays 13-15 (usually 14); lateral-line scales 24; developed gill rakers (higher than their base) 2-3 + 11-14; preopercular edge serrate, the largest serrae at angle; large canine teeth in jaws, including a pair at front of lower jaw; body depth 3.0-3.6 in standard length; grey dorsally, shading to silvery with lavender and pale blue iridescence on side and ventrally, with ten to thirteen narrow dark brown stripes which alternate in width and intensity; a very large bright yellow area posteriorly on caudal peduncle and base of caudal fin containing in its centre a black spot larger than pupil (spot diameter 2.5-3.6 in peduncle depth); pale interspaces anteriorly on head golden; first dorsal fin dusky distally. Reaches about 15 cm. A shallow-water species presently known only from the Arabian Gulf to southern Oman (more common in northern Oman than in the south).

400. *Cheilodipterus persicus*, about 10 cm (J. Randall)

FIVELINE CARDINALFISH

Cheilodipterus quinquelineatus Cuvier, 1828

Dorsal rays VI + I,9; anal rays II,8; pectoral rays 12-13 (usually 12); lateral-line scales 24; developed gill rakers (higher than their base) 1-2 + 7-12; preopercular edge serrate at corner and at most adjacent half of posterior and ventral margins; no canine teeth at front of lower jaw; body depth 3.1-3.7 in standard length; iridescent silvery grey with five, sharply defined, narrow, black stripes on body, the third from front of snout through eye, along middle of body, ending posteriorly at edge of a large yellow spot centred on caudal-fin base; a small black spot in middle of large yellow spot, its diameter 2.9-5.3 in peduncle depth; fifth dark stripe on body straight from anal-fin base to isthmus (not arching upward on chest); no small black spot dorsally or ventrally on caudal peduncle. Attains 12 cm; sexually mature at about 6 cm. Indo-Pacific; not yet known from the Arabian Gulf, but occurs in Gulf of Oman and in the south. Usually found in protected waters of bays or lagoons, often sheltering among the branches of live coral or the spines of *Diadema*, but may be seen in the deeper areas of seaward reefs (to at least 40 m).

401. *Cheilodipterus quinquelineatus*, about 10 cm (J. Hoover)

402. *Fowleria abocellata*, 4.8 cm (L. McCarthy)

403. *Fowleria aurita*, 9 cm (J. Randall)

MOTTLED CARDINALFISH

Fowleria abocellata Goren and Karplus, 1980

Dorsal rays VII + I,9; anal rays II,8; pectoral rays 13-14; lateral-line scales 22-23, the first 9-11 with tubes; predorsal scales 4; gill rakers 3 + 12-13 (1 + 5 developed); preopercular edge and ridge not serrate; villiform teeth in jaws and on vomer, but none on palatines (true of other species of *Fowleria*); body depth 2.7-3.5 in standard length; caudal fin rounded (also generic); mottled brown or reddish brown and white, often with six to eight narrow whitish bars; indistinct dark bands radiating from posterior half of eye; no ocellated dark spot on opercle. Attains 5 cm. Although not described until 1980 (from the northern Red Sea), it is now known to range widely in the Indo-Pacific; collected by the author in the Arabian Gulf, Mauritius, Seychelles, Maldives, Indonesia, New Guinea, Solomons, Great Barrier Reef, Philippines, Ruykyus, Marshall Islands, Line Islands, and Society Islands from the depth range of 5-52 m; occurs in a variety of habitats from isolated reefs to seagrass and algal substrates. Mistakenly classified in the genus *Foa* by Hayashi in Masuda et al. (1984).

CROSSEYED CARDINALFISH

Fowleria aurita (Valenciennes, 1831)

Dorsal rays VII + I,9; anal rays II,8; pectoral rays 13-14; lateral-line scales 23, the first 9-13 with tubes; predorsal scales 6; gill rakers 3-4 + 12-14 (1 + 4-6 developed); posterior preopercular edge smooth, the ventral edge membranous and crenulate; preopercular ridge smooth; body depth 2.6-3.05 in standard length; reddish to orangish brown, the edges of scales darker than centres; a yellow-rimmed black spot larger than pupil basally on opercle; fin rays red or orange, the membranes translucent. Reaches 9 cm. Red Sea south to Natal and east to Samoa; the illustrated specimen was collected in 1 m at Barr al Hikman, central coast of Oman; other localities from various habitats to depths of 21 m.

VARIEGATED CARDINALFISH
Fowleria variegata (Valenciennes, 1832)

Dorsal rays VII + I,9; anal rays II,8; pectoral rays 12-14 (usually 13); lateral-line scales 22-23, the first 10-13 with tubes; predorsal scales 4; gill rakers 3-4 + 11-12 (1 + 5-6 developed); upper preopercular margin smooth, the ventral edge firmly membranous and crenulate; preopercular ridge smooth; body depth 2.5-2.95 in standard length; a faint pattern of narrow pale and dark bars on body obscured by numerous small dark brown spots; a black spot larger than pupil, narrowly rimmed by yellow and encircled by a dark brown line, basally on opercle; all fins except pectorals with numerous small dark brown spots. Reaches 7 cm. Red Sea and Arabian Gulf south to Kenya and east to Samoa; in the western Pacific from the Ryukyu Islands to the Great Barrier Reef; collected by the author in the depth range of 0.3-27 m; occurs in seagrass beds, algal flats, mangrove areas, and silty reefs. Highly cryptic, like other species of the genus.

TITAN CARDINALFISH
Holapogon maximus (Boulenger, 1887)

Dorsal rays VIII + I,9 (the eighth spine of adults usually hidden beneath scales); anal rays II,7; pectoral rays 13-14; lateral-line scales 23-25; predorsal scales 5; gill rakers 5-7 + 15-17; preopercular edge nearly fully serrate, the ridge smooth; villiform teeth in bands in jaws and on vomer and palatines; body depth 2.6-2.8 in standard length; second dorsal fin higher than first; caudal fin emarginate with rounded lobes; pinkish tan to brownish yellow dorsally, shading to brassy with pink iridescence on side and ventrally, the body and nape with numerous small dark brown spots, some on ventral part of body tending to merge to form irregular stripes; two slightly diagonal brown bars on head, one from top of iris

404. *Fowleria variegata*, 7.1 cm (J. Randall)

405. *Holapogon maximus*, 20 cm (J. Randall)

across lower cheek, the second (containing some dark brown spots) from nape across operclum; fins yellowish, the first dorsal with a black spot anteriorly at base. Largest specimen, 25 cm. Known only from the Gulf of Oman and the southern Arabian coast; two were collected from a small aggregation in 38 m at Fahl Island by the author; the species probably ranges to 100 m or more. Fraser (1973), who created the genus *Hola-*

pogon for this fish, regards it as close to the ancestral line of living apogonid fishes.

SWALLOWTAIL CARDINALFISH
Rhabdamia cypselura Weber, 1909

Dorsal rays VI + I,9; anal rays II,9; pectoral rays 14-16; lateral-line scales 25; predorsal scales 4; scales cycloid and deciduous; gill rakers 4-5 + 12-14 (1-2 + 10-12 developed); preopercular edge and ridge smooth; no canine teeth; no palatine teeth; body elongate, the depth 3.8-4.3 in standard length; fin spines slender; caudal fin strongly forked; transparent with tiny orange dots, silvery to golden over abdomen and operculum; a short black stripe on side of snout (often only as a spot), continuing faintly behind eye onto opercle; a submarginal dusky band in each lobe of caudal fin. Reaches 6 cm. Reported from Mozambique, Seychelles, Maldives, Chagos Archipelago, Indonesia, New Guinea, and the Philippines; the Oman record is based on specimens collected by the author from the Strait of Hormuz. Forms dense aggregations in caves.

406. School of *Rhabdamia cypselura*, 4-5 cm (J. Randall)

SEA-URCHIN FISH
Siphamia versicolor (Smith and Radcliffe, 1911)

Dorsal rays VII + I,9; anal rays II,8; pectoral rays 14-16 (rarely 14; usually 15); lateral-line scales 23-24; predorsal scales 4; scales cycloid, thin, and easily lost; developed gill rakers (higher than their base) 1 + 7-8; preopercular edge serrate; a subcutaneous tubular luminous organ, unique to the genus, ventrally on body from anteriorly in the gill chamber to lower caudal peduncle; body depth 2.4-2.6 in standard length; caudal fin forked with rounded lobes; colour varying from black to silvery or silvery with three blackish stripes; fins transparent to orange-red (red pigment concentrated on rays); first dorsal fin with scattered small black dots; surface of tongue with a large blackish patch on each side. Reaches 4 cm. Gulf of Oman and southern Oman (in 6-15 m) to western Pacific; often found among the spines of long-spined sea urchins, especially those of the genus *Diadema*. A revision of the species of *Siphamia* is needed.

407. *Siphamia versicolor* hiding among spines of *Diadema* (J. Hoover)

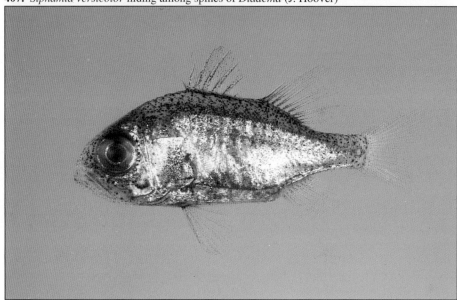

408. *Siphamia versicolor*, 3.8 cm (J. Randall)

SILLAGOS
FAMILY SILLAGINIDAE

Also known as whitings, these fishes are found only in shallow marine waters and estuaries of the tropical to warm temperate western Pacific and Indian Oceans, usually on sand or mud bottoms. They are characterised by an elongate body; opercle with a single sharp spine; small terminal mouth with villiform teeth in bands in jaws; small teeth anteriorly on vomer, none on palatines; maxilla slipping under preorbital when mouth closed; small ctenoid scales; complete lateral line; two dorsal fins with little or no space between, the first of IX to XII slender spines, the second of one spine and 16 to 26 rays; anal fin with two slender spines and 14 to 26 rays; caudal fin emarginate to truncate; pelvic fins I,5, inserted beneath the pectorals. The swim bladder may be absent or vestigial (*Sillaginopsis*) or complex with numerous extensions. There are three genera, the monotypic *Sillaginodes* and *Sillaginopsis* and *Sillago* with 29 species. The family was revised by McKay (1985, 1992). Burchmore et al. (1988) reported on the biology of four species of *Sillago* from New South Wales; the fishes fed principally on polychaete worms, crustaceans (amphipods, copepods, and various shrimps, including *Callianassa*), and bivalve molluscs.

409. *Sillago arabica*, about 7 cm (J. Randall)

ARABIAN SILLAGO
Sillago arabica McKay and McCarthy, 1989

Dorsal rays XII-XIII + I,22-24; anal rays II,22-24; lateral-line scales 75-80; scale rows above lateral line to origin of first dorsal fin 6; cheek scales in 3-4 rows; vertebrae 38-40; body depth 5.0-6.25 in standard length; head 3.45-4.15 in standard length; snout short, its length 2.65-3.2 in head length; caudal fin slightly forked; swim bladder with a single posterior extension and none anterior; silvery without dark markings. Largest specimen, 13.6 cm. Known only from the Arabian Gulf; caught by beach seines.

410. *Sillago arabica*, 13.8 cm (L. McCarthy)

SLENDER SILLAGO
Sillago attenuata McKay, 1985

Dorsal rays XII-XIII + I,19-21; anal rays II,18-20; lateral-line scales 73-77; scale rows above lateral line to origin of first dorsal fin 5; scales on cheek cycloid, in 2 rows; vertebrae 37-39; body slender, the depth 5.9-6.7 in standard length; head length 3.6-3.85 in standard length; snout 2.45-2.7 in head; caudal fin slightly emarginate; swim bladder delicate and nearly transparent; two longitudinal series of faint dark spots on body, the upper of eight to nine spots and the lower midlateral row of ten; anterior interspinous membranes of first dorsal fin dusky; membranes of second dorsal fin sparsely dotted with black; corners of caudal fin dusky. Largest specimen, 22 cm. Presently known only from the Arabian Gulf.

411. *Sillago attenuata*, 11.3 cm (L. McCarthy)

CLUBFOOT SILLAGO
Sillago chondropus Bleeker, 1849

Dorsal rays XI-XII + I,20-21; anal rays II,22-23; first pelvic ray modified into a laterally compressed, club-like structure; lateral-line scales 66-73; scales above lateral line to origin of first dorsal fin 6; cheek scales in 3-4 rows; vertebrae 35; body depth 6.25-6.7 in standard length; head 4.0 in standard length; snout length 2.85-3.1 in head length; caudal fin slightly emarginate; swim bladder reduced in size; pale brown dorsally, with a silver-grey midlateral stripe; tip of first dorsal fin dusky. Reported to 36 cm. South Africa north to the Gulf of Aden and Gulf of Oman, east to the Indo-Malayan region and Taiwan.

INDIAN SILLAGO
Sillago indica McKay, Dutt, and Sujatha, 1985

Dorsal rays XI + I,20-23; anal rays II,21-24; lateral-line scales 67-77; vertebrae 34; scales above lateral line to origin of first dorsal fin 4; scales on cheek mostly cycloid, in 2-3 rows; body depth 4.75-5.55 in standard length; head length 3.45-3.6 in standard length; snout length 2.5-2.7 in head length; caudal fin forked; swim bladder with a very slender anterior projection on each side which curves and passes posteriorly; other shorter anterior and lateral extensions; posterior end of swim bladder bifurcating to two slender postcoelomic extensions; silvery grey dorsally, silvery whitish ventrally, the two zones separated by a midlateral white stripe containing a series of dusky blotches of about pupil size. Reaches about 20 cm. Previously known only from India; five specimens obtained by the author in the Salalah market.

412. *Sillago chondropus* (after Bleeker, 1878)

413. *Sillago indica*, 17.5 cm (J. Randall)

SILVER SILLAGO
Sillago sihama (Forsskål, 1775)

Dorsal rays XI + I,20-23; anal rays II,21-23; lateral-line scales 66-72; scales above lateral line to origin of first dorsal fin 4-5 (usually 5); scales on cheek cycloid, in 2-3 rows (usually 2); vertebrae 34; body depth 5.0-6.25 in standard length; head length 3.35-4.15 in standard length; snout length 2.4-2.85 in head length; caudal fin slightly emarginate to truncate; swim bladder similar to that of *S. indica*, but lacking lateral extensions; silvery grey dorsally, shading to silvery on sides and ventrally; corners of caudal fin dusky. Attains about 30 cm. The most wide-ranging species of the family, occurring along the entire east coast of Africa, the Red Sea and Arabian Gulf to the western Pacific where it ranges from Korea to Queensland; insular localities include Madagascar, Comoros, Seychelles, Palau, and the Solomons. Occurs along sandy shores and in estuaries. Like most members of the family, it is able to bury in the sand with the approach of danger; it may escape a seine this way.

414. *Sillago sihama*, 18.6 cm (J. Randall)

TILEFISHES
FAMILY MALACANTHIDAE

This family is now regarded as consisting of two subfamilies, the Malacanthinae, the sand tilefishes, and the Latilinae (= Branchiosteginae), the tilefishes. Some authors have preferred to regard the two as separate families. At the family level they are diagnosed by having an elongate body; opercle with a single spine; mouth terminal or slightly inferior, with small canine teeth and villiform teeth in jaws, but no teeth on roof of mouth; pharygneal teeth well-developed; 6 branchiostegal rays; scales ctenoid on most of body, cycloid on head; dorsal and anal fins long and without a notch, the dorsal with two to ten spines, the anal with one or two; pelvic fins I,5. The species of Latilinae are less elongate, in general, more blunt-headed, and have a characteristic median predorsal ridge; there are three genera, none of which have representatives

in Oman, though species of *Branchiostegus* should be expected in the deeper water. The Malacanthinae contains two genera, *Malacanthus* with three species (one in the Atlantic) and *Hoplolatilus* (only Indo-Pacific, with nine species). Dooley (1978) revised the family.

BLUE BLANQUILLO
Malacanthus latovittatus (Lacepède, 1802)

Dorsal rays III-IV,43-47; anal rays I,37-40; pectoral rays 16-17 (usually 17); lateral-line scales 116-132; opercular spine large and sharp; edge of preopercle smooth; body elongate, the depth 5.0-6.7 in standard length, and little compressed; head length 3.1-4.0 in standard length; snout long and pointed, 2.1-2.7 in head length; lips fleshy; caudal fin truncate with the upper rays slightly prolonged; head and anterior part of body blue, becoming bluish white posteriorly, with a broad midlateral dark stripe on body continuing into caudal fin, the stripe progressively blacker posteriorly; juveniles white with a broader black stripe that extends to the front of the head. Attains about 40 cm. Occurs from the Red Sea and coast of East Africa to Samoa and the Line Islands; rare in Oman. A shallow-water species that builds burrows in sand and rubble areas near reefs. Difficult to approach underwater. It has been suggested that the juvenile is a mimic of the cleaner wrasse *Labroides dimidiatus*; however, this seems unlikely because one would then expect the juvenile to be blue with a black stripe like its adult and the cleaner wrasse. The reproduction was studied by Clark and Pohle (1992) who determined that this species forms monogamous pairs.

415. *M. latovittatus*, about 15 cm (J. Randall)

416. *Malacanthus latovittatus*, about 30 cm (J. Randall)

FALSE TREVALLY
FAMILY LACTARIIDAE

This family is represented by a single species, *Lactarius lactarius*, discussed below.

FALSE TREVALLY
Lactarius lactarius (Bloch and Schneider, 1801)

Dorsal rays VII-VIII + I,20-22; anal rays III,24-30; pectoral rays 17-18; pelvic rays I,5, inserted below lower base of pectoral fins; lateral-line scales 62-68; scales cycloid, easily shed; branchiostegal rays 7; mouth large, the maxilla extending to or posterior to a vertical at centre of eye, and strongly oblique with projecting lower jaw; a pair of small canine teeth anteriorly in jaws; swim bladder present; body ovate, the depth 2.5-3.0 in standard length, and strongly compressed; second dorsal spine longest; second dorsal fin about equal in height to first dorsal; origin of anal fin distinctly anterior to origin of second dorsal fin; pectoral fins moderately long and pointed; caudal fin forked; silvery grey with blue iridescence dorsally, shading to silvery white ventrally; a blackish spot posteriorly on operculum. Largest specimen, 35 cm (Talwar and Kacker, 1984). Occurs from the Arabian Gulf and Gulf of Oman (Blegvad, 1944) along the Asian coast to the Indo-Malayan region, north to China and south to Queensland; generally found on sandy bottoms; caught mostly in trawls and gill nets, the larger individuals usually at depths greater than 30 m. Known to form schools.

417. *Lactarius lactarius*, 18.1 cm (J. Randall)

embedded); pectoral rays 16-17; pelvic rays I,5; lateral-line scales 90-100; scales ctenoid, present on operculum and basally on median fins; branchiostegal rays 7; opercle ending in a flat spine; edge of preopercle partially serrate; mouth large, the maxilla reaching to or beyond rear edge of eye, the lower jaw slightly projecting; a single series of compressed, very sharp teeth in jaws, the upper jaw with an inner row of conical teeth; villiform teeth on vomer, palatines, and tongue; swim bladder present; body moderately elongate, the depth 3.3-4.0 in standard length; first dorsal fin low, the spines slender, folding into a groove; second dorsal and anal fins elevated anteriorly, more than twice height of first dorsal; caudal fin moderately forked; silvery green on back (chang-

ing to blue after death), silvery on sides and ventrally; a black spot at base of pectoral fins (more evident in young). Attains 130 cm. A subtropical-warm temperate species; occurs along the coast of East Africa, Madagascar, southern Oman, southwest India, Australia (where known as the Tailor) except the Northern Territory, New Zealand, the Malay Peninsula, and both sides of the Atlantic, including the Mediterranean Sea. A highly prized gamefish; the world record, 14.4 kg. An inshore pelagic fish; migratory and schooling. A voracious feeder; about 87% of the diet is small fishes. In South Africa (where called the Elf) there is a closed season September 1 through November and a size limit of 27.7 cm fork length.

418. *Pomatomus saltatrix*, 30 cm (J. Randall)

BLUEFISH
FAMILY POMATOMIDAE

The monotypic *Pomatomus* is here treated as the sole genus of the family Pomatomidae (see discussion of the species below). Some authors also classify the genus *Scombrops* as a pomatomid.

BLUEFISH
Pomatomus saltatrix (Linnaeus, 1766)

Dorsal rays VII-VIII + I,23-28; anal rays II,23-27 (the spines small and may be partly

COBIA
FAMILY RACHYCENTRIDAE

This family is also represented by a single species; see following account.

COBIA
Rachycentron canadum (Linnaeus, 1766)

Dorsal rays VII-IX (as short isolated spines, each with separate membrane) + I,33-36; anal rays II-III,22-28; pectoral rays 21-22; pelvic rays I,5; scales very small (over 300 in longitudinal series), and embedded; branchiostegal rays 7; head broad and depressed; mouth large, the lower jaw projecting; villiform teeth in bands in jaws, on vomer, palatines, and tongue; preopercle smooth; no swim bladder; body elongate, the depth 5.55-8.0 in standard length, and little compressed; second dorsal and anal fins somewhat elevated anteriorly; caudal fin truncate in young, progressively more emarginate with growth; a broad dark brown stripe from front of snout through eye to upper base of caudal fin, bordered above by a narrow pale olive stripe; back and top of head above olive stripe dark brown; body below lateral dark stripe white with a faint dark stripe on lower side. Largest reported, 200 cm, 68 kg. The world angling record, 61.5 kg, from Shark Bay, Australia. Found in all warm seas except the eastern Pacific, more in continental than insular waters. The specific name *canadum* is inappropriate because the species is not known from Canada. Semipelagic and migratory; feeds mainly on crustaceans, especially crabs; also important in the diet, small fishes and squids.

REMORAS
FAMILY ECHENEIDAE

These hitch hikers of the sea, also called sharksuckers or discfishes, have a broad flat head bearing a unique, transversely laminated, oval, sucking disk with which they may attach, depending on the species of remora, to other fishes, cetaceans, or sea turtles. The disc is derived during development from the precursor of

419. *Rachycentron canadum*, 32 cm (J. Randall)

the spinous dorsal fin. These fishes are further characterised by lacking a spine on the opercle, having small cycloid scales which are often embedded; 8 to 11 branchiostegal rays; a projecting lower jaw; villiform teeth in the jaws and on the vomer (in some species on the palatines and tongue as well); no swim bladder; an elongate body; long dorsal and anal fins without spines which are elevated anteriorly; and pelvic fins I,5. The family consists of four genera and eight species (Lachner in Whitehead et al., 1986 treated the seven known from the northeastern Atlantic). Only the two remoras presented below are positively known from Oman seas, but *Remorina albescens* (Temminck and Schlegel), which is most often commensal with mantas, *Remora osteochir* (Cuvier) and *R. brachyptera* (Lowe) which usually attach to billfishes, and the slender *Phtheirichthys lineatus* (Menzies) which often attaches to barracudas, might be expected. Most remoras are found in association with only one or a few hosts, but others are not host-specific, and the two species of *Echeneis* are free-living part of the time. Some of the remoras, especially when small, enter the mouths or gill chambers of their hosts; parasitic copepods from their hosts form an important part of the diet of *Remora remora* and *R. osteochir* (Cressey and Lachner, 1970).

SHARKSUCKER
Echeneis naucrates Linnaeus, 1758

Disc laminae 21-28, the disc extending to above middle of pectoral fins; dorsal rays 34-42; anal rays 31-41; pectoral rays 21-24; lower-limb gill rakers 11-16 (excluding rudiments); body slender, the depth 8-14 in standard length; dorsal and anal fins long; caudal fin lanceolate in young, emarginate in large adults; grey with a white-edged lateral black stripe from tip of lower jaw to base of caudal fin. Attains 90 cm. Circumglobal in tropical to warm temperate seas. Fischer and Bianchi (1984) wrote that it is probably absent from the Red Sea and Arabian Gulf; however, the species occurs in both. Found on a wide variety of hosts, but most often sharks; frequently observed free-living. One detached from a hawksbill turtle in the Virgin Islands and attached to the chest of the author.

420. *Echeneis naucrates* (Hagen Schmid)

REMORA
Remora remora (Linnaeus, 1758)

Disc laminae 16-20, the disk extending nearly to above end of pectoral fins, its length 2.4-2.95 in standard length; dorsal rays 21-27; anal rays 20-24; pectoral rays 25-32; lower-limb gill rakers 26-28 (including 1 or 2 rudiments); body depth about 6-8 in standard length; caudal fin emarginate; uniform tan to dark brown. Reaches 65 cm. Found most often on offshore species of sharks (reported from 12 different species of sharks representing eight different genera). As mentioned above, it feeds in part on crustacean parasites of its host (especially when young).

421. *Remora remora*, 21 cm (J. Randall)

DOLPHINFISHES
FAMILY CORYPHAENIDAE

This family consists of a single genus, *Coryphaena*, with two circumglobal epipelagic species. They are distinctive in having an elongate, compressed body; very small cycloid scales; mouth large with a projecting lower jaw; bands of small teeth in jaws and on vomer, palatines, and tongue; no swim bladder; no spines in dorsal and anal fins; a long dorsal fin commencing on the nape; a deep-ly forked caudal fin (emarginate with rounded lobes in juveniles); pectoral fins usually with 19 or 20 rays; pelvic fins I,5, thoracic in position, fitting into a groove in the abdomen. Adult males develop a bony crest on the head, resulting in a very steep dorsal profile and elevated forehead. Dolphinfishes are blue-water species, hence normally come close to land only when deep water is near. Juveniles are often associated with drifting weed such as *Sargassum* and are sometimes carried into coastal waters. The species of *Coryphaena* are beautifully coloured in life, but fade to dull silvery and yellowish after death. Although these fishes are often called dolphins, it is preferred that we use the common name dolphinfish because of confusion with the marine mammals called dolphins. It would be better to adopt the Spanish common name dorado for the fishes. Gibbs and Collette (1959) reviewed the systematics and biology of the Coryphaenidae.

POMPANO DOLPHINFISH
Coryphaena equiselis Linnaeus, 1758

Dorsal rays 48-60 (usually 52-56); anal rays 23-29 (usually 24-27); lateral-line scales 160-200; vertebrae 33; patch of teeth on tongue large and nearly forming a square; body depth more than 4.0 in standard length, the greatest depth near middle of body; outer margin of anal fin straight to slightly convex; brilliant metallic blue-green on back, the sides silvery with a golden sheen and numerous small dark spots; juveniles nearly uniformly dark (sometimes a faint barring on body, more evident on dorsal fin); entire posterior margin of caudal fin broadly clear; pelvic fins clear. Attains 75 cm. As noted by Gibbs and Collette (1959), the exact distribution of this species is not known because it is often not distinguished from the more common *C. hippurus*; reported from the Gulf of Oman by Norman (1939). Feeds on fishes and squids.

COMMON DOLPHINFISH
Coryphaena hippurus Linnaeus, 1758

Dorsal rays 50-67 (usually 56-63); anal rays 25-30 (usually 26-28); lateral-line scales 200-318 (usually 245-280); vertebrae 31; patch of teeth on tongue small and round; body depth less than 4.0 in standard length, the greatest depth of body anteriorly; outer margin of anal fin slightly concave; brilliant metallic blue-green on back, shading to golden on sides and ventrally, with numerous small blue-green spots; juveniles dark with about 15 black bars that extend into dorsal and anal fins; only the tips of caudal lobes clear; pelvic fins blackish. Reported to reach 200 cm. Known throughout tropical and warm temperate seas to latitudes as great as 35°. Although Collette in Fischer and Bianchi (1984) failed to include the Red Sea and Arabian Gulf in the distribution of this species, there are records from both; the author obtain a specimen of *C. hippurus* from fishermen at Mutrah.

422. *Coryphaena equiselis*, 26 cm (J. Randall)

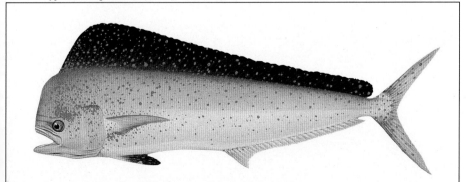

423. *Coryphaena hippurus* (Illustration by R.A. Swainston)

Famous as a gamefish for its spectacular leaps and strong fight on a line; the world angling record is 39.5 kg, from Costa Rica. Males begin to develop a bony crest on the head at a length of about 30 cm. Feeds mainly on fishes (a wide variety of species as postlarvae) but also cephalopods and occasional crustaceans; flyingfishes are believed to be a major food item, but food-habit studies do not show them as the dominant food source. *C. hippurus* has a phenomenal growth rate; males in Hawaiian waters grow to 126 cm fork length in one year, and females to 112 cm (Uchiyama et al., 1986); because of this and its high quality as a food fish, the dolphinfish has potential for mariculture (Kraul, 1989). This fish is also amazing for reaching sexual maturity in four to five months (three months for captive fish).

JACKS
FAMILY CARANGIDAE

The jacks are a large and very important family of strong-swimming, open-water, carnivorous fishes which are usually silvery in colour. They are highly variable in shape from fusiform, like the scads of the genus *Decapterus*, to deep-bodied like the species of *Alectis*; the caudal peduncle is slender and usually reinforced with a series of external overlapping bony plates called scutes. The eye is usually protected and streamlined with the so-called adipose eyelid. There is no spine on the opercle, and the preopercular edge is smooth. The mouth is moderate to large, varying from slightly to strongly oblique. Most species have small teeth in rows or bands in the jaws, but the species of *Caranx* have strong conical teeth, those of *Alepes* have a single row of slender teeth, and those of the genera *Selaroides* and *Gnathanodon* lack teeth in the upper jaw. The gill openings are large, the gill membranes not united and free from the isthmus; the branchiostegal rays vary in number from 6 to 10 (usually 7). The vertebrae vary from 24 to 27 (usually 24). The scales are small and cycloid (sometimes embedded); in the species of *Scomberoides* the scales are slender and pointed to lanceolate; the lateral line is arched over the pectoral region, becoming midlateral posteriorly and extending onto caudal fin. There are two dorsal fins, at least in juveniles (the first dorsal fin obsolete or embedded in adults of some species), the first of IV to VIII spines, the second with one spine and numerous soft rays; some species have one to several finlets following the dorsal and anal fins. The anal fin has two anterior spines (except *Elagatis* and *Seriolina* with one), separated by a gap from the rest of the fin which has an initial spine and numerous soft rays (in large individuals of some species, the first two anal spines may become embedded). The caudal fin is strongly forked or lunate. The pectoral fins vary from short to long and falcate; the pelvic fins I,5, thoracic in position (these fins rudimentary in some species and lost in the adults of *Parastromateus niger*). The carangids are provisionally divided into four subfamilies: Caranginae, Naucratinae, Somberoidinae, and Trachinotinae (although *Parastromateus* would seem to warrant a subfamily of its own); there are about 32 genera and 140 species (Smith-Vaniz in Moser et al., 1984). Because of the scutes of most carangid fishes, standard length (to end of vertebral column) cannot be measured accurately, so fork length (tip of snout to end of middle caudal rays) is used for proportional measurements involving length in these fishes.

424. Subadults of *Caranx heberi* (J. Earle)

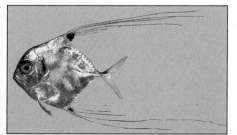

THREADFIN JACK
Alectis ciliaris (Bloch, 1788)

Dorsal rays VII + I,18-20 (spines of first dorsal fin embedded at a fork length greater than about 17 cm); anal rays II + I,15-17 (first two anal spines also embedded with growth); anterior four or five soft rays of dorsal and anal fins of juveniles filamentous

425. *Alectis ciliaris*, juv., 13.2 cm (J. Randall)

and extremely long; scales minute and embedded; scutes 12-30; gill rakers 4-6 + 12-17 (excluding rudiments); villiform teeth in bands in jaws, becoming obsolete with age; body very deep and strongly compressed, becoming more elongate with growth; dorsal profile of head very steep, becoming broadly rounded above eye; suborbital depth 1.7-3.0 in length of upper jaw; silvery blue dorsally, silvery on sides and ventrally; juveniles with five dark bars, slightly chevron-shaped, and a black blotch at base of third to sixth dorsal soft rays; dorsal and anal filaments banded with black. Reaches at least 130 cm. World angling record, 22.9 kg. Circumtropical, including the Arabian Gulf (location of juvenile illustrated herein). Adults are solitary; reported to feed mainly on crustaceans, occasionally on small fishes. The juveniles with their long dorsal and anal rays may be mimicking venomous jellyfishes such as cubomedusae. *A. crinitis* (Mitchill) and *Carangoides ajax* Snyder are synonyms.

426. *Alectis ciliaris*, 56.4 cm (J. Randall)

INDIAN THREADFISH
Alectis indicus (Rüppell, 1830)

Dorsal rays VI + I,18-20 (the spines of the first dorsal embedded at a fork length of about 17 cm or more); anal rays II + I,15-17 (first two anal spines also embedded with growth); anterior dorsal and anal soft rays of juveniles extremely long and filamentous; scales minute and embedded; scutes 6-11; gill rakers 8-11 + 21-26 (excluding rudiments); body very deep and compressed, becoming more elongate with growth; dorsal profile of head very steep and straight to above eye where distinctly angular, then straight to origin of dorsal fin; suborbital depth 0.8-1.0 in upper jaw length; dusky green dorsally, shading to silvery below, with a blackish spot dorsally at posterior end of opercle; juveniles with five dark bars. Reported to 150 cm; South African spearfishing record, 21.4 kg. Known from continental waters of the Indian Ocean (including the Red Sea, Arabian Gulf, and Madagascar) and the western Pacific. Adults said to form schools; juveniles solitary and may enter estuaries. Adults reported to feed on fishes, small squids, and crustaceans.

428. *Alectis indicus*, subadult, 22 cm (J. Randall)

427. *Alectis indicus*, 77.4 cm (J. Randall)

SHRIMP SCAD
Alepes djedaba (Forsskål, 1775)

Dorsal rays VIII + I,23-25; anal rays II + I,18-20; anterior curved part of lateral line with 31-36 scales (of which 0-3 posteriorly are scutes); straight part of lateral line with 0-1 scales and 39-51 scutes; total lateral-line scales and scutes (not including caudal scales) 77-85; juncture of curved and straight sections of lateral line below first three rays of second dorsal fin; gill rakers 10-14 + 27-33 (including rudiments); jaws with a single row of small, incurved, conical teeth; adipose eyelid well-developed only on posterior half of eye; posterior edge of maxilla slightly concave; supramaxilla with a spinelike anterior extension; last ray of second dorsal and anal fins about 1.3-1.5 times longer than penultimate ray; grey-green to bluish dorsally, shading to silvery white below, with a black spot posteriorly on opercle at level of eye, bordered above by a white spot; caudal fin yellowish. Attains 33 cm. Ranges from South Africa to the Red Sea and Arabian Gulf (including Madagascar and the Seychelles), east along south Asian shores to Thailand and Sumatra, north to the Philippines and Taiwan; a recent immigrant to the eastern Mediterranean via the Suez Canal. An inshore species, generally found in somewhat turbid water; often forms schools; reported to feed mainly on plank-

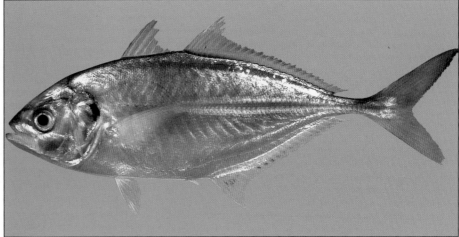

429. *Alepes djedaba*, 20.5 cm (J. Randall)

tonic crustaceans such as decapod larvae; when larger also on small fishes.

SHARPBELLY SCAD
Alepes kleinii (Bloch, 1793)

Dorsal rays VIII + I,23-26; anal rays II + I,19-22; curved part of lateral line with 32-46 scales (of which 0-2 are scutes); straight part of lateral line with 0-2 scales and 35-45 scutes; total lateral-line scales and scutes 72-86; juncture of curved and straight parts of lateral line below fourth to sixth dorsal soft rays; gill rakers 10-12 + 27-32 (includ-

430. *Alepes kleinii*, 11.2 cm (J. Randall)

431. *Alepes melanoptera*, 25 cm (J. Randall)

ing rudiments); body oval, the ventral profile a little more convex than the dorsal; adipose eyelid well-developed only on posterior half of eye; upper jaw with two irregular rows of conical teeth, narrowing posteriorly to one row, the teeth progressively shorter and less sharp on side of jaw; two to three irregular rows of small nubbin-like teeth medially on upper jaw; lower jaw with a single row of conical teeth, becoming progressively smaller and blunter posteriorly in jaw; silvery, sometimes with dark bars on upper half of body; a large black spot at upper end of gill opening; caudal fin yellowish, more so on upper lobe which has a narrow dusky edge; tongue dark except tip which is pale. Attains 18 cm. *Caranx kalla* Cuvier and *C. para* Cuvier are synonyms. Although resembling the species of *Alepes*, this fish is very different in dentition and probably will require placement in a new monotypic genus (Gunn, 1990, after W.F. Smith-Vaniz).

BLACKFIN SCAD
Alepes melanoptera Swainson, 1839

Dorsal rays VIII + I,23-26; anal rays II + I,18-21; curved part of lateral line with 31-50 scales, of which 0-2 are scutes; straight part of lateral line with 0-4 scales and 49-69 scutes; total lateral-line scales and scutes 95-114; juncture of curved and straight portions of lateral line below first three soft dorsal rays; gill rakers 7-9 + 17-24 (including rudiments); adipose eyelid well-developed only on posterior half of eye; posterior end of maxilla slightly rounded; supramaxilla small, without an anterior spinelike extension; bluish silver dorsally, shading to silvery below; a dusky spot posteriorly on opercle; first dorsal fin black; caudal fin dusky yellow. Largest specimen examined, 25 cm. Known from the Arabian Gulf to Sri Lanka, and Indonesia to the Gulf of Thailand; an inshore species which feeds mainly on planktonic crustaceans.

HERRING SCAD
Alepes vari (Cuvier, 1833)

Dorsal rays VIII + I,24-27; anal rays II + I,20-23; curved portion of lateral line with 42-50 scales, of which 0-2 are scutes; straight portion of lateral-line with 0-7 scales and 48-69 scutes; total lateral-line scales and scutes 86-119; juncture of curved and straight parts of lateral line below first three dorsal soft rays; adipose eyelid well-developed only on posterior half of eye; posterior end of maxilla nearly straight; supramaxilla relatively large with an anterior spinelike projection; silvery with a dusky spot posteriorly on opercle; caudal fin dusky. Largest specimen reported, 56 cm. Red Sea and Arabian Gulf to Gulf of Thailand, north to Taiwan and Okinawa. A shallow-water coastal species; feeds on small fishes and the larger crustaceans of the zooplankton.

CLEFTBELLY JACK
Atropus atropos (Bloch and Schneider, 1801)

Dorsal rays VIII + I,19-22; anal rays II + I,17-18; straight part of lateral line with 31-37 scutes; juncture of curved and straight portions of lateral line below fifth to seventh dorsal soft rays; entire chest to rear base of pelvic fins scaleless; gill rakers 8-11 + 19-22 (including rudiments); eye without adipose eyelid; body deep and strongly compressed; dorsal profile of head steep and straight to above eye, then convex; upper jaw with a narrow band of small teeth; lower jaw with two or three rows of small teeth anteriorly, soon narrowing to a single row along side of jaw; a deep median groove on abdomen into which the long pelvic fins fold; mature males with 6 to 12 soft rays in middle-anterior part of fin prolonged into filaments, and anal fin with about 5 comparable prolonged rays; blue-green dorsally, silvery below; membranes of pelvic fins black, the rays white basally; a dusky spot posteriorly on opercle; juveniles with faint

432. *Alepes vari*, about 30 cm (J. Hoover)

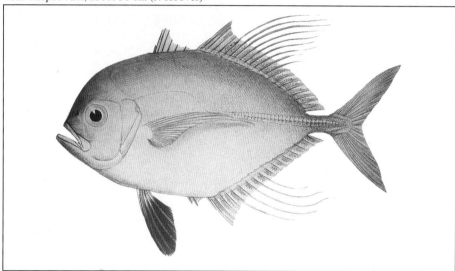

433. *Atropus atropos* (after Bleeker, 1983)

dark bars. Largest specimen reported, 26.5 cm. Arabian Gulf to Indo-Malayan region, north to Japan.

YELLOWTAIL SCAD
Atule mate (Cuvier, 1833)

Dorsal rays VIII + I,22-25; anal rays II + I,18-21; curved part of lateral line with 39-57 pored scales; straight part of lateral line with 0-10 scales and 36-49 scutes; total scales and scutes in lateral line 92-103; juncture of curved and straight parts of lateral line below sixth to eighth dorsal soft rays; gill rakers 10-13 + 26-31 (including rudiments); adipose eyelid covering eye except for a vertical slit in centre; body moderately elongate; front of upper jaw with two to three rows of small canines; rest of jaw and all of lower jaw with a single row of small teeth; last ray of dorsal and anal fins about twice as long as penultimate ray and more separated, though still joined basally by membrane; silvery blue-green dorsally, shading to silvery with golden sheen on sides and silvery white ventrally; a black spot posteriorly on opercle at level of eye; soft dorsal fin yellowish; caudal fin yellow. Reaches 30 cm. Western Indian Ocean (including the Red Sea and Arabian Gulf) to Samoa and the Hawaiian Islands; in the western Pacific from Japan to Queensland. A schooling species which occurs to depths of at least 50 m; feeds on zooplankton.

434. *Atule mate*, 25.4 cm (J. Randall)

LONGFIN JACK
Carangoides armatus (Rüppell, 1830)

Dorsal rays VIII + I,19-22; anal rays II + I,16-18; straight part of lateral line with 11-24 small scutes, the total pored scales and scutes in straight section 25-43; curved part of lateral line (measured as a straight line) longer than straight part, the juncture of the two below 11th and 12 dorsal soft rays; chest entirely naked to base of pectoral fins and rear base of pelvics; gill rakers 10-15 + 20-24 (including rudiments); adipose eyelid not well-developed (true of other species of *Carangoides*); body deep, the depth 1.85-2.2 in fork length; anterior lobe of second dorsal and anal fins much longer than head, becoming filamentous, the longest ray of second dorsal 2.0-2.7 in fork length; mature males larger than about 21 cm fork length developing filamentous central rays of second dorsal and anal fins; first dorsal fin small; pectoral fins long and falcate, reaching to or beyond juncture of curved and straight sections of lateral line; silvery blue-grey dorsally, shading on sides to silvery, with a small, vertically elongate, black spot posteriorly on operculum at level of upper part of eye; margins of dorsal filament blackish; juveniles with five or six broad dusky bars on body, the pelvic fins blackish. Attains about 57 cm. Madagascar and coast of Africa to Red Sea (type locality), Gulf of Oman, Arabian Gulf (juvenile photograph herein establishes the occurrence in the Gulf), east to the Gulf of Thailand, north to Hong Kong and Japan; reported as an inshore species swimming along edges of reefs (Smith-Vaniz in Fischer and Bianchi, 1984).

ORANGESPOTTED JACK
Carangoides bajad (Forsskål, 1775)

Dorsal rays VIII + I,24-26; anal rays II + I,21-24; straight part of lateral line with 14-26 scales, followed by 20-30 small scutes; curved portion of lateral line longer than straight part, the juncture of the two parts below 11th to 15th dorsal soft rays; chest completely scaled or with a narrow median scaleless zone on isthmus; gill rakers 7-9 + 18-21; body depth 2.7-3.1 in fork length; head length 3.4-4.2 in fork length; dorsal profile of head to above eye nearly straight; anterior lobes of second dorsal and anal fins not long, the dorsal lobe about half head length; pectoral fins long and falcate, reaching junction of curved and straight sections of lateral line; brassy dorsally, shading to silvery below, with numerous, conspicuous, yellow-orange spots on body; no obvious black spot on operculum; able to assume an overall golden yellow colour (but yellow-

435. *Carangoides armatus*, female, 15.2 cm (J. Randall)

436. *Carangoides bajad*, 18 cm (J. Randall)

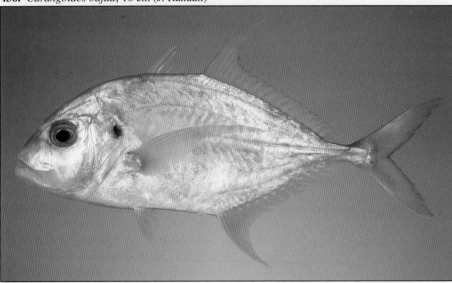

437. *Carangoides chrysophrys*, 27.8 cm (J. Randall)

orange spots still evident). Attains 55 cm. Known in the Indian Ocean only from the Red Sea to the Arabian Gulf; the most common jack seen on inshore reefs in the Arabian Gulf and Gulf of Oman, but rare in southern Oman; also reported from the Gulf of Thailand, Indonesia, Philippines, and Ryukyu Islands.

LONGNOSE JACK
Carangoides chrysophrys (Cuvier, 1833)

Dorsal rays VIII + I,18-20; anal rays II + I,14-17; small scutes in straight part of lateral line 20-37; curved part of lateral line nearly twice as long as straight part, the juncture below 12th to 14th dorsal soft rays;

entire chest scaleless to rear base of pelvic fins; gill rakers 5-9 + 15-18 (including rudiments); body depth 2.4-2.8 in fork length; head length 3.2-3.4 in fork length; dorsal profile of head sloping, forming an angle of about 45° to the horizontal; second dorsal and anal fin lobes filamentous in young, becoming shorter with age but still long in adults (though usually a little shorter than head length); pectoral fins long and falcate, but not reaching junction of curved and straight parts of lateral line; silvery with a black spot a little smaller than pupil posteriorly on operculum at level of eye; caudal fin yellowish. Attains at least 45 cm (reports to 60 cm). Continental shores of the Indian Ocean, including the Red Sea and Arabian Gulf, to the western Pacific where it ranges from New South Wales to the Ryukyu Islands; insular localities in the Indian Ocean include Madagascar, Comoros, and the Seychelles; most common at depths of 30-60 m. Feeds on small fishes and benthic crustaceans.

COASTAL JACK
Carangoides coeruleopinnatus (Rüppell, 1830)

Dorsal rays VIII + I,20-23 (usually 22 or 23); anal rays II + I,16-20; curved part of lateral line with 77-97 scales; straight part of lateral line with 16-38 small scutes; curved part of lateral line longer than straight, the juncture beneath 12th to 14th dorsal soft rays; chest scaleless to behind base of pelvic fins (rarely a narrow band of scales in front of pectoral-fin base); gill rakers 6-8 + 15-17 (including rudiments); body moderately deep, the depth 2.3-2.5 in fork length; lobe of second dorsal fin filamentous in young, shorter than head and shorter than anal-fin lobe in individuals longer than about 10 cm fork length; pectoral fins long and falcate, reaching to juncture of curved and straight parts of lateral line; silvery blue-green dorsally, becoming silvery on sides and ventrally; numerous small yellow spots usually present on body; a small black spot posteriorly on operculum at level of upper part of eye. Attains 40 cm. Coastal continental waters of the Indian Ocean to the western Pacific where it ranges from Queensland to Japan. Also known from the Seychelles (the *C. malabaricus* of Smith and Smith, 1963: pl. 11 B, is *C. coeruleopinnatus*) and Maldives (Randall and Anderson, 1993).

WHITEFIN JACK
Carangoides equula Temminck and Schlegel, 1844

Dorsal rays VIII + I,22-25; anal rays II + I,21-24; straight part of lateral line with 0-6 scales, followed by 22-32 small scutes; curved portion of lateral line much longer than straight part, the juncture of the two below 12th to 15th dorsal soft rays; chest fully scaled; gill rakers 7-10 + 18-23 (including rudiments); body depth 2.3-2.4 in fork length; dorsal profile of head strongly sloping, forming an angle of about 45° to the horizontal; vomerine tooth patch diamond-shaped with a long median posterior part; first dorsal fin equal in height or a little higher than second dorsal; pectoral fins not reaching junction of curved and straight parts of lateral line; silvery blue-green dorsally, shading to silvery on side and ventrally; a small black spot posteriorly on operculum; second dorsal and anal fins with a submarginal black zone, the margins white; spines and rays of first dorsal and pelvic fins white; juveniles with seven dusky bars. Attains about 28 cm. Known in the Indian Ocean only from South Africa, Somalia, Gulf of Oman, and western Australia from 8° to 28° S; in the Pacific from Japan (type locality) and Taiwan. Largely restricted to shelf slope habitats in the depth range of 100-200 m; feeds on a wide variety of fishes, crustaceans, and cephalopods (Gunn, 1990). Classified by some authors such as Gushiken (1983) in the genus *Kaiwarinus*. The related *C. dasson* (Jordan and Snyder) from Hawaii and Easter Island is larger (to 50 cm), more elongate (depth 2.9-3.2 in fork length), and has prolonged last dorsal and anal rays.

438. *Carangoides coeruleopinnatus*, about 26 cm (J. Randall)

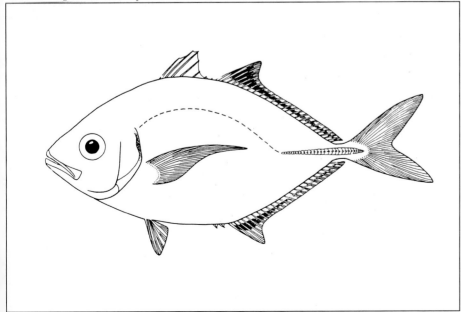

439. *Carangoides equula*, (after Fischer and Bianchi, 1984)

BARRED JACK
Carangoides ferdau (Forsskål, 1775)

Dorsal rays VIII + I,26-34; anal rays II + I,21-26; straight part of lateral line with 10-30 scales and 21-37 small scutes; curved portion of lateral line much longer than straight, the junction of the two sections below 15th to 20th dorsal soft rays; chest scaled except for a broad midventral scaleless zone, narrowing to origin of pelvic fins and pectoral-fin base; gill rakers 7-10 + 17-20 (including rudiments); lips not papillose; body depth 2.25-2.75 in fork length; head length 3.55-3.9 in fork length; second dorsal and anal fins with prominent anterior lobes, the dorsal longest, 2.75-4.0 in fork length; first dorsal fin small, about one-fourth height of second dorsal; pectoral fins long and falcate, reaching junction of curved and soft portions of lateral line; silvery blue-green dorsally, shading to silvery on sides and ventrally, with seven dusky bars on upper two-thirds of body nearly as broad as pale interspaces; numerous small yellow spots often present, mostly on upper half of body. Largest specimen, 53 cm. Indo-Pacific; usually seen over sand near coral reefs, sometimes in small schools, from inshore to depths of at least 60 m. Feeds mainly on benthic crustaceans, occasionally on small fishes. *C. gilberti* (Jordan and Seale) is a synonym. The closely related *C. orthogrammus* (Jordan and Gilbert) is unknown from Oman waters and the Red Sea.

YELLOWSPOTTED JACK
Carangoides fulvoguttatus (Forsskål, 1775)

Dorsal rays VIII + I,25-30; anal rays II + I,21-26; straight part of lateral line with 18-27 scales, followed by 15-21 small scutes; curved part of lateral line longer than straight part, the juncture of the two beneath 13th to 16th dorsal soft rays; chest nearly scaleless or with a scaled zone separating naked pectoral base from broad ventral scaleless area; gill rakers 6-8 + 17-21 (including rudiments); body depth 3.0-3.45 in fork length; head length 3.35-3.9 in fork length; dorsal profile of snout nearly straight; anterior lobes of second dorsal and anal fins moderately long, the dorsal 6.5-7.0 in fork length; first dorsal fin about half as high as anterior lobe of second dorsal; pectoral fins long and falcate, nearly or just reaching juncture of curved and straight sections of lateral line; silvery blue-green dorsally, shading to silvery with iridescence on side and ventrally; often with numerous yellow spots on upper two-thirds of body which tend to be arranged in vertical bars (spots may not be evident on large individuals);

440. *Carangoides ferdau*, about 29 cm (J. Randall)

441. *Carangoides fulvoguttatus*, about 60 cm (J. Hoover)

442. *Carangoides gymnostethus*, 57 cm (J. Randall)

dark opercular spot indistinct; three dusky spots frequently evident on lateral line, the first beneath first dorsal fin, the second at juncture of curved and straight portions, and the last on straight portion; also about five broad dusky bars sometimes apparent; caudal fin yellowish. Largest reported, 103 cm. Found throughout the Indian Ocean and the western Pacific from southern Queensland to Japan; also to Palau and New Caledonia; often seen in small schools; reported from offshore banks to 100 m.

BLUDGER
Carangoides gymnostethus (Cuvier, 1833)

Dorsal rays VIII + I,28-32; anal rays II + I,24-26; straight part of lateral line with 14-25 scales and 20-31 small scutes; curved part of lateral line longer than straight, the juncture of the two beneath the 16th to 20th dorsal soft rays; chest entirely scaleless to rear base of pelvic fins; body elongate, the depth 3.0-3.7 in fork length; head length 3.45-3.7 in fork length; dorsal profile of head prominently convex; anterior lobes of second dorsal and anal fins not very high, the dorsal lobe less than half head length; pectoral fins long and falcate, nearly or just reaching junction of curved and straight sections of lateral line; silvery blue-green dorsally, silvery below, sometimes with a few scattered brown or yellow spots on side; opercular spot small and blackish to dusky. Reported to attain 90 cm; South African spearfishing record, 14.5 kg. Occurs from Mauritius, Seychelles (type locality), Madagascar, and coast of Indian Ocean, including Red Sea and Arabian Gulf, to the western Pacific where it ranges from the Great Barrier Reef and New Caledonia to the Ryukyu Islands. Adults are said to be solitary and juveniles to form small schools. *C. gymnostethoides* Bleeker is a synonym.

MALABAR JACK
Carangoides malabaricus (Bloch and Schneider, 1801)

Dorsal rays VIII + I,20-23; anal rays II + I,17-19; straight part of lateral line with 19-36 small scutes, the total number of pored scales and scutes in this section 31-55; curved part of lateral line longer than straight part, the juncture of the two below 12th to 14th dorsal soft rays; chest entirely scaleless to behind pelvic fins and to above pectoral-fin base; gill rakers 8-12 + 21-27; body moderately deep, the depth 2.25-2.5 in fork length; head length 3.3-3.75 in fork length; dorsal profile of snout steep and nearly straight; anterior lobes of dorsal and anal fins not greatly elevated, the dorsal lobe about 1.7 in head length; first dorsal fin about three-fourths height of second dorsal lobe; pectoral fins long and falcate, but not reaching juncture of curved and straight parts of lateral line; silvery blue-green above and silvery with iridescence below, with a black spot posteriorly on operculum at level of upper part of eye; interradial membranes of anal fin with a basal white spot; tongue dark brown. Largest specimen, 27.5 cm. A continental shelf species from South Africa to the Arabian Gulf (but not the Red Sea), east to the Indo-Malayan region, south to Queensland and north to Japan (where rare); usually taken by trawls; known from depths of 30-140 m.

443. *Carangoides malabaricus*, 24.7 cm (J. Randall)

444. *Carangoides praeustus* (S. Marthen)

BLACKTIP JACK
Carangoides praeustus (Bennett, 1830)

Dorsal rays VIII + I,22-25; anal rays II + I,18-21; straight part of lateral line with 4-12 scales, followed by 24-34 small scutes; curved and straight portions of lateral line of about equal length, the junction of the two below 7th to 11th dorsal soft rays; chest scaleless except ventrally; gill rakers 11-15 + 28-32; vomerine tooth patch anchor-shaped, with a long narrow median posterior extension; body elongate and compressed, the depth 2.9-3.2 in fork length; head length 3.65-4.0 in fork length; anterior lobes of second dorsal and anal fins only slightly elevated, the dorsal lobe about 1.7 in head length; pectoral fins shorter than head; silvery blue-grey dorsally, shading to silvery on sides and ventrally, sometimes with a broad brassy midlateral zone; upper half to three-fourths of dorsal fin lobe jet black, sometimes with a white tip; caudal fin yellow. Reaches about 25 cm. Arabian Gulf to the Indo-Malayan region.

IMPOSTER JACK
Carangoides talamparoides Bleeker, 1852

Dorsal rays VIII + I,20-23; anal rays II + I,17-19; straight part of lateral line with 20-32 small scutes, the total number of pored scales and scutes in straight part 32-52; curved part of lateral line longer than straight part, the juncture of the two below 12th to 14th

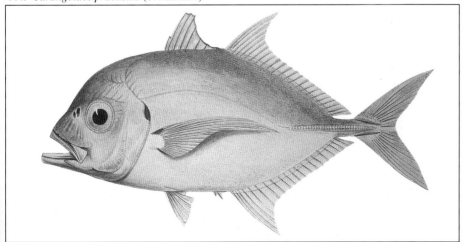

445. *Carangoides talamparoides* (after Bleeker, 1983)

dorsal soft rays; chest entirely scaled to behind base of pectoral fins and above pectoral-fin base; gill rakers 6-9 + 19-22; body moderately deep, the depth 2.2-2.6 in fork length; head length 3.1-3.3 in fork length; dorsal profile of head to above eye steep and nearly straight; second dorsal and anal-fin lobes not greatly elevated, the dorsal lobe about 1.6 in head length; pectoral fins long and falcate, but not reaching juncture of curved and soft portions of lateral line; silvery blue-grey dorsally, silvery white below, the operculum with a black spot at level of upper third of eye; tongue white to pale grey. Attains 30 cm. Gulf of Oman to Indo-Malayan region and Australia.

BLACKTIP TREVALLY
Caranx heberi (Bennett, 1828)

446. *Caranx heberi* (J. Hoover)

Dorsal rays VIII + I,19-21; anal rays II + I,15-17; straight part of lateral line with 0-4 scales, followed by 30-40 strong scutes; curved part of lateral line (measured as a straight line) shorter than straight part (true of other species of *Caranx*); chest varying from completely scaled to scaleless ventrally (when naked ventrally, a patch of prepelvic scales usually present); adipose eyelid short anteriorly but reaching to edge of pupil posteriorly; upper jaw with an outer row of stout canine teeth and an inner band of small teeth; lower jaw with a single row of strong conical teeth (dentition similar in other species of the genus); upper jaw reaching to below posterior edge of pupil or a little beyond; body depth varying greatly with growth, from 2.5 in fork length of a 17-cm specimen to 3.8 in a 68.5-cm one; anterior lobe of second dorsal fin moderately long, 5.3-7.4 in fork length; two small well-developed keels on side of caudal fin, one above and one below posterior scutes (also found on other *Caranx*); pectoral fins long and falcate, reaching beyond juncture of curved and straight portions of lateral line (also generic); brassy dorsally, silvery below; central part of scutes blackish; fins usually yellow, the outer half of upper caudal lobe generally black, the second dorsal and anal lobes often tipped with white. Attains at least 85 cm. Coastal in the Indian Ocean, including the Arabian Gulf (but not yet known from the Red Sea), to the Indo-Malayan region. The most common jack inshore on the southern coast of Oman. *Caranx sem* Cuvier is a synonym.

GIANT TREVALLY
Caranx ignobilis (Forsskål, 1775)

Dorsal rays VIII + I,18-21; anal rays II + I,15-17; straight part of lateral line with 0-4 scales, followed by 26-38 strong scutes; chest scaled except for median prepelvic area which is naked with a patch of scales; gill rakers 5-7 + 15-17; adipose eyelid short anteriorly, to edge of pupil posteriorly; upper jaw extending to below rear edge of pupil or a little beyond; body depth varying with growth, the depth of adults about 3.0-3.5 in fork length; dorsal profile of snout very steep and nearly straight to above eye, then smoothly convex to nape; anterior lobe of dorsal fin 4.4-6.2 in fork length; silvery grey, shading to silvery white ventrally, with numerous, scattered, very small, black spots; centres of scutes blackish; mature males may be almost entirely black. The largest of the carangid fishes; reaches at least 165 cm; world angling record, 66 kg, from the Hawaiian Islands. Occurs throughout the Indo-Pacific region; feeds primarily on fishes.

447. *Caranx ignobilis*, about 50 cm (J. Randall)

BLACK TREVALLY
Caranx lugubris Poey, 1860

Dorsal rays VIII + I,20-22; anal rays II + I,16-19; straight part of lateral line with 26-32 strong scutes; chest completely scaled; gill rakers 6-8 + 17-22; adipose eyelid short anteriorly, to centre of eye posteriorly; upper jaw nearly or just reaching a vertical through middle of eye; body depth of adults 2.4-2.8

448. *Caranx lugubris*, subadults (J. Hoover)

in fork length; dorsal profile of snout relatively steep and straight or slightly concave to above eye where it is distinctly angular as it curves to nape; anterior lobe of second dorsal fin often prolonged, its length 2.3-5.3 in fork length; dark olive grey to almost black dorsally, shading to bluish grey ventrally, the scutes black; a small black spot at upper end of gill opening; fins dark grey to black. Reaches at least 80 cm; world angling record, 12.9 kg, from the Revillagigedo Islands, Mexico. Circumtropical; usually seen on outer reef slopes at depths greater than 30 m. The author opened the stomachs of 22 specimens, 38-65 cm fork length caught at night at Easter Island. Eight were empty, 11 had fish remains (included were *Synodus* sp., *Aulostomus chinensis* and myc-tophids), two contained stomatopods, and one an isopod. *Caranx ascensionis* Cuvier is an older but little-used name for this species. Smith-Vaniz and Randall (1994) successfully petitioned the International Commission on Zoological Nomenclature to suppress this name in favour of *Caranx lugubris*.

BLUEFIN TREVALLY
Caranx melampygus Cuvier, 1833

Dorsal rays VIII + I,21-24; anal rays II + I,17-20; straight portion of lateral line with 0-10 scales, followed by 27-42 strong scutes; chest completely scaled; gill rakers 5-9 + 17-21 (including rudiments); adipose eyelid short anteriorly, extending to edge of pupil posteriorly; upper jaw reaching posteriorly to or beyond a vertical at front edge of eye; body depth of adults 2.85-3.2 in fork length; dorsal profile of head forming an angle of about 45° to the horizontal, nearly straight to above eye, then smoothly convex; anterior lobe of second dorsal and anal fins moderately long, the dorsal lobe 4.2-6.7 in fork length; brassy dorsally, shading to silvery with iridescence below; body finely blotched with bright blue and dotted with small black spots; centres of scutes a little blackish; fins blue. Reported to 100 cm; world angling record, 43.5 kg, from Christmas Island, Line Islands. Common throughout the Indo-Pacific region (though not recorded from the Arabian Gulf or Gulf of Oman) and tropical eastern Pacific. Randall (1980) opened the stomachs of 61 specimens, of which 44 contained food; all consisted of fishes, but one individual had eaten a squid. The prey fishes included *Caranx* sp., anthiines, priacanthids, caesionids, cirrhitids, mullids, pomacentrids, labrids, microdesmids, and acanthurids, thus indicating heavy feeding on reef species. *C. stellatus* Eydoux and Souleyet is a synonym.

449. *Caranx melampygus*, about 50 cm (J. Hoover)

450. *Caranx sexfasciatus*, about 40 cm (J. Hoover)

BIGEYE TREVALLY
Caranx sexfasciatus Quoy and Gaimard, 1824

Dorsal rays VIII + I,19-22; anal rays II + I,14-17; straight portion of lateral line with 0-3 scales, followed by 27-36 strong scutes; chest completely scaled; gill rakers 6-8 + 15-19 (including rudiments); eye large; adipose eyelid conspicuous, short anteriorly, extending to rear of pupil posteriorly; mouth large, the upper jaw reaching posterior to rear edge of eye; body depth varying with growth from about 2.5 in fork length of juveniles to 3.9 in large adults; anterior lobe of second dorsal and anal fins moderately high, the dorsal lobe 5.0-6.6 in fork length; silvery grey dorsally, shading to silvery white ventrally, the scutes blackish; a small black spot on operculum at upper end of gill opening; fins grey, the second dorsal and anal lobes tipped with white, the caudal with a black posterior margin; juveniles brassy yellow with five or six dark bars. Reaches 85 cm; world angling record, 7.05 kg, from the Hawaiian Islands. Common throughout the Indo-Pacific region and tropical eastern Pacific (where often identified as *C. marginatus* Gill, a synonym). Forms large semi-stationary schools by day; feeds individually at night, mainly on fishes. Courtship observed to commence at dusk with pairs swimming together, the male assuming black colouration. Juveniles commonly found in estuaries, even penetrating fresh water.

MACKEREL SCAD
Decapterus macarellus Cuvier, 1833

Dorsal rays VIII + I,27-31; anal rays II + I,28-32 (last dorsal and anal soft rays as a well-separated, single filament); straight part of lateral line with 18-38 scales, followed by 25-39 scutes; scales on top of head extending forward to anterior margin of pupil; gill rakers 10-13 + 34-41 (including rudiments); adipose eyelid well-developed anteriorly and posteriorly, leaving only a narrow gap over pupil (also applies to other species of the genus); jaws with a single row of minute teeth (also true of other *Decapterus*); posterior edge of maxilla straight but slanting anteroventrally; edge of shoulder girdle (under operculum) with a small upper and large lower papilla (also generic); body elongate and little compressed, the depth 5.0-5.65 in fork length; pectoral fins short, 1.4-1.7 in head length; silvery blue-green above, shading to silvery on sides and ventrally, with a small black spot on margin of operculum at level of eye; caudal fin usually yellowish. Reaches 32 cm. Circumtropical; a schooling species known from near the surface to about 200 m. Feeds on zooplankton, like others of the genus,

SHORTFIN SCAD
Decapterus macrosoma Bleeker, 1851

Dorsal rays VIII + I,33-39; anal rays II + I,27-31 (last dorsal and anal soft rays as a separate finlet); straight part of lateral line with 14-29 scales, followed by 24-40 scutes; scales on top of head not reaching posterior margin of pupil; gill rakers 10-12 + 34-38 (including rudiments); posterior end of maxilla straight above and prominently convex below; body slender, the depth 5.7-6.45 in fork length; pectoral fins very short, 1.35-1.65 in head length; metallic blue-green on back, silvery below, with a black spot posteriorly on operculum at level of eye; caudal fin slightly dusky. Reaches about 30 cm. Indo-Pacific, including the Gulf of Oman, but no record for the Arabian Gulf; also occurs in the eastern Pacific. A schooling species known from depths of about 30 to at least 170 m.

INDIAN SCAD
Decapterus russelli (Rüppell, 1830)

Dorsal rays VIII + I,28-33; anal rays II + I,25-29 (last dorsal and anal soft rays as separate finlet); straight part of lateral line with 0-4 scales, followed by 30-40 scutes; scales on top of head not extending anterior to centre of eye; gill rakers 10-14 + 30-39 (including rudiments); posterior edge of

451. *Decapterus macarellus*, photographed in Hawaii, about 20 cm (J. Randall)

452. *Decapterus macrosoma* (Yasumasa Kobayashi)

453. *Decapterus russelli*, 17.4 cm (J. Randall)

maxilla slightly concave; body moderately elongate, the depth 4.4-5.0 in fork length; pectoral fins generally reaching or extending slightly beyond a vertical at origin of second dorsal fin; metallic blue-green dorsally, silvery below, with a black spot posteriorly on operculum; caudal fin dusky to light brown, sometimes orangish. Largest specimen, 39 cm. Broadly distributed in the Indian Ocean where it is the most common species of the genus in coastal waters to depths of at least 100 m; also in the western Pacific from Australia to Japan. *D. kiliche* (Cuvier) is a synonym.

454. *Elagatis bipinnulata*, about 70 cm (J. Randall)

RAINBOW RUNNER
Elagatis bipinnulata (Quoy and Gaimard, 1824)

Dorsal rays VI + I,25-30; anal rays I + I,20-24 (the last two dorsal and anal rays as a single separate finlet); lateral-line scales about 100, none as scutes; gill rakers 9-10 + 25-28; body moderately elongate, the depth 4.0-4.8 in standard length; head pointed; mouth small, the maxilla not reaching to below anterior edge of eye; first dorsal fin low, about one-third height of anterior part of second dorsal; caudal peduncle and base of caudal fin of adults with a lateral keel; caudal fin deeply forked, a groove dorsally and ventrally in peduncle in front of upper and lower lobes; pectoral fins small, about 2.0 in head; olive green on back, side of body with two narrow blue stripes, separated by a broader yellow stripe, the lower blue stripe bordered below by a yellow stripe; ventral part of body white. Reaches 120 cm; world angling record, 17.05 kg, from the Revillagigedo Islands, Mexico. Circumtropical; pelagic but usually not far offshore; often occurs in small schools from near the surface to at least 150 m. Feeds primarily on small fishes and the larger crustaceans of the zooplankton.

455. *G. speciosus*, juvenile (J. Randall)

GOLDEN TREVALLY
Gnathanodon speciosus (Forsskål, 1775)

Dorsal rays VII + I,18-20; anal rays II + I,15-17; straight part of lateral line with 17-24 scales, followed by 17-26 scutes; junction of curved and straight parts of lateral line below 9th to 14th dorsal soft rays; chest fully scaled; gill rakers 7-9 + 19-22 (including rudiments); adipose eyelid weakly developed; lips fleshy; mouth strongly protractile; upper jaw without teeth; lower jaw with a few small teeth in juveniles, none in adults; body depth 2.3-3.5 in fork length; first dorsal fin short, about two-thirds height of anterior lobe of second dorsal fin; pectoral fins long and falcate, reaching juncture of curved and straight parts of lateral line; juveniles golden yellow with a narrow black bar through eye, one from nape across posterior operculum, and eight of alterating width on body; tips of caudal lobes black; adults silvery with iridescence, the dark bars faint or absent, with a few scattered blackish blotches on body. Attains about 120 cm; South African spearfishing record, 14.8 kg. Indo-Pacific and eastern Pacific. Usually encountered over sandy bottoms; observed to root into the sand in search of its usual prey of sand-dwelling invertebrates and occasional small fishes. The young sometimes act like pilotfish with sharks and other large fishes.

TORPEDO SCAD
Megalaspis cordyla (Linnaeus, 1758)

Dorsal rays VIII + I,18-20, the last 7-9 as separate finlets; anal fin II + I,16 -17, the last 8 to 10 as separate finlets; curved anterior part of lateral line short, with 21-28 scales, the straight part with 51-59 extemely large scutes; lower part of chest scaleless; gill rakers 8-11 + 18-22 (including rudiments); adipose eyelid well-developed, only a narrow slit over pupil; body depth 3.6-4.3 in fork length; body slightly compressed; caudal peduncle very slender, the scutes forming a lateral keel; first dorsal fin three-fourths or more length of anterior lobe of second dorsal fin; pectoral fins very long and falcate, extending posterior to origin of anal-fin lobe; silvery bluish grey dorsally, shading to silvery on sides and ventrally, with a large black spot posteriorly on operculum at level of eye; fins grey, the caudal with a blackish posterior margin. Reported to attain 80 cm. Occurs throughout the tropical and subtropical Indian Ocean to the western Pacific where it it is distributed from New South Wales and New Caledonia to southern Japan. A pelagic schooling species but ranges into inshore waters; feeds mainly on fishes and squids.

456. *Gnathanodon speciosus*, about 65 cm (J. Randall)

457. *Megalaspis cordyla*, 49 cm (J. Randall)

PILOTFISH
Naucrates ductor (Linnaeus, 1758)

Dorsal rays IV-V + I,25-29 (first spine minute and last spine embedded in adults); anal rays II + I,15-17 (first spine embedded with growth); no scutes but a fleshy keel on each side of caudal peduncle; peduncle with a groove dorsally and ventrally in front of origin of caudal lobes; gill rakers 6-7 + 15-20 (including rudiments); body depth 3.5-4.5 in fork length; dorsal spines very short and not joined by membrane; lobes of second dorsal and anal fins slightly elevated, the dorsal lobe 7.1-8.2 in fork length; pectoral fins very short, about 2 in head; bright blue dorsally, shading to silvery white ventrally, with five broad black bars on body and a sixth at caudal-fin base. Reported to reach 70 cm. Worldwide in tropical to warm temperate seas. Pelagic; often seen riding the bow wave of sharks and other large fishes, sometimes of ships. Juveniles tend to be associated with jellyfishes or drifting seaweed.

BLACK POMFRET
Parastromateus niger (Bloch, 1795)

Dorsal rays IV-V + I,41-44 (the spines very short, soon embedded with growth); anal rays II + I, 35-39 (first two anal spines embedded with growth); pelvic fins absent in individuals of about 10 cm fork length or larger; lateral line only slightly arched anteriorly, the straight part with 8-19 small scutes which form a low keel on side of caudal peduncle and caudal-fin base; small scales nearly covering dorsal and anal fins; gill rakers 5-6 + 13-14; body deep, the depth 1.85-2.2 in fork length, and compressed, the width nearly 3.0 in depth; anterior part of second dorsal and anal fins elevated as lobes, as long or slightly longer than head length; pectoral fins long, falcate, and slender, about 2.8 in fork length; purplish to brownish grey, the front of the head orangish; edges of dorsal and anal fins and posterior margin of caudal fin blackish. Reported to 55 cm. Widespread in continental waters of the Indian Ocean (including the Arabian Gulf but not the Red Sea), ranging to Mauritius and Seychelles; in the western Pacific from Australia to China and southern Japan. Usually found over mud bottoms at depths of about 15-40 m by day, but rising to the surface at night; feeds on zooplankton. Only a single species in the genus. *Apolectus* and *Formio* are synonyms. Formerly classified in its own family, Apolectidae (or Formionidae).

TALANG QUEENFISH
Scomberoides commersonianus Lacepède, 1802

Dorsal rays VI-VII + I,19-21; anal rays II + I,16-19; posterior dorsal and anal rays joined only basally by membrane; lateral line wavy and slightly arched over pectoral fin, then straight to caudal-fin base, without scutes (true of other species of *Scomberoides*); scales pointed and partially embedded; gill rakers short, 0-3 + 7-12 (excluding rudiments); mouth very large, the upper jaw extending well beyond eye; body depth 2.75-3.9 in fork length; body strongly compressed; dorsal profile of head slightly con-

458. *Naucrates ductor*, 33 cm (J. Randall)

459. *Parastromateus niger*, 17 cm (J. Randall)

460. *Scomberoides commersonianus*, 75.2 cm (J. Randall)

vex; dorsal spines very short, anteriorly-posteriorly flattened, folding into a shallow groove, and joined by membrane only basally in groove (true of other species of the genus); anterior lobe of second dorsal and anal fins elevated, the dorsal lobe 5.1-6.9 in fork length; pectoral fins short, about 1.5 in head; pelvic fins joined by membrane to abdomen, depressible into a groove (also generic); bluish grey to lateral line with a series of five to eight large roundish dark spots just above lateral line (spots vary from dark grey to silvery depending on angle of light); body below lateral line silvery to brassy yellow; a blackish spot basally on lower part of pectoral fins. Reported to 120 cm; world angling record 14.5 kg, from Mozambique. Continental waters of the Indian Ocean, including the Red Sea and Arabian Gulf; also in Madagascar and Seychelles; in the western Pacific from southern Queensland to Okinawa. Usually swims in small schools; feeds principally on fishes and squids; the young rasp scales and epidermal tissue from fishes. In their revision of *Scomberoides*, Smith-Vaniz and Staiger (1973) showed that this species has often been misidentified as *S. lysan* (the correct name for the species of the following account).

461. *Scomberoides lysan*, about 35 cm (J. Hoover)

462. *Scomberoides tol*, about 40 cm (J. Hoover)

463. School of *Selar crumenophthalmus* (J. Hoover)

DOUBLESPOTTED QUEENFISH
Scomberoides lysan (Forsskål, 1775)

Dorsal rays VI-VII + I,19-21; anal rays II + I,17-19; posterior dorsal and anal soft rays joined only basally by membrane; scales strongly pointed and partially embedded; gill rakers 3-8 + 15-20 (excluding rudiments); mouth large, the upper jaw extending to below posterior edge of eye; body elongate and strongly compressed, the depth 3.7-4.8 in fork length; dorsal profile of head slightly concave; anterior lobe of second dorsal and anal fins not greatly elevated, the dorsal lobe length 7.05-11.0 in fork length; pectoral fins short, about 1.5 in head; silvery grey-green dorsally, shading on sides and ventrally to silvery white, with a double series of six to eight dark spots on side, one above and one below lateral line (spots varying from dark grey to silvery depending on angle of light); outer half or more of anterior lobe of second dorsal fin black. Largest specimen, 67 cm. Wide-ranging in the Indo-Pacific; occurs as solitary individuals or in small aggregations, from the surface to 100 m. *Chorinemus sanctipetri* Cuvier is a synonym.

NEEDLESCALE QUEENFISH
Scomberoides tol Cuvier, 1832

Dorsal rays VI-VII + I,19-21; anal rays II + I,18-20; posterior dorsal and anal rays joined by membrane only basally; scales lanceolate and partially embedded; gill rakers 4-7 + 17-20 (excluding rudiments); upper jaw of adults extending posteriorly to below rear margin of pupil; body elongate and strongly compressed, the depth 4.05-5.0 in standard length; dorsal profile of head slightly concave; anterior lobe of dorsal and anal fins not very long, the dorsal lobe 8.9-13.0 in fork length; pectoral fins short, about 1.6 in head; bluish silver dorsally, silvery on side and ventrally, with five to eight vertically oblong dark grey (silvery depending on light angle) spots, the first four or five located on lateral line, the second to fourth spots generally largest; outer three-fifths of lobe of dorsal fin black. Largest specimen, 51 cm. Red Sea and Arabian Gulf south to Natal and east to Fiji; in the western Pacific from southern Queensland to Japan. Usually found in small schools in coastal waters near the surface.

BIGEYE SCAD
Selar crumenophthalmus (Bloch, 1793)

Dorsal rays VIII + I,24-27; anal rays II + I,21-23; curved part of lateral line with 48-56 scales and 0-4 scutes; straight part of lateral line with 0-11 scales, followed by 29-42 scutes; gill rakers 9-12 + 27-31 (including rudiments); adipose eyelid well-developed, with a vertically elongate gap over pupil; shoulder girdle beneath operculum with a small upper and large lower papilla and a deep furrow below the latter; body depth 3.4-4.1 in fork length; first dorsal fin and elevated anterior lobe of second dorsal fin about equal in height; no finlets; pectoral fins nearly as long as head; silvery blue-green dorsally, shading to iridescent silvery below, usually with a brassy yellow stripe from upper end of gill opening to upper caudal-fin base; a blackish spot posteriorly on opercle at level of eye. Reaches 28 cm. Worldwide in tropical and subtropical seas; forms small to large schools from near shore to depths as great as 170 m; feeds primarily on zooplankton.

YELLOWSTRIPE SCAD
Selaroides leptolepis (Cuvier, 1833)

Dorsal rays VIII + I,24-26; anal rays II + I,21-23; curved part of lateral line longer than straight part, the straight with 13-25 scales followed by 24-29 small scutes; gill rakers 10-14 + 27-32 (including rudiments); adipose eyelid well-developed only on posterior part of eye; shoulder girdle without papillae and a deep furrow; no teeth on upper jaw or roof of mouth; upper jaw reaching to or slightly beyond front edge of eye, posterior end of maxilla concave above, convex and protruding below; body depth 3.1-3.7 in fork length; first dorsal fin and anterior lobe of second dorsal fin about equal in height; pectoral fins longer than head but not reaching

464. *Selaroides leptolepis*, about 11 cm (J. Randall)

juncture of curved and straight parts of lateral line; silvery blue above, silvery below, with a brassy yellow stripe from upper part of eye to caudal peduncle; a black spot about as large as pupil posteriorly on opercle at level of dorsal part of eye. Attains 20 cm. Arabian Gulf to western Pacific where it ranges from southern Queensland to southern Japan; forms schools over mud bottoms, generally in less than 50 m; feeds mainly on zooplankton; females sexually mature at a length of 12 cm.

GREATER AMBERJACK
Seriola dumerili (Risso, 1810)

Dorsal rays VII + I,29-35 (first spine in adults usually minute or embedded); anal rays II + I,18-22; lateral-line scales 141-163; no scutes; gill rakers in juveniles less than 7 cm fork length 5-6 + 20-24, decreasing in number with growth, the total count 11-19 (excluding rudiments) in adults; upper jaw reaching to below rear edge of pupil, the posterior edge very broad (supramaxilla large); body depth 3.1-4.1 in fork length; a dorsal and ventral precaudal groove present (true of other *Seriola*); anterior lobe of second dorsal fin more than twice height of first dorsal fin, its length 5.6-7.7 in fork length; anal-fin base 1.4-1.7 in base of second dorsal fin; pelvic fins longer than pectoral fins; silvery blue-grey to silvery olive-grey dorsally, shading to silvery ventrally (brassy in juveniles), with a midlateral yellow stripe extending posteriorly from eye; a diagonal olive-brown band from eye to nape; tip of lower caudal lobe, anal-fin lobe, and pelvic fins often white. Reported to 188 cm and 80.6 kg; world angling record, 70.6 kg, from Bermuda. Circumtropical; ranges from near shore to depths as great as 360 m (larger fish, generally, in deeper water); feeds primarily on fishes. Juveniles often associated with drifting algae or debris.

465. *Seriola dumerili*, about 80 cm (J. Hoover)

ALMACO JACK
Seriola rivoliana Valenciennes, 1833

Dorsal rays VII + I,27-33; anal rays II + I,18-22; lateral-line scales 122-143; no scutes; gill rakers of juveniles less than 7 cm fork length 6-9 + 18-20, decreasing with growth to total count of 22-26 (excluding rudiments) in adults; upper jaw reaching to or nearly to a vertical at middle of eye, the posterior edge broad (supramaxilla large); body depth 2.9-3.8 in fork length; anterior lobe of second dorsal fin about four times higher than first dorsal fin, its length 4.5-5.55 in fork length; anal-fin base 1.5-1.6 in base of second dorsal fin; pelvic fins longer than pectorals; silvery violet, silvery blue-green, or silvery olive dorsally, shading to silvery ventrally, with a midlateral brassy yellow stripe and a diagonal olive-brown band from eye to nape (may be faint in adults). Reaches about 120 cm. Found in all tropical to warm temperate seas; more oceanic in its distribution than *S. dumerili*.

BLACKBANDED JACK
Seriolina nigrofasciata (Rüppell, 1829)

Dorsal rays VII-VIII + I,30-37 (one or two posterior spines may be embedded in adults); anal rays I + I,15-18 (initial anal spine often embedded); scales small; no scutes; gill rakers 1-2 + 5-8, mostly as rudiments; upper jaw reaching to below rear

466. *Seriola rivoliana*, about 40 cm (J. Hoover)

edge of eye, its posterior edge rounded and not broad (supramaxilla slender); body depth 3.3-3.9 in fork length; dorsal and ventral precaudal groove present; anterior lobe of second dorsal fin about three times higher than first dorsal fin, the dorsal-lobe length 5.0-6.65 in fork length; anal-fin base contained 2.1-2.3 times in base of second dorsal fin; pelvic fins longer than pectorals; dark silvery blue-grey, shading to silvery grey

467. *S. nigrofasciata*, juv., 9.2 cm (J. Randall)

below, with five diagonal dark bands or series of large blotches on dorsal half of body (these markings often fading in adults); first dorsal, caudal, and pelvic fins dark grey. Reported to 70 cm; South African angling record, 5.2 kg. Widely distributed in the western Indian Ocean, including the Red Sea and Arabian Gulf, to the western Pacific where it ranges from southern Queensland to Japan. Usually encountered as solitary individuals; recorded from depths of 20-150 m; feeds on demersal fishes, cephalopods, and shrimps.

AFRICAN POMPANO
Trachinotus africanus Smith, 1967

Dorsal rays VI + I,21-23 (anterior spines embedded in large adults); anal rays II + I,19-21 (first two anal spines may be embedded with growth); scales small and partially embedded, none as scutes (applies to other species of *Trachinotus*); lateral line slightly arched anteriorly and a little irregular (true of other species of the genus); gill rakers 7-10 + 11-14 (including rudiments); body ovate and compressed, the depth decreasing with age; first dorsal fin very low, the membranes deeply incised (also generic); lobe of second dorsal fin high, its length (in individuals larger than 10 cm fork length) 4.0-5.25 in fork length; pectoral fins about 1.2 in head length; pelvic fins about half length of pectorals; bluish silver dorsally, shading to silvery on sides and ventrally; fins yellowish. Reported to have exceeded 25 kg in the Durban Aquarium (van der Elst, 1981); a 92-cm fish weighed about 9 kg. Occurs from South Africa to the Gulf of Aden and Oman; Pakistan is the easternmost record reported by Smith-Vaniz in Fischer and Bianchi (1984); the author obtained the illustrated specimen in Bali. Occurs inshore, particularly on hard bottom, the young often in estuaries. Principal food items in South Africa are rock mussels, sand mussels, sand dollars, crabs, and mole crabs; these hard-shelled prey are crushed by the powerful pharyngeal dentition.

468. *Seriolina nigrofasciata*, about 60 cm (J. Randall)

469. *Trachinotus africanus*, 71 cm (J. Randall)

SMALLSPOTTED POMPANO
Trachinotus baillonii (Lacepède, 1801)

Dorsal rays VI + I,20-24; anal rays II + I,20-24; gill rakers 7-13 + 15-19 (including rudiments); body depth 2.4-2.9 in fork length; body strongly compressed; dorsal and ventral profiles of head about equally convex; anterior lobes of dorsal and anal fins long, slender, and posteriorly curved, the anal lobe of adults longer than the dorsal, its length 2.5-4.2 in fork length; caudal fin very large and deeply forked; pectoral fins about 1.4 in head length; pelvic fins small, about half length of pectorals; bluish silver dorsally, shading to silvery below, with one to five black spots smaller than pupil along lateral line (number of spots increasing, in general, with growth; spots absent in fish less than about 10-13 cm fork length); lobes of caudal fin and leading edge and distal part of dorsal and anal-fin lobes dark grey to black.

Largest reported, 53.5 cm. Natal to the Red Sea and Arabian Gulf, east to the Marshall, Line, and Society Islands. Occurs in shallow water, often near the surface or along sandy beaches; usually encountered in small aggregations.

470. *Trachinotus baillonii*, about 28 cm (J. Randall)

471. *Trachinotus blochii* (J. Hoover)

472. *Trachinotus botla*, 50.8 cm (J. Randall)

SNUBNOSE POMPANO
Trachinotus blochii (Lacepède, 1801)

Dorsal rays VI + I,18-20; anal rays II + I,16-18; gill rakers 5-8 + 8-10 (including rudiments); body depth varying from 1.8 in fork length of a 20-cm fish to 2.5 in a 69-cm fish; dorsal profile of head steep and strongly convex, the snout short and bluntly rounded; anterior lobe of second dorsal fin longer than anal-fin lobe, varying from 2.75-3.55 in fork length in the same two fish; pectoral fins about 1.2 in head length; pelvic fins small, 1.7-2.0 in pectorals; bluish silvery dorsally, shading to silvery or golden yellow on sides and ventrally; fins dusky yellow to yellowish grey. Reaches at least 70 cm. Indo-Pacific from South Africa north to the Red Sea and Arabian Gulf, east to the Marshall Islands and Samoa. A coastal species sometimes seen in small schools; observed feeding on sand bottoms; a 64.5-cm specimen collected by the author in the Solomon Islands had eaten gastropods (mainly *Strombus*, some *Conus*) and hermit crabs.

LARGESPOTTED POMPANO
Trachinotus botla (Shaw, 1803)

Dorsal rays VI + I,22-24; anal rays II + I,19-22; gill rakers 6-9 + 11-15 (including rudiments); body depth 2.1-2.8 in fork length (deeper in smaller fish); dorsal profile of head only slightly more convex than ventral profile; second dorsal and anal-fin lobes very long, slender, and posteriorly curved, the dorsal longest, 2.3-3.0 in fork length; caudal fin very large and deeply forked; pectoral fins about 1.3 in head length; pelvic fins about 1.7 in length of pectorals; silvery grey, darker dorsally, with one to five, large, vertically oblong, dark grey spots along lateral line (spots touching to one-third below lateral line, increasing in number with growth, none on fish less than 10-13 cm fork length); lobes of median fins bluish black. Reported to attain 75 cm. South Africa north to the Gulf of Oman, east to western Australia. Inhabits coastal waters; often seen along exposed sandy beaches. In South Africa, feeds mainly on mole crabs, but also takes small clams, sand mussels, and worms (van der Elst, 1981). *T. russelii* Cuvier is a synonym.

INDIAN POMPANO
Trachinotus mookalee Cuvier, 1832

Dorsal rays VI + I,18-20 (the anterior spines may be completely embedded in

473. *T. mookalee*, juvenile, 12.5 cm (J. Randall)

474. *Trachinotus mookalee*, 71.5 cm (J. Randall)

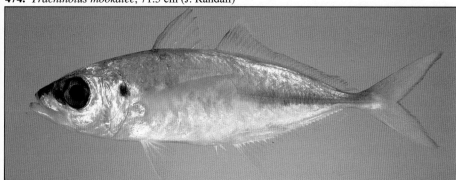

475. *Trachurus indicus*, 24.3 cm (J. Randall)

476. *Ulua mentalis* (J. Randall)

large adults); anal rays II + I,16-18 (first two anal spines often embedded in large adults); gill rakers 5-8 + 8-10 (including rudiments); body depth varying from 2.0 in fork length in a 12.5-cm fish to 2.75 in a 71.5-cm, 3.7-kg specimen; snout very short, rounded, and overhanging the mouth; rest of dorsal profile very steep and convex; second dorsal and anal-fin lobes long, the dorsal lobe 2.95-4.2 in fork length; pectoral fins of adults nearly as long as head; pelvic fins about 2.3 in length of pectoral fins; silvery grey dorsally, shading to silvery or golden yellow on sides and ventrally; fins dirty yellow except pelvics nearly white; juveniles with the outer

half or more of lobe of second dorsal fin black. Reported to 90 cm and a weight of 8.1 kg. Gulf of Oman east to the Gulf of Thailand, north to Hong Kong; a shallow coastal species.

ARABIAN SCAD
Trachurus indicus Nekrasov, 1966

Dorsal rays VIII + I,28-35; anal rays II + I,24-30; scales and scutes of curved part of lateral line 33-41; scales and scutes in straight portion 33-40 (enlarged scales and scutes of large specimens may be obscured by overgrowth of small scales); an accessory lateral line dorsally on body, ending below fifth to ninth dorsal spines; gill rakers 13-17 + 39-47 (including rudiments); shoulder girdle with a small furrow at upper end (beneath operculum), but no papillae; adipose eyelid developed, leaving a vertically oval gap over pupil; body depth 3.8-4.3 in fork length; first dorsal fin about equal to height of lobe of second dorsal fin; no finlets; pectoral fins about as long as head; pelvic fins about half length of pectorals; bluish silver dorsally, shading to silvery white ventrally, with a black spot posteriorly on opercle at level of eye. Reaches 35 cm. Red Sea to Arabian Gulf, south to Somalia and east to Pakistan. In view of the numerous gill rakers, probably feeds on zooplankton.

LONGRAKERED JACK
Ulua mentalis (Cuvier, 1833)

Dorsal rays VIII + I,21-22; anal rays II + I,17-18; curved part of lateral line about equal in length to straight part, the juncture of the two below tenth to twelfth dorsal soft rays; straight part of lateral line with 0-5 scales followed by 26-38 scutes; chest scaleless to behind base of pelvic fins; gill rakers 23-27 + 51-61 (including rudiments), very long, projecting into mouth along side of tongue; body depth 2.0-2.9 in fork length; body strongly compressed; lower jaw becoming prominent and strongly jutting in large adults; dorsal profile of head to above eye straight to slightly concave; lobe of second dorsal and anal fins very long and filamentous in juveniles, the dorsal reaching to

477. *U. mentalis*, juvenile, 8.4 cm (J. Randall)

tip of upper caudal lobe; dorsal lobe of adults shorter than head; pectoral fins long and falcate, reaching beyond juncture of curved and straight portions of lateral line; pelvic fins short, about one-third length of pectorals; silvery blue-green dorsally, shading to silvery below; a dusky to blackish blotch posteriorly on operculum of adults. Reported to 100 cm. Madagascar and Mozambique north to the Red Sea and Arabian Gulf, east to the western Pacific where it ranges from Queensland to Taiwan. The numerous fine gill rakers suggest feeding on the smaller animals of the zooplankton.

WHITETONGUE JACK
Uraspis helvola (Forster and Schneider, 1801)

Dorsal rays VIII + I,25-30 (the posterior two or three spines embedded with growth); anal rays II + I,19-22 (the first two spines soon embedded with growth); curved part of lateral line usually longer than straight part, with 48-66 scales; straight part with 23-40 small scutes; chest scaleless ventrally to origin of pelvic fins, separated by a broad scaled zone from naked base of pectoral fins; gill rakers 5-8 + 13-17 (including rudiments); one or two rows of small, sharp, usually recurved, conical teeth in jaws; no teeth on roof of mouth or tongue; body depth 2.1-2.9 in fork length; first dorsal fin small, its height about one-third that of anterior part of second dorsal fin; anterior second dorsal and anal fins not elevated into a lobe; pecto-

478. *Uraspis helvola*, 16.1 cm (J. Randall)

ral fins long, reaching or nearly reaching juncture of curved and straight parts of lateral line; pelvic fins long in juveniles, shortening with growth; adults dark grey-brown, paler below, with a silvery sheen; juveniles silvery grey with seven dark grey bars on body more than twice as broad as pale interspaces (bars more distinct ventrally; may be faintly evident in specimens as large as 25 cm fork length); most of tongue, roof of mouth, and median floor of mouth white or cream-coloured, the rest of mouth black. Attains 54 cm. Red Sea and Arabian Gulf to the Indo-Malayan region, north to Japan; also recorded from the Hawaiian Islands and St Helena in the Atlantic; bottom-oriented, generally at depths greater than 30 m.

MOONFISH
FAMILY MENIDAE

This family consists of a single species (see following account).

MOONFISH
Mene maculata (Bloch and Schneider, 1801)

Dorsal rays III-IV,40-45; anal rays 30-33; pectoral rays 15-16; pelvic rays I,5, the first two rays greatly prolonged; scales small, cycloid, and highly deciduous; body extremely deep, the depth 1.3-1.5 in standard length and highly compressed, the maximum width about 6 in depth; dorsal profile moderately convex; ventral profile extremely steep and nearly straight to pelvic-fin origin, then broadly convex to the narrow caudal peduncle; ventral edge of body sharp; mouth small, protusible, very strongly oblique, with a band of villiform teeth in jaws, none on roof of mouth; caudal fin forked; blue-green on back with three to four rows of dark grey spots on upper side, silvery below. Attains nearly 30 cm. Wide-ranging in the Indian Ocean, including the Red Sea and Arabian Gulf; in the western Pacific from Queensland to Japan; not common.

479. *Mene maculata*, 21.4 cm (J. Randall)

PONYFISHES
FAMILY LEIOGNATHIDAE

The ponyfishes, also called slip-mouths and soapies, are known only from the Indo-Pacific region (except one Red Sea species which has immigrated via the Suez Canal to the Mediterranean). They are characterised by a compressed body; three bony ridges dorsally on the head which converge on nape, and a median bony ridge on nape anterior to dorsal-fin origin; two short spines behind nostrils above front edge of the eye; ventral edge of preopercle serrate; a small mouth which is highly protractile and tubular when protruded; teeth villiform in jaws except for the two species of the genus *Gazza* which have a row of canines; no teeth on vomer or palatines; gill membranes attached to isthmus; branchiostegal rays 4 or 5; scales small, thin, cycloid, and easily shed; dorsal fin VII-IX (usually VIII),14-17; anal fin III,13-15; second dorsal and second anal spines longest; base of dorsal and anal fins with a series of retrorse spines; caudal peduncle slender; caudal fin forked. There are three genera and about 24 species; the largest genus, *Leiognathus*, is in need of revision. These fishes are bottom-dwelling on mud and sand substrata, mainly in shallow coastal waters, often entering estuaries. They generally occur in schools. Most feed on small invertebrates from the bottom, but the two species of *Gazza* take larger prey, including small fishes. The anterior dorsal and anal spines of leiognathids can be locked in an erect position (Seigel, 1982). Upon capture, ponyfishes exude a large quantity of mucus. They are also known for their unique light organ that encircles the posterior part of the esophagus (Haneda and Tsuji, 1976). The light is produced continuously by luminous bacteria but is not normally visible due to an opaque membrane covering the organ except for two window-like areas; a layer of guanine crystals between the light organ and the esophagus reflects the light through the two windows. The light from the ventral window shines through the translucent muscles of the isthmus and chest; that from the dorsal window enters the anteroventral end of the swim bladder which reflects it into the translucent abdominal muscles.

TOOTHPONY
Gazza minuta (Bloch, 1797)

Dorsal rays VII-VIII,15-17; anal rays III,13-14; pectoral rays 16-17; lateral-line scales 58-60; no scales on head, chest, or abdomen; gill rakers 4-6 + 16-17; body depth 2.2-2.5 in standard length; lower jaw slightly projecting when mouth closed; mouth moving forward when protruded; moderate canine teeth in jaws; grey dorsally with dark orange-yellow to dark grey markings, shading to silvery below; edge of dorsal fin blackish; anterior part of anal fin yellow; caudal fin yellowish. Reported to reach 20 cm. Occurs throughout the tropical and subtropical Indian Ocean and the western Pacific from Queensland to the Ryukyu Islands, east to Samoa. Feeds on small fishes, shrimps and other crustaceans, and polychaete worms.

ORANGEFIN PONYFISH
Leiognathus bindus (Valenciennes, 1835)

Dorsal rays VIII,16; anal rays III,14; pectoral rays 18-19; lateral-line scales 54-58; scales present on chest; gill rakers 5-6 + 16-18; body depth 1.8-2.2 in standard length; head length 3.2-3.5 in standard length; mouth projecting ventroanteriorly when protruded (applies to other species of *Leiognathus*); second dorsal spine 4.9-6.1 in standard length; silvery grey dorsally, usu-

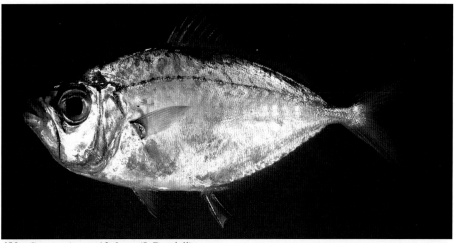
480. *Gazza minuta*, 13.6 cm (J. Randall)

481. *Leiognathus bindus*, 8.7 cm (J. Randall)

ally with irregular dark grey markings, silvery below; a dark spot as large as pupil may be present on each side of nape; outer part of interspinous membranes of dorsal fin between second and fifth to seventh spines orange. Maximum length 11 cm. Red Sea and Arabian Gulf to the Indo-Malayan region, north to Japan.

GOLDSTRIPE PONYFISH
Leiognathus daura (Cuvier, 1829)

Dorsal rays VIII,16; anal rays III,14; pectoral rays 18-19; lateral-line scales 60-68; chest scaleless; gill rakers 5-6 + 14-16; body depth 2.0-2.4 in standard length; head length 3.3-3.6 in standard length; second dorsal spine 4.5-5.1 in standard length; silvery blue-green to grey dorsally, shading to silvery below, with a broad, diffuse, golden yellow stripe from behind and above upper part of eye, following lateral line to end at dark upper part of caudal peduncle; front of snout blackish; a large black spot covering outer two-thirds of membranes between second and sixth dorsal spines except white membrane at tip of second spine; spinous portion of anal fin and distal part of anterior half of soft portion yellow. Attains 14 cm. Gulf of Aden and southern Oman to the Indo-Malayan region, generally in shallow muddy areas.

DECORATED PONYFISH
Leiognathus decorus De Vis, 1884

Dorsal rays VIII,16 (rarely 15); anal rays III,14; pectoral rays 17-18 (rarely 17); lateral-line scales 56-59; chest scaleless; gill rakers 5-6 + 16-18; slender teeth in villiform bands in jaws; body depth 2.2-2.45 in standard length; head length 3.2-3.4 in standard length; second dorsal spine not long, 4.2-4.6 in standard length; second anal spine 6.0-6.45 in standard length; bluish silver dorsally with irregular narrow dark bands which extend to or slightly below lateral line, shading to silvery on side and ventrally; a large dark brown spot with a grey centre dorsally on nape above upper end of gill opening; front of snout above upper lip dusky; a large orange-yellow spot on dorsal fin between second and sixth spines, this spot partially edged with dark grey (broadest above spot); axil of pectoral fins black. Reported to 13.5 cm. Queensland and Papua New Guinea to the Arabian Gulf; the above diagnosis based on 17 specimens, 64-86 mm standard length, taken by trawl off Bahrain. This is the species identified by James (1975) and James in Fischer and Bianchi (1984) from the coasts of India to Australia as *L. brevirostris* (Valenciennes); however, Jones (1985)

482. *Leiognathus daura*, 11.7 cm (J. Randall)

483. *Leiognathus decorus*, 8.8 cm (J. Randall)

484. *Leiognathus equulus*, 16.4 cm (J. Randall)

examined Valenciennes' syntypes and noted that they have scales on the chest and a single row of teeth in the jaws, hence not the *brevirostris* of James.

COMMON PONYFISH
Leiognathus equulus (Forsskål, 1775)

Dorsal rays VIII,15-16; anal rays III,14-15; pectoral rays 18-20; lateral-line scales 55-64; gill rakers 5-6 + 16-17; body depth 1.7-2.1 in standard length; head length 2.9-3.3 in standard length; second dorsal spine 3.85-4.85 in standard length; silvery grey dorsally with narrow, slightly irregular, dark grey bars extending to or slightly below lateral line, silvery below; dorsal edge of caudal peduncle dark brown; margin of soft portion of dorsal fin blackish; posterior margin of caudal fin broadly dusky; anal and paired fins pale to yellowish. The largest of the leiognathids; reaches 24 cm. South Africa to Red Sea and Arabian Gulf, including Mauritius and Seychelles, to the western Pacific, ranging from Queensland and New Caledonia to the Ryukyu Islands, east to the Mariana Islands, Caroline Islands, and Samoa. Shallow coastal waters, including estuaries, to depths of 40 m. The young feed on plankton, the larger fish on benthic crabs, shrimps, and marine worms (van der Elst, 1981).

BARRED PONYFISH
Leiognathus fasciatus (Lacepède, 1803)

Dorsal rays VIII,16; anal rays III,14; pectoral rays 19-20; lateral-line scales 58-64; no scales on chest; gill rakers 5-6 + 15-17; body depth 1.6-1.9 in standard length; head length 2.95-3.5 in standard length; second dorsal fin elongate, its length 1.6-2.8 in standard length; silvery grey dorsally, with narrow, slightly irregular, dark grey bars extending a short distance below lateral line, shading to silvery ventrally; often with a few dusky yellow spots in a longitudinal row below lateral line (adults trawled from 28 m in the Gulf of Oman had two rows of elliptical yellow spots along side of body); anterior part of anal fin yellow; axil of pectoral fins yellow. Reaches 21 cm. Red Sea south to Madagascar and Mauritius, east to the western Pacific where the range extends from Queensland and New Caledonia to the Ryukyu Islands and east to the Mariana Islands and Samoa.

OBLONG PONYFISH
Leiognathus oblongus (Valenciennes, 1835)

Dorsal rays VIII,16; anal rays III,14; pectoral rays 17-18; lateral-line scales about 55; gill rakers 4-6 + 12-14; body depth 2.5-2.9 in standard length; head length 3.5-3.7 in standard length; a slight concavity in dorsal profile of head above eye leading to the slightly convex nape; ventral profile of head to below front of eye slightly concave; second dorsal spine 4.6-4.8 in standard length; silvery grey dorsally with numerous, short, dark grey vermiculations extending a short distance below lateral line; anterior edge of snout blackish; borders of dorsal and anal fins yellow; caudal fin yellowish grey; axil of pectoral fins blackish. Attains 10 cm. Occurs from the Red Sea south to Zanzibar and east to the Indo-Malayan region. The illustrated specimen was taken by trawling in 20 m over mud bottom off Kuwait. This species has been identified as *L. berbis* (Valenciennes), as by James (1975), and as *L. lineolatus* (Valenciennes), as by Blegvad (1944) and Kuronuma and Abe (1986).

485. *Leiognathus fasciatus*, 8.1 cm (J. Randall)

486. *Leiognathus oblongus*, 10.2 cm (J. Randall)

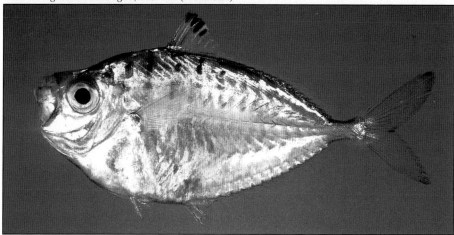

487. *Secutor insidiator*, 7.1 cm (J. Randall)

Günther (1860) and Day (1876) are followed in regarding *L. oblongus* as the correct name. Forsskål (1775) described *Scomber equula* from the Red Sea and listed a second variety, providing the local name "Berbîs". Valenciennes in Cuvier and Valenciennes (1835) copied Forsskål's brief description and named the variety as a species, *L. berbis*. There is no type specimen (Klausewitz and Nielsen, 1965). *L. lineolatus* was described from a specimen from Java with vertical dark lines on the back.

PUGNOSE PONYFISH
Secutor insidiator (Bloch, 1787)

Dorsal rays VIII-IX,15-17; anal rays III,14; pectoral rays 17-18; lateral-line scales 82-92; gill rakers 6-7 + 17-21; body

193

depth 1.95-2.2 in standard length; head length 3.6-4.0 in standard length; head very distinctive in shape, the dorsal profile slightly sloping to above front of eye, then convex to dorsal-fin origin; ventral profile nearly vertical for a distance of about one eye diameter below lower lip, then broadly convex; mouth directed slightly upward when protruded; second dorsal spine not long, 5.5-7.0 in standard length; silvery dark greenish grey with four rows of small, slightly irregular, black spots on upper third of body; a black streak from below front of eye to angle of ventral head profile; a large black spot on outer part of interspinous membranes between second and sixth dorsal spines; caudal fin yellowish with a blackish posterior margin. Maximum length, 10.5 cm. Western Indian Ocean, including Madagascar, Seychelles, Red Sea, and Arabian Gulf, to the Indo-Malayan region and northwestern Australia; occurs in coastal waters from inshore to depths of 150 m; also common in brackish lagoons and estuaries; feeds on zooplankton, including copepods, mysids, and larval fishes and crustaceans (van der Elst, 1981).

MOJARRAS
FAMILY GERREIDAE

The following characters collectively identify the fishes of this family: body compressed but variable in depth; ventral profile of head to below front of eye concave; mouth very protractile, angling downward when protruded; teeth in jaws brushlike (very small, close-set, and numerous), none on roof of mouth; maxilla broad posteriorly and exposed on the cheek (except *Pentaprion*); gill membranes free from isthmus; a single dorsal fin, elevated anteriorly, with IX or X spines and 9-18 soft rays; anal fin with II-VI spines and 6-18 soft rays; dorsal and anal fins fold into a scaly sheath at base; caudal fin deeply forked; pelvic rays I,5; branchiostegal rays 6; head scaled; scales thin, cycloid, moderately large, and easily lost; colour dominantly silvery. The mojarras, also known as silver biddies, are found in tropical to warm temperate seas on sand or mud bottoms,

generally in shallow water. They feed by taking in mouthfuls of sediment and expelling the inorganic material from the gill openings. They may be encountered as solitary individuals or in small schools. Eight genera and about 40 species are recognised; a systematic revision of the family is needed.

LONGTAIL MOJARRA
Gerres acinaces Bleeker, 1854

Dorsal rays IX-X,9-11; anal rays III,7; pectoral rays 15-16 (usually 16); lateral-line scales 40-47; scales above lateral line to base of fifth dorsal spine 5-5.5; body depth

2.4-2.9 in standard length; head length 2.9-3.35 in standard length; second dorsal spine longest (true of other species of the genus), 3.9-4.4 in standard length; caudal fin large, longer than head, 2.6-2.9 in standard length; pectoral fins extending to above origin of anal fin; silvery with vertical series of pink to bluish spots on side of body (spots may be faint); no black on dorsal fin; posterior margin of caudal fin dusky. Reaches 37 cm. Indo-Pacific; usually solitary in clear water over sand bottoms, often in the vicinity of coral reefs.

WHIPFIN MOJARRA
Gerres filamentosus Cuvier, 1829

Dorsal rays IX,10; anal rays III,7; pectoral rays 15-16 (usually 16); lateral-line

488. *Gerres acinaces*, about 15 cm (J. Randall)

489. *Gerres filamentosus*, 15.4 cm (J. Randall)

scales 43-47; scales above lateral line to base of fifth dorsal spine 4.5-5; body depth 2.0-2.5 in standard length (body more elongate in juveniles, up to 3.0 in standard length); head length 2.9-3.1 in standard length; second dorsal spine very long and filamentous, 1.5-3.0 in standard length; pectoral fins long, extending posteriorly to above base of third anal spine; caudal fin length less than head length; silvery, the juveniles with about ten narrow dusky bars on upper two-thirds of body which break up into vertical series of oval dark spots in adults; a longitudinal row of small dusky spots, one per membrane, in dorsal fin. Attains 25 cm. Red Sea and Arabian Gulf south to South Africa and east to the Indo-Malayan region and northern Australia, north to China and Japan; also recorded from Yap in the Caroline Islands. Tends to occur in deeper water than *G. acinaces*; adults were trawled from the Gulf of Oman in 37 m.

490. *Gerres oyena*, about 9 cm (J. Randall)

491. *Gerres oyena*, about 9 cm, night (J. Randall)

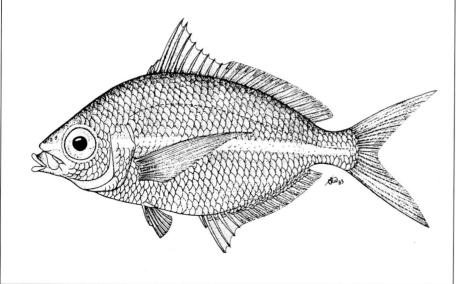

492. *Pentaprion longimanus* (after Fischer and Bianchi, 1984)

BLACKTIP MOJARRA
Gerres oyena (Forsskål, 1775)

Dorsal rays IX,10; anal rays III,7; pectoral rays 15 (rarely 14 or 16); lateral-line scales 36-40; scales above lateral line to base of fifth dorsal spine 3-3.5; body depth 2.8-3.1 in standard length; head length 2.8-3.2 in standard length; second dorsal spine 4.1-4.9 in standard length; caudal fin equal to or shorter than head; pectoral fins not reaching to above origin of anal fin; silvery; tip of dorsal fin black, the rest of fin margin often blackish; a row of small dusky spots, one per membrane, near base of dorsal fin; posterior margin of caudal fin dusky. Attains about 20 cm. Occurs throughout the tropical and subtropical Indian Ocean to the western Pacific, south to Queensland and New Caledonia, north to Japan, and east to Samoa. Generally found in shallow water along sandy shores, but also in estuaries and mangrove sloughs; taken in beach seines, sometimes in trawls to depths of at least 20 m.

LONGFIN MOJARRA
Pentaprion longimanus (Cantor, 1850)

Dorsal rays IX-X,14-15; anal rays V-VI,12-14; pectoral rays 15-17; lateral-line scales 44-48; gill rakers 4-5 + 13-14; body depth 2.5-2.8 in standard length; head length about 3.2 in standard length; upper part of maxilla slipping under edge of preorbital bone when mouth closed (maxilla exposed in *Gerres*); third dorsal spine longest, its length about 5.0 in standard length; base of anal fin longer than base of soft portion of dorsal fin; pectoral fins reaching to above base of about third anal soft ray; silvery greenish to pinkish grey with a midlateral silver stripe. Arabian Gulf to Indo-Malayan region and northern Australia, north to Japan. Arabian Gulf specimens collected in trawls in 15-20 m.

ROVERS
FAMILY EMMELICHTHYIDAE

The one character that unites the fishes of this family as distinct from other perciforms is the upper-jaw morphology; the maxilla is broadly expanded posteriorly, scaled, and not partially covered by the preorbital bone when the mouth is closed; the supramaxilla is well-developed; the premaxilla has a broad median ascending process joined to a large rostral cartilage, and there is a prominent midlateral process. Other characters are as follows: jaws without teeth or with only a few minute conical teeth anteriorly; no teeth on vomer or palatines; two flat spines on opercle (in some species a small third spine dorsally); edge of preopercle broadly rounded at corner and projecting posterior to upper margin; 7 branchiostegal rays; scales small and ctenoid; head scaled; body depth varying from 2.8-5.8 in standard length; dorsal fin continuous or divided, with XI-XIV spines (posterior spines not visible externally in two species of *Emmelichthys*); anal fin with III spines; dorsal and anal fins with a basal scaly sheath; pelvic fins I,5; caudal fin forked. The rovers are bottom-oriented and are generally found in the depth range of 100-400 m; limited data suggest that they feed on the larger animals of the zooplankton for which their highly protractile mouth is adapted. Three genera are recognised: *Emmelichthys*, *Erythrocles*, and *Plagiogeneion* (Heemstra and Randall, 1977) and 14 species.

RUBY ROVER
Erythrocles schlegelii (Richardson, 1846)

Dorsal rays XI,10-11; anal rays III,9-10 (usually 10); pectoral rays 18-20; lateral-line scales 66-72; head scaled except for a narrow zone at front of snout; gill rakers 9-10 + 25-29; body depth 3.85-4.55 in standard length; head length 3.2-3.6 in standard

493. *Erythrocles schlegelii*, 42 cm (J. Randall)

length; two prominent fleshy protuberances posteriorly at edge of gill cavity; a low median lateral keel on caudal peduncle; dorsal fin almost completely divided between tenth and eleventh spines; dorsal and anal fins with a basal scaly sheath; reddish brown dorsally, silvery pink on sides and ventrally; lips and caudal fin red; remaining fins with red rays and translucent membranes; juveniles with four to six dark bars dorsally on body. Largest reported, 53 cm. Known only from Japan (type locality), Korea, Natal, Kenya, and Gulf of Oman (Oman record from Boulenger, 1889).

SNAPPERS
FAMILY LUTJANIDAE

The snappers are among the most important commercial fishes of tropical and subtropical seas. In addition to the general characteristics of perciform fishes, they are distinctive in having a moderately large mouth with equal jaws or the lower jaw protruding; upper edge of maxilla slipping under the preorbital bone when mouth closed; no supramaxilla; teeth in jaws varying from small and conical to large and caniniform (none incisiform or molariform); vomer and palatines usually with small teeth; no spines on opercle; scales ctenoid; dorsal rays X-XII,9-17; anal rays III,7-11; dorsal fin continuous or with a notch between spinous and soft portions; dorsal spines heteracanthus (successive spines alternating slightly left to right when fin folded); caudal fin truncate, emarginate, or forked, the principal rays 17; pelvic rays I,5, their base slightly posterior to base of pectoral fins. All snappers are carnivorous; most feed heavily on crustaceans, but a few are primarily piscivorous (those that feed on fishes generally have large canine teeth). Many snappers are nocturnal; during the day some species of *Lutjanus* form semi-stationary aggregations. The family is represented by 13 genera and 103 species (Allen, 1985); it is divisible into four subfamilies of which only the Lutjaninae and Etelinae are represented in Oman waters. The 39 Indo-Pacific species of *Lutjanus* were revised by Allen and Talbot (1985). Allen (1985) included Oman on his distribution maps for *Aphareus furca* (Lacepède) and *Aprion virescens* Valenciennes, and although these roving snappers might be expected off southern Oman, the author knows of no definite record of them.

RUSTY JOBFISH
Aphareus rutilans Cuvier, 1830

Dorsal rays X,11; anal rays III,8; pectoral rays 15-16; lateral-line scales 70-75; gill rakers 17-19 + 32-34; body depth 3.3-4.0 in standard length; head length 3.0-3.3 in standard length; lower jaw projecting; mouth large, the maxilla reaching to or slightly beyond a vertical through centre of eye; small teeth in a narrow band in jaws, none on roof of mouth; dorsal fin without a notch; last dorsal and anal rays filamentous, about three time length of penultimate rays; caudal fin large and very deeply forked; pectoral fins about as long as head; silvery lavender dorsally, silvery pink on sides and ventrally; lower lip, edge of maxilla, and maxillary groove black; inside of mouth silvery; caudal and pectoral fins red. Reaches 80 cm. Indo-Pacific (absent from the Arabian Gulf), generally at depths of 100 m or more (once observed by the author in 20 m).

MANGROVE SNAPPER
Lutjanus argentimaculatus (Forsskål, 1775)

Dorsal rays X,13-14; anal rays III,8; pectoral rays 16-17; lateral-line scales 44-48; scale rows on back usually parallel to lateral line below spinous portion of dorsal fin, ascending obliquely upward posteriorly; small scales basally on soft portions of dorsal and anal fins (true of other species of *Lutjanus*); gill rakers 6-8 + 9-12; body depth 2.5-3.0 in standard length; head length 2.3-2.7 in standard length; preopercular notch not well developed; interopercular knob small or absent; large canine teeth at front of jaws; vomerine teeth in a V-shaped band without a median posterior extension; tongue with a patch of small granular teeth; caudal fin truncate; greenish brown to reddish brown, the scale edges silvery on sides and ventrally; juveniles and subadults often with two, near-horizontal, blue lines

494. *Aphareus rutilans*, 37 cm (J. Randall)

495. *Lutjanus argentimaculatus* (J. Hoover)

under eye; juveniles with about eight narrow pale bars on body. Reported to 120 cm, but 100 cm seems a more likely maximum. Red Sea (and via Suez Canal to eastern Mediterranean) to South Africa and east to Samoa; in the western Pacific from New South Wales to southern Japan. Occurs on sheltered coral reefs, often in silty dead-reef areas; has been taken in trawls as deep as 120 m. The young are usually found in estuarine areas, even in freshwater.

BENGAL SNAPPER
Lutjanus bengalensis (Bloch, 1790)

Dorsal rays XI-XII,12-14; anal rays III,8; pectoral rays 16-17; lateral-line scales 47-49; scale rows above lateral line ascending obliquely; gill rakers 8-9 + 17-19; body depth 2.5-2.9 in standard length; head length 2.5-2.7 in standard length; preopercular notch and interopercular knob well developed; vomerine teeth in a V-shaped band without a median posterior extension; no teeth on tongue; caudal fin slightly emarginate; upper three-fifths of body yellow with four dark-edged blue stripes, the uppermost narrow, passing from interorbital space to below middle of spinous portion of dorsal fin; lower two-fifths of body white; iris yellow; dorsal and caudal fins yellow; remaining fins whitish. Attains nearly 30 cm. Red Sea and Gulf of Oman south to Kenya and Mauritius, east to Indonesia; a coral-reef species usually found at depths of about 10-25 m. More common in the Gulf of Oman than the Arabian Sea. Very similar in colour to *L. kasmira*, but easily distinguished with specimens in hand by having XI-XII dorsal spines, in contrast to X for *L. kasmira*.

496. *Lutjanus bengalensis*, about 20 cm (J. Hoover)

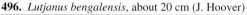

TWINSPOT SNAPPER
Lutjanus bohar (Forsskål, 1775)

Dorsal rays X,13-14; anal rays III,8; pectoral rays 16-17; lateral-line scales 48-51; scale rows above lateral line ascending obliquely; gill rakers 6-7 + 16; body depth 2.4-2.9 in standard length; head length 2.4-2.9 in standard length; preopercular notch and interopercular knob moderately developed; nostrils of adults in a prominent oblique groove passing forward from eye (unique to this species); canine teeth at front of jaws very large; vomerine teeth in a narrow V-shaped band without a median posterior extension; tongue with one or two patches of fine granular teeth; caudal fin slightly forked; dark reddish brown on back, shading to red on sides, the scales with a whitish spot, thus forming a linear pattern; juveniles and subadults below about 20 cm in standard length with one or two whitish spots on back, the first below middle of dorsal fin and the last below base of posterior dorsal soft rays; anterior soft portion of dorsal fin, leading edge of anal fin, lateral edge of pelvic fins, and often upper and lower edges of caudal fin whitish with a broad dark brown submarginal band (these fin markings obscure in large adults); upper part of pectoral fin darker than rest of fin, with a small black spot at upper base. Attains 80 cm. Indo-Pacific; especially common on seaward reefs of atolls and low islands. Observed occasionally in Oman only on the Arabian Sea coast. The food habits were studied by Talbot (1960), Helfrich et al. (1968), and Randall (1980); the principal prey are fishes (about 70% by volume of stomach contents), especially reef species, followed by crustaceans and cephalopods. The young have been reported to mimic the damselfishes *Chromis ternatensis*, *C. margaritifer*, and *C. iomelas* (Russell et al., 1976).

497. *Lutjanus bohar*, about 22 cm (J. Randall)

498. *Lutjanus coeruleolineatus*, about 27 cm (J. Randall)

BLUELINED SNAPPER
Lutjanus coeruleolineatus (Rüppell, 1830)

Dorsal rays X,12-14; anal rays III,8-9; pectoral rays 16-17; lateral-line scales 46-49; scale rows above lateral line ascending obliquely; gill rakers 7-8 + 14-15; body depth 2.4-2.6 in standard length; head length 2.5-2.7 in standard length; preopercular notch and interopercular knob poorly developed; vomerine teeth in a narrow V-shaped band without a median posterior extension; tongue without teeth; caudal fin truncate to slightly emarginate; yellow with seven or eight narrow blue stripes and a large oval black spot on lateral line below anterior soft portion of dorsal fin (about two-thirds of spot above lateral line); fins yellow. Reaches about 40 cm. Red Sea to Gulf of Oman.

BLACKSPOT SNAPPER
Lutjanus ehrenbergii (Peters, 1879)

Dorsal rays X,13-14; anal rays III,8; pectoral rays 15-16; lateral-line scales 42-47; scales on back parallel to lateral line; gill rakers 6-7 + 10-14; body depth 2.5-3.0 in standard length; head length 2.5-2.8 in standard length; preopercular notch indistinct; interopercular knob small or absent; vomerine teeth of adults in a triangular patch with a median posterior extension (crescentic in juveniles); tongue of adults with a patch of fine granular teeth; caudal fin truncate to slightly emarginate; body grey-brown dorsally, the edges of the scales darker than centres, shading to silvery grey on sides and ventrally, with four or five narrow yellow stripes on body below lateral line and a large black spot on lateral line below juncture of spinous and soft portions of dorsal fin; head silver-grey; fins yellow. Maximum length about 35 cm. Red Sea and Arabian Gulf south to Natal and east to the Marianas and Caroline Islands; in the western Pacific north to Taiwan and south to northern Queensland; the dominant inshore snapper in the Gulf of Oman. Occurs on coral reefs and rocky substrata, the young sometimes in estuaries; often encountered by day in small aggregations.

499. *Lutjanus ehrenbergii* (J. Hoover)

CRIMSON SNAPPER
Lutjanus erythropterus Bloch, 1790

Dorsal rays XI,12-14; anal rays III,8-9; pectoral rays 16-17; lateral-line scales 46-50; scales on side rising obliquely from below and above lateral line; gill rakers 5-6 + 13-14; body depth 2.5-3.0 in standard length; head length 2.5-2.8 in standard length; dorsal profile of head convex; preopercular notch poorly developed; interopercular knob indistinct or absent; mouth relatively small, the upper-jaw length distinctly less than greatest depth of caudal peduncle; vomerine teeth in a V-shaped or triangular patch without a median posterior extension; tongue without teeth; caudal fin truncate to slightly emarginate; red dorsally, shading to silvery pink on sides and ventrally; fins largely red; juveniles with an oblique dark band from snout through eye to nape, and a large black saddle-like spot on caudal peduncle preceded by a white bar. Attains about 60 cm. Gulf of Oman to western Pacific where it ranges from Queensland to southern Japan; usually caught by handline or trawls to depths of at least 100 m.

DORY SNAPPER
Lutjanus fulviflamma (Forsskål, 1775)

Dorsal rays X,12-14; anal rays III,8; pectoral rays 15-17; lateral-line scales 46-49;

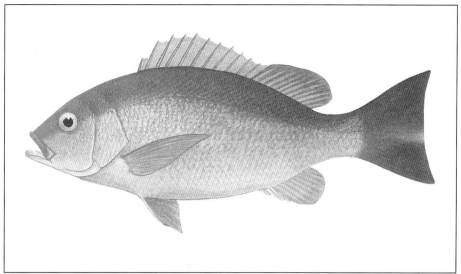

500. *Lutjanus erythropterus* (after Allen, 1985)

scales on back rising obliquely above lateral line; gill rakers 6-7 + 9-12; body depth 2.6-2.9 in standard length; head length 2.4-2.7 in standard length; preopercular notch shallow; interopercular knob indistinct or absent; vomerine teeth in a triangular or diamond-shaped patch with a median posterior extension (except in juveniles); tongue of adults with a patch of small granular teeth; caudal fin slightly emarginate; greenish to grey on back, silvery white on sides and ventrally, with about six narrow orange-yellow stripes and a black spot (usually oblong) on lateral line below anterior soft portion of

501. *Lutjanus fulviflamma*, 11 cm (J. Randall)

502. *Lutjanus fulvus*, about 20 cm (J. Hoover)

dorsal fin (most of spot below lateral line); fins yellowish; juveniles and subadults usually with a dark brown streak from side of snout through eye to end of opercle. Reaches about 35 cm. Red Sea and Arabian Gulf to South Africa, east to Samoa; in the western Pacific from New South Wales to the Ryukyu Islands. Occurs mainly on coral reefs or rocky substrata from inshore to depths of at least 35 m; the young enter brackish habitats.

BLACKTAIL SNAPPER
Lutjanus fulvus (Forster and Schneider, 1801)

Dorsal rays X,13-14; anal rays III,8; pectoral rays 16; lateral-line scales 47-50; scale rows above lateral line ascending obliquely; gill rakers 6-7 + 10-13; body depth 2.3-2.8 in standard length; head length 2.4-2.7 in standard length; preopercular notch deep; interopercular knob well developed; vomerine teeth in a V-shaped band without a median posterior extension; tongue edentate; caudal fin slightly emarginate; brownish to yellowish grey dorsally, paler below, with narrow yellow stripes following centres of scale rows below lateral line; dorsal fin dark reddish to grey, the soft portion with a white margin and a broad red to blackish submarginal band; caudal fin reddish black with a white posterior margin; remaining fins largely yellow. Reported to 40 cm. Southern Oman to South Africa, east to French Polynesia; introduced to the Hawaiian Islands; a coral-reef fish known from the shallows to depths of at least 40 m; the young often found in estuaries and mangrove sloughs. Randall and Brock (1960) reported the food habits of adults in the Society Islands (where it is the most common snapper) as 54.3% crustaceans (mainly crabs) and 42.4% fishes. *L. vaigiensis* (Quoy and Gaimard) is a synonym.

HUMPBACK SNAPPER
Lutjanus gibbus (Forsskål, 1775)

Dorsal rays X,13-14; anal rays III,8; pectoral rays 16-17; lateral-line scales 47-51; scales on side rising obliquely from below and above lateral line; gill rakers 9-10 + 15-20; body depth 2.2-2.5 in standard length; head length 2.4-2.6 in standard length; dorsal profile of head of adults a sinuous curve, the forehead and nape prominently convex; preopercular notch very deep, the conspicuous interopercular knob fitting into notch; patch of teeth on vomer V-shaped without a median posterior extension; caudal fin forked with broadly rounded lobes (giving rise to another common name, Paddletail Snapper); reddish grey to red (those from deeper water more red); lower part of opercle and axil of pectoral fins yellow; median fins dark reddish with white distal margin; paired fins red; juveniles bluish grey with dark lines following scale rows on body and a large black area posteriorly on caudal peduncle and basally on caudal fin. Attains about 50 cm. Indo-Pacific; known from Oman only in the south. When abundant, forms large, nearly stationary schools by day; feeds individually at night. Randall (1980) summarised the food habits of his and previous studies: crabs dominated the diet of most studies, followed by shrimps, fishes, and molluscs (cephalopods, prosobranchs, opisthobranchs, and amphineurans), and echinoids, but fishes were the main food item found by Helfrich et al. (1968).

JOHN'S SNAPPER
Lutjanus johnii (Bloch, 1792)

Dorsal rays X,13-14; anal rays III,8; pectoral rays 16-17; lateral-line scales 46-49; scales on back parallel to lateral line; gill rakers 6-7 + 11-12; body depth 2.4-2.9 in standard length; head length 2.5-2.7 in standard length; preopercular notch shallow; interopercular knob poorly developed; vomerine teeth in a V-shaped band without a median posterior extension; adults with a patch of small granular teeth on tongue; caudal fin truncate; grey dorsally, silvery grey on sides and ventrally, with a crescentic dark brown spot on each scale; a large blackish spot on lateral line below anterior soft portion of dorsal fin (more of spot above than below lateral line), the spot larger, darker, and broadly white-edged in juveniles; fins yellowish grey. Reported to 70 cm. Djibouti to South Africa, east to Fiji; in the western Pacific from northern Queensland to the Ryukyu Islands; recorded from the Strait of Hormuz by Blegvad (1944). Juveniles have been found inshore in estuaries, but

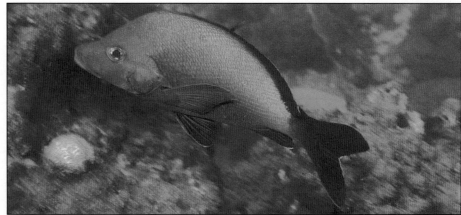

503. *Lutjanus gibbus*, 35 cm (J. Randall)

504. *Lutjanus johnii*, 29.7 cm (J. Randall)

505. *Lutjanus kasmira*, 20 cm (J. Randall)

adults occur in deeper water (to at least 80 m) where they are often taken in trawls.

BLUESTRIPED SNAPPER
Lutjanus kasmira (Forsskål, 1775)

Dorsal rays X,14-15; anal rays III,7-8; pectoral rays 15-16; lateral-line scales 48-51; scale rows above lateral line on back rising obliquely; gill rakers 7-8 + 13-14; body depth 2.4-2.8 in standard length; head length 2.3-2.7 in standard length; preopercular notch moderately deep, the interopercular knob well developed; vomerine teeth in a crescentic band without a median posterior extension; tongue without teeth; caudal fin slightly forked; yellow with four dark-edged blue stripes on upper three-fifths of body, whitish, yellowish, or pale pink on lower two-fifths with bluish to grey lines following scale rows; fins yellow, the upper part of pectorals dusky; a faint blackish spot sometimes present below anterior soft part of dorsal fin (the spot can be turned on or off by the fish). Largest specimen, 34 cm. Indo-Pacific; known from Oman only in the south; introduced to the Hawaiian Islands where it has undergone a population explosion. When abundant, forms large aggregations by day; feeds at night, mainly on crustaceans. Generally found at depths greater than 15 m; the author caught one by hook and line in the Red Sea from 265 m. Spawning and development documented by Suzuki and Hioki (1979).

LUNARTAIL SNAPPER
Lutjanus lunulatus (Park, 1797)

Dorsal rays X,13-14; anal rays III,8; pectoral rays 16-17; lateral-line scales 47-48; scales above lateral line ascending obliquely; gill rakers 7 + 8-10; body depth 2.5-2.6 in standard length; head length 2.4-3.0 in standard length; preopercular notch shallow; interopercular knob poorly developed; vomerine teeth in a V-shape without a median posterior extension; tongue with a patch of small granular teeth; caudal fin slightly forked; red on back, shading to silvery red on sides and yellow ventrally; caudal fin with a broad, crescent-shaped, black bar reaching nearly to tips of lobes. Attains about 35 cm. Gulf of Oman to Indo-Malayan region; usually found on coral reefs in about 10-30 m; rare in Oman.

YELLOWLINED SNAPPER
Lutjanus lutjanus Bloch, 1790

Dorsal rays X-XII,12; anal rays III,8; pectoral rays 16-17; lateral-line scales 48-50; scale above lateral line ascending obliquely; gill rakers 6-8 + 17-19; body elongate, the depth 2.9-3.3 in standard length; head length 2.4-2.9 in standard length; eye large, 2.9-3.7 in head length; preopercular notch shallow; interopercular knob not apparent; vomerine teeth in a triangular patch with a median posterior extension; tongue with a patch of fine granular teeth; caudal fin slightly forked; silvery grey on back with diagonal brownish yellow lines following scale rows, silvery on sides and ventrally with a narrow midlateral yellow stripe commencing behind eye and longitudinal yellow lines following scales rows on lower half of body; fins yellow. Maximum length about 30 cm. Western Indian Ocean, including Red Sea and Arabian Gulf, to Indo-Malayan region and Australia, north to Ryukyu Islands; a schooling species. *L. lineolatus* (Rüppell) is a synonym.

MALABAR SNAPPER
Lutjanus malabaricus (Bloch and Schneider, 1801)

Dorsal rays XI,12-14; anal rays III,8-9; pectoral rays 16-17; lateral-line scales 46-50; scales above lateral line ascending obliquely; gill rakers 4-7 + 12-14; body depth 2.2-2.8 in standard length; head length 2.4-2.8 in standard length; dorsal profile of head to above eye straight; preopercular notch slight; interopercular knob not apparent; mouth relatively large, the upper-jaw length about equal to greatest depth of caudal peduncle; vomerine teeth in a triangular patch without a median posterior extension; tongue without teeth; caudal fin truncate to slightly emarginate; pink above lateral line with oblique orange-red lines following scale rows, the sides and ventral part of body silvery pink; fins light red; juveniles silvery pink with reddish lines following scale rows with a large, white-bordered, saddle-like, black spot on caudal peduncle, and an oblique dark band from snout to nape. Reported to attain 100 cm, but 70 cm would be unusually large. Arabian Gulf to Fiji; in the western Pacific from New South Wales to Taiwan. Allen (1985) recorded the depth range as about 12-100 m. An important food fish caught by trawls and handlines. Adults not observed by the author while diving.

506. *Lutjanus lunulatus*, 33.3 cm (J. Randall)

507. School of *Lutjanus lutjanus* (J. Hoover)

508. *Lutjanus malabaricus*, 48.7 cm (J. Randall)

509. *L. malabaricus*, juv., 9.8 cm (J. Randall)

ONESPOT SNAPPER
Lutjanus monostigma (Cuvier, 1828)

Dorsal rays X,12-14 (rarely 14); anal rays III,8; pectoral rays 15-17; lateral-line scales 47-50; scales above lateral line ascending obliquely; gill rakers 6-7 + 11-12; body depth 2.6-3.0 in standard length; head length 2.5-2.7 in standard length; preopercular notch shallow; interopercular knob little-developed; canine teeth at front of jaws very large; vomerine teeth in a crescentic band without a median posterior extension; tongue without teeth; caudal fin slightly forked; silvery grey dorsally, the edges of the scales above lateral line dark grey-brown, pinkish to yellowish silvery below, with an oval blackish spot smaller than eye on lateral line below anterior soft portion of dorsal fin (spot may be faint or absent in large adults); fins yellow. Reaches about 60 cm. Indo-Pacific; not known from the Arabian Gulf, but occasional in the Gulf of Oman and southern Oman. Occurs from a few to at least 30 m on coral reefs or irregular hard bottom, often in the vicinity of caves; may be seen as solitary individuals or in small groups. Nocturnal; stomach-content analyses revealed fishes about 90% by volume (Randall, 1980).

510. *Lutjanus monostigma*, about 40 cm (J. Hoover)

511. Aggregation of *Lutjanus quinquelineatus* (J. Hoover)

FIVESTRIPE SNAPPER
Lutjanus quinquelineatus (Bloch, 1790)

Dorsal rays X,13-15; anal rays III,8; pectoral rays 16-17; lateral-line scales 47-50; scales on back rising obliquely above lateral line; gill rakers 7-8 + 13-15; body depth 2.3-2.8 in standard length; head length 2.5-2.7 in standard length; preopercular notch moderately deep, the interopercular knob well developed; vomerine teeth in a crescentic band without a mean posterior extension; tongue without teeth; caudal fin slightly forked; yellow, becoming greyish red anteriorly on head, with five, slightly irregular, dark-edged blue stripes on body and six on head; a black spot as large or larger than eye on body between second and third blue stripes below anterior soft portion of dorsal fin, the lower edge of spot adjacent to lateral line; fins yellow. Largest specimen examined, 25 cm. Arabian Gulf to Fiji; New South Wales to southern Japan; rare in Oman waters. Occurs on rocky substrata or coral reefs to depths of at least 40 m; often seen in aggregations by day. *L. spilurus* (Bennett) is a synonym.

SPECKLED SNAPPER
Lutjanus rivulatus (Cuvier, 1828)

Dorsal rays X,15-16; anal rays III,9; pectoral rays 17-18; lateral-line scales 47-49; scales above lateral line ascending obliquely; gill rakers 6 + 11-13; body moderately deep, the depth 2.1-2.4 in standard length; head length 2.4-2.5 in standard length; suborbital deep, its depth 3.1-4.5 in head length; preopercular notch moderately developed, the interopercular knob indistinct; lips of adults thick (hence another common name, Blubberlip Snapper); vomerine teeth in a V-shaped band without a median posterior extension; tongue without teeth; soft portion of anal fin pointed; caudal fin slightly forked; adults brown dorsally, shading to silvery light brown on sides and ventrally, the scales of body with one to four small bluish white spots; head with numerous, undulating, yellowish brown and blue lines; juveniles with narrow dark bars and a half-white, half-black spot on lateral line below anterior soft part of dorsal fin. Attains at least 80 cm. Red Sea and Gulf of Oman south to Natal and east to Society Islands; in the western Pacific from northern Queensland to the Ryukyu Islands; occurs to depths of at least 100 m; usually solitary and difficult to approach underwater.

512. *Lutjanus rivulatus* (J. Hoover)

513. *Lutjanus rivulatus*, juvenile (J. Hoover)

RUSSELL'S SNAPPER
Lutjanus russelli (Bleeker, 1849)

Dorsal rays X,14; anal rays III,8; pectoral rays 16-17; lateral-line scales 47-50; scale rows above lateral line rising obliquely; gill rakers 5-7 + 11-13; body depth 2.6-2.8 in standard length; head length 2.5-2.7 in standard length; preopercular notch shallow; interopercular knob slightly developed; vomerine teeth in a triangular or diamond-shaped patch with a median posterior extension; tongue with a patch of small granular teeth; caudal fin truncate to slightly emarginate; silvery grey dorsally, the scale edges dark grey-brown, shading to silvery white on side and ventral part of body with five or six brownish orange to yellowish brown lines (two below lateral line horizontal, three or four above oblique), and a large oval black spot on lateral line below anterior soft portion of dorsal fin (most of spot above lateral line); fins light grey; juveniles with four broader and darker stripes, the third interrupted by a white-edged black spot on lateral line. Reaches 45 cm. Red Sea and Arabian Gulf south to Natal and east to Fiji; in the western Pacific from New South Wales to southern Japan. A coral-reef and rocky bottom species occurring from a few to about 75 m; juveniles may be found in brackish habitats.

HUMPHEAD SNAPPER
Lutjanus sanguineus (Cuvier, 1828)

Dorsal rays XI,13-14; anal rays III,8-9; pectoral rays 16-17; lateral-line scales 47-50; scales above lateral line ascending obliquely; gill rakers 6-7 + 13-14; body depth 2.3-2.5 in standard length; head length 2.3-2.7 in standard length; a distinct convexity in dorsal profile of head of adults above posterior part of eye; horizontal grooves on head behind eye in specimens more than about 20 cm standard length; preopercular notch and interopercular knob poorly developed; vomerine teeth in a V-shaped band without a median posterior extension; caudal fin slightly emarginate; red dorsally, the scale centres silver-grey, silvery red on side and ventrally; fins red. Attains about 85 cm. Western Indian Ocean; localities include Red Sea (type locality), Djibouti, Arabian Gulf, Oman, west coast of India, Kenya, Zanzibar, Natal, Seychelles, and Madagascar; occurs to depths of at least 100 m; not observed by the author while diving.

EMPEROR SNAPPER
Lutjanus sebae (Cuvier, 1828)

Dorsal rays XI,15-16 (rarely 15); anal rays III,10; pectoral rays 17; lateral-line scales 46-50; scales on side rising obliquely above and below lateral line; gill rakers 6-7 + 10-12; body moderately deep, the depth 2.1-2.4 in standard length; head length 2.3-2.5 in standard length; dorsal profile of head to above posterior part of eye straight to slightly concave; preopercular notch moderately deep; interopercular knob small; vomerine teeth in a V-shaped or triangular patch without a median posterior extension; tongue without teeth; lips in adults thick; soft portions of dorsal and anal fins pointed; caudal fin slightly emarginate to slightly forked; silvery red (scales silvery with red edges) with three dark brown bands, the first from front of side of snout through eye to nape, the second a broad bar from under fourth to sixth dorsal spines to below basal half of pectoral fin, and the last a curved band from below anterior soft portion of dorsal fin to lower lobe of caudal fin (bands black in small juveniles, faint or absent in large adults). Reported to about 100 cm. Red Sea and southern Oman to South Africa, east to the western Pacific (New South Wales to southern Japan); ranges in depth from a few to at least 100 m, the large adults generally in the greater depths. Juveniles may occur in estuaries; they sometimes take refuge among the spines of long-spined sea urchins.

514. *Lutjanus russelli* (J. Hoover)

515. *Lutjanus sanguineus*, 58.9 cm (J. Randall)

516. *Lutjanus sebae*, 36.5 cm (J. Randall)

SMALLSCALE SNAPPER
Paracaesio sordidus Abe and Shinohara, 1962

Dorsal rays X,9-10; anal rays III,8; pectoral rays 16-17; lateral-line scales 68-73; scale rows on back parallel to lateral line; maxilla scaleless; no scales on dorsal and anal fins; gill rakers 5-11 + 19-22; body depth 2.5-2.7 in standard length; head small, its length 3.85-4.1 in standard length; mouth small and strongly oblique, the maxilla reaching slightly posterior to anterior edge of eye; jaws with an outer row of moderate conical teeth and an inner band of villiform teeth; vomer and palatines with villiform teeth; dorsal fin without a notch; caudal fin large and deeply forked; pectoral fins long, reaching to above origin of anal fin or beyond, 3.2-3.6 in standard length; bluish to purplish brown dorsally (centres of scales blue to lavender, the edges brown, giving a linear effect), whitish ventrally; dorsal and caudal fins varying from dull red to yellowish brown. Reaches 35 cm. Red Sea (Randall, 1983) and southern Oman to Samoa and Ryukyu Islands (type locality); semipelagic from 20 to about 200 m. Solitary or in small schools; feeds on zooplankton.

PINJALO
Pinjalo pinjalo (Bleeker, 1850)

Dorsal rays XI,14-15 (rarely 15); anal rays III,9-10 (usually 10); pectoral rays 17-19; lateral-line scales 48-51; scale rows on body oblique; dorsal and anal fins with a basal sheath of small scales; gill rakers 6-8 + 16-18; body depth 2.9-4.2 in standard length (relatively shorter in larger individuals); snout short, 3.4-4.25 in head length; mouth small and oblique, not reaching or just reaching below front edge of eye; an outer row of conical teeth and inner band of villiform teeth in jaws; teeth on vomer and palatines minute; dorsal fin without a notch; caudal fin moderately emarginate; pectoral

517. *Paracaesio sordidus*, about 26 cm (J. Randall)

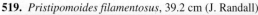

518. *Pinjalo pinjalo*, 56 cm (J. Randall)

fins longer than head, 3.05-3.9 in standard length; pink to silvery lavender, shading to pale pink or silvery white ventrally, with diagonal yellowish brown to brownish red lines following scale rows. Largest specimen 61 cm. Arabian Sea to the Indo-Malayan region, north to China and Taiwan; recorded from Oman by Randall et al. (1987). Occurs in schools from depths of about 15 to at least 60 m. There is only one other species in the genus, *P. lewisi* Randall, Allen, and Anderson, not known from Oman seas; it differs in having XII,13 dorsal rays and 8-9 anal soft rays.

ROSY JOBFISH
Pristipomoides filamentosus (Valenciennes, 1830)

Dorsal rays X,11; anal rays III,8; pectoral rays 15-16; lateral-line scales 58-65; scales on body parallel to lateral line; no scales on dorsal and anal fins (true of other species of the genus); gill rakers 5-8 + 14-17; body elongate, the depth 3.3-3.8 in standard length; head length 3.2-3.6 in standard length; jaws with an outer row of strong conical teeth (of canine proportions anteriorly) and an inner band of small incurved teeth; villiform teeth on vomer and palatines, those on vomer in a triangular shape; no teeth on tongue; dorsal fin without a notch; last dorsal and anal rays prolonged as filaments, about twice or more length of penultimate rays; caudal fin deeply forked; colour variable, from silvery red to silvery lavender-brown dorsally, progressively more silvery ventrally. Attains about 80 cm. Red Sea and Gulf of Oman to South Africa, east to Samoa and Hawaii; occurs at depths of about 90-360 m. Moves to the upper part of its depth range at night to feed on small fishes, crustaceans, and the larger animals of the zooplankton. Estimated maximum age, 18 years.

519. *Pristipomoides filamentosus*, 39.2 cm (J. Randall)

GOLDBANDED JOBFISH
Pristipomoides multidens (Day, 1870)

Dorsal rays X,11; anal rays III,8; pectoral rays 15-16; lateral-line scales 48-52; scale rows on body parallel with lateral line; gill rakers 5-9 + 11-15; body depth 3.1-3.4 in standard length; head length 3.0-3.3 in standard length; dentition as in preceding species, but canines at front of jaws larger; dorsal fin without a notch; last ray of dorsal and anal fins prolonged as a filament, twice or more length of penultimate rays; caudal fin large and deeply forked; reddish to lavender-brown on back, the scale centres silvery, becoming progressively more silvery ventrally; side of snout and cheek below eye with two broad yellow stripes bordered with red and lavender; top of head with transverse yellow bands and arcs. Reaches a maximum length of about 90 cm. Red Sea to Samoa, north to the Ryukyu Islands; found on rocky substrata in the depth range of 40-200 m.

LAVENDER JOBFISH
Pristipomoides sieboldii (Bleeker, 1857)

Dorsal rays X,11; anal rays III,8; pectoral rays 16; lateral-line scales 70-74; scale rows on body parallel with lateral line; gill rakers 8-10 + 19-22; body elongate, the depth 3.2-3.8 in standard length; head length 3.4-3.8 in standard length; conical teeth in outer row in jaws not of canine proportions, with an inner band of small teeth; villiform teeth on vomer in a diamond-shaped patch; tongue with a heart-shaped patch of small teeth; dorsal fin without a notch; last dorsal and anal rays prolonged as a filament twice or more length of penultimate rays; caudal fin moderately large and deeply forked; lavender-brown dorsally, shading to silvery with lavender and light blue iridescence on sides and whitish ventrally. Maximum length about 60 cm. Indo-Pacific; occurs over rocky bottom in the depth range of 100-360 m.

FUSILIERS
FAMILY CAESIONIDAE

The fusiliers are sometimes classified as a subfamily of the Lutjanidae. Following Carpenter (1987) who monographed the group, they are given full family status. These fishes have oblong to fusiform bodies, the body depth varying from 2.2-6.0 in standard length; the mouth is small,

520. *Pristipomoides multidens*, 60.5 cm (J. Randall)

521. *Pristipomoides sieboldii*, 25.5 cm (J. Randall)

terminal, oblique, and highly protrusible; the long median ascending premaxillary process is a separate ossification; one or two slender bony processes present dorsally on side of premaxilla which slide medial to the maxilla; teeth very small and conical (absent in *Dipterygonotus*); scales small to moderate and weakly ctenoid (lateral-line scales 45-88); a supratemporal band of scales separated by a narrow naked zone from scales of rest of nape (this scale band not distinct in *Dipterygonotus*); dorsal fin with X-XV slender spines, the third or fourth spines longest, and 8-22 soft rays; anal fin III,9-13; pelvic fins I,5, their origin distinctly posterior to base of pectoral fins; caudal fin deeply forked. Caesionids are diurnal, midwater, zooplankton-feeding fishes that are usually encountered in aggregations, generally over or in the vicinity of coral reefs; they do not take refuge in reefs by day but depend on their swift swimming and elusive movement to escape predators. They come readily to cleaning stations on reefs and retire to the shelter of reefs at night. There are four genera and 20 species, all in the Indo-Pacific region.

522. School of *Caesio lunaris*, about 27 cm (J. Randall)

LUNAR FUSILIER
Caesio lunaris Cuvier, 1830

Dorsal rays X,13-15 (usually 14); anal rays III,10-11; pectoral rays 18-21; lateral-line scales 45-53; supratemporal band of scales usually interrupted medially by a narrow scaleless zone; dorsal and anal fins scaled (true of other species of *Caesio*); a single bony process dorsally on side of pre-maxilla (also characteristic of the genus); posterior end of maxilla not tapered (also generic); body depth 2.5-3.5 in standard length; head length 2.6-3.5 in standard length; blue-green dorsally, shading to silvery white ventrally, with longitudinal yellow lines following scales rows below lateral line, those on side of body coalescing into a yellow stripe posteriorly which is continuous with yellow of caudal fin; tips of caudal-fin lobes black; axil and upper base of pectoral fins black. Reaches about 30 cm. Red Sea and Arabian Gulf south to Kenya, east to the Solomon Islands, and north to the Ryukyu Islands. Arabian Gulf and Oman fish of this species retain the yellow caudal peduncle and fin as adults which is seen elsewhere only on juveniles.

523. *Caesio lunaris*, night (R. Bedford)

524. School of *Caesio varilineata* (J. Hoover)

525. *Dipterygonotus balteatus*, 7.9 cm (J. Randall)

YELLOWSTRIPED FUSILIER
Caesio varilineata Carpenter, 1987

Dorsal rays X,14-16 (usually 15); anal rays III,11-13; pectoral rays 20-23 (usually 21); lateral-line scales 57-67; supratemporal band of scales often interrupted medially by a scaleless zone; body depth 3.0-3.9 in standard length; head length 3.2-3.6 in standard length; blue-green, shading to silvery white ventrally, with four or five yellow stripes on body, the broadest above and adjacent to lateral line (which is apparent as a thin black line); caudal-fin lobes tipped with black, often with a dark streak in each lobe; a triangular black spot at upper base of pectoral fins; pectoral axil black. Reaches 28 cm. Red Sea and Arabian Gulf south to Natal and east to western Sumatra (including Seychelles, Maldives, and Sri Lanka). The colour note given above applies to the species in Oman; there is variation in the number and width of the yellow stripes in other parts of the range.

DWARF FUSILIER
Dipterygonotus balteatus (Valenciennes, 1830)

Dorsal rays XII-XV,8-11; anal rays III,9-11; pectoral rays 16-19; lateral-line scales 68-80; supratemporal band of scales indistinct; posterior end of maxilla tapered; two slender bony processes on side of premaxilla; no teeth in jaws; margin of opercle with a prominent dorsoposterior flap; body elongate, the depth 4.4-5.7 in standard length; head length 3.3-4.0 in standard length; pelvic fins short, 1.4-1.7 in head length; green dorsally, shading to silvery white or silvery pink ventrally, with a yellow stripe from upper edge of eye along straight part of lateral line to upper base of caudal fin; two irregular, longitudinal, yellow lines on back (sometimes broken into segments); no dark markings in caudal fin. The smallest of the fusiliers; maximum length, 14 cm. Known from Djibouti south to Seychelles, east to the Indo-Malayan region and Australia, north to Taiwan and China. Unlike other caesionids, may occur well away from coral reefs; sometimes schools with clupeids. Used as bait for tunas, and so on.

GOLDBAND FUSILIER
Pterocaesio chrysozona (Cuvier, 1830)

Dorsal rays X-XI,14-16; anal rays III,11-13; pectoral rays 17-20; lateral-line scales 62-72; supratemporal band of scales distinct, not interrupted medially; scales present on median fins; two bony processes dorsally on side of premaxilla; posterior end of maxilla tapered; small conical teeth in jaws; body depth 3.3-4.6 in standard length; head length 3.0-3.5 in standard length; green dorsally, the scales edged with brown, becoming silvery white or silvery pink ventrally, with a broad yellow stripe from snout through upper part of eye, tapering as it passes along straight part of lateral line (the dark line of which forms upper edge of stripe) to upper base of caudal fin; tip of caudal lobes black; axil of pectoral fins black. Maximum length, 21 cm. Red Sea and Gulf of Oman south to Kenya and Seychelles, east to the Indo-Malayan region and Australia, north to Taiwan and China. Often schools with other caesionids.

526. *Pterocaesio chrysozona* (J. Hoover)

GRUNTS

FAMILY HAEMULIDAE

This family of fishes was long named the Pomadasyidae in the Indo-Pacific and the Haemulidae in the Atlantic and eastern Pacific; Haemulidae is the older family name. Grunts get their common name from the sounds they produce by grinding their pharyngeal teeth together; the swim bladder acts as a resonating chamber to amplify the sounds. The haemulid fishes resemble snappers in general form and a number of characters, such as the maxilla slipping under the edge of the preorbital when the mouth is closed (even less of the maxilla is exposed in haemulids); no supramaxilla; no obvious spines on opercle; 7 branchiostegal rays; ctenoid scales; a continuous dorsal fin; similar spine and soft-rays counts of the dorsal and anal fins; and pelvic fins I,5, their origin below or slightly posterior to base of pectoral fins. They differ in having a smaller mouth which is often slightly inferior, never with the lower jaw projecting; small conical teeth in bands in jaws (outer row usually slightly enlarged, but none approaching canine proportions); well developed pharyngeal teeth; no teeth on vomer or palatines; serrate preopercle (the serrae may be lost in large individuals); the second anal spine longest and usually much stronger than the other anal spines (second spine of lutjanids usually smaller or equal to third spine and not much stronger), and enlarged pores on the chin. The family is divisible into three subfamilies, two of which are represented in Oman, the Haemulinae (Pomadaysinae a synonym) with a median pit and two enlarged pores on the chin, and the Plectorhinchinae (Gateininae a synonym) with six large pores on chin, no median pit, and very thick lips. In Australia the fishes of the latter subfamily are called sweetlips; in South Africa they are known as rubberlips; the common name thicklips is adopted here. The young of the species of Plectorhinchinae are coloured very differently from the adults, and not all have been definitively linked to the adult stage. The family contains 17 genera and about 150 species. Only three genera occur in Oman seas. Most grunts are nocturnal; they feed chiefly on benthic invertebrates, especially crustaceans. The species of *Pomadasys* tend to occur in brackish water of estuaries and sheltered lagoons, the species of *Plectorhinchus* mainly on reefs. Records of *Pomadasys multimaculatum* (Playfair and Günther) from the Arabian Gulf or Gulf of Oman (as by Randall et al., 1978 and Sivasubramaniam and Ibrahim, 1982) are misidentifications of *P. argenteum* (Forsskål); Smith and McKay in Smith and Heemstra (1986) wrote that *P. multimaculatum* is known only from Zanzibar to Algoa Bay, South Africa.

527. School of *Pomadasys taeniatus* (J. Hoover)

SUBFAMILY PLECTORHINCHINAE

PAINTED THICKLIP
Diagramma pictum (Thunberg, 1792)

Dorsal rays IX-X,21-26; anal rays III,7; pectoral rays 16-17; lateral-line scales about 59; gill rakers 6-8 + 14-15; body depth of adults 2.7-3.0 in standard length; head length of adults 3.2-3.6 in standard length; caudal peduncle slender and long, its length nearly as great as head length; six pores on chin and no median pit; outer row of teeth in jaws not enlarged; second dorsal spine longest, the first spine about one-third its length; dorsal fin without a notch; caudal fin of juveniles rounded, becoming truncate with age; adults purplish grey with a small bronze spot on each scale and usually a few scattered large dark blotches; dorsal and caudal fins with numerous small brown spots; juveniles with two broad black stripes on body, the fins yellow, all but the pectorals with one or more black bands; additional stripes appear on body of juveniles with growth; with further growth the stripes break into small spots. Reported to 90 cm (Smith, 1962). Red Sea and Arabian Gulf south to Natal and east to Indo-Malayan region and Australia, north to Taiwan; usually seen in silty reef areas, moving little during daylight hours.

528. *Diagramma pictum*, juvenile (J. Randall)

529. *Diagramma pictum*, subadult (J. Hoover)

530. *Diagramma pictum*, adult (J. Hoover)

208

LEMON THICKLIP
Plectorhinchus flavomaculatus (Cuvier, 1830)

Dorsal rays XII-XIII (usually XIII),19-22; anal rays III,7; pectoral rays 17; lateral-line scales 56-59; gill rakers 11-14 + 17-20; body depth 2.6-2.8 in standard length; head length 3.0-3.3 in standard length; six prominent pores and no median pit on chin (true of other species of the genus); outer row of teeth in jaws slightly enlarged (also characteristic of the genus); fourth or fifth dorsal spines longest, about 2.6 in head; dorsal fin with a very slight notch between spinous and soft portions; caudal fin of adults slightly emarginate; juveniles bluish grey with yellow-orange stripes that break into spots on body and dorsally on head with growth; spots on large adults tend to disappear, although the stripes on lower half of head persist, alternating with blue; lower edge of caudal fin broadly dusky. Attains 60 cm. Red Sea to South Africa, and northwestern Australia north to Japan; observed in Oman only in the south.

BLACKSPOTTED THICKLIP
Plectorhinchus gaterinus (Forsskål, 1775)

Dorsal rays XIII,19-20; anal rays III,7; pectoral rays 16; lateral-line scales 55-60; gill rakers 8 + 18-19; body depth of adults 2.5-2.7 in standard length; head length of adults about 3.5 in standard length; third to fifth dorsal spines longest, about 2.2 in head; caudal fin of juveniles rounded, becoming truncate in adults; head and nape grey; body whitish with numerous small black spots (smaller than pupil), none on chest and ab-

531. *Plectorhinchus flavomaculatus*, about 38 cm (J. Randall)

532. *Plectorhinchus gaterinus* (J. Hoover)

domen; fins light yellow, the median fins with black spots; lips pale salmon; inside of mouth orange-red; juveniles with three pairs of black stripes on head and body which break into spots at a length of about 12 cm. Reaches 50 cm. Red Sea and Arabian Gulf to Natal, Madagascar, and Mauritius; common in the Arabian Gulf and Gulf of Oman, occasional to the south.

533. *P. gaterinus*, juv., about 11 cm (J. Randall)

DUSKY THICKLIP
Plectorhinchus gibbosus (Lacepède, 1802)

Dorsal rays XIV,15-16; anal rays III,7; pectoral rays 17; lateral-line scales 50-55; gill rakers 8-10 + 18-20; body deep, the depth 2.1-2.8 in standard length (juveniles deeper-bodied); head length 2.8-3.0 in standard length; lips extremely thick in adults; dorsal spines long, the fourth and fifth longest, 1.7-2.0 in head (spines relatively longer in juveniles); dorsal fin strongly notched between spinous and soft portions; base of spinous portion of dorsal fin nearly twice as long as soft portion; caudal fin rounded in juveniles, slightly rounded to truncate in adults; dark grey, the centres of scales paler than edges; opercular membrane and a narrow zone adjacent to posterior edge of preopercle black. Attains 70 cm. Red Sea and Gulf of Oman to South Africa, east to the Indo-Malayan region, north to Japan. *P. nigrus* (Cuvier) is a synonym.

534. *Plectorhinchus gibbosus* (J. Hoover)

209

TROUT THICKLIP
Plectorhinchus pictus (Tortonese, 1935)

Dorsal rays XII,15-16; anal rays III,7-8; pectoral rays 17-18; lateral-line scales 50-54; gill rakers 7 + 15; body depth of adults 2.2-2.5 in standard length; head length 3.0-3.2 in standard length; fourth and fifth dorsal spines longest, about 1.8 in head length; dorsal fin deeply notched between spinous and soft portions; caudal fin rounded in juveniles, truncate in adults; light grey with black spots of variable size (some larger than pupil) on dorsal and caudal fins and body posterior to a diagonal from origin of dorsal fin to rear base of anal fin. Reaches 60 cm. Arabian Gulf to Sri Lanka; not seen in southern Oman. Some authors regard *P. cinctus* Temminck and Schlegel from Japan, Taiwan, and China as a senior synonym of *P. pictus*; however, the two appear to be distinct species. *P. cinctus* has a similar pattern of black spots, but differs in having two broad curved blackish bands on the body, a broad blackish bar anteriorly on the head, and yellowish dorsal and caudal fins.

WHITEBARRED THICKLIP
Plectorhinchus playfairi (Pellegrin, 1914)

Dorsal rays XII,19-20; anal rays III,7; pectoral rays 16; lateral-line scales about 58-60; gill rakers 11 + 21-23; body depth 2.4-2.5 in standard length; head length 3.0-3.2 in standard length; fourth and fifth dorsal spines longest, 2.2-2.4 in head length; dorsal fin slightly notched between spinous and soft portions; caudal fin truncate to slightly emarginate; upper half of body black with three narrow white bars on anterior two-thirds; lower half of body abruptly silvery white; head black dorsally, white ventrally, with a narrow white bar across operculum; fins blackish. Reaches about 50 cm. Red Sea and southern Oman to South Africa and Madagascar; ranges from a few to about 80 m. Reported as active diurnally, feeding on shrimps, worms, small crabs, and occasionally juvenile fishes (van der Elst, 1981).

MINSTREL
Plectorhinchus schotaf (Forsskål, 1775)

Dorsal rays XII,18-21; anal rays III,7; pectoral rays 16-17; lateral-line scales about 55; gill rakers 11-13 + 17-18; body depth 2.5-3.0 in standard length; head length 3.3-3.7 in standard length; fourth and fifth dorsal spines longest, 2.3-2.6 in head length; base of soft portion of dorsal fin (measured to rear base of last dorsal spine) slightly longer than base of spinous portion; dorsal fin very slightly notched between spinous and soft

535. *Plectorhinchus pictus*, about 40 cm (J. Randall)

536. *Plectorhinchus playfairi*, about 24 cm (J. Randall)

537. *Plectorhinchus schotaf* (J. Hoover)

portions; caudal fin truncate in young, slightly emarginate in adults; silver-grey, shading to whitish ventrally; upper part of opercular membrane, axil of pectoral fins, maxillary groove, and inside of mouth red. Reported to reach 80 cm. Red Sea and Gulf of Oman to South Africa; more common in southern Oman than in the Gulf of Oman.

538. *P. sordidus*, juvenile, 5.6 cm (J. Randall)

SORDID THICKLIP
Plectorhinchus sordidus (Klunzinger, 1870)

Dorsal rays XII,18-20; anal rays III,7-8 (usually 7); pectoral rays 16-17; lateral-line scales 55-56; gill rakers 10-12 + 15-17; body depth 2.5-2.8 in standard length; head length 3.1-3.4 in standard length; fourth or fifth dorsal spines longest, 2.6-2.9 in head length; base of spinous and soft portions of dorsal fin about equal; dorsal fin not notched; caudal fin of adults truncate; grey, often with a bronze cast; opercular membrane dark brown to black; iris a mixture of brown and yellow except dorsally where all yellow; juveniles yellow, shading to whitish ventrally, with five blue lines on body and a sixth posteriorly at base of dorsal fin (blue lines break into blue dots with growth, and ultimately disappear). Reported to reach a maximum length of only 30 cm. Red Sea to Arabian Gulf where abundant; also reported from Mozambique, Madagascar, Seychelles, and Mauritius. Difficult to distinguish from *P. schotaf*. The red of the opercular membrane and pectoral axil of the latter seems to be a consistent colour difference; also, *schotaf* has more gill rakers, longer dorsal spines, the soft portion of the dorsal fin a little longer than the spinous, and a smaller eye at any given length.

SUBFAMILY HAEMULINAE

YELLOWBACK GRUNT
Pomadasys aheneus McKay and Randall, 1995

Dorsal rays XII,13-14; anal rays III,7-8; pectoral rays 16-17 (usually 17); lateral-line scales 51-53; circumpeduncular scales 26; gill rakers 5-6 + 12-13; body depth 2.3-2.6 in standard length; head length 2.9-3.0 in standard length; dorsal profile of head nearly straight to above posterior margin of preopercle; fourth dorsal spine longest (but third and fifth subequal), 1.95-2.1 in head length; last dorsal spine slightly shorter than penultimate spine; brassy dorsally on postorbital head and anterodorsal part of body, shading to silver-grey elsewhere; fins dusky,

539. *Plectorhinchus sordidus* (J. Hoover)

540. *Pomadasys aheneus* (J. Hoover)

the caudal fin and soft portion of dorsal fin dark grey to black; juveniles yellow with two dark brown stripes on upper half of body and a narrower brown stripe between (midlateral stripe the last to persist; still evident on a 13-cm fish). Reaches 27 cm. Known only from southern and central Oman; an inshore species associated more with rocky than sandy substrata. Closely related to *P. guoraca* (Cuvier) from India and Sri Lanka which differs in having 22 circumpeduncular scales, yellow stripes

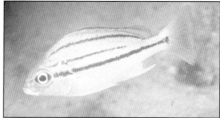

541. *Pomadasys aheneus*, juvenile (J. Hoover)

below lateral line, yellow anal and paired fins, and a white posterior margin on the caudal fin.

SILVER GRUNT
Pomadasys argenteus (Forsskål, 1775)

Dorsal rays XII,14; anal rays III,7; pectoral rays 16-17; lateral-line scales 47-50; gill rakers 5-6 + 11-13; body depth 2.7-2.8 in standard length; head length 2.75-2.9 in standard length; dorsal profile of head steep and nearly straight to above posterior pre-opercular margin; chin with two prominent pores and a medial pit (characteristic of the species of *Pomadasys*); posterior margin and prominent rounded corner of preopercle serrate, the serrae largest and well separated on corner (also true of other species of the genus); snout pointed, 2.8-3.0 in head length; fourth or fifth dorsal spines longest, 1.7-1.8 in head length; penultimate dorsal spine about three-fourths length of last spine; caudal fin slightly emarginate; silvery with small black spots on upper three-fifths of body and on nape and dorsal fin; juveniles with blackish stripes, which break into spots with growth, and a large dark spot on opercle. Reported to 52 cm. Red Sea (type locality) and Arabian Gulf to the western Pacific.

542. *Pomadasys argenteus*, 21.5 cm (J. Randall)

543. *Pomadasys commersonnii*, 65.4 cm (J. Randall)

544. *Pomadasys kaakan*, 21.9 cm (J. Randall)

SPOTTED GRUNT
Pomadasys commersonnii (Lacepède, 1802)

Dorsal rays XI,13-16; anal rays III,9-10; pectoral rays 17-19; lateral-line scales 52-54; gill rakers 9-10 + 16-17; body relatively elongate, the depth 2.9-3.7 in standard length; head length 3.0-3.15 in standard length; dorsal profile of head straight to above posterior edge of eye; snout pointed, 2.55-2.7 in head length; third and fourth dorsal spines longest, 1.9-2.5 in head length; last dorsal spine about equal in length to penultimate spine; caudal fin emarginate; silvery with small black spots on about upper two-thirds of body and on nape; a bluish black spot posteriorly on opercle. Attains about 80 cm and a weight of 10 kg. Northwest coast of India to southern Oman, south to South Africa, Seychelles, and Madagascar; frequently found in brackish habitats and can tolerate freshwater. Able to jet a stream of water into the mud to expose crustaceans, worms, and small bivalves on which it feeds (van der Elst, 1981). *P. opercularis* (Playfair and Günther) is a synonym.

JAVELIN GRUNT
Pomadasys kaakan (Cuvier, 1830)

Dorsal rays XII,13-15; anal rays III,7-8; pectoral rays 17-18; lateral-line scales 43-47; gill rakers 5-6 + 13-14; body depth 2.65-2.8 in standard length; head length 2.7-2.9 in standard length; snout length 3.0-3.2 in head length; dorsal and anal spines very stout; third or fourth dorsal spines longest, 1.6-2.1 in head length; penultimate dorsal spine about three-fourths length of last spine; caudal fin emarginate; six to ten vertical series of blackish spots or double spots in four rows on body, the third row along lateral line (spots less distinct with growth and eventually disappear); a row of small dark spots along base of dorsal fin. Reaches about 50 cm. Coastal in the western Indian Ocean, including the Red Sea, Arabian Gulf, and Madagascar, east to the Indo-Malayan region, Australia, and Palau. Often found in shallow, turbid, estuarine waters, but reported to depths as great as 75 m; feeds in the same way as the preceding species. Sometimes misidentified as *P. hasta*(Bloch).

SADDLE GRUNT
Pomadasys maculatus (Bloch, 1797)

Dorsal rays XII,14-15; anal rays III,7; pectoral rays 17-18; lateral-line scales 50-52; gill rakers 5-6 + 13-16; body depth 2.6-3.0 in standard length; head length 2.9-3.2 in standard length; snout short, its length 3.0-4.0 in head length; dorsal profile of head smoothly convex; third or fourth dorsal spines longest, 1.7-2.3 in head length; last two dorsal spines subequal; caudal fin slightly emarginate; silvery with a broad, curved, blackish bar from nape to below anterior part of lateral line, and three broken blackish bars below dorsal fin, none extending onto lower half or third of body; a large black spot in dorsal fin between third and sixth or seventh spines. Attains 50 cm. Coastal throughout the Indian Ocean and western Pacific where it ranges from Queensland to southern Japan.

OLIVE GRUNT
Pomadasys olivaceus (Day, 1875)

Dorsal rays XII,15-17; anal rays III,11-13; pectoral rays 16-17; lateral-line scales 51-54; gill rakers 5-7 + 13-15; body depth 2.5-2.8 in standard length; head length 2.7-3.2 in standard length; dorsal profile of head nearly straight to above posterior margin of preopercle; dorsal spines slender; fourth dorsal spine longest, 2.1-2.2 in head length; last dorsal spine shortest; caudal fin moderately forked; silvery, the dorsal part of body silvery greenish grey or silvery with brassy reflections, shading to silvery white on side and ventrally; a large dark brown spot or double spot irregularly edged in yellow posteriorly on opercle. Largest specimen, 31 cm. South Africa to the Gulf of Aden and along the southern Asian coast to Malaysia. Juveniles and subadults are found inshore on shallow reefs (the illustrated specimen was taken from a tidepool) where they feed mainly on shrimps; adults are found on deeper reefs.

LINED GRUNT
Pomadasys punctulatus (Rüppell, 1838)

Dorsal rays XII,15; anal rays III,8; pectoral rays 16; lateral-line scales 51; gill rakers 5-6 + 12-13; body depth 2.3-2.5 in standard length; head length 3.0-3.2 in standard length; snout length 2.8-3.0 in head length; dorsal profile of head slightly convex; third or fourth dorsal spine longest, 2.1-2.15 in head length; last dorsal spine shortest; caudal fin slightly forked; silvery, the back with a yellow-green iridescence, with slightly irregular, longitudinal, dark brown lines on about upper three-fourths of body (some

545. *Pomadasys maculatus*, 22.2 cm (J. Randall)

546. *Pomadasys olivaceus*, 9.4 cm (J. Randall)

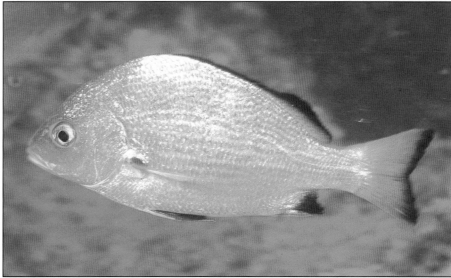

547. *Pomadasys punctulatus*, about 22 cm (J. Randall)

lines may be partially broken into rows of dots); fins dusky, the caudal darkest, especially posteriorly; a large diffuse blackish blotch on membranes anteriorly in middle of pelvic fins; palate and part of sides of mouth dull orange-red. Attains about 30 cm. Red Sea (type locality) to Gulf of Oman; observed inshore on rocky substrata. Formerly regarded as a synonym of *P. furcatus* (Bloch and Schneider).

213

STRIPED GRUNT
Pomadasys stridens (Forsskål, 1775)

Dorsal rays XII,13-16; anal rays III,8-9; pectoral rays 16-18; lateral-line scales 57-60; gill rakers 7-8 + 14-16; body depth 3.0-3.2 in standard length; head length 2.95-3.2 in standard length; snout length 2.8-3.0 in head length; dorsal profile of head convex; posterior margin of preopercle nearly straight (concave on other species of the genus); dorsal spines slender; third to fifth dorsal spines longest, 1.7-2.1 in head length; penultimate dorsal spine one-half to three-fourths length of last dorsal spine; no scaly sheath at base of spinous portion of dorsal fin and only slightly developed on soft portion (but well developed on anal fin); second and third anal spines subequal, the second only slightly thicker; caudal fin slightly to moderately forked; greenish silver dorsally, silvery on sides and ventrally, with three stripes on upper half of body which vary from brassy yellow to yellowish brown, the broadest midlateral; a black spot posteriorly on operculum. Maximum length 16 cm. Red Sea and Arabian Gulf to Natal; has penetrated the Mediterranean Sea via the Suez Canal.

BRONZESTRIPED GRUNT
Pomadasys taeniatus McKay and Randall, 1995

Dorsal rays XII,15; anal rays III,8; pectoral rays 16-17 (rarely 17); lateral-line scales 52-53; circumpeduncular scales 26; gill rakers 5-6 + 12-13; body moderately deep, the depth 2.3-2.4 in standard length; head length 2.9-3.1 in standard length; maxilla ending slightly posterior to a vertical at front edge of orbit, its posterior edge slightly concave; third to fifth dorsal spines subequal, 2.2 in head length; last dorsal spine shortest; caudal fin slightly forked; silvery with seven bronze stripes on body which converge without bifurcating as they pass onto head;

548. *Pomadasys stridens*, 14.3 cm (J. Randall)

549. *Pomadasys taeniatus*, about 20 cm (J. Hoover)

a black spot posteriorly on operculum superimposed on fifth bronze stripe and extending above it; fins grey. Attains about 25 cm. Known only from the southern coast of the Arabian Peninsula. Occurs inshore over rocky or rock-sand substrata; usually observed in schools. Previously misidentified as *P. furcatus* (Bloch and Schneider), a wide-ranging Indian Ocean–Indo-Malayan species which differs in having six dark stripes, the second to fourth bifurcating anteriorly.

550. *Scolopsis ghanam*, about 12 cm (J. Randall)

BREAMS
FAMILY NEMIPTERIDAE

This Indo-Pacific family of five genera and 64 species is remarkable in its uniformity of the number of dorsal and anal rays; all have X dorsal spines and 9 soft rays and III anal spines and 7 soft rays, except for one species of *Nemipterus* with III,8 anal rays. The dorsal fin is continuous without a notch; the pelvic fins are I,5, with an axillary scale, their origin slightly posterior to the base of the pectoral fins; the caudal fin varies from emarginate to deeply forked, some species with a filamentous upper lobe; the opercle has a single flat spine; the second suborbital below eye with a free margin which varies from smooth to serrate and may bear a retrorse spine; there are 10 + 14 vertebrae and 6 branchiostegal rays, the gill membranes free from the isthmus; the gill rakers are short and knob-like; the mouth is terminal, small to moderate in size; the maxilla slips under edge of first (preorbital) and second suborbital bones when mouth closed; no supramaxilla; jaws with small conical teeth (small canines anteriorly in jaws of the species of *Nemipterus* and *Pentapodus*); no teeth on vomer or palatines; supraneural (predorsal) bones 2; scales finely ctenoid and moderate in size. Species of three of the five genera are found in Omani seas, those of the genera *Nemipterus* and *Parascolopsis* mostly from greater-than-diving depths. Many of the species of *Nemipterus* are of commercial importance; they are caught mainly by trawling and by handlines. The family was reviewed by Russell (1990); a few species remain to be described. The species of *Scolopsis* are sometimes called spinecheeks because of the strong retrorse spine on the second suborbital bone; they are also called monocle breams.

DELAGOA THREADFIN BREAM
Nemipterus bipunctatus (Valenciennes, 1830)

Dorsal rays X,9; anal rays III,7; pectoral rays 16; lateral-line scales 48-50; scale rows below lateral line obliquely ascending anteriorly on body, curving to near-horizontal posteriorly; gill rakers 10-14; three or four pairs of small recurved canine teeth anteriorly in upper jaw; edge of preopercle smooth (true of other Oman species of *Nemipterus*); body depth 3.4-3.9 in standard length; caudal fin forked, the lobes about equal in length, the upper lobe slightly rounded; pectoral fins moderately long, 1.2-1.5 in head length; pelvic fins long, reaching to or a little beyond origin of anal fin; silvery pink with five to seven narrow silvery yellow stripes following oblique scale rows below lateral line; iris yellow; dorsal fin pale translucent pink with a narrow red margin and submarginal yellow line; anal fin pale bluish white with two to four irregular yellow stripes; caudal fin pale yellowish pink. Reaches 27 cm. Red Sea and Arabian Gulf south to Delagoa Bay, Mozambique and east to the Andaman Sea; known from the depth range of 18-100 m. Reported to feed on crustaceans, squids, small fishes, and polychaetes. *N. bleekeri* (Day) and *N. delagoae* Smith are synonyms.

551. *Nemipterus bipunctatus*, 21 cm (J. Randall)

552. *Nemipterus japonicus*, 25.6 cm (J. Randall)

553. *Nemipterus peronii*, 13.5 cm (J. Randall)

JAPANESE THREADFIN BREAM
Nemipterus japonicus (Bloch, 1791)

Dorsal rays X,9; anal rays III,7; pectoral rays 17-18; lateral-line scales 44-45; scale rows horizontal; gill rakers 14-17; four or five pairs of small recurved canine teeth anteriorly in upper jaw; body depth 2.7-3.5 in standard length; caudal fin moderately forked, the upper lobe longer than lower and produced into a long filament; pectoral fins long, 1.0-1.3 in head length; pelvic fins reaching to or just beyond anus; silvery pink with 11 narrow greenish yellow stripes following scale rows; an elongate light red and yellow spot (about as long as eye diameter) just below anterior part of lateral line; iris red; dorsal fin translucent with a narrow red margin and a longitudinal pale yellow stripe near base of fin which broadens posteriorly; caudal fin pink, the upper tip and filament yellow. Reaches 32 cm, discounting caudal filament. Red Sea and Arabian Gulf south to Kenya, east to southern Indonesia, north to southern Japan. Abundant in coastal waters on mud or sand bottoms in the depth range of about 5 to at least 80 m, usually in schools. Russell (1990) reviewed the literature on the biology.

NOTCHFIN THREADFIN BREAM
Nemipterus peronii (Valenciennes, 1830)

Dorsal rays X,9; anal rays III,7; pectoral rays 16-18; lateral-line scales 46-51; scale rows below lateral line horizontal; gill rakers 9-12; three or four pairs of small recurved canine teeth anteriorly in upper jaw; body depth 3.3-3.5 in standard length; membranes of spinous portion of dorsal fin distinctly incised, more so in larger individuals (other species of *Nemipterus* without notched membranes); caudal fin deeply forked, the upper lobe longer and pointed, but without a filament; pectoral fins short, 1.1-17 in head; pelvic fins not reaching or just reaching anus; silvery pink dorsally, shading to silvery white ventrally, with seven or eight darker pink saddle-like bars on body which reach to or below lateral line; a diffuse light red spot below anterior part of lateral line; tips of spinous membranes of dorsal fin yellow. Attains 23 cm. Red Sea and Arabian Gulf; Sri Lanka to western Pacific, ranging from Queensland and New Caledonia to southern Japan. A benthic species found over sand or mud substrata from 17 to about 100 m (usually less than 60 m). *N. tolu* (Valenciennes) is a synonym.

RANDALL'S THREADFIN BREAM
Nemipterus randalli Russell, 1986

Dorsal rays X,9; anal rays III,7; pectoral rays 16-17; lateral-line scales 47-48; scales below lateral line horizontal; gill rakers 12-15; three or four pairs of small recurved canine teeth anteriorly in upper jaw; body depth 2.9-3.5 in standard length; first dorsal spine 1.3-1.4 in longest dorsal spine; caudal fin strongly forked, the upper lobe with a long trailing filament; pectoral fins long, 1.0-1.4 in head length; pelvic fins with a filamentous first soft ray reaching to or beyond origin of anal fin; silvery pink, shading to silvery white ventrally, with two to four faint yellow stripes on side below lateral line; a broad yellow stripe on either side of ventral midline; a pink to yellow blotch sometimes present under anterior part of lateral line; iris salmon pink; dorsal fin pale blue with numerous irregular yellow spots on basal three-fourths and a narrow red margin; anal fin pale bluish with a broken pale yellow stripe in middle of fin; caudal fin, including filament, pink. Reaches 26 cm, discounting caudal filament. Red

554. *Nemipterus randalli*, 26 cm (J. Randall)

555. *Parascolopsis aspinosa*, 14.4 cm (J. Randall)

Sea and Arabian Gulf south to South Africa, including Madagascar and Seychelles, east to southwest India. Occurs on sand or mud substrata in the depth range of 22-225 m.

SPOTFIN BREAM
Parascolopsis aspinosa (Rao and Rao, 1981)

Dorsal rays X,9; anal rays III,7; pectoral rays 16-17; lateral-line scales 35-36; scales dorsally on head reaching to above posterior nostrils; suborbital and maxilla scaleless; posterior and ventral part of preopercle scaleless; posterior edge of preopercle serrate (true of other species of *Parascolopsis*); gill rakers short, 5-6 + 6-7; second suborbital ending with a small posteriorly-directed spine, the rest of margin smooth or with a few fine serrae; body depth 2.5-3.0 in stan-

dard length; caudal fin slightly forked; silvery pink dorsally, shading to silvery white below, usually with six darker pink saddle-like bars on body; a black spot basally in dorsal fin between eighth spine and first soft ray. Reaches 21 cm. Gulf of Aden and Arabian Gulf to the Andaman Sea; known from the depth range of 20-225 m on mud or sand bottoms.

ROSY BREAM
Parascolopsis eriomma (Jordan and Richardson, 1909)

Dorsal rays X,9; anal rays III,7; pectoral rays 16-17; lateral-line scales 34-36; scales dorsally on head extending forward to above centre of eye; suborbital and maxilla scaleless; posterior and ventral part of preopercle scaleless; gill rakers short, 5-6 + 11-13; second suborbital ending in a small retrorse spine, the posterior margin finely serrate; body depth 2.6-2.9 in standard length; caudal fin slightly to moderately forked; salmon pink to light red dorsally, shading on side to silvery with salmon or light red edges on scales, and to silvery white ventrally (reported to have a yellow stripe on side by Russell, 1990, but not seen on Oman specimens; perhaps this is juvenile colouration); dorsal, caudal, and pectoral fins salmon pink; anal and pelvic fins whitish. Maximum length, 32 cm. Red Sea and Gulf of Oman south to Mozambique, east to central Indonesia, and north to Taiwan (type locality).

556. *Parascolopsis eriomma*, 28.9 cm (J. Randall)

TOWNSEND'S BREAM
Parascolopsis townsendi Boulenger, 1901

Dorsal rays X,9; anal rays III,7; pectoral rays 15-17; lateral-line scales 37-40; scales dorsally on head reaching forward to above posterior nostrils; maxilla with or without scales; suborbital scaled; scales on preopercle extending to margins; lower-limb gill rakers 6-7; body depth 2.4-2.7 in standard length; caudal fin slightly forked; uniform reddish with a silvery lateral stripe. Reaches about 20 cm. Red Sea to the Gulf of Oman (type locality) and the west coast of India. Reported from mud or sand bottoms in the depth range of 100-410 m.

THUMBPRINT BREAM
Scolopsis bimaculatus Rüppell, 1828

Dorsal rays X,9; anal rays III,7; pectoral rays 17-19; lateral-line scales 45-48; scales dorsally on head reaching forward to above posterior nostrils; suborbital bones scaleless; scales on preopercle extending to margins; gill rakers short, usually 4-5 + 5 (true of other Omani species of the genus); second suborbital bone with a large retrorse spine and two spinules posteriorly, but no antrorse spine; posterior margin and posteriorly bulging corner of preopercle strongly serrate (applies to other species of *Scolopsis*); body depth 2.7-3.3 in standard length; caudal fin moderately forked; pale brownish grey dorsally, the scale edges darker than centres, shading to silvery white ventrally, with a large elongate blackish blotch on lateral line below juncture of spinous and soft portions of dorsal fin; a narrow blue band across anterior interorbital space; upper lip bluish; fins pale, the dorsal with a very narrow yellow margin. Reaches 31 cm. Red Sea and Arabian Gulf south to Mozambique and Madagascar; also reported from Pakistan, southern India, and Sri Lanka. Occurs on or near silty reefs from a few to at least 60 m. Feeds on a variety of benthic prey including crustaceans, molluscs, echinoderms, and small fishes.

DOTTED BREAM
Scolopsis ghanam (Forsskål, 1775)

Dorsal rays X,9; anal rays III,7; pectoral rays 15-18; lateral-line scales 44-47; scales dorsally on head extending forward to above middle of eyes; suborbital bones and lower limb of preopercle scaleless; posterior edge of second suborbital bone with a large retrorse spine and four or five spinules, but no antrorse spine; body depth 2.9-3.3 in standard length; caudal fin moderately forked; light olive-grey dorsally, shading to whitish

557. *Parascolopsis townsendi* (after Boulenger, 1901)

558. *Scolopsis bimaculatus*, 23 cm (J. Randall)

559. *Scolopsis ghanam*, about 19 cm (J. Randall)

560. *Scolopsis taeniatus*, about 23 cm (J. Hoover)

ventrally, with a white-edged brown stripe following curved part of lateral line and continuing as a white stripe forward to upper edge of eye; a row of blackish spots above brown stripe and above this a pale greenish line from above eye, bifurcating below soft portion of dorsal fin; side of body below lateral line with a blackish spot on each scale. Attains 18 cm. Arabian Gulf and Red Sea south to Mozambique and Madagascar, east to northwestern India; also reported from the Andaman Islands; abundant throughout Oman waters. Usually found inshore on coral reefs or sandy bottom near reefs.

BLACKSTREAK BREAM
Scolopsis taeniatus Cuvier, 1830

Dorsal rays X,9; anal rays III,7; pectoral rays 17-18; lateral-line scales 45-48; scales dorsally on head extending forward to above posterior nostrils; suborbital bones scaleless; scales extending to margin posteriorly on preopercle, but ventral limb scaleless; posterior margin of second suborbital with a large retrorse spine and usually three spinelets, but no antrorse spine; body depth 2.8-3.1 in standard length; caudal fin moderately forked; greenish with iridescence

217

dorsally, shading to pale silvery blue-green on sides and ventrally, with a broad dark brown stripe beginning above about seventh lateral-line scale, following lateral line until it deflects ventrally, then continuing dorsally on caudal peduncle; scales above lateral line with a blackish basal spot, the spots smaller posteriorly (spots obscure within dark brown band); an oblique narrow pale blue band from lower margin of orbit to edge of upper lip a little anterior to corner of mouth. Reaches 36 cm. Arabian Gulf and Arabian Sea to the Red Sea; also reported from the Gulf of Manaar; a shallow-water species, common in the Arabian Gulf and Gulf of Oman.

WHITECHEEK BREAM
Scolopsis vosmeri (Bloch, 1792)

Dorsal rays X,9; anal rays III,7; pectoral rays 17-19; lateral-line scales 39-45; scales dorsally on head extending forward to anterior nostrils; suborbital bones naked; scales on preopercle extending to margins; posterior edge of second suborbital with a large retrorse spine, an antrorse spine above it, and a fully serrate posterior edge below; body deep, the depth 2.0-2.6 in standard length; dorsal profile of head steeply convex; caudal fin moderately forked; brown, often with a reddish or purplish cast, with a dark brown spot basally on each scale; head dark brown with a broad curved whitish bar from top of head across operculum, its posterior edge bordered with bright orange-red ventrally; lips and side of snout whitish. Reaches 20 cm. Coastal Indian Ocean, including Madagascar, Red Sea, and Arabian Gulf, east to the Indo-Malayan region and northwestern Australia, north to the Ryukyu Islands; occurs on mud and sand bottoms near reefs, but generally at greater depths than the preceding two species.

EMPERORS
FAMILY LETHRINIDAE

The fishes of this family are found only in the tropical and subtropical Indo-Pacific region except for one species of *Lethrinus* which occurs in the tropical eastern Atlantic. They appear to be most closely related to the Nemipteridae, sharing such features as a continuous dorsal fin with X spines and 9 (or 10) soft rays; a forked or emarginate caudal fin; pelvic fins I,5, with an axillary scale,

561. *Scolopsis vosmeri*, about 16 cm (J. Hoover)

and thoracic in position; 10 + 14 vertebrae; 6 branchiostegal rays; mouth terminal, small to moderate, and protrusible; maxilla largely slipping beneath the suborbital bones when mouth closed; no supramaxilla; no teeth on the vomer or palatines; gill membranes not attached to the isthmus; gill rakers knob-like and few in number; opercle with a single flat spine; and scales finely ctenoid, moderate in size. The lethrinids differ from the nemipterids notably in having anal rays III,8-10, pectoral rays 13-15 (14-19 in nemipterids), 3 supraneural (predorsal) bones (nemipterids have 2), no free margin on suborbital bones below eye (free and often with spines in nemipterids), and in dentition which varies greatly within the family. Lethrinids have an outer row of small to moderate canine teeth anteriorly in the jaws, these either continuing in progressively smaller size along side of jaws

562. *Lethrinus nebulosus* (J. Hoover)

or giving way to molariform or nodular teeth; there is an inner band of villiform teeth in the jaws which continues progressively narrower posteriorly in jaws; Emperors are carnivorous, bottom-feeding, coastal fishes usually associated with coral reefs or rocky substrata or nearby sand, rubble, or weedy bottoms. Their prey varies from hard-shelled invertebrates for species with molariform teeth to fishes for the larger species with strong canines. When fishes of the genus *Lethrinus* come to rest near the substratum, they quickly take on a coarse, near-reticular pattern of dark blotches. The family consists of five genera, the monotypic *Gnathodentex*, *Monotaxis*, and *Wattsia*, and *Gymnocranius* and *Lethrinus*. At the present time only *Monotaxis* and *Lethrinus* are represented by species in Oman waters. Carpenter and Allen (1989) reviewed the family, recognising 39 species.

SNUBNOSE EMPEROR
Lethrinus borbonicus Valenciennes, 1830

Dorsal rays X,9; anal rays III,8; pectoral rays 13; lateral-line scales 46-48; scales above lateral line to base of middle dorsal spines 5.5; no scales on cheek (true of other species of the genus); lower series of scales around caudal peduncle (including lateral-line scale on each side) 13-15 (rarely 15); 6-8 scales in supratemporal patch; inner base of pectoral fins with numerous small scales (applies to other Oman species of *Lethrinus*); outer surface of maxilla with a distinct longitudinal ridge; lateral teeth in jaws as molars; body moderately deep, the depth 2.7-2.9 in standard length; dorsal profile of head to above eye nearly straight; snout short, its length without lip 2.0-2.2 in head length; fourth or fifth dorsal spine longest, 2.5-3.1 in body depth; caudal fin moderately forked; body silvery greenish grey dorsally, silvery on sides, the scale edges grey to yellowish brown; body often with irregular broken dusky bars and vertically elongate dusky blotches; head olivaceous dorsally; soft rays of median and pectoral fins often light red. Attains 40 cm. Arabian Gulf and Red Sea south to Mozambique, Madagascar, Seychelles, and Mascarenes. Usually found over sand near reefs from near shore to depths of about 40 m; feeds at night, mainly on echinoderms, molluscs, and crustaceans. Misidentified as *L. fletus* Whitley and *L. kallopterus* Bleeker by Kuronuma and Abe (1972, 1986) and *L. mahsenoides* Valenciennes by Randall (1983) and Sato in Fischer and Bianchi (1984).

563. *Lethrinus borbonicus* (J. Hoover)

BLACKSPOT EMPEROR
Lethrinus harak (Forsskål, 1775)

Dorsal rays X,9; anal rays III,8; pectoral rays 13; lateral-line scales 46-47; scales above lateral line to base of middle dorsal spines 4.5-5.5 (usually 5.5); lower series of scales around caudal peduncle (including lateral-line scale of each side) 13-14; 4-7 scales in supratemporal patch; outer surface of maxilla with or without a longitudinal ridge; teeth on side of jaws molariform or nodular; body moderately deep, the depth 2.7-2.9 in standard length; snout short, its length without lip 2.1-2.6 in head length; dorsal profile of head straight to in front of eye, then convex; fifth dorsal spine usually longest, 2.5-3.1 in body depth; caudal fin slightly forked; olive-grey dorsally, shading to pale grey or whitish ventrally, the scale edges dark; a large, horizontally elongate, black spot, broadly edged in dull yellow, on side of body between tip of pectoral fin and lateral line. Attains about 45 cm. Red Sea to southern Oman (where rare), south to Natal and islands of the western Indian Ocean; southern India and Sri Lanka, and Indo-Malayan region, north to southern Japan, south to northern Queensland, east to Samoa. A shallow-water species usually seen over sand, rubble, or seagrass bottoms, sometimes in mangrove areas; feeds on polychaetes, crustaceans, molluscs, echinoderms, and small fishes.

REDSPOT EMPEROR
Lethrinus lentjan (Lacepède, 1802)

Dorsal rays X,9; anal rays III,8; pectoral rays 13; lateral-line scales 46-47; scales above lateral line to base of middle dorsal spines 5.5; lower series of scales around caudal peduncle (including lateral-line scale of each side) 15-16; 4-9 scales in supratemporal patch; outer surface of maxilla with a longitudinal ridge; teeth at side of jaws nodular or as small molars; body moderately deep, the depth 2.6-2.8 in standard length; snout short, its length without lip 2.0-2.4 in head length; dorsal profile of head nearly straight to above eye; fourth dorsal spine usually longest, 2.7-3.4 in body depth; first anal soft ray longest; caudal fin slightly to moderately forked; greenish grey dorsally, shading to white ventrally, the scale edges darker; a white or pale greenish spot on scales of upper half of body; opercular membrane pink to red, especially the part above opercular spine; base of pectoral fins sometimes pink or red; caudal fin bluish grey, sometimes with two or three irregular, narrow, chevron-shaped, dark bars. Reaches about 40 cm. Indian Ocean and Red Sea to western Pacific; east in Oceania to Palau and Tonga; common in the Arabian Gulf; occurs over sandy or weedy bottoms, often in the vicinity of coral reefs, from the shallows to about 50 m. Feeds mainly on crustaceans and molluscs. This species has 12 junior synonyms, among them *L. mahsenoides* Valenciennes (Carpenter in Carpenter and Allen, 1989).

564. *Lethrinus harak* (J. Randall)

565. *Lethrinus lentjan* (J. Hoover)

MAHSENA
Lethrinus mahsena (Forsskål, 1775)

Dorsal rays X,9; anal rays III,8; pectoral rays 13; lateral-line scales 46-48; scales above lateral line to base of middle dorsal spines 4.5; lower series of scales around caudal peduncle (including lateral-line scale of each side) 14-15; 3-6 scales in supratemporal patch; body deep, the depth 2.3-2.5 in standard length; snout short, its length without lip 1.7-2.3 in head length; dorsal profile of head straight to slightly concave to above eye; outer surface of maxilla usually with a longitudinal ridge; teeth along side of jaws nodular to molariform; third or fourth dorsal spine longest, 2.9-3.8 in body depth; caudal fin moderately forked, the posterior margin of lobes rounded; body pale greenish grey dorsally, shading to white below, the scale edges darker; usually 10 dusky yellowish bars on body about three times broader than pale interspaces; head purplish grey except for scales on opercle; a red streak submarginal to upper edge of pectoral fin; base of pectoral fins with a red bar; a variable amount of red basally on spinous portion of dorsal fin; some adults with even more red on pectoral and dorsal fins, sometimes on opercular membrane, anteriorly on base of anal fin, below eye, and on caudal fin. Reported to 65 cm. Indian Ocean from Sri Lanka to the west, including the Gulf of Oman (but not the Arabian Gulf) and the Red Sea. Occurs on or near coral reefs to depths of about 100 m; feeds on a wide variety of benthic invertebrates, especially echinoids, and occasionally on fishes; the purple dots on the head of the illustrated fish are from wounds from the long spines of the sea urchin *Diadema* on which it often feeds. *L. sanguineus* Smith is a synonym based on specimens with heavy red colouration.

SMALLTOOTH EMPEROR
Lethrinus microdon Valenciennes, 1830

Dorsal rays X,9; anal rays III,8; pectoral rays 13; lateral-line scales 47-48; scales above lateral line to base of middle dorsal spines 4.5; lower series of scales around caudal peduncle (including lateral-line scale of each side) usually 15; 9-11 scales in supratemporal patch; body elongate for the genus, the depth 2.9-3.4 in standard length; snout moderately long, its length without lip 1.8-2.2 in head length; head pointed; dorsal profile of head to above gill opening straight to slightly convex; outer surface of maxilla without a ridge; teeth on side of jaws conical; fourth or fifth dorsal spine longest, 2.4-3.0 in body depth; caudal fin deeply emarginate; greenish grey, shading to white ventrally, the edges of the scales darker; body

566. *Lethrinus mahsena*, about 35 cm (J. Randall)

567. *Lethrinus microdon*, about 28 cm (J. Randall)

568. *Lethrinus nebulosus*, 28 cm (J. Randall)

often with large, irregular, dusky blotches nearly forming a coarse reticular pattern; three narrow blackish streaks often present extending forward from eye (the author observed one fish turn these dark streaks on and off). Reaches about 70 cm. Arabian Gulf and Red Sea south to Mozambique and the islands of the western Indian Ocean, east to the Indo-Malayan region and northwestern Australia, north to southern Japan. Inhabits reefs and adjacent habitats to depths of about 80 m; feeds mainly on fishes, crustaceans, and cephalopods, both by night and day. *L. elongatus* Valenciennes is a synonym. Often confused with *L. olivaceus* Valenciennes which differs in having an even longer snout, 5.5 scales above the lateral line, and usually 7-9 scales in supratemporal

569. *L. nebulosus*, juv., about 10 cm (J. Randall)

patch. Although not yet known from Oman, it occurs in the Gulf of Aden and is reported from Pakistan, so it should be expected in Oman seas.

SPANGLED EMPEROR
Lethrinus nebulosus (Forsskål, 1775)

Dorsal rays X,9; anal rays III,8; pectoral rays 13; lateral-line scales 46-48; scales above lateral line to base of middle dorsal spines 5.5; lower series of scales around caudal peduncle (including lateral-line scale on each side) usually 15; 5-9 scales in supratemporal patch; body depth 2.5-2.8 in standard length; snout length without lip 1.8-2.3 in head length; dorsal profile of snout straight to slightly concave to above eye, then convex; outer surface of maxilla sometimes with a longitudinal ridge; teeth on side of jaws bluntly conical anteriorly, becoming progressively more molarifom posteriorly; fourth or fifth dorsal spine longest, 2.8-3.5 in body depth; caudal fin slightly forked; body pale yellowish brown with dark brown edges on scales, shading to white ventrally, with a light blue spot on many scales of upper half of body; head bronze except for scales on opercle, with scattered, short, bright blue streaks (some radiating from eye) and spots. Reaches about 80 cm. Indo-Pacific, the easternmost record, Samoa. Occurs in a variety of habitats from coral reefs to seagrass beds and mangroves sloughs, from near shore to at least 75 m, sometimes in small aggregations. Feeds mainly on echinoderms, molluscs, and crustaceans. Carpenter in Carpenter and Allen (1989)

listed a surprising 19 junior synonyms for this emperor.

ORANGESTRIPED EMPEROR
Lethrinus obsoletus (Forsskål, 1775)

Dorsal rays X,9; anal rays III,8; pectoral rays 13; lateral-line scales 45-48; scales above lateral line to base of middle dorsal spines 5.5; lower series of scales around caudal peduncle (including lateral-line scale from each side) 15 or 16; 5-7 scales in supratemporal patch; body depth 2.6-2.9 in standard length; snout length without lip 1.8-2.3 in head length; dorsal profile of head straight to in front of eye, then convex; outer surface of maxilla with a distinct knob; teeth on side

570. *L. obsoletus*, juvenile, 5.6 cm (J. Randall)

of jaws bluntly conical anteriorly, becoming molariform posteriorly; fourth or fifth dorsal spine longest, 2.5-3.4 in body depth; caudal fin slightly forked, the lobes with a rounded posterior margin; light greenish grey to tan dorsally, the edges of the scales dark brown, shading to white ventrally; a broad orange-yellow stripe on lower side at level of pectoral-fin base, often with two less distinct orange-yellow stripes above and one below; head purplish grey except for scales on opercle. Attains 45 cm. Red Sea and southern Oman south to Natal, east to Samoa and the Marshall Islands; in the western Pacific from Queensland to the Ryukyu Islands; occurs on coral reefs and adjacent habitats from a few to about 30 m, sometimes in small aggregations. Often identified as *L. ramak* (Forsskål); however, Smith (1959b) showed that *L. obsoletus* has priority and indicated that *L. ramak* was intended as a listing of the Arabic name.

BIGEYE EMPEROR
Monotaxis grandoculis (Forsskål, 1775)

Dorsal rays X,10; anal rays III,9; pectoral rays 14; lateral-line scales 44-47; scales above lateral line to base of middle dorsal spines 5; body depth 2.2-2.9 in standard length (depth increasing with age); dorsal profile of head of adults very steep and straight to front of eye, then angling sharply to a second nearly straight section to origin of dorsal fin (juveniles with a pointed head and sloping dorsal profile); eye very large, its diameter 2.5-3.2 in head length; posterior margin of preopercle finely serrate (smooth on the species of *Lethrinus*); side of maxilla with a denticulated ridge; side of jaws with a row of six or seven large molariform teeth; caudal fin moderately forked, the posterior margin of each lobe rounded; greenish grey dorsally, the edges of the scales dark brown, shading to silvery white ventrally; can quickly assume a pattern of four broad blackish bars on body; juveniles with four permanent dark brown bars on body, two of which extend into dorsal fin, the more posterior ending in a large black spot. Indo-Pacific, but known in Oman only in the south (where rare). Nocturnal; feeds heavily on molluscs, but crabs, sea urchins, and hermit crabs are important items of the diet.

573. *M. grandoculis*, juv., about 7.5 cm (J. Randall)

571. *Lethrinus obsoletus*, about 22 cm (J. Randall)

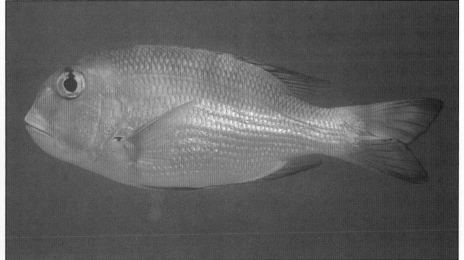

572. *Monotaxis grandoculis*, about 35 cm (J. Randall)

PORGIES AND SEABREAMS
FAMILY SPARIDAE

The three perciform families Sparidae, Lethrinidae, and Nemipteridae have been grouped together as the superfamily Sparoidea, along with the Centracanthidae (no representatives in Oman seas) (Johnson, 1981). The sparids share many of the characters with nemipterids and lethrinids such as the maxilla not fully exposed on the cheek, no teeth on the palate; a single flat spine on opercle; 10 + 14 vertebrae; 6 branchiostegal rays; a continuous dorsal fin (the spines, however, vary from X to XIII); caudal fin emarginate or forked; and pelvic fins thoracic with I,5 rays and an axillary scale. They are very diverse in general form, the shape varying from elongate to deep-bodied, and the dorsal profile from very steep to sloping. They are also unusual as a group in having highly variable dentition; the teeth may be conical, caniniform, molariform, or incisiform, with or without crenulations. The mouth is small to moderate, usually not reaching posterior to a vertical through middle of eye, and slightly protrusible, with the posterior end of the premaxilla overlapping the maxilla; the margin of the preopercle is usually smooth or with a few fine serrae; the scales are finely ctenoid or secondarily cycloid; most species have a scaly sheath at the base of the dorsal and anal fins, and most have long pointed pectoral fins. The majority of these fishes are carnivorous, feeding principally on molluscs and crustaceans which they crush with their molariform teeth, but some, such as species of *Diplodus*, are omnivorous, feeding in part on benthic plants. Many species of the family have been shown to be hermaphroditic; some have both male and female gonads developing simultaneously; others change sex with age from males to females (protandrous) or from females to males (protogynous). Sparid fishes range from tropical to temperate seas, nearly all in continental waters or the insular shelves of large islands; none extend their range to the islands of Oceania. Many occur in moderately deep water, and a few species penetrate brackish habitats. There are 29 genera and about 100 species in the family.

574. Mixed school dominated by *Acanthropagus bifasciatus* and *Diplodus cervinus omanensis* (J. Hoover)

PICNIC SEABREAM
Acanthopagrus berda (Forsskål, 1775)

Dorsal rays XI-XII (rarely XII),10-13 (usually 11 or 12); anal rays III,8-9; pectoral rays 14-15; lateral-line scales 43-46; scales above lateral line to base of fourth dorsal spine 4; gill rakers 6-7 + 9-11; body depth 1.9-2.4 in standard length; dorsal profile of head steep and nearly straight to above posterior edge of eye; snout pointed; suborbital depth about 7.5-8.0 in head length; usually three pairs of large, compressed, conical teeth at front of jaws; side of upper jaw with a lateral row of bluntly conical teeth and four inner rows of molars; side of lower jaw with four rows of molars; dorsal spines laterally compressed, seeming to alternate broad and narrow (based on attachment of interspinous membranes) (true of other species of the genus); fourth or fifth dorsal spine longest; second anal spine stout, laterally flattened, and distinctly longer than third spine; caudal fin slightly forked; young silvery, the lateral line clearly evident as a dark line, the paired and pelvic fins often blackish distally; adults with increasing amount of dark pigment on scales (those in muddy water may be almost completely black); pelvic, anal, and caudal fins dark grey. Maximum length, 75 cm. Continental shelf of the Indian Ocean, including the Red Sea and Arabian Gulf, to the western Pacific where it ranges from Australia to southern Japan. A shallow-water species that freely enters estuaries, and even freshwater; feeds mainly on echinoids (especially sand dollars), crustaceans, polychaete worms, and molluscs (primarily small bivalves).

DOUBLEBAR SEABREAM
Acanthopagrus bifasciatus (Forsskål, 1775)

Dorsal rays XI,12-15; anal rays III,10-12; pectoral rays 15; lateral-line scales 48-50; scales above lateral line to base of dorsal spines 4.5; gill rakers 6-7 + 11-12; body deep, the depth 1.8-2.2 in standard length; dorsal profile of head steep and convex; dentition as in the preceding two species, but outer row of teeth on side of upper jaw less conical; third dorsal spine usually longest; second anal spine slightly longer than third; caudal fin slightly forked; body silvery with a blackish spot on each scale; head silvery with two black bars, the narrower anterior one passing through eye, the broad posterior one from nape across operculum; side of snout yellow; pelvic and anal fins black; remaining fins yellow. Reaches 50 cm. Western Indian Ocean, including the Arabian Gulf, Red Sea, Madagascar, and the Mascarene Islands. Red Sea individuals differ

575. *Acanthopagrus berda*, about 25 cm (J. Randall)

576. *Acanthopagrus bifasciatus*, about 20 cm (J. Randall)

577. *Acanthopagrus latus*, 41 cm (J. Randall)

from Oman and Arabian Gulf fish in lacking the rows of black spots, one per scale, on the body. Generally found in sheltered waters of bays and estuaries, often in the vicinity of coral reefs.

YELLOWFIN SEABREAM
Acanthopagrus latus (Houttuyn, 1782)

Dorsal rays XI,11-12; anal rays III,8-9; pectoral rays 15; lateral-line scales 43-48; scales above lateral line to base of fourth dorsal spine 4.5; gill rakers 5-8 + 9-11; body depth 2.1-2.5 in standard length; dorsal profile of head steep and slightly convex, adults often with a slight bump in front of upper part of eye; dentition similar to preceding species; a juvenile with three instead of four rows of molars in jaws; suborbital depth 5.0-6.5 in head length; third to fifth dorsal spines longest; second anal spine lat-

578. *A. latus*, juvenile, 17 cm (J. Randall)

erally flattened and distinctly longer than third spine; caudal fin moderately forked; silvery grey dorsally, shading to silvery on sides and ventrally, the centres of scales brassy to yellowish; a blackish blotch at upper part of gill opening; anal and pelvic fins of young yellow, yellowish in adults; caudal fin yellowish with a dusky posterior margin; pectoral fins yellowish with small black spot at upper base. Reaches 50 cm. Arabian Gulf along the southern Asian continent to the western Pacific; Australia to southern Japan. Occurs from inshore to depths of about 50 m; enters brackish areas.

KING SOLDIERBREAM
Argyrops spinifer (Forsskål, 1775)

Dorsal rays XI-XII,10-11; anal rays III,8-9; pectoral rays 15; lateral-line scales 49-53; gill rakers 6 + 10-11; body deep and compressed, the depth 1.75-2.0 in standard length; dorsal profile of head steep with a slight bump before eye, the large adults (perhaps only males) developing a grotesque hump on nape; front of upper jaws with two pairs of stout canine teeth; side of jaws with two rows of teeth, the outer row as blunt conical teeth, becoming molariform posteriorly, the inner row molariform; first two dorsal spines very short; third to seventh spines laterally flattened, these spines elongate and filamentous in young, reaching beyond base of caudal fin; caudal fin slightly forked; silvery pink (scale centres pink, the edges silvery); edge of opercular membrane above spine red; young with five faint pink bars on body, the dorsal filaments bright red. Reaches 70 cm. Red Sea and Arabian Gulf to South Africa, east to the western Pacific where the range is Queensland to China and Taiwan; reported from the depth range of 5 to at least 100 m. Occurs over mud or sand substrata; feeds on benthic invertebrates, especially molluscs. *A. filamentosus* (Valenciennes) which ranges from the Red Sea to Natal might be expected from Oman; it differs in having 8-10 dorsal soft rays and only the third dorsal spine elongate in the young. The fish from the Arabian Gulf identified as *A. filamentosus* by Abe and Kuronuma (1986) is *A. spinifer*.

579. *Argyrops spinifer*, 62 cm (J. Randall)

580. *Argyrops spinifer*, 42 cm (J. Randall)

581. *A. spinifer*, juvenile, 15 cm (J. Randall)

STRIPED BOGA
Boops lineatus (Boulenger, 1892)

Dorsal rays XIII,13-14; anal rays III,13-14; lateral-line scales 70; scales above lateral line to base of dorsal spines 6; body moderately elongate, the depth 3.4-3.6 in standard length; eye diameter greater than snout length; mouth small and oblique, the maxilla reaching slightly posterior to a vertical at anterior edge of orbit; teeth in a single row in jaws, incisiform, the distal edges truncate sold denticulate; dorsal spines slender, the fourth to sixth longest; caudal fin deeply forked; pectoral fins short, about

582. *Boops lineatus*, about 20 cm (J. Hoover)

three-fourths head length; silvery blue-green dorsally, shading to silvery with iridescence ventrally, with six dark reddish brown stripes (the third following all but posterior part of lateral line, the sixth on lower side faint); caudal fin yellowish. Reaches 25 cm. Known only from the Gulf of Oman to Yemen. A shallow-water species usually seen in schools.

SANTER SEABREAM
Cheimerius nufar (Valenciennes, 1830)

Dorsal rays XII,10-11 (usually 10); anal rays III,8; pectoral rays 16; lateral-line scales 58-63; scales above lateral line to base of fourth dorsal spine 6.5; gill rakers 9 + 13-15; body depth 2.3-2.6 in standard length; dorsal profile of head straight to in front of eye, then convex; mouth slightly oblique; two pairs of slender canine teeth anteriorly in upper jaw and three in lower (the medial pair small); side of jaws with a row of compressed conical teeth; an inner band of villiform teeth (no molars); first two dorsal spines very short; remaining dorsal spines and anal spines laterally compressed; third dorsal spine longest and filamentous, 1.0-1.2 in head length; remaining spines progressively shorter; second and third anal spines subequal; caudal fin deeply forked; pectoral fins long, reaching to above first anal soft ray; silvery pink with five pink bars on body and a pink bar through eye; front of snout pink. Attains 60 cm. Western Indian Ocean, including the Red Sea, Arabian Gulf, Madagascar, and Mascarene Islands. Bauchot and Smith in Fischer and Bianchi (1984) recorded the depth range as 60 to about 100 m; however, the species was observed by the author off Masirah Island, central coast of Oman, in less than 8 m.

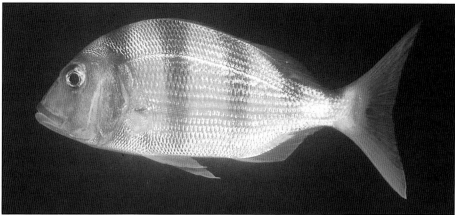

583. *Cheimerius nufar* (J. Hoover)

KARANTEEN SEABREAM
Crenidens crenidens indicus Day, 1873

Dorsal rays XI,11; anal rays III,10; pectoral rays 13-14; lateral-line scales 52-60; scales above lateral line to base of fourth dorsal spine 5-5.5; gill rakers 6-7 + 9-11; body depth 2.1-2.4 in standard length; dorsal profile of head slightly convex with a broad-based, slight convexity centred in front of upper edge of eye; mouth horizontal and small, the maxilla reaching to below nostrils; an outer series of four pairs of upper and five pairs of lower incisiform teeth, the curved distal edge of each with five denticulations; two inner lower series of similar teeth in each jaw (probably as replacement teeth), and small granular teeth lingual to these; dorsal spines somewhat flattened laterally, the third to sixth longest; caudal fin slightly forked; pectoral fins reaching a vertical through anus; silvery with a dusky spot in scale centres, resulting in a striped effect; a blackish spot dorsally in pectoral-fin axil and extending above pectoral-fin base; dorsal and caudal fin dusky distally. Maximum length about 30 cm. Nicobar Islands and coast of India to the Arabian Gulf. Omnivorous, but feeds principally on algae (also ingests crustaceans, worms, etc.); tends to occur in schools. A second subspecies, *C. c. crenidens* from the Red Sea and east coast of Africa, is more slender (body depth 2.4-2.75 in standard length).

OMAN PORGY
Diplodus cervinus omanensis Bauchot and Bianchi, 1984

Dorsal rays XI,12; anal rays III,10-11; pectoral rays 15; lateral-line scales 61-63; gill rakers 9-10 + 8-10; body depth 2.0-2.25 in standard length; dorsal profile of head slightly convex; mouth horizontal and small, the maxilla reaching to below anterior margin of eye, and completely concealed under suborbitals with mouth closed; five or six pairs of projecting incisiform teeth in upper jaw and four pairs in lower jaw; side of jaws with two or three rows of small molars; fourth dorsal spine usually longest; second and third anal spines subequal; caudal fin forked; pectoral fins reaching to above third anal spine; body silvery with four broad black bars (the first and second may bifurcate ventrally); two short narrow black bars ventrally in first silver interspace on body and one in second; head with a black bar through eye; snout partly yellow. Reaches about 30 cm. This subspecies is known only from southern Oman where it occurs inshore over rocky bottom; its sister subspecies, *D. c. hottentotus* (Smith), occurs only in southern Mozambique and South Africa (Bauchot and Bianchi, 1984).

584. *Crenidens crenidens indicus*, 20.3 cm (J. Randall)

585. *Diplodus cervinus omanensis* (J. Hoover)

CAPE PORGY
Diplodus sargus capensis (Smith, 1844)

Dorsal rays XII,14-15; anal rays III,13-14; pectoral rays 16-17; lateral-line scales 62-72; gill rakers 6-8 + 8-11; body depth 2.0-2.25 in standard length; dorsal profile of head slightly convex; mouth horizontal and small, the maxilla reaching to below anterior edge of eye, not completely concealed beneath suborbitals when mouth closed; four pairs of projecting incisiform teeth anteriorly in jaws; side of jaws with rows of small molars (three or four rows in upper jaw and two or three in lower); fifth or sixth dorsal spine usually longest; caudal fin forked; pectoral fins reaching to above spinous portion of anal fin; silvery to brassy with a very large saddle-like black spot anteriorly on caudal peduncle, sometimes extending to ventral margin; ten narrow dusky bars on upper two-thirds of body, alternating in intensity. Reaches about 35 cm. Known from Angola, southern Africa, southern Madagascar, and Oman; the illustrated fish was photographed off Raysut, southern Oman. Mann and Buxton (1992) analysed the stomach contents of numerous specimens from South Africa; they found a large variety of benthic invertebates, especially echinoids, polychaetes, and crustaceans, and little algae.

586. *Diplodus sargus capensis* (J. Randall)

587. *Diplodus sargus kotschyi* (J. Randall)

ONESPOT PORGY
Diplodus sargus kotschyi (Steindachner, 1876)

Dorsal rays XII,13-15; anal rays III,12-14; pectoral rays 15-16; lateral-line scales 60-68; scales above lateral line to base of fourth dorsal spine 6.5; gill rakers 7 + 9-11; body depth 2.1-2.35 in standard length; mouth horizontal and small, the maxilla reaching to below front of eye; four pairs of incisiform teeth at front of jaws, the symphyseal pair the largest; side of jaws with rows of small molariform teeth (three or four rows in upper jaw and two or three in lower); fourth to sixth dorsal spines longest; second

anal spine slightly longer than third; caudal fin forked; pectoral fins reaching to above third anal spine; silvery grey dorsally, silvery with brassy reflections on side and ventrally, with a black spot nearly as large as eye anteriorly on side of caudal peduncle; a black spot in axil of pectoral fins and extending slightly above; juveniles with eight or nine dark bars. Attains 30 cm. Arabian Gulf (where common) to northwestern India. Abou-Seedo et al. (1990) determined that most fish undergo sex reveral from female to male in the second year of life; spawning takes place in Kuwait Bay from November to March. De la Paz (1978) regarded *Diplodus noct* (Valenciennes) from the Red Sea and *D. kotschyi* (Steindachner) as sister species; however, Bauchot and Smith in Fischer

and Bianchi (1984) treated them as subspecies.

BARRED SEABREAM
Lithognathus mormyrus (Linnaeus, 1758)

Dorsal rays XI,12-13; anal rays III,10-11; pectoral rays 15-17; lateral-line scales 60-65; gill rakers 8-10 + 15-17; body depth 2.6-2.8 in standard length; snout long and pointed; mouth slightly oblique and moderately large, the maxilla reaching or nearly reaching a vertical at anterior edge of eye; slender conical teeth anteriorly in jaws, the outer series larger; outer row of teeth on side of jaw progressively more molariform posteriorly; three or four inner rows of molariform teeth in jaws, those of the second row greatly enlarged posteriorly; third or fourth dorsal spine longest; caudal fin forked; pectoral fins short, not reaching beyond anus; silvery with about 15 narrow dark bars on about upper three-fourths of body, including three on nape. Reported to 55 cm. Mediterranean Sea to Bay of Biscay, west coast of Africa around Cape of Good Hope to southern Mozambique, and southern Oman (and rarely in the Gulf of Oman); a protandrous hermaphrodite; feeds on crustaceans, worms, molluscs, and echinoids. Often seen in schools, usually over sand, silty sand, or seagrass bottoms; known from shallow water to depths as great as 150 m.

588. *Lithognathus mormyrus* (J. Hoover)

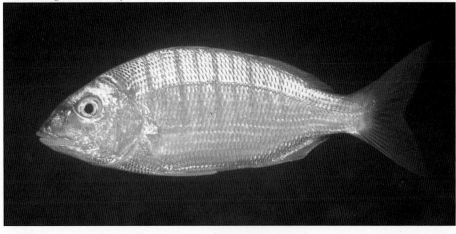

ARABIAN PANDORA
Pagellus affinis Boulenger, 1887

Dorsal rays XII,10-11; anal rays III,10; pectoral rays 16; lateral-line scales 59-63; scales above lateral line to base of fourth dorsal spine 6; gill rakers short, 6 + 9-11; body depth 2.6-3.0 in standard length; dorsal profile of head smoothly convex; eye near middle of head; four pairs of moderate conical teeth anteriorly in upper jaw and five pairs in lower; row of teeth along side of jaws progressively more molariform posteriorly; an inner posterior row of moderate molars in each jaw and very small molars medial to this; dorsal spines slender, the third to fifth longest; last dorsal and anal soft rays a little longer than penultimate rays; second and third anal spines subequal; caudal fin deeply forked; pectoral fins long, extending to above base of second anal soft ray; pinkish silver with a pale blue spot in centres of scattered scales above lateral line but on nearly all scales below lateral line; opercular membrane light red; a few iridescent blue markings on head. Largest reported, 37 cm. Arabian Gulf to the Gulf of Aden and northern coast of Somalia; not observed while diving; occurs to depths of at least 150 m.

589. *Pagellus affinis*, 27.5 cm (J. Randall)

HAFFARA
Rhabdosargus haffara (Forsskål, 1775)

Dorsal rays XI,12-14; anal rays III,10-12; pectoral rays 14-15 (usually 15;); lateral-line scales 58-66; scales above lateral line to base of fourth dorsal spine 5.5-6; lower-limb gill rakers 7-9; body depth 2.5-2.7 in standard length; dorsal profile convex with a bump before eye; mouth low on head, almost horizontal, the lower jaw inferior; maxilla reaching to below anterior half of eye; three pairs of bluntly pointed incisiform teeth anteriorly in jaws; side of upper jaw with an outer row of bluntly conical teeth, becoming more nodular posteriorly, and four rows of molariform teeth, the inner posterior tooth greatly enlarged; side of lower jaw with three rows of molariform teeth, the inner posterior tooth greatly enlarged; dorsal spines slender, the third to fifth longest; second and third anal spines subequal; caudal fin forked; pectoral fins reaching to above anus; bluish silver dorsally, silvery on side and ventrally, with faint brassy stripes following centres of scale rows; a little blackish pigment on first few lateral-line scales. Attains 35 cm. Red Sea to Arabian Gulf; a shallow-water species usually encountered over sand or silty sand substrata; may occur in small schools.

590. *Rhabdosargus haffara*, 8 cm (J. Randall)

591. *Rhabdosargus sarba*, 23 cm (J. Randall)

GOLDSTRIPED SEABREAM
Rhabdosargus sarba (Forsskål, 1775)

Dorsal rays XI,12-13; anal rays III,11; pectoral rays 15; lateral-line scales 56-59; scales above lateral line to base of fourth dorsal spine 6.5-7; gill rakers 6-7 + 7-9; body moderately deep, the depth 2.0-2.3 in standard length; dorsal profile of head smoothly convex; mouth almost horizontal, the lower jaw slightly inferior; dentition similar to that of *R. haffara*; third or fourth dorsal spine longest; second and third anal spines subequal; caudal fin forked; pectoral fins long, reaching posterior to spinous portion of anal fin; silvery with brassy yellow stripes following scale rows; an orange-yellow streak on lower side of abdomen commencing at origin of pelvic fin; a little blackish pigment on first few lateral line scales; paired and anal fins yellow; lobes of caudal fin (especially the lower) yellow, the posterior margin blackish. Reported to reach 60 cm; the South African angling record is 7.3 kg. Western Indian Ocean, including Red Sea, Arabian Gulf, Madagascar, Seychelles, and Mascarenes; collected by the author off southwestern India. Coastal, including estuaries, to a maximum of about 60 m; often encountered in small schools. Feeds heavily on bivalve molluscs, but also on sand dollars, sea urchins, and sand-dwelling crustaceans.

SOBAITY
Sparidentex hasta (Valenciennes, 1830)

Dorsal rays XI,11-12; anal rays III,8-9; pectoral rays 15-16; lateral-line scales 47-50; scales above lateral line to base of fourth dorsal spine 4.5-5; lower-limb gill rakers 9; body moderately elongate, the depth 2.7-3.2 in standard length; dorsal profile of head straight to above eye, then convex; mouth slightly oblique and moderately large, the maxilla extending to or beyond a vertical at middle of eye; three pairs of stout canine teeth at front of jaws; a row of conical teeth along side of jaws, those in the middle largest; a band of small granular teeth behind anterior canines and extending posteriorly along inner side of jaws; fourth dorsal spine longest, but fifth and sixth nearly as long; second anal spine a little longer than third but not notably heavier; caudal fin slightly to moderately forked; pectoral fins reaching posterior to anus; silvery grey, only the edges of scales silvery; about nine faint dark bars dorsally on body; a blackish spot at front of lateral line; opercular membrane blackish; blackish streaks following scale rows on cheek and behind eye; dorsal and caudal fins dark grey; a black spot at upper axil of pectoral fins. Attains about 50 cm; Blegvad (1944) recorded one of 7 kg from Iran. Arabian Gulf to west coast of India. An active fish ranging over reefs and adjacent habitats; food habits not recorded. *S. cuvieri* (Day) is a synonym.

592. *Sparidentex hasta*, about 30 cm (J. Randall)

DRUMS AND CROAKERS
FAMILY SCIAENIDAE

The sciaenids are another large perciform family which is confined to continental waters or the insular shelfs of large continental islands. The Indo-Pacific species are characterised by a moderately elongate, compressed body, a long dorsal fin with VI to XIII slender spines, deeply notched between the last and penultimate spines (except *Panna*), and 20-44 soft rays; anal rays II,5-12, the first spine very short; pelvic fins thoracic with I,5 rays; caudal fin varying from slightly emarginate to truncate, rhomboid, rounded, or pointed; mouth often inferior, but some species with a projecting lower jaw; maxilla largely concealed when mouth closed; jaws with rows of small conical teeth, a few species with canines; no teeth on roof of mouth; some species with a single barbel or a pair of small barbels on chin; opercle with two spines, gill membranes free from isthmus, the branchiostegal rays 7; scales ctenoid or cycloid or a mixture of the two, largely covering head and caudal fin; lateral line extending to end of caudal fin; head with enlarged cavernous canals; prominent pores on front of snout and on chin (in species with inferior mouths); swimbladder variable in structure, often with diverticula that may be complexly branched (unfortunately, swimbladder morphology is of major importance in classification). Nearly all are drably coloured, the dominant hue silvery. As their common names imply, the drums and croakers are well known for sound production, for which the swimbladder acts as a resonating chamber. The family consists of about 70 genera and about 330 species which are found in shallow water of tropical to temperate seas. They generally occur over sand or mud substrata; many penetrate brackish habitats, and a few are restricted to freshwater. All are carnivorous, feeding mainly on crustaceans, but some also prey on fishes. The larger species are important food fishes. Trewavas (1977) reviewed the Indo-Pacific species; Lal Mohan in Fischer and Bianchi (1984) reviewed western Indian Ocean species; Sasaki (1989) recognised 10 subfamilies.

593. School of *Argyrosomus heinii*, about 20 cm (J. Randall)

ARABIAN SEA MEAGRE
Argyrosomus heinii (Steindachner, 1907)

Dorsal rays XI,32-33; anal rays II,7; pectoral rays 17; lateral-line scales about 50; scales on body finely ctenoid; axil of pectoral fins scaleless; gill rakers slender, 9 on lower limb; body depth 3.4-3.6 in standard length; mouth terminal or slightly inferior and large, the maxilla reaching or nearly reaching to below rear edge of eye; a series of enlarged well-spaced conical teeth in outer row of upper jaw and an inner band of small teeth; inner row of teeth of lower jaw enlarged, well-spaced, and incurved, with a single outer row of small teeth; snout with 5 rostral pores (may be absent in large specimens) and five marginal pores; chin with 3 pairs of pores; caudal fin truncate, becoming slightly emarginate in adults; swim-

594. *Argyrosomus heinii*, 59.2 cm (J. Randall)

bladder carrot-shaped with about 30 pairs of arborescent appendages, progressively larger and more complexly branched anteriorly; grey dorsally, shading to silvery on slides and ventrally; a black spot at upper base of pectoral fins. Attains 60 cm. Known only from the Gulf of Oman and southern coast of Oman. The young may occur in schools.

595. *Argyrosomus hololepidotus*, adults (J. Hoover)

SOUTHERN MEAGRE
Argyrosomus hololepidotus (Lacepède, 1802)

Dorsal rays XI,26-29; anal rays II,7; pectoral rays 17; lateral-line scales 46-54; scales finely ctenoid, becoming cycloid on snout and below eye; axil of pectoral fins scaleless; gill rakers slender, 8-10 on lower limb; body depth 3.4-3.9 in standard length; mouth terminal or lower jaw slightly projecting; mouth large, the maxilla nearly or

just reaching to below posterior edge of eye; outer row of conical teeth in upper jaw enlarged and well spaced with inner series of small conical teeth; inner row of teeth in lower jaw enlarged and well spaced, the outer series small (small teeth not apparent in large specimens); snout with 5 rostral pores (lateral pair absent in large specimens) and 5 pairs of marginal pores; 3 pairs of pores on chin; caudal fin slightly rhomboid, the upper half slightly emarginate, the lower half truncate; swimbladder carrot-shaped

with 25-35 pairs of arborescent appendages; silvery grey, the median fins dark yellowish grey; a blackish spot at upper base of pectoral fins. Reported to attain 200 cm and a weight of 70 kg. Known from West Africa from Zaire to Namibia, east coast of South Africa, Madagascar, Gulf of Oman to northwest India, and the southern half of Australia. Generally found on mud bottoms from depths of 15-150 m; may occur in estuaries.

BELANGER'S CROAKER
Johnius belangerii (Cuvier, 1830)

Dorsal rays X-XI,26-30; anal rays II,7-8; pectoral rays 17; lateral-line scales 48-52; scales ctenoid, becoming cycloid on snout and below eye; gill rakers 2-5 + 6-11; body depth 3.1-4.0 in standard length; mouth inferior, slightly oblique, the maxilla ending below pupil; teeth of upper jaw with an outer row of enlarged curved conical teeth and an inner band of villiform teeth in four or five series; lower jaw with a band of villiform teeth; rostral pores of snout 5, marginal pores of snout 5; pores on chin 5; caudal fin rhomboid; second anal spine long, about half length of head; swimbladder hammer-shaped with 11-15 pairs of arborescent appendages, the first entering head; silvery grey with a blackish blotch on opercle; outer part of dorsal fin blackish. Reaches 30 cm. Ranges from the coast of China south to Indonesia and the east coast of Australia, and west to the Arabian Gulf.

596. *Johnius belangerii*, 13.3 cm (J. Randall)

597. *Johnius carutta*, 20.1 cm (J. Randall)

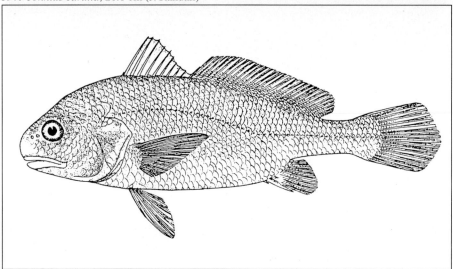

598. *Johnius sina* (after Fischer and Bianchi, 1984)

KARUT CROAKER
Johnius carutta Bloch, 1793

Dorsal rays X-XI,26-30; anal rays II,7; pectoral rays 17; lateral-line scales about 50; scales of head and anterodorsal part of body cycloid, weakly ctenoid elsewhere; gill rakers 3-4 + 8-10; body depth 3.2-4.0 in standard length; mouth inferior, nearly horizontal, the maxilla extending to below posterior edge of pupil; upper jaw with an outer enlarged series of teeth and an inner band of small teeth; lower jaw with small teeth; snout with 5 rostral pores and 5 marginal pores; 3 pairs of pores on chin, the anterior pair close together in a common pit; caudal fin rhomboid in young, truncate or sigmoid in adults; second anal spine about 4 in head length; swimbladder hammer-shaped with about 16 pairs of arborescent appendages; silvery grey dorsally, shading to silvery below; darker individuals with a narrow pale streak along lateral line. Maximum length about 30 cm. Southern Asian coast from western Thailand to the Arabian Gulf; illustrated specimen trawled in Kuwait Bay.

SIN CROAKER
Johnius sina (Cuvier, 1830)

Dorsal rays X-XI,26-29; anal rays II,7-8; pectoral rays 17; lateral-line scales about 46; scales ctenoid on body, cycloid on head; gill rakers 6-7 + 13-15; body depth about 3.6 in standard length; mouth inferior, the gape forming an angle of about 30° to horizontal axis of body, the maxilla nearly reaching a vertical at rear edge of eye; upper jaw with an outer row of enlarged, well-spaced teeth and an inner band of very small teeth; lower jaw with an inner row of moderately large teeth (about half length of large upper teeth) and two irregular outer rows of small teeth; snout with 5 rostral and 5 marginal pores; chin with 3 pairs of pores, the anterior pair close together; caudal fin rhomboid; second anal spine about 3 in head length; swimbladder hammer-shaped with 12-17 pairs of arborescent appendages; brownish grey dorsally, shading to silvery below; a large dark blotch on opercle; outer part of spinous dorsal fin blackish. Attains about 30 cm. Coastal waters of the Indian Ocean from Natal (except the Red Sea) to the Malay Peninsula (Trewavas, 1977).

SHARPTOOTH CROAKER
Johnius vogleri (Bleeker, 1853)

Dorsal rays XI,27-28; anal rays II,7; pectoral rays 19; lateral-line scales about 48; scales on body ctenoid, on head cycloid; gill rakers short and coarsely toothed in adult, 4-6 + 9-13; body depth 3.1-3.3 in standard length; eyes large and interorbital space narrow; mouth inferior, the gape forming an angle of about 20° to horizontal axis of body, the maxilla reaching to below posterior edge of pupil; enlarged widely-spaced teeth in both jaws, the outer series of upper jaw and the inner series of lower jaw large; snout with 3 minute rostral pores and 5 marginal pores; chin with 3 pairs of pores, the anterior pair close together and joined by a groove; caudal fin rhomboid; second anal spine short, about 4 in head length; swimbladder hammer-shaped with 14-16 pairs of arborescent appendages; silvery grey dorsally, becoming silvery below. Largest specimen reported, 26 cm. Taiwan and coast of China south to New South Wales and west to the Arabian Gulf.

LESSER TIGERTOOTH CROAKER
Otolithes cuvieri Trewavas, 1974

Dorsal rays X,29-31; anal rays II,7-8; pectoral rays 15; lateral-line scales about 50; scales cycloid, becoming finely ctenoid posteriorly; gill rakers 7 + 12-14; body moderately elongate, the depth 3.25-4.5 in standard length; mouth large and oblique, the lower jaw projecting, the gape forming an angle of about 30° to horizontal axis of body; maxilla extending posterior to centre of eye; one or two pairs of large canine teeth at front of upper jaw, and one pair at tip of lower jaw; no rostral pores on snout; 3 small marginal pores; chin pores indistinct or absent; caudal fin rhomboid; swimbladder of adults carrot-shaped with about 28 pairs of arborescent appendages, somewhat swollen at their bases; silvery, the scale centres brown on upper two thirds of body, forming narrow oblique bands. Reaches 20 cm. East coast of India to southern Oman.

TIGERTOOTH CROAKER
Otolithes ruber (Bloch and Schneider, 1801)

Dorsal rays X-XI,27-30; anal rays II,7; pectoral rays 17; lateral-line scales 48-50; scales cycloid, becoming weakly ctenoid ventroposteriorly on body; gill rakers 4-5 + 8-11; body elongate, the depth 4.2-5.1 in standard length; mouth large and oblique, the lower jaw projecting, the gape forming an angle of about 35° to horizontal axis of

599. *Johnius vogleri*, 17.5 cm (J. Randall)

600. *Otolithes cuvieri* (J. Hoover)

601. *Otolithes ruber*, 42.8 cm (J. Randall)

body, the maxilla extending to or nearly to a vertical at rear margin of eye; a pair of very large canines teeth at front of upper jaw and a pair of smaller canines between; side of jaw with an outer row of close-set conical teeth and inner rows of very small teeth; front of lower jaw with a pair of very large canines at symphysis (often one of this pair is missing); side of lower jaw with an inner row of close-set conical teeth and an outer row of much smaller teeth; no rostral pores on snout; 3 small marginal pores; chin pores indistinct or absent; caudal fin rhomboid

(pointed in juveniles); second anal spine slender and short, about 8 in head length; swimbladder of adults carrot-shaped with 32-37 pairs of arborescent appendages; silvery, the scale centres dusky, thus forming faint oblique lines following scale rows. Reaches 75 cm. Philippines and coast of China south to Queensland and west to the Asian and East African coasts where it extends south to Natal. Common in the Arabian Gulf and Gulf of Oman, but not reported from the Red Sea. Feeds primarily on fishes.

GREYFIN CROAKER
Pennahia anea (Bloch, 1773)

Dorsal rays X-XI,23-24; anal rays II,7; pectoral rays 18; lateral-line scales 50-55; scales ctenoid on nape, a narrow band dorsally on body, and posteriorly on body, cycloid elsewhere; gill rakers 4-7 + 10-13; body depth 3.1-3.5 in standard length; mouth strongly oblique, the lower jaw projecting, the maxilla reaching to below middle of eye; a narrow villiform band of teeth in jaws, the upper jaw with an outer row of larger teeth, approaching canine proportions at symphysis, the lower jaw with an inner row of larger teeth; rostral pores on snout absent or minute; 2 pairs of pores on chin; caudal fin usually truncate, but may vary from slightly rhomboid to slightly emarginate; swimbladder with about 30 complexly branched appendages on each side; silvery grey dorsally, shading to silvery on sides ventrally; a blackish blotch sometimes present on opercle; outer part of spinous portion of dorsal fin blackish. Attains about 25 cm. Known from China and the Philippines to Indonesia, India (type locality, Malabar coast), and the Arabian Gulf. *Pennahia macrophthalma* (Bleeker) is a synonym (Sasaki, 1994).

SPOTTED CROAKER
Protonibea diacantha (Lacepède, 1802)

Dorsal rays X-XI,22-24; anal rays II,7-8; pectoral rays 18-19; lateral-line scales about 51 scales strongly ctenoid except on snout and below eye where cycloid; gill rakers 5-6 + 6-8; body depth moderately elongate, the depth 3.3-4.2 in standard length; mouth slightly inferior and slightly oblique, the maxilla nearly reaching a vertical at rear edge of eye; upper jaw with an outer row of large broadly spaced conical teeth and irregular inner rows of small teeth; lower jaw with an inner row of slightly enlarged conical teeth and an outer row of small teeth; snout with 3 small rostral pores and 5 marginal pores, the outer pair notching the snout edge; chin with 3 pairs of pores, the most anterior close to symphysis; caudal fin strongly rhomboid; second anal spine 3 in head length; swimbladder carrot-shaped with 16-20 pairs of arborescent appendages; whitish with five dark brown bars and numerous small black spots on upper half of body; dorsal and caudal fins black-spotted; pectoral fins, lower half of caudal fin, and outer part of anal and pelvic fins blackish (dark bars and spots less evident on large adults). Reported to 150 cm by Talwar and Kacker (1984) who wrote that it is the most esteemed table fish among the offshore sciaenids of India. Ranges from southern

602. *Pennahia anea*, 22.8 cm (J. Randall)

603. *Protonibea diacantha*, 26.5 cm (J. Randall)

604. *Umbrina ronchus* (J. Hoover)

Japan and coast of China south to Queensland and west along the southern Asian continent to the Arabian Gulf; the author obtained specimens by trawling off Kuwait.

OBLIQUEBANDED CROAKER
Umbrina ronchus Valenciennes, 1843

Dorsal rays XI,23-26; anal rays II,7; pectoral rays 18; lateral-line scales 49-51; scales mostly ctenoid; gill rakers 5-6 + 9-11; body depth 2.9-3.5 in standard length; mouth small, inferior, and slightly oblique; teeth villiform; snout with five upper and five marginal pores; chin with a short rigid barbel having a pore at tip and two pores to each side; second anal spine 3.0-3.5 in head

605. *U. ronchus*, juvenile, 15.9 cm (J. Randall)

length; caudal fin slightly rhomboid (in juveniles and subadults) to slightly emarginate (in large adults); swimbladder carrot-shaped without lateral appendages; silvery with oblique wavy dark bands on body, continuing onto postorbital head (bands progressively less distinct with growth); fins dark grey, the pelvics and outer part of anal fin nearly black. Able to change its colour from silvery to almost black. Reported to 70 cm. Western Mediterranean to Angola (including the Canary Islands, the type locality), South Africa to the Arabian Gulf (though not recorded from some intermediate coastal areas or the Red Sea); usually seen over sandy bottoms, but may be near reefs. *U. canariensis* Valenciennes has been reported from Oman, but the author has not examined any Omani specimens; supposedly it differs from *U. ronchus* in having 25-29 dorsal soft rays and a longer second anal spine.

THREADFINS
FAMILY POLYNEMIDAE

The pectoral fins of this family are the most distinctive feature; they are low on the body and divisible into an upper part with the rays joined by membrane and a lower part of three to seven separate rays (in one species 14 or 15); the rays are very long in juveniles, becoming relatively shorter with growth. Other family characters include an obtusely conical, overhanging snout; mouth ventral, near-horizontal, and large, the maxilla extending far beyond eye; adipose eyelid (firm transparent gelatinous tissue) covering eye; teeth in villiform bands in jaws and on palatines (sometimes on vomer); two well-separated dorsal fins, the first with VII-VIII spines, the second with an initial spine and 11-15 soft rays; caudal fin deeply forked to lunate; pelvic fins subabdominal, with I,5 rays; scales weakly ctenoid, extending onto head; small scales covering most of second dorsal, anal, and caudal fins; lateral line complete, continuing onto caudal fin, usually with a branch in each lobe; gill openings wide, the gill membranes separate and not attached to isthmus; branchiostegal rays 7; vertebrae 24-25; bones of the skull with a well-developed muciferous system similar to that of the Sciaenidae. Threadfins are shallow-water fishes which occur mainly in tropical continental seas, but some extend their distributions to warm temperate areas, and a few range to oceanic islands; they are usually found on sand or mud substrata; some occur mainly in estuaries and may penetrate freshwater. The lower separate pectoral rays are held against the ventral side of the body when actively swimming, but they can be extended outward and forward to make contact with the bottom when searching for food. Limited data suggest that the principal food consists of benthic crustaceans, polychaete worms, and occasionally small fishes. The family contains seven genera and about 33 species.

FOURFINGER THREADFIN
Eleutheronema tetradactylum (Shaw, 1804)

Dorsal rays VIII + I,13-15; anal rays II,15-17; pectoral rays 16-17 + 4 free lower rays; lateral-line scales 78-80; body elongate, the depth 3.6-4.0 in standard length; head length 3.3-3.9 in standard length; lips absent except for a short lower lip near corner of mouth; teeth extending onto outer part of jaws; a triangular patch of small teeth on vomer; posterior margin of preopercle serrate; no swimbladder; caudal fin large and deeply forked; bluish to greenish grey dorsally, becoming silvery on sides and ventrally; fins whitish to yellowish, the dorsal and caudal fins blackish on margins, especially the leading edges; a broad dusky streak on pectorals, the free rays white. Often reported to 200 cm, but Talwar and Kacker (1984) list the maximum length as about 4 feet (120 cm). Arabian Gulf in continental waters to western Pacific where it ranges from Taiwan to Queensland; inhabits muddy inshore environments and will enter rivers.

BLACKSPOT THREADFIN
Polydactylus sextarius Bloch and Schneider, 1801

Dorsal rays VIII + I,12-13; anal rays II-III,12-13; pectoral rays 13-15 + 6 lower free rays; lateral-line scales 44-50; a short spine at front of lateral line; body depth 2.9-3.1 in standard length; head length 2.9-3.3 in standard length; lower lip present except anteriorly; teeth in jaws not extending onto outer surface; vomerine teeth absent; posterior margin of preopercle serrate; swimbladder simple and small; caudal fin deeply forked; silvery with some golden iridescence; a blackish spot larger than pupil on lateral line above posterior end of operculum; fins whitish to yellowish, the pectorals often dusky to blackish, the lower free rays white. Reaches 30 cm. Papua New Guinea to Arabian Gulf, south to Cape Province, South Africa; not recorded from the Red Sea. Although usually found along sandy shores and estuaries, it has been taken as deep as 60 m in trawls in the Bay of Bengal.

606. *Eleutheronema tetradactylum*, 21.6 cm (J. Randall)

607. *Polydactylus sextarius*, 21.5 cm (J. Randall)

MULLETS
FAMILY MUGILIDAE

Mullets are moderately elongate and little-compressed, except posteriorly; the head is somewhat depressed, the interorbital space broad and scaled. The mouth is small, terminal to slightly inferior, usually shaped like an inverted V when viewed from the front, the tip of the upper lip of most species with a fleshy symphyseal knob; the preorbital is serrate; the teeth are minute or absent, usually loosely attached on the lips. Many species have an adipose eyelid partially covering the eye anteriorly and posteriorly. Most have a gizzard-like stomach; the intestine is very long. There are two widely-spaced, short-based dorsal fins, the first of IV spines (anterior three spines close together at the base, the fourth spine more distant); the caudal fin varies in shape from truncate to deeply emarginate or forked; the pelvic fins of I,5 rays lie well behind the pectorals. The scales are moderately large and cycloid or finely ctenoid; there is no single lateral line on the side of the body; however, most scales on the body have a longitudinal groove with a neuromast. Vertebrae 24-26. The colour is silvery, the back generally dark silvery grey. Mullets are shallow-water fishes found in all tropical to temperate seas. Many species occur in brackish habitats, and a few such as *Chelon abu* (Heckel) of the Tigris-Euphrates and other southern Asian river systems live in freshwater, returning to the sea only for spawning. Mullets often form schools, and some are prone to leap free of the surface, a habit which may enable them to escape an approaching seine. These fishes have a branchial filter-feeding mechanism involving their numerous, slender gill rakers. Typically they feed on fine algal and detrital material from the surface of bottom sediments; they may be seen expelling the inorganic material from their gill openings. Some ingest algal scums from the surface. There may be opportunistic feeding on small benthic crustaceans or worms or on zooplankton. Many mullets are of commercial importance, and a few species have been successfully cultured. Opinions vary as to the phylogenetic position of the mullet family. Senou and Okiyama (MS) revised the family; they are followed here in placing the Mugilidae in the Perciformes. They recognised two subfamilies, the Agonostominae with three genera and seven species, and the Mugilinae with 14 genera and 64 species.

608. School of *Crenimugil crenilabis* (J. Hoover)

KLUNZINGER'S MULLET
Chelon klunzingeri (Day, 1888)

Dorsal rays IV + 9; anal rays III,9; pectoral rays 15-17; longitudinal scale series 32-38; scales finely ctenoid; body depth 3.4-3.7 in standard length; head length 3.35-3.55 in standard length; a median predorsal ridge extending to above opercle; adipose eyelid covering about half of iris; mouth terminal, the posterior part of maxilla exposed when mouth closed, its end extending to or slightly posterior to a vertical at front edge of eye; edge of upper lip with a single row of tiny teeth (true of other species of *Chelon*); origin of first dorsal fin equidistant to tip of snout and caudal-fin base; origin of second dorsal fin over end of anterior quarter of anal fin; caudal fin forked; pectoral fins without a distinct pointed axillary scale, the fins usually just reaching a vertical at origin of first dorsal fin; greenish grey dorsally, soon shading to silvery on sides and ventrally; golden iridescence often present dorsally on head; posterior edge of caudal fin narrowly blackish. Attains 20 cm. Arabian Gulf to India. Senou et al. (1987) showed that there is a complex of three species of mullets characterized by a distinct predorsal ridge: *C. carinata* (Valenciennes) from the Red Sea, *C. klunzingeri*, and *C. affinis* from China, Taiwan, and Japan.

609. *Chelon klunzingeri*, 19.8 cm (J. Randall)

LARGESCALE MULLET
Chelon macrolepis (Smith, 1849)

Dorsal rays IV + 8-9 (rarely 8); anal rays III,9; pectoral rays 15-18 (rarely 15 or 18); longitudinal scale series 30-34; scales finely ctenoid; body depth 3.65-4.25 in standard length; head length 3.75-4.15 in standard length; adipose eyelid covering little or none of iris; slender part of maxilla showing between corner of mouth and serrate notched part of preorbital bone when mouth closed, its posterior end not reaching anterior edge of eye; origin of first dorsal fin closer to caudal-fin base than tip of snout; origin of second dorsal fin over middle of anal-fin base; caudal fin forked; pectoral fins without an obvious axillary scale, their tips not approaching a vertical at origin of first dorsal fin; greenish grey dorsally, shading to silvery on sides and ventrally; posterior edge of caudal fin dusky; a yellow bar often present at base of pectoral fins. Attains 40 cm. Indo-Pacific, including Red Sea and Gulf of Oman; enters freshwater.

PERSIAN MULLET
Chelon persicus Senou, Randall, and Okiyama, 1995

Dorsal rays IV + 9; anal rays III,8-9; pectoral rays 15-17; longitudinal scale series 34-36 (most often 36); scales weakly ctenoid; predorsal scales with a single elongate groove; body depth 3.6-4.2 in standard length; head length 4.0-4.3 in standard length; no adipose eyelid; maxilla hooked downward at corner of mouth, its posterior tip reaching beyond corner of mouth and remaining exposed when mouth closed; edge of lower lip thin and projecting horizontally forward; origin of first dorsal fin closer to caudal-fin base than front of snout; origin of second dorsal fin over middle or slightly anterior to middle of base of anal fin; caudal fin slightly forked; silvery green dorsally, the edges of the scales dark, shading to silvery on sides and ventrally; caudal fin and second dorsal fin with a blackish margin, broadest posteriorly on caudal. Reaches 30 cm. Known at the present time only from Bahrain and Qatar in the Arabian Gulf.

610. *Chelon macrolepis*, 23.8 cm (J. Randall)

611. *Chelon persicus*, 26.5 cm (J. Randall)

235

GREENBACK MULLET
Chelon subviridis (Valenciennes, 1836)

Dorsal rays IV + 9; anal rays III,8-10 (rarely 8 or 10); pectoral rays 14-17; longitudinal scale series 27-33; scales finely ctenoid; body depth 3.45-4.25 in standard length; head length 3.85-4.15; adipose eyelid covering about half of iris; posterior end of maxilla nearly or just reaching anterior edge of eye; origin of first dorsal fin slightly closer to base of caudal fin than tip of snout; origin of second dorsal fin over anterior third to half of anal-fin base; caudal fin emarginate; axillary scale of pectoral fins rudimentary, the fin tips not approaching a vertical at origin of first dorsal fin; silvery grey dorsally, the edges of the scales green, shading to silvery on sides and ventrally, with a linear pattern from a dusky spot on each scale; distal margin of second dorsal and caudal fins broadly blackish. Reaches 30 cm. Arabian Gulf to western Pacific. *Mugil dussumieri* Valenciennes is a synonym.

FRINGELIP MULLET
Crenimugil crenilabis (Forsskål, 1775)

Dorsal rays IV + 8-10 (usually 9); anal rays III,8-9 (rarely 8); pectoral rays 16-18; longitudinal scale series 36-41; scales cycloid with membraneous edge; body depth 3.5-3.95 in standard length; head length 3.7-4.0 in standard length; adipose eyelid absent; maxilla concealed when mouth closed, its posterior edge anterior to a vertical at front edge of eye; upper lip broad anteriorly, its lower part with a fringe of small papillae (absent in very small juveniles); lower lip finely folded with a forward-directed fringe of flattened papillae; no teeth on edge of lips; origin of first dorsal fin slightly closer to caudal-fin base than snout tip; origin of second dorsal fin slightly posterior to origin of anal fin; caudal fin deeply emarginate; an elongate axillary scale above base of pectoral fins; tips of pectoral fins nearly or just reaching a vertical at origin of first dorsal fin; silvery olive-grey dorsally, shading to silvery below; caudal fin grey-blue with a blackish posterior border; pectoral fins yellowish with a prominent black spot at upper base. Largest specimen examined, 55 cm. Indo-Pacific (but not the Hawaiian Islands for which there is an erroneous record); usually seen in small schools inshore, often over coral reefs; juveniles may be found in tidepools. Spawning occurs in large aggregations near the surface at night (Helfrich and Allen, 1975).

SQUARETAIL MULLET
Ellochelon vaigiensis (Quoy and Gaimard, 1825)

Dorsal rays IV + 8-10 (rarely 10); anal rays III,8; pectoral rays 15-18 (rarely 15 or 18); longitudinal scale series 25-29; scales finely ctenoid, the sensory groove on scales long; body moderately elongate, the depth 3.6-4.2 in standard length; head length 3.5-3.8 in standard length; head broad; interorbital space only slightly convex except at edges; no adipose eyelid; a little of maxilla exposed when mouth closed, reaching to below anterior margin of eye; edge of upper lip with a row of extremely small teeth; lower lip thin, the edge directed forward; origin of first dorsal fin closer to caudal-fin base than tip of snout; base of second dorsal fin short, but fin distinctly higher than first dorsal; origin of second dorsal fin over posterior third of anal-fin base; caudal fin slightly emarginate to nearly truncate; no pectoral axillary scale; pectoral fins approaching but not reaching below origin of first dorsal fin; silvery grey dorsally, the edges of the scales dark, shading to silvery below; narrow dark stripes on midside of body along centres of scale rows; caudal fin yellow to yellowish; pectoral fins largely black. Reported to attain 55 cm. Indo-Pacific; an inshore species usually seen in schools in protected waters such as lagoons or mangrove sloughs; tolerant of low salinity.

612. *Chelon subviridis*, 26.6 cm (J. Randall)

613. *Crenimugil crenilabis* (J. Hoover)

614. *Ellochelon vaigiensis*, 35.7 cm (J. Randall)

WEDGESNOUT MULLET
Moolgarda cunnesius (Valenciennes, 1836)

Dorsal rays IV + 9; anal rays III,9; pectoral rays 16-17 (usually 17); longitudinal scale series 32-39; scales cycloid with a fringed membranous edge; body depth 3.7-4.0 in standard length; head length 3.6-3.9 in standard length; snout slightly wedge-shaped when viewed from above; adipose eyelid well developed, covering most of iris; maxilla exposed when mouth closed, its posterior end below or slightly posterior to anterior edge of eye; edge of upper lip a little fleshy; edge of lower lip thin, projecting forward nearly horizontally near symphysis; minute teeth along edge of lips (fewer visible on upper lip); origin of dorsal fin nearer snout than caudal-fin base; first and second dorsal fins about equal in height; origin of second dorsal fin below middle of anal-fin base; caudal fin moderately forked; pectoral fins reaching posterior to a vertical at base of third dorsal spine; pectoral axillary scale 2.8-3.5 in fin length; silvery blue-green dorsally, shading to silvery on sides and ventrally; a blackish spot at upper base of pectoral fins, becoming a streak in axil; outer edge of dorsal fins blackish; caudal fin slightly yellowish, blackish distally on upper and posterior margins. Said to attain 35 cm, but none seen by author approach this size. Red Sea and Arabian Gulf south to Transkei, South Africa and east to the western Pacific, ranging there from Japan to Queensland. Reported by van der Elst (1981) as common in coastal lagoons of Natal that infrequently open to the sea; feeds mainly on organic detritus.

LONGFIN MULLET
Moolgarda pedaraki (Valenciennes, 1836)

Dorsal rays IV + 9; anal rays III,9; pectoral rays 17-19; longitudinal scale series 33-37; scales cycloid with membraneous edge; body depth 3.3-3.65 in standard length; head length 3.6-4.0 in standard length; no adipose

615. *Moolgarda cunnesius*, 12.5 cm (J. Randall)

616. *Moolgarda pedaraki*, 20.4 cm (J. Randall)

eyelid; maxilla concealed when mouth closed, its end a little posterior to anterior edge of eye; edges of lips thin; juveniles with a row of tiny teeth on their edge, disappearing with growth; origin of dorsal fin equidistant to snout tip and caudal-fin base; second dorsal fin 1.5 times or more higher than first dorsal, its origin over or slightly posterior to origin of anal fin; second dorsal and anal fins strongly falcate; caudal fin deeply emarginate, the caudal concavity 1.2-1.8 in head length; pectoral fins nearly as long as head, their tips reaching a little posterior to origin of first dorsal fin; pectoral axillary scale about one-third length of fin; silvery blue-grey on back, silvery on sides and ventrally; pectoral fins yellowish with a black spot at upper base. Reaches about 60 cm. Coast of East Africa south to Knysna, South Africa, east to the western Pacific; Arabian Gulf

record by Kuronuma and Abe (1986). *Mugil buchanani* Bleeker is a synonym (H. Senou, pers. comm.).

BLUESPOT MULLET
Moolgarda seheli (Forsskål, 1775)

Dorsal rays IV + 8-9 (rarely 8); anal rays III,8-9 (rarely 8); pectoral rays 17-19; longitudinal scale series 38-42; scales cycloid with a crenulate to serrate membraneous edge; body depth 3.5-3.9 in standard length; head length 3.6-4.0 in standard length; no adipose eyelid; maxilla concealed when mouth closed, its posterior end not reaching or just reaching a vertical at front edge of eye; margin of lips thin with a series of tiny teeth; origin of first dorsal fin about equidistant to snout tip and caudal-fin base; second dorsal fin only slightly higher than first dorsal, its origin over or a little posterior to anal fin origin; second dorsal and anal fins falcate; caudal fin forked, the caudal concavity 1.8-2.7 in head length; pectoral fins usually reaching to below origin of first dorsal fin; pectoral axillary scale long, about 38% length of fin; silvery grey dorsally, silvery on sides and ventrally, with narrow dark stripes, one per longitudinal scale row; median fins bluish grey; pectoral fins pale yellowish with a deep blue to black spot at upper base. Attains 50 cm. Red Sea to South Africa, east to the Mariana Islands and Samoa. An inshore schooling species which enters brackish and freshwater habitats.

617. *Moolgarda seheli*, 24.6 cm (J. Randall)

THICKLIP MULLET
Oedalechilus labiosus (Valenciennes, 1836)

Dorsal rays IV + 8-9; anal rays III,9; pectoral rays 16-18; longitudinal scale series 32-37; scales finely ctenoid; body depth 3.3-3.7 in standard length; head length 4.0-4.5 in standard length; no adipose eyelid; preorbital bone deeply notched, only the rounded ventral edge serrate; a slender posterior part of maxilla exposed below preorbital when mouth closed, its posterior end reaching slightly posterior to front edge of eye; mouth ventral to thick overhanging upper lip; base of upper lip with two margins, each bearing a dense series of low horny ridges, and separated by a deep groove, the lower margin divisible into four lobes; lower lip forward-projecting, with a similar series of horny ridges, also divisible into four lobes; origin of first dorsal fin clearly closer to caudal-fin base than tip of snout; origin of second dorsal fin over posterior quarter of anal fin; caudal fin emarginate, the caudal concavity about 4-5 in head length; pectoral fins longer than head but not reaching a vertical at origin of first dorsal fin; silvery grey dorsally, soon shading to silvery on side and ventrally; a small black spot at upper base of pectoral fins. Reaches about 25 cm. Red Sea and Gulf of Oman east to the Marshall Islands; the photograph of the small school in the family account above was taken off Musandam. More common in insular than continental areas; usually seen in small schools over coral reefs.

618. *Oedalechilus labiosus* (J. Randall)

GOATFISHES
FAMILY MULLIDAE

The most distinctive feature of the goatfishes is the pair of long barbels on the chin. Only the species of the beryciform family Polymixiidae have a similar pair of chin barbels, but these fishes are easily distinguished by their blunt snout and single dorsal fin. Goatfishes have two well-separated dorsal fins, the first of VI to VIII spines (the initial spine may be very small), the second of 9 or 10 (usually 9) soft rays; the anal fin has a small initial spine and 6 or 7 soft rays; the caudal fin is forked. The body is moderately elongate and compressed, the snout relatively long and somewhat pointed. The scales are finely ctenoid and moderately large, 27-38 in the lateral line. There are five genera, of which three occur in Oman waters. The genera are distinguished primarily on dentition; the species of *Mulloidichthys* and *Parupeneus* lack teeth on the roof of the mouth, whereas those of *Upeneus* have small teeth on the vomer and palatines. The species of *Mulloidichthys* and *Upeneus* have bands of villiform teeth in the jaws in contrast to those of *Parupeneus* which have a single row of moderately large conical teeth. *Upeneus* spp. generally live on open mud or sand bottoms, in contrast to those of *Mulloidichthys* and *Parupeneus* which are usually seen in the vicinity of reefs. Goatfishes are carnivorous, feeding mainly on invertebrates, particularly worms and crustaceans but also brittle stars, small heart urchins, and small molluscs, that live in the bottom sediment. They use their barbels, which possess chemosensory organs, to probe into the bottom in search of prey. Once food is found, they thrust their snouts into the sediment to capture it. The large *Parupeneus cyclostomus*, which has very long barbels, often feeds on small fishes. It has been observed to insert its barbels into small holes and crevices in the reef in an attempt to frighten out small fishes. When not searching for food, the barbels of goatfishes are held back between the lower part of the gill covers (except males in courtship who rapidly wriggle their barbels). Night colouration is usually dominated by large irregular red blotches.

619. School of *Parupeneus macronemus*, about 23 cm (J. Randall)

238

YELLOWSTRIPE GOATFISH
Mulloidichthys flavolineatus (Lacepède, 1801)

Dorsal rays VIII + 9; anal rays I,7; pectoral rays 16-17; lateral-line scales usually 34-35; gill rakers 7-9 + 18-22; body depth 3.8-4.8 in standard length; head length 3.0-3.5 in standard length; snout length 1.9-2.2 in head length; barbels 1.25-1.55 in head; silvery white with a yellow stripe on body at level of eye; often a blackish spot in yellow stripe below first dorsal fin; fins whitish, the caudal often yellowish. Largest specimen examined, 36.5 cm; reported to 40 cm. Indo-Pacific; occasional in the Gulf of Oman, but rare in the south; not yet recorded from the Arabian Gulf. Frequently seen in semistationary aggregations during the day. *Mulloides samoensis* Günther is a synonym.

YELLOWFIN GOATFISH
Mulloidichthys vanicolensis (Valenciennes, 1831)

Dorsal rays VIII + 9; anal rays I,7; pectoral rays 16-17; lateral-line scales 35-37; gill rakers 8-10 + 22-25; body depth 3.5-4.3 in standard length; head length 3.05-3.45 in standard length; snout length 2.2-2.6 in head length; barbels 1.2-1.5 in head; yellowish dorsally, the scale edges darker than centres, shading to white or pink ventrally, with a pale blue-edged yellow stripe from eye to base of caudal fin; fins yellow. A second colour form (see illustration), which occurs in the western Indian Ocean, has the blue edges of the yellow stripe much brighter, a third narrower blue stripe usually evident ventrally, and often a longitudinal row of small blue spots dorsally on body. A sample of both colour forms collected in southern Oman failed to reveal any differences in counts or measurements. Both colour phases may at times be seen in the same aggregation. The author has observed the form with prominent blue stripes schooling with the Bluestriped Snapper (*Lutjanus kasmira*) off Kenya, suggesting that the goatfish is mimicking the snapper, as proposed for *M. mimicus* and the same snapper in the Marquesas and Line Islands (Randall and Guézé, 1980). Largest specimen examined, 38 cm, from Muscat. Indo-Pacific; more common in Oman waters than *M. flavolineatus*; also not reported from the Arabian Gulf. Closely related to *M. martinicus* of the western Atlantic and *M. dentatus* of the eastern Pacific. Stepien et al. (1994) documented differences in the populations of *M. vanicolensis* in the Indian Ocean and Pacific but concluded they are not at the specific level.

DASH-DOT GOATFISH
Parupeneus barberinus (Lacepède, 1801)

Dorsal rays VIII + 9; anal rays I,7; pectoral rays 16-18; lateral-line scales 27-28 (true of other species of the genus); gill rakers 6-7 + 20-24; body depth 3.35-3.7 in standard length; head length 2.6-3.0 in standard length; snout length 1.5-2.05 in head length (snout relatively longer in larger fish); barbels 1.4-1.6 in head; pale tan, the scale edges darker, shading to whitish ventrally, with a dark brown to brownish red stripe from front of snout through eye to below end of second dorsal fin; a dark brown to brownish red spot as large or larger than eye at base of caudal fin. The largest of the goatfishes; reaches at least 50 cm. Indo-Pacific; usually seen over sand or sand-rubble bottoms near reefs. Observed in Oman only in the south.

620. *Mulloidichthys flavolineatus*, about 21 cm (J. Randall)

621. *Mulloidichthys vanicolensis*, large school of adults showing different colour patterns (J. Hoover)

622. *Parupeneus barberinus*, about 28 cm (J. Randall)

623. *Parupeneus barberinus*, night colour, about 23 cm (J. Randall)

DOUBLEBAR GOATFISH
Parupeneus bifasciatus (Lacepède, 1801)

Dorsal rays VIII + 9; anal rays I,7; pectoral rays 15-16 (usually 16); gill rakers 7-9 + 27-30; body depth 2.7-3.35 in standard length (larger fish, in general, deeper bodied); head length 2.9-3.3 in standard length; dorsal profile of snout slightly concave, its length 1.7-2.05 in head length; barbels 1.6-1.9 in head; yellowish grey to reddish with two broad blackish bars on body, one below each dorsal fin; a faint third bar sometimes present dorsally on caudal peduncle; a dusky patch usually present on head, partially enclosing eye and extending below and anterior to eye. Reported to 35 cm. Indo-Pacific (slightly different in colour in the Pacific); rare in Oman (seen only in the south). *P. trifasciatus* (Lacepède) is a synonym.

GOLDSADDLE GOATFISH
Parupeneus cyclostomus (Lacepède, 1801)

Dorsal rays VIII + 9; anal rays I,7; pectoral rays 15-17 (usually 16); gill rakers 6-7 + 22-26; body depth 3.3-3.9 in standard length; head length 2.85-3.1 in standard length; snout length 1.6-1.9 in head length; barbels long, reaching to or beyond posterior end of head; two colour phases, one yellowish grey with blue markings on scales and a yellow saddle-like spot on caudal peduncle, the other all yellow with a brighter yellow peduncular spot. Reported to 50 cm. Indo-Pacific. Unusual among goatfishes in its heavy feeding on fishes (about 70% of the diet). *P. chryserydros* (Lacepède) and *P. luteus* (Valenciennes) are synonyms.

CINNABAR GOATFISH
Parupeneus heptacanthus (Lacepède, 1801)

Dorsal rays VIII + 9; anal rays I,7; pectoral rays 15-17 (usually 16); gill rakers 6-7

624. *Parupeneus bifasciatus*, about 22 cm (J. Randall)

625. *Parupeneus cyclostomus* (J. Hoover)

+ 20-23 (rarely 20 or 23); body depth 3.15-3.4 in standard length; head length 2.9-3.2 in standard length; snout length 1.75-2.1 in head; barbels 1.2-1.35 in head; posterior end of maxilla symmetrically convex (in other Omani species of the genus, there is a dorso-posterior lobe to the maxilla); yellowish to pink dorsally, the scales with a pale blue spot, shading to silvery white on sides and ventrally; a small reddish brown spot usually present just below lateral line beneath seventh and eighth dorsal spines. Largest specimen examined, 36 cm. Red Sea, coast of East Africa, and Arabian Gulf to the Marshall Islands; usually found over silty sand substrata or seagrass beds. *P. cinnarabinus* (Cuvier) and *P. pleurospilos* (Bleeker) are synonyms.

626. *Parupeneus heptacanthus*, about 22 cm (J. Randall)

INDIAN GOATFISH
Parupeneus indicus (Shaw, 1803)

Dorsal rays VIII + 9; anal rays I,7; pectoral rays 15-17 (usually 16); gill rakers 5-7 + 19-21; body depth 3.3-3.75 in standard length; head length 2.95-3.2 in standard length; snout length 1.65-2.0 in head length; barbels 1.3-1.55 in head; grey dorsally, the scale edges darker, shading to white ventrally, with a large horizontally elongate yellow spot centred on lateral line in middle of body and a black spot larger than eye posteriorly on caudal peduncle, centred slightly above midlateral line. Reaches at least 35 cm. East Africa to the Samoa Islands; observed in Oman only in the south where not common; usually seen over silty sand or seagrass bottoms.

LONGBARBEL GOATFISH
Parupeneus macronemus (Lacepède, 1801)

Dorsal rays VIII + 9; anal rays I,7; pectoral rays 15-17 (usually 16); gill rakers 7-9 + 27-30; body depth 3.35-3.7 in standard length; head length 2.85-3.25 in standard length; snout 1.75-1.9 in head length; barbels long, 1.1-1.25 in head; last dorsal and anal rays prolonged; tan, the scale edges darker, with a blackish stripe from eye to front of caudal peduncle, followed by a black spot larger than eye on caudal-fin base; region between stripe and spot paler than rest of body; ventral third of head and body usually lavender to magenta; a dusky band from eye to front of snout; basal part of second dorsal fin blackish. Largest specimen collected by author, 29.5 cm, from Bahrain. Red Sea and coast of East Africa to Indonesia and the Philippines; common in the Gulf of Oman, but not seen in the south.

PEARLY GOATFISH
Parupeneus margaritatus Randall and Guézé, 1984

Dorsal rays VIII + 9; anal rays I,7; pectoral rays 15-17 (usually 16); gill rakers 6-8 + 22-25; body depth 3.5-4.35 in standard length; head length 2.75-3.0 in standard length; snout length 1.75-2.3 in head length (relatively longer in larger fish); barbels 1.45-1.65 in head; grey to tan dorsally, the scale edges darker, shading to lighter grey or mottled red on sides and ventrally, the scales on and below lateral line with a small pale blue spot; a horizontally elongate whitish spot anterodorsally on caudal peduncle; an indistinct dark brown to reddish brown stripe from front of snout through eye, ending anteriorly on body. Largest specimen, 23 cm. Known from the Arabian Gulf to Masirah Island on the central Oman coast; the most common species of the genus in the Arabian Gulf and Gulf of Oman.

627. *Parupeneus indicus*, subadult (J. Hoover)

628. *Parupeneus macronemus*, about 22 cm (J. Randall)

629. *Parupeneus margaritatus*, about 19 cm (J. Randall)

241

SIDESPOT GOATFISH
Parupeneus pleurostigma (Bennett, 1830)

Dorsal rays VIII + 9; anal rays I,7; pectoral rays 15-17 (usually 16); gill rakers 6-8 + 22-25; body depth 3.45-3.95 in standard length; head length 2.95-3.1 in standard length; snout length 1.7-2.1 in head length; barbels 1.3-1.55 in head; whitish to pink with a black spot about four scales in width on lateral line beneath posterior part of first dorsal fin; behind this a large oval white spot, followed by a dusky area; basal part of second dorsal fin blackish. Attains 33 cm. Indo-Pacific; rare in Oman waters (only a few individuals observed along the southern coast).

630. *Parupeneus pleurostigma*, about 17 cm (J. Randall)

ROSY GOATFISH
Parupeneus rubescens (Lacepède, 1801)

Dorsal rays VIII + 9; anal rays I,7; pectoral rays 15-17 (nearly always 16); gill rakers 6-7 + 21-24; body depth 2.95-3.5 in standard length; head length 2.8-3.15 in standard length; snout length 1.8-2.15 in head length; barbels 1.3-1.6 in head; tan to light reddish brown dorsally, the scale edges darker, shading to whitish or light red ventrally, with a white-edged dark stripe from front of snout through eye, gradually fading to about middle of body; a very large saddle-like black spot dorsally on caudal peduncle, preceded by a pale red to white spot. Largest specimen, 41 cm, from Réunion. Western Indian Ocean including the Red Sea and Gulf of Oman; usually found on silty sand, seagrass or weedy bottoms. *P. fraterculus* (Valenciennes), *P. dispilurus* (Playfair and Günther), and *P. pleurospilus* (Playfair and Günther) are synonyms.

631. *Parupeneus rubescens* (J. Hoover)

OCHREBAND GOATFISH
Upeneus sundaicus (Bleeker, 1855)

Dorsal rays VIII + 9; anal rays I,7; pectoral rays 14-15 (usually 14); gill rakers 4-6 + 14-16; body moderately elongate, the depth 3.55-4.0 in standard length; head length 3.3-3.65 in standard length; snout length 2.05-2.5 in head length; barbels 1.35-1.7 in head length; first dorsal spine minute; second dorsal spine longest, 1.1-1.3 in head length; bronze to silvery green dorsally, shading to silvery white on sides and ventrally, with a narrow brownish yellow stripe on body at level of upper part of eye containing three darker zones, one under each dorsal fin and one below anterior caudal peduncle; lobes of caudal fin without dark cross bands or with faint irregular narrow ones; lower lobe of caudal fin with a broad dusky posterior border (broader toward midline), this part containing the faint dark bars, when present; fins yellowish; barbels yellow; peritoneum pale. Largest specimens examined, 17.2 cm. Arabian Gulf to northern Australia, north to Philippines. *U. luzonius* Jordan and Seale appears to be a synonym.

632. *Upeneus sundaicus*, 10 cm (J. Randall)

GILDED GOATFISH
Upeneus doriae (Günther, 1869)

Dorsal rays VIII + 9, the first spine very small; anal rays I,7; pectoral rays 16-17 (usually 16); lateral-line scales 33-34; gill rakers 8-9 + 22-24; body depth 3.2-3.7 in standard length; head length 2.9-3.3 in standard length; snout length 2.4-2.7 in head length; barbels 1.6-1.85 in head; silvery with orange, pink, or blue iridescence on back, shading to silvery white ventrally, with a narrow yellow stripe on body at level of upper part of eye; tip of first dorsal fin broadly dusky yellow, with three white and two yellow cross bands below; caudal fin grey with a whitish posterior margin (becoming submarginal to a narrow blackish border centrally). Attains 20 cm. Known only from the Arabian Gulf and Gulf of Oman. Gallotti (1971) mistakenly regarded *U. doriae* as a synonym of *U. moluccensis*. Actually, it is a close relative of *U. sulphureus* Cuvier, the latter differing in having 34-36 lateral-line scales, 18-22 (usually 20-21) lower-limb gill rakers, longer barbels, a second (though less distinct) yellow stripe on side of body at level of pectoral fins, and a black-tipped first dorsal fin. Previous records of *U. sulphureus* from the Arabian Gulf (as by Kuronuma and Abe, 1986: pl. 22) appear to be *U. doriae*. Blegvad (1944: pl. 7, fig. 1) misidentified the species as *Mulloidichthys auriflamma*.

633. *Upeneus doriae*, 19.7 cm (J. Randall)

634. *Upeneus pori* (J. Hoover)

635. *Upeneus tragula*, about 13 cm (J. Randall)

POR'S GOATFISH
Upeneus pori Ben-Tuvia and Golani, 1989

Dorsal rays VII + 9; anal rays I,7; pectoral rays 13-15 (usually 14); lateral-line scales 28-30; gill rakers 6-8 + 18-21; body elongate, the depth 4.1-4.6 in standard length; head length 3.25-3.6 in standard length; snout length 2.35-2.65 in head length; barbels 1.45-1.8 in head; no small first dorsal spine (first spine longest); bluish to greenish grey, shading to silvery white ventrally, each scale dorsally and on side of body with a red to brown blotch; a red bar below eye often present; barbels white to yellow; upper lobe of caudal fin of adults with five or six transverse reddish brown bands; ventral border of lower lobe white with seven to ten short transverse reddish black bands, the rest of lobe dark reddish brown with a few white flecks; dorsal, anal, and pelvic fins with alternating orangish brown and white bands or rows of spots (the white mainly on rays). Largest specimen, 19 cm. Known only from the Red Sea to the south coast of Oman; has entered the Mediterranean Sea via the Suez Canal and is now abundant in the eastern part.

FRECKLED GOATFISH
Upeneus tragula Richardson, 1846

Dorsal rays VIII + 9, the first spine very small; anal rays I,7; pectoral rays 13-14 (usually 13); lateral-line scales 28-29; gill rakers 5-7 + 15-18 (usually 6 + 16 or 17); body moderately elongate, the depth 3.9-4.6 in standard length; head length 3.4-3.6 in standard length; snout length 2.25-2.65 in head; barbels 1.45-1.7 in head; a reddish brown to blackish stripe from front of snout through eye to upper base of caudal fin (four or five zones along stripe may be darker than rest of stripe); back above stripe greenish grey, finely flecked with reddish brown (dusky bars on back may be present which end at the darker zones in lateral stripe); body below stripe whitish with small reddish spots (but large red blotches may also be present); barbels yellow; lobes of caudal fin with four to seven transverse dark reddish brown to black bands (the number increasing with growth); tip of first dorsal fin broadly brownish red to nearly black with a few small pale yellow spots; tip of second dorsal fin white with a broad submarginal dark reddish brown to black spot. Attains 30 cm. Red Sea and coast of East Africa to the western Pacific where it ranges from southern Japan to New South Wales. Lachner (1954) described *U. oligospilus* from the Arabian Gulf, but the differences he listed are subspecific at best.

SWEEPERS
FAMILY PEMPHERIDAE

This small family consists of only two genera, *Pempheris* with about 20 species and *Parapriacanthus* with perhaps four. All are Indo-Pacific in distribution except for two western Atlantic species of *Pempheris*. The fishes of this family are distinctive in having a single short dorsal fin with IV-VII progresively longer spines and 7-12 soft rays, and a longer anal fin of III (rarely II) spines and 17-45 soft rays. The body shape of the species of *Pempheris* is unusual in being deep below the origin of the dorsal fin but strongly tapering to the narrow caudal peduncle; the species of *Parapriacanthus* are more elongate. Other pempherid features are very large eyes; a strongly oblique mouth with projecting lower jaw; maxilla broad posteriorly and exposed on the cheek, reaching at most to below rear of pupil; teeth small with incurved tips, in bands in jaws, on palatines, and in a V-shaped patch on vomer; gill rakers long; scales either ctenoid and adherent or cycloid and deciduous; caudal fin usually slightly forked, with 15 branched rays; pelvic fins I,5, their origin below base of pectorals. The species of *Parapriacanthus* and some of *Pempheris* have bioluminescent organs associated with the digestive tract (Haneda and Johnson, 1958, 1962). Sweepers are nocturnal; they are usually seen in large aggregations in caves or deep crevices by day, dispersing at night to feed on zooplankton.

636. School of *Parapriacanthus ransonneti* (J. Hoover)

637. *Pempheris vanicolensis*, 15.3 cm (J. Randall)

abdomen, the rest of body translucent pink; a narrow blackish bar at base of caudal fin; tips of caudal lobes blackish. Attains 10 cm. Red Sea to South Africa, east to New Caledonia and the Marshall Islands. Forms dense aggregations in caves during the day. *P. guentheri* (Klunzinger), *P. beryciformis* Franz, and *P. unwini* Ogilby are synonyms (Randall D. Mooi, pers. comm., currently conducting a systematic research on the family).

GOLDEN SWEEPER
Parapriacanthus ransonneti Steindachner, 1870

Dorsal rays V-VI (usually V),7-10; anal rays III,18-24; pectoral rays 16-17; lateral-line scales 52-70 to caudal fin base, the pored scales extending to middle of caudal fin; scales ctenoid; no scales on fins; gill rakers 15-20; body depth 2.4-3.3 in standard length; golden yellow on head, silvery over

VANIKORO SWEEPER
Pempheris vanicolensis Cuvier, 1831

Dorsal rays VI,9; anal rays III,39-44; pectoral rays 16-18; lateral-line scales 49-68; scales on body cycloid except on chest where ctenoid; gill rakers 7-9 + 19-20; body depth 2.2-2.4 in standard length; adults bronze, the scale edges of silvery, thus giving a slightly oblique striped pattern following scale rows;

638. *P. vanicolensis*, subadults (J. Randall)

centres of lateral-line scales silvery; fins brownish orange-yellow, the dorsal fin broadly tipped with black; juveniles and subadults more solid bronze, the scale edges narrowly dark; leading edge of dorsal fin as well as apex blackish; base of anal fin dark brown to black; upper and lower edges of caudal fin blackish. Reaches 18 cm. Western Indian Ocean, including the Red Sea, to Samoa; more common on the Arabian Sea coast of Oman than in the Gulf of Oman.

RED SWEEPER
Pempheris sp.

Dorsal rays VI,9; anal rays III,46; pectoral rays 19; lateral-line scales 69; scales above lateral line 7; scales below lateral line 16; cheek scale rows 7; circumpeduncular scales 23; scales finely ctenoid (more coarsely ctenoid on chest) except below and above pectoral fin to lateral line where cycloid; gill rakers 8 + 19; body depth 2.3 in standard length; a slight but distinct midventral ridge on chest, bifurcating to a V-shape before pelvic fins; two patches of villiform teeth outside gape at front of lower jaw; red, the edges of scales on body silvery (except anteriorly above lateral line where entirely red); fins red, without dark markings. A single 15.7-cm specimen of this fish was speared by the author at the wreck of the "Electra" off Masirah Island, central coast of Oman. It is under study by R.D. Mooi. More specimens are needed.

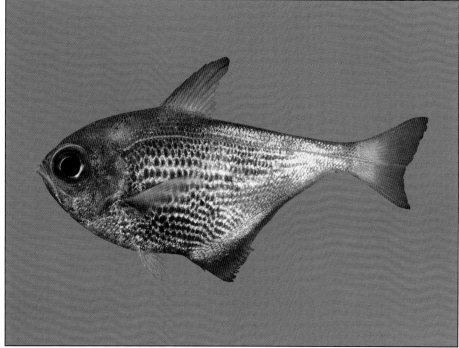

639. *Pempheris* sp., 15.7 cm (J. Randall)

MONOS
FAMILY MONODACTYLIDAE

This small family is characterised by a deep compressed body; a short angular snout; a small highly oblique mouth with lower jaw slightly protruding; small brush-like teeth in jaws and villiform teeth on vomer and palatines; a single dorsal fin with VII-VIII small spines and 26-36 soft rays; anal fin with III small spines and 27-37 soft rays; anterior soft portions of dorsal and anal fins elevated; caudal fin slightly emarginate; scales small and weakly ctenoid; dorsal and anal fins nearly fully scaled; and the predominant colour silvery. Monos are usually encountered in schools.

They are more apt to be found in estuaries or mangrove areas than in full-saline marine environments; able to tolerate freshwater. The family consists of two genera, *Monodactylus* with three species and the Australian *Schuettea* with two.

SILVER MONO
Monodactylus argenteus (Linnaeus, 1758)

Dorsal rays VII-VIII,27-30; anal rays III,27-30; pectoral rays 16-18; pelvic fins I,2-3, absent or vestigial in adults; lateral-line scales 52-58; gill rakers 8 + 18-22; upper jaw shorter than eye diameter; teeth small, compressed, tricuspid (middle cusp the longest), in bands in jaws; silvery, the juveniles with a dark bar through eye, and sometimes a second bar from nape through pectoral-fin base; median fins yellowish, the scaled basal part silvery, the tips of the dorsal and anal lobes blackish. Reported to 25 cm, but rarely exceeds 20 cm. Red Sea south to South Africa and east to Samoa; in the western Pacific from southern Japan to New South Wales.

641. *M. argenteus*, subadult (J. Hoover)

640. *Monodactylus argenteus*, 11.8 cm (J. Randall)

245

SEA CHUBS
FAMILY KYPHOSIDAE

The sea chubs are shore fishes of rocky substrata or coral reefs of exposed coasts. Opinions vary on the limits of this family; many authors include the Girellidae as a subfamily, and still others expand the Kyphosidae to include the Scorpididae, Microcanthidae, and Parascorpididae. Since only the genus *Kyphosus* occurs in Oman seas, the general remarks below refer just to the Kyphosinae which also contains the monotypic genera *Neoscorpis*, *Hermosilla*, and *Sectator*. These fishes are moderately deep-bodied and compressed, with a small head, and a small terminal or slightly inferior mouth; the maxilla slips partially under the preorbital bone when mouth closed; the teeth are incisiform, uniserial, and close-set, each curving to a large horizontal root (*Kyphosus*) or in bands in jaws with the outer row enlarged (*Neoscorpis*); scales small, ctenoid, those of *Kyphosus* covering most of head and soft portions of median fins; dorsal fin continuous, with VI-XI spines (*Neoscorpis* with VI-VIII, the rest with XI, rarely X), and 11-15 soft rays (except *Neoscorpis* with 20-22); anal fin with III spines and 10-14 rays (except *Neoscorpis* with 23-26); caudal fin forked; swimbladder bifurcate posteriorly, extending into tail. The sea chubs are omnivorous, but they feed mainly on benthic plants (with the probable exception of the more pelagic *Sectator*); the digestive tract is very long, as would be expected of fishes with a diet dominated by plants. These fishes are often encountered in aggregations; this can be advantageous when feeding on benthic algae; in schools the sea chubs are able to overwhelm the defenses of the territorial damselfishes and surgeonfishes. Juveniles of the species of *Kyphosus* and *Sectator* are sometimes found well offshore drifting with masses of *Sargassum* or other floating material.

GREY CHUB
Kyphosus bigibbus Lacepède, 1802

Dorsal rays XI,12 (rarely 11 or 13); anal rays III,11; pectoral rays 18-19; lateral-line scales 53-59; gill rakers 7-9 + 18-20; body depth 2.2-2.5 in standard length; head length 3.4-3.65 in standard length; soft portion of dorsal fin not higher than longest dorsal spine; base of spinous portion of dorsal fin longer than soft portion; silvery grey, the edges of the scales brown, resulting in a longitudinal linear pattern on body; opercular membrane dark brown to black; suborbital region of head silvery, interrupted by a diagonal dark brown streak extending posteriorly from corner of mouth; fins dark; an occasional entirely yellow color phase may be seen, and sometimes the apparent offspring of a cross of a xanthic individual and a normal-coloured fish; even more rare are albino individuals. Reported to attain 70 cm. Widespread in the Indo-Pacific, but appears to have an antiequatorial distribution: in the Indian Ocean, Red Sea and Oman in the north and South Africa to the south; in the Pacific, southern Japan and Hawaii in the north and New South Wales, Lord Howe Island, Rapa, Pitcairn Group, and Easter Island in the south.

HIGHFIN CHUB
Kyphosus cinerascens (Forsskål, 1775)

Dorsal rays XI,12; anal rays III,11-12 (usually 11); pectoral rays 18-19; lateral-line scales 65-72; gill rakers 8-10 + 18-20; body depth 2.25-2.5 in standard length; dorsal profile of snout forming an angle of about 70° to horizontal axis of body; soft portion of dorsal fin distinctly higher than spinous (longest dorsal spine of adults 1.3-1.7 in longest soft ray); base of spinous portion of dorsal fin longer than soft portion; silvery grey, the edges of the scales brown, especially upper and lower edges, resulting in a pattern or narrow brown stripes on body; opercular membrane dark brown. Reported to 50 cm. Indo-Pacific.

642. *Kyphosus bigibbus*, about 40 cm (J. Randall)

643. *Kyphosus cinerascens* (J. Hoover)

246

BRASSY CHUB

Kyphosus vaigiensis (Quoy and Gaimard, 1825)

Dorsal rays XI,14 (rarely 13); anal rays III,13; pectoral rays 19-20; lateral-line scales 52-54; gill rakers 9-10 + 20-24; body depth 2.3-2.5 in standard length; soft rays of dorsal fin not higher than longest dorsal spine; base of spinous portion of dorsal fin shorter than soft portion; silvery grey with brassy stripes along upper and lower edges of scales of body; two oblique brassy bands on snout and cheek, one from upper lip to upper corner of preopercle, the other from front of snout through lower part of eye; opercular membrane usually yellowish brown. Reaches 60 cm. Indo-Pacific.

644. *Kyphosus vaigiensis* (J. Randall)

BUTTERFLYFISHES
FAMILY CHAETODONTIDAE

Twenty years ago the butterflyfishes and the angelfishes were regarded as subfamilies of the Chaetodontidae. Burgess (1974) showed that there are sufficient morphological differences to warrant recognition of these two groups as families. The butterflyfishes are characterized by a deep, ovate, compressed body; no spine at the corner of the preopercle; mouth small, not extending posterior to front of eye, terminal, and protractile; teeth small and setiform (*Chaetodon* means bristle tooth), in one or more bands in jaws, none on roof of mouth; scales ctenoid, extending onto head and most of caudal fin and soft portions of dorsal and anal fins; dorsal fin continuous or with a slight notch, with VI-XVI strong spines (no initial procumbent spine), and 15-30 soft rays; anterior interspinous membranes of dorsal fin deeply incised; anal fin with III-V (usually III) spines and 14-23 rays; caudal fin varying from slightly emarginate to slightly rounded; pelvic fins I,5, thoracic, with a scaly axillary process; intestine long and coiled; vertebrae 24. The postlarval stage, termed the tholichthys larva, has large bony plates on the head and anterior body. Most butterflyfishes are brightly and distinctly coloured. Many of the species feed on coral polyps or other coelenterates (those that are obligate coral-polyp feeders are not good candidates as aquarium fishes); such feeding generally does not kill the coral, because the polyps are able to regenerate (however, when the crown-of-thorns starfish feeds on coral, the coral dies where the feeding took place). Other butterflyfishes feed heavily on benthic algae and small benthic invertebrates such as polychaete worms and crustaceans; some such as the species of *Hemitaurichthys* are primarily zooplankton feeders. A few, such as *Heniochus diphreutes*, form aggregations, but most are solitary or occur as pairs of long duration. Some have relatively small territories, while others wander over a large area of reef. Butterflyfishes are diurnal; at night they take cover in the reef and enter into a state of torpor, usually exhibiting some change in colour pattern (generally not as bright as the day pattern). Most species occur on coral reefs or rocky substrata in less than 30 m, but a few are restricted to reefs or rocky bottom as deep as 200 m. The family consists of 120 species which are classified in 10 genera (Burgess, 1978; Steene, 1978; Allen, 1980). The species most recently described is *Chaetodon dialeucos* Salm and Mee (1989), endemic to the Arabian Sea coast of Oman.

645. Aggregation of *Chaetodon dialeucos* (J. Hoover)

THREADFIN BUTTERFLYFISH
Chaetodon auriga Forsskål, 1775

Dorsal rays XIII,22-25; anal rays III,19-22; pectoral rays 15-17; longitudinal scale series 31-40, ending beneath rear of dorsal fin (true of other species of the genus); body depth 1.6-1.75 in standard length; snout moderately pointed, 2.2-2.8 in head; fourth to sixth dorsal soft rays prolonged to a posteriorly-directed filament which may extend beyond caudal fin; caudal fin slightly rounded; white with two series of diagonal black-ish lines set at right angles, shading posteriorly to orange-yellow; a black spot often present in outer part of soft portion of dorsal fin; a black bar through eye, very broad below eye. Reaches 20 cm. Indo-Pacific; most often found on coral reefs in the depth range of 1-35 m; feeds mainly on coral polyps, polychaete worms, algae, and small shrimps.

EXQUISITE BUTTERFLYFISH
Chaetodon austriacus Rüppell, 1836

Dorsal rays XIII,20-21; anal rays III,19-20; pectoral rays 13-15; longitudinal scale

646. *Chaetodon auriga* (J. Hoover)

series 39-42; body depth 1.6-1.8 in standard length; snout short, 3.5-4.0 in head length; caudal fin rounded; orange-yellow with dark longitudinal lines (blackish dorsally orangish ventrally); two diagonal black bands on head, the anterior through eye; upper lip and chin black; dorsal fin whitish, the soft portion black distally; caudal and anal fins

largely black. Reaches 14 cm. Red Sea and Gulf of Aden, rarely to southern Oman (probably only as waifs from the Gulf of Aden). A close relative of *C. trifasciatus* Park and *C. melapterus* Guichenot; all three feed primarily on coral polyps, hence impractical as aquarium fishes.

648. *Chaetodon austriacus*, about 10 cm (J. Randall)

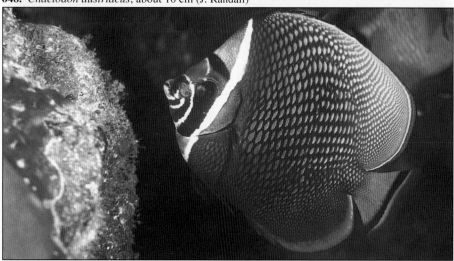

649. *Chaetodon collare* (J. Hoover)

647. *C. austriacus*, juv., about 4.5 cm (J. Randall)

COLLARED BUTTERFLYFISH
Chaetodon collare Bloch, 1787

Dorsal rays XII,25-28; anal rays III,20-22; pectoral rays 14-15; longitudinal scale series 37-40; body depth 1.4-1.6 in standard length; snout length 3.3-4.2 in head length; caudal fin truncate to slightly rounded; tan, the edges of scales dark brown, thus forming dark oblique lines on body; head brown with a prominent white bar from dorsal-fin origin to chest, preceded by a black bar below eye which is edged anteriorly with white, snout and chin black with white markings; caudal fin red with a whitish posterior margin and black submarginal band. Attains 16 cm. Philippines and Indonesia to the southern coast of Oman; more common in the Gulf of Oman than in the south; also occurs in the Laccadives and Maldives. Often seen in small aggregations. Said to feed heavily on coral polyps; does not do well, in general, in aquaria.

650. *C. dialeucos*, juv., about 4 cm (J. Randall)

OMAN BUTTERFLYFISH
Chaetodon dialeucos Salm and Mee, 1989

Dorsal rays XII,21-22; anal rays III,19; pectoral rays 15-16; longitudinal scale series 31-35; body depth 1.45-1.7 in standard length; snout length 2.5-2.65 in head length; caudal fin slightly rounded; body pale grey-brown, the scale edges narrowly dark grey-brown, to a demarcation from base of fourth dorsal spine to origin of pelvic fins; body and head anterior to this demarcation white except for a broad black bar from origin of dorsal fin to interorbital space, narrowing as it passes downward (enclosing eye) to ventral corner of operculum; dorsal fin pale grey-brown with a black border which broadens posteriorly; anal, caudal, and pelvic fins blackish except for a white posterior

651. *Chaetodon dialeucos* (J. Hoover)

border on caudal. Reaches 18 cm. Known only from Oman from Ra's al Hadd at the southwestern entrance to the Gulf of Oman nearly to the Yemen border; it appears to be most abundant in the vicinity of Barr al Hikman. Usually found on rocky reefs from less than 1 to more than 10 m; has not been observed to feed directly on live coral; one individual did well in an aquarium when it finally commenced to feed on prepared flake food.

GARDINER'S BUTTERFLYFISH
Chaetodon gardineri Norman, 1939

Dorsal rays XII,20-22; anal rays III,18-19; pectoral rays usually 14; longitudinal scale series 33-37; body depth 1.6-1.7 in standard length; snout length 2.5-2.9 in head length; caudal fin slightly rounded; white, becoming black posteriorly, this extending broadly into middle of dorsal fin; black bar through eye, edged posteriorly with yellow; opercular membrane yellow; outer part of dorsal fin, base of caudal fin, and most of anal fin yellow. Reported to 17 cm. Sri Lanka to Gulf of Aden; one record from the Arabian Gulf; more common in the Gulf of Oman than southern Oman; usually found at depths below 15 m; often seen in pairs. Closely related to *C. selene* Bleeker of the western Pacific.

652. *Chaetodon gardineri*, about 13 cm (J. Randall)

JAYAKAR'S BUTTERFLYFISH
Chaetodon jayakari Norman, 1939

Dorsal rays XI,21-23; anal rays III,17-18; pectoral rays 14-15; longitudinal scale series 45-49; body deep, the depth 1.3-1.6 in standard length; snout 2.8-3.3 in head length; caudal fin rounded; white with two broad dark brown bars on body, the first extending into dorsal fin, the second into both the dorsal and anal fins; white interspace in middle of body broader ventrally; a dark brown bar from high on nape through eye, ending at lower edge of preopercle; a white-edged black spot about as large as eye on soft portion of dorsal fin in upper posterior part of second brown bar. Attains about 16 cm. Known from west coast of India to the Red Sea in the depth range of 33-274 m; the photograph was taken by the author at Fahl Island off Muscat in 34 m. Klausewitz and Fricke (1985) reported the species from the Red Sea and differentiated it from its close relatives, *C. modestus* Temminck and Schlegel from the western Pacific and *C. excelsa* (Jordan) from the Hawaiian Islands.

653. *Chaetodon jayakari*, about 14.5 cm (J. Randall)

ORANGEFACE BUTTERFLYFISH
Chaetodon larvatus Cuvier, 1831

Dorsal rays XI-XII (usually XI),24-27; anal rays III,21-22; pectoral rays 15-16; longitudinal scale series 31-37; body deep, the depth 1.3-1.45 in standard length; snout length 3.2-3.9 in head length; dorsal and anal spines progressively longer, the anterior soft portions of these fins still longer, resulting in an overall triangular shape; caudal fin truncate to slightly rounded; head (except posterior part of operculum) orange without a black bar through eye; body bluish grey with chevron-shaped, vertical, yellow lines; caudal peduncle, most of caudal fin, and posterior part of dorsal fin black. Attains 12 cm. Red Sea to Gulf of Aden; two individuals seen in the Juzor al Hallaniyat (Kuria Muria Islands), southern Oman, one of which was photographed; another photographed in Hoon's Bay. Often seen in pairs. Feeds mainly on coral polyps; defends a relatively small territory of live coral. Some authors have classified this and two related species in the genus *Gonochaetodon*, now considered by most as a subgenus.

SOMALI BUTTERFLYFISH
Chaetodon leucopleura Playfair and Günther, 1867

Dorsal rays XII,21-23; anal rays III,18-19; pectoral rays 14-15; longitudinal scale series 31-37; body depth 1.45-1.7 in standard length; snout length 2.3-2.8 in head length; caudal fin rounded to double emarginate; white, the scale edges dorsally on body blackish, becoming black posteriorly and dusky ventrally; a black bar on head through eye; opercular membrane, outer part of dorsal and anal fins, pelvic fins, and caudal fin yellow except for hyaline posterior border of caudal. Maximum length about 18 cm. Zanzibar north to southern Red Sea, east to southern Oman; common off Dhofar, generally at depths greater than 20 m; not observed in the Gulf of Oman. Does well in aquaria.

RACOON BUTTERFLYFISH
Chaetodon lunula (Lacepède, 1802)

Dorsal rays XI-XIII,22-25; anal rays III,17-19; pectoral rays 15-16; longitudinal scale series 35-44; body depth 1.4-1.7 in standard length; snout 2.9-3.4 in head length; caudal fin rounded; orange-yellow, the body with oblique brownish bands, overlaid dorsally with dusky pigment; a yellow-edged curved black band centred at base of eighth dorsal spine, broadening as it passes to edge of gill opening; a wide black bar

654. *Chaetodon larvatus* (J. Hoover)

655. *Chaetodon leucopleura*, about 16 cm (J. Hoover)

656. *Chaetodon lunula*, about 13 cm (J. Hoover)

through eye, broadly bordered posteriorly by white; a yellow-edged black bar on caudal peduncle, continuing upward as an arc into base of dorsal fin. Attains 20 cm. Indo-Pacific, but unknown from the Red Sea or Gulf of Oman; rare along the southern coast of Oman. Sometimes seen in small aggregations. Diet variable: opisthobranch gastropods, tubeworm tentacles, benthic algae, coral polyps, other benthic invertebrates, and zooplankton.

ARABIAN BUTTERFLYFISH
Chaetodon melapterus Guichenot, 1862

Dorsal rays XIII,19-21; anal rays III,18-20; pectoral rays 14-15; longitudinal scale series 35-39; body depth 1.5-1.7 in standard length; snout short, 3.5-4.1 in head length; caudal fin rounded; bright orange-yellow, abruptly black posteriorly, with slightly oblique reddish lines on body; two black bars on nape and head, the anterior passing through eye; front of snout and chin black; median fins jet black except for pale posterior edges. Reaches about 13 cm. Arabian Gulf to southern Red Sea; common on coral reefs in the Gulf of Oman and Arabian Gulf. Feeds mainly on coral polyps. Randall (1994) showed that the alleged type locality of *C. melapterus*, the island of Réunion, is a probable error.

657. *C. melapterus*, juv., about 4.5 cm (J. Randall)

658. *Chaetodon melapterus*, about 10 cm (J. Hoover)

BLACKSPOTTED BUTTERFLYFISH
Chaetodon nigropunctatus Sauvage, 1880

Dorsal rays XIII,21-23; anal rays III,18-20; pectoral rays 14-15; longitudinal scale series 36-39; body depth 12.5-1.6 in standard length; snout length 2.8-3.2 in head length; caudal fin truncate to slightly rounded; brown to yellowish brown with a blackish spot on each scale; juveniles with a black bar from nape at origin of dorsal fin through eye, persisting only dorsally on adult; head anterior to eye, ventral part of head, and median zone of forehead whitish; dorsal and anal fins with a black border; caudal fin brown, shading to blackish posteriorly and at edges, with a broad clear posterior border and narrow white submarginal band. Attains 14 cm. Known only from the Arabian Gulf to the central coast of Oman (only a few individuals seen at Masirah Island); the most common butterflyfish in the Arabian Gulf and Gulf of Oman. *C. obscurus* Boulenger is a synonym.

659. *C. nigropunctatus*, juv., about 3 cm (J. Randall)

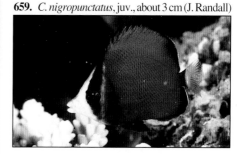

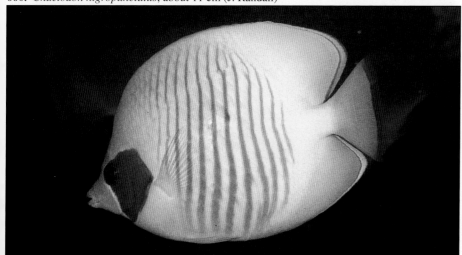

660. *Chaetodon nigropunctatus*, about 11 cm (J. Randall)

MASKED BUTTERFLYFISH
Chaetodon semilarvatus Cuvier, 1831

Dorsal rays XII,25-27; anal rays III,20-22; pectoral rays 16; longitudinal scale series 28-32; body deep, the depth 1.3-1.5 in standard length; snout length 3.0-3.4 in head length; caudal fin slightly rounded; deep yellow with about 13 vertical orange lines following scale rows, gradually broadening as they pass ventrally; a large bluish black spot posteroventrally on head, just enclosing eye. Reaches about 23 cm. Red Sea to Gulf of Aden; one individual sighted by John P. Hoover at Al Mahallah in southern Oman, hence probably a stray from the Gulf of Aden. Usually seen in pairs, occasionally in aggregations.

661. *Chaetodon semilarvatus* (J. Hoover)

CHEVRON BUTTERFLYFISH
Chaetodon trifascialis Quoy and Gaimard, 1825

Dorsal rays XIII-XV,14-16; anal rays IV-V (rarely V),13-15; pectoral rays 14-15; scales large, the longitudinal scale series 22-29; body elongate for the genus, the depth 1.7-2.2 in standard length; snout length 2.8-3.4 in head length; caudal fin slightly rounded; white with purplish to blackish lines forming a chevron pattern on body; a black bar through eye; caudal fin largely black; dorsal and anal fins mainly orange-yellow (these fins on juveniles black posteriorly, linked with a black bar across caudal peduncle). Reaches 17 cm. Indo-Pacific; occurs in southern Oman but not seen in the Gulf of Oman. Vigorously defends a relatively small territory of live coral (generally plate-like species of *Acropora*) on which it feeds. Sometimes classified in its own genus *Mega-protodon*, now regarded by most authors as a subgenus.

VAGABOND BUTTERFLYFISH
Chaetodon vagabundus Linnaeus, 1758

Dorsal rays XIII,23-25; anal rays III,19-22; pectoral rays 15-16; longitudinal scale series 34-40; body depth 1.5-1.7 in standard length; snout length 2.6-3.1 in head length; caudal fin slightly rounded; body white with bluish black lines in two series set at right angles; head white with a black bar from high on nape through eye; a black bar across caudal peduncle, extending basally into dorsal and anal fins; rest of these and the caudal fin largely yellow, the caudal with a black bar in the middle, a clear posterior border, and a blackish submarginal band. Reaches 18 cm. Indo-Pacific, but not recorded from the Red Sea or Arabian Gulf; the predominant butterflyfish of southern Oman, ranging into the Gulf of Oman; in the western

662. *Chaetodon trifascialis*, about 12 cm (J. Randall)

663. *Chaetodon vagabundus*, about 13.5 cm (J. Randall)

Pacific from Tokyo to Sydney. Feeds mainly on coral polyps and algae; adapts well to aquarium life and prepared flake food.

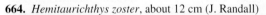
664. *Hemitaurichthys zoster*, about 12 cm (J. Randall)

BELTED BUTTERFLYFISH
Hemitaurichthys zoster (Bennett, 1831)

Dorsal rays XI-XII,24-26; anal rays III,20-21; pectoral rays 17-18; scales small, the longitudinal scale series 67-73; body depth 1.5-1.6 in standard length; snout length 3.0-3.6 in head length; caudal fin slightly rounded; dark brown with a very wide white bar in middle-anterior part of body, broader ventrally; outer part of dorsal spines above white bar yellow; caudal fin white with a brown posterior border. Attains 18 cm. Western Indian Ocean, but not known from the Red Sea, Arabian Gulf; observed in Oman only at Ra's al Had. Usually seen in aggregations feeding on zooplankton well above the substratum. The species name is from the Greek meaning belt or girdle. One of four species of the genus, of which the most closely related is *H. polylepis* (Bleeker) of the Pacific.

LONGFIN BANNERFISH
Heniochus acuminatus (Linnaeus, 1758)

Dorsal rays XI (rarely XII),24-27; anal rays III,15-18; pectoral rays 16-18; lateral line complete (i.e. to base of caudal fin), the pored scales 47-54; body deep, the depth 1.25-1.45 in standard length; snout pointed, 2.7-3.3 in head length; fourth dorsal spine extremely elongate (often longer than standard length); caudal fin truncate to slightly rounded; white with two broad black bands, the first from front of dorsal fin to abdomen and pelvic fins, the second from middle of spinous portion of dorsal fin to rear of anal fin; snout and interorbital space largely blackish; caudal fin and posterior part of dorsal fin mainly yellow. Reaches 20 cm. Indo-Pacific except the Red Sea and Hawaii; common in the Arabian Gulf and Gulf of Oman, less so in southern Oman. Almost identical in colour to *H. diphreutes* Jordan which was not recognized as a valid species until Allen and Kuiter (1978) differentiated it by its dorsal- fin count of XII,23-25 and shorter snout (3.3-3.7 in head). *H. diphreutes* appears to be more subtropical in distribution, in general, occurring in the northern

665. *Heniochus acuminatus*, about 13 cm (J. Randall)

Red Sea, South Africa, southern Japan, southeast Australia, and Hawaii; but it is known from some tropical localities such as the Maldive Islands. There is also a difference, in general, in life style; *H. acuminatus* usually occurs as solitary individuals or in pairs and is closely oriented to the bottom,

whereas *H. diphreutes* tends to form aggregations that feed on zooplankton well above the substratum. *H. acuminatus* is unusual in the Gulf of Oman in sometimes forming zooplankton-feeding aggregations (perhaps due to the abundance of plankton).

666. *Apolemichthys xanthotis*, juv. (J. Hoover)

ANGELFISHES
FAMILY POMACANTHIDAE

As mentioned in the above family discussion for butteflyfishes, the angelfishes were once classified as a subfamily of the Chaetodontidae. They share many of the characters with butterflyfishes such as the deep compressed body, small mouth with brushlike teeth, ctenoid scales which extend onto head and well out on median fins, and a single unnotched dorsal fin. They differ significantly in having a prominant spine at the corner of the preopercle, no scaly axillary process at the base of the pelvic fins, more strongly ctenoid scales with distinct ridges on the exposed part, and auxiliary scales in adults. Also, the postlarvae lack bony plates on the head and anterior body so characteristic of chaetodontid postlarvae. Angelfishes are diurnal; the

species of *Pomacanthus* and *Apolemichthys* as adults feed mainly on sponges, occasionally on algae; the species of *Centropyge* are grazers on algae and detritus. Because of the beautiful colours of most of the angelfishes, they are popular aquarium fishes. The young of the species of *Pomacanthus* are very different in colour from adults.

YELLOW-EAR ANGELFISH
Apolemichthys xanthotis Fraser-Brunner, 1950

Dorsal rays XIV,17-19; anal rays III,17-18; pectoral rays 16-17; lateral line ending

667. *Apolemichthys xanthotis* (J. Hoover)

beneath soft portion of dorsal fin, the pored scales 55-57; gill rakers 5 + 13-14; posterior margin of preopercle finely serrate, the ventral margin with a few small spines; preorbital serrate; soft portions of dorsal and anal fins rounded; caudal fin slightly rounded, the uppermost branched ray of adults prolonged; large central portion of body pale yellowish grey, the edges of the scales narrowly blackish, the body abruptly black posteriorly; head and anterior body dark brown; a bright yellow spot about as large as pupil above upper end of gill opening; edge of long spine at corner of preopercle blue; dorsal part of body black; dorsal and anal fins black, the dorsal with a bluish white margin, the anal fin with blue; caudal fin yellow. Attains about 20 cm. Red Sea to the Gulf of Oman; the most common angelfish off Dhofar, progressively less common to the east; found more often on rocky substrata than coral reefs. Closely related to *A. xanthurus* (Bennett) from elsewhere in the western Indian Ocean which differs in a slightly deeper body, shorter snout, 52-54 lateral-line scales, and a reduction of the dark colouration, as shown by Klausewitz and Wongratana (1970).

AFRICAN CHERUBFISH
Centropyge acanthops (Norman, 1922)

Dorsal rays XIV,16-17; anal rays III,16-18; pectoral rays 15-16 (usually 16); lateral-line scales 33-37; longitudinal scale series 43-44; gill rakers 5-6 + 15-16; lower edge of preorbital with 1-4 large spines; body depth 2.1-2.25 in standard length; caudal fin slightly rounded; head, chest, dorsal part of body, and most of dorsal fin bright yellow; rest of body, anal fin, and pelvic fins deep blue; spines of head and most of edge of orbit bright blue; posterior margin of dorsal fin, most of margin of anal fin, and lateral margin of pelvic fins bright blue; caudal fin whitish to yellowish, the upper and lower edges dusky. Maximum length 7 cm. East coast of Africa to Mauritius and Seychelles; the unexpected Oman record is based on an underwater photograph by Philip Woodhead taken on the southern coast near Marbat.

668. *Centropyge acanthops* (P. Woodhead)

669. *Centropyge multispinis* (J. Hoover)

670. *Pomacanthus asfur* (J. Randall)

Very similar in colour to *C. aurantonotus* Burgess from the West Indies.

MANYSPINE CHERUBFISH
Centropyge multispinis (Playfair and Günther, 1867)

Dorsal rays XIII-XV,15-17 (rarely 15); anal rays III,17-18; pectoral rays 15-17 (rarely 15); lateral-line scales 36-38; longitudinal scale series 46-48; gill rakers 4-5 + 12-13; body depth 1.75-2.0 in standard length; posterior margin of preopercle coarsely serrate, the ventral margin with one to a few small spines; preorbital, suborbital, and interopercle coarsely serrate; caudal fin rounded; brown to yellowish brown with irregular black vertical lines on body; a large deep blue and black spot behind upper end of gill opening; median and pelvic fins dark brown, sometimes with black bands across rays; lateral edge of pelvic fins and most of margin of anal fin bright blue; posterior margin of caudal fin pale yellowish. Attains about 11 cm. Widespread in the Indian Ocean, including the Red Sea; in Oman waters, only on the southern coast.

ARABIAN ANGELFISH
Pomacanthus asfur (Forsskål, 1775)

Dorsal rays XII,19-21; anal rays III,18-20; pectoral rays 17-18; lateral-line complete, the pored scales 44-46; longitudinal scale series 52-53; body depth 1.5-1.7 in standard length; posterior margin of preopercle finely serrate (serrae may be absent in large adults), the ventral margin with a few moderate serrae; preorbital serrate; soft portions of dorsal and anal fins of adults prolonged into long filaments that extend posterior to caudal fin; pelvic fins long; caudal fin rounded; head black; anterior body, including chest and nape, blue, the scale edges black; a broad bright yellow bar in middle of body centred above anus and extending into dorsal fin between sixth and twelfth spines; body posterior to yellow bar bluish black; caudal fin and posterior caudal peduncle abruptly bright yellow; juveniles dark brown with slightly irregular, near-vertical, blue lines, some broader and lighter blue than others (juveniles as small as 5.5 cm already developing the yellow bar on body and the filament on the soft portion of the dorsal and anal fins – see figure of juvenile). Reaches about 35 cm. Red Sea and Gulf of Aden to Dhofar, Oman (only a few sightings, hence probably strays). Usually found on protected inshore reefs of reduced visibility, often with heavy growth of soft corals; difficult to approach underwater.

671. *Pomacanthus imperator*, juv. (J. Hoover)

EMPEROR ANGELFISH
Pomacanthus imperator (Bloch, 1787)

Dorsal rays XIII-XIV (usually XIV),19-21; anal rays III,19-21; pectoral rays 19-20 (usually 20); longitudinal scale series 77-79 (pored scales about 49); gill rakers 6-7 + 13-14; body depth 1.6-1.8 in standard length; posterior margin of preopercle finely serrate, the ventral edge with a few moderate serrae; middle rays of soft portion of dorsal fin of large adults produced into a filament; soft portion of anal fin rounded; caudal fin rounded; body and basal part of soft portion of dorsal and anal fins of adults with alternating, slightly oblique stripes of purple and yellow; throat, chest, anterior abdomen, and a broad dorsal extension covering posterior head and anterior body black, the part on head with a blue margin; a blue-edged black band across interorbital, enclosing eye, narrowing to end at base of preopercular spine; head anterior to this band pale grey to white, posterior to it dark yellow; caudal fin orange-yellow; juveniles deep blue to black with alternating narrow blue and wider white lines which are vertical anteriorly and progressively more curved posteriorly, one white line forming a complete circle anterior to caudal peduncle. Reaches about 40 cm. Indo-Pacific; more common in the Gulf of Oman than the Arabian Sea coast of Oman. Usually found in outer coral-reef or rocky areas, often in the vicinity of caves. Adults are capable of producing a loud thumping sound when alarmed.

YELLOWBAR ANGELFISH
Pomacanthus maculosus (Forsskål, 1775)

Dorsal rays XII-XIII (usually XII),21-23; anal rays III,19-20; pectoral rays 18-20; lateral-line scales 44-48; longitudinal scale series 71-78; gill rakers 5-6 + 13-14; body depth 1.6-1.8 in standard length; posterior margin of preopercle usually finely serrate, the ventral margin with a few small spines;

672. *Pomacanthus imperator* (J. Hoover)

673. *Pomacanthus maculosus* (J. Hoover)

soft portion of dorsal and anal fins of adults elevated and angular, the middle rays prolonged into a posteriorly-directed filament (dorsal filament developing first); caudal fin rounded; adults yellowish brown to blue, with a broad irregular yellow bar in middle of body; posterior head, nape, and anterior body with black spots, most of which are vertically elongate; posterior part of dorsal and anal fins with interconnected blue lines, the margin of these fins narrowly bright blue; caudal fin pale yellow with a finely reticular blue pattern, a narrow blue posterior margin and black submarginal line; juveniles black with numerous vertical blue lines and three wider bluish white lines (one on head and two on body); juveniles reach a larger size than *P. asfur* before developing the yellow bar on body (one of 6.7 has the bar, the soft portions of the dorsal and anal fins angular but not yet showing a filament).

674. *P. maculosus*, juv., about 8 cm (J. Randall)

Red Sea and Arabian Gulf south to Mozambique (type locality of *Pomacanthops filamentosus* Smith), Seychelles (type locality of *Holacanthus ignatius* Playfair), and Madagascar. Unusually abundant in the Arabian Gulf and Gulf of Oman for an angelfish.

SEMICIRCLE ANGELFISH
Pomacanthus semicirculatus (Cuvier, 1831)

Dorsal rays XIII,21-23; anal rays III,20-22; pectoral rays 19-21; lateral-line scales 48-52; longitudinal scale series 78-82; gill rakers 4-5 + 13; body depth 1.5-1.75 in standard length; edge of preorbital and posterior margin of preopercle finely serrate; fifth to seventh dorsal soft rays developing into a posteriorly-directed filament in adults; a comparable but less pronounced filament in anal fin; caudal fin rounded; broad middle zone of body greyish yellow with numerous small round black spots and somewhat larger vertically oval black spots, shading anteriorly and posteriorly to dark yellowish grey, the black spots gradually replaced posteriorly on body and median fins with small greenish yellow spots and irregular lines; head dark yellowish grey, the opercular membrane, edge of preopercle, and opercular spine bright blue; margins of all fins except pectorals bright blue; juveniles black with alternating narrow white bars and more numerous vertical blue lines which are more curved posteriorly (one white band forming a near-perfect semicircle). Red Sea and coast of East Africa to Samoa; in the western Pacific from southern Japan to New South Wales; the dominant species of the genus in southern Oman; rare in the Gulf of Oman.

675. *Pomacanthus semicirculatus*, subadult (J. Hoover)

676. *P. semicirculatus*, juvenile (J. Hoover)

additional papers by Hardy (1983b), and Humphreys et al. (1989).

ARMOURHEADS
FAMILY PENTACEROTIDAE

This family of eight genera and 12 species is distinctive in having the head encased in exposed striated bones; a moderately to very deep compressed body; small terminal mouth; no supramaxilla; teeth small, in bands in jaws; teeth sometimes present on vomer but none on palatines; scales small and ctenoid; a single dorsal fin with IV-XV strong spines and 8-29 soft rays; anal fin with II-VI strong spines and 6-17 soft rays; pelvic fins large, with a spine and 5 soft rays. The family is primarily Indo-Pacific (one species ranging to the west coast of North America and two to the South Atlantic). Most of the fishes occur in deep water; only one is known from Oman. The family was revised by Hardy (1983a);

SAILFIN ARMOURHEAD
Histiopterus typus Temminck and Schlegel, 1844

Dorsal rays IV,23-29; anal rays III,8-10; pectoral rays 16-18; lateral-line scales 58-70; gill rakers 3-6 + 14-16; body depth 1.3-1.9 in standard length; head length 2.4-2.9 in standard length; head covered with rugose, striated bones; mouth slightly oblique, the maxilla reaching to below posterior nostril; teeth short and conical, in a band in jaws, the outer row largest; no teeth on vomer; first two dorsal spines short, the last two long, the third longest and much stouter than fourth; anterior soft dorsal rays long, sometimes extending posterior to caudal-fin base when depressed; adults with four faint dark bars on body; juveniles with large, close-set, round to elliptical dark brown spots. Attains 36 cm. Known from Japan, Taiwan, South China Sea, New Britain, Western Australia, west coast of India, Gulf of Oman, and South Africa in the depth range of 46-421 m.

677. *H. typus*, juv. (after Smith and Heemstra, 1985)

678. *Histiopterus typus* (after Temminck and Schlegel, 1844)

DAMSELFISHES
FAMILY POMACENTRIDAE

The Pomacentridae is a large family of small, often colourful, shallow-water fishes, most of which are associated with coral reefs or rocky substrata. They are characterised by a moderately deep compressed body; a small mouth with conical or incisiform teeth; no teeth on vomer or palatines; scales moderately large and ctenoid; head largely scaled, as are the basal parts of the median fins; lateral line interrupted, the anterior part ending below dorsal fin, consisting of tubed scales and often a few pored scales at the end, the peduncular part only of pored scales; the count of lateral-line scales given below is just the tubed scales of the anterior series; a single dorsal fin of VIII-XVII spines and 10-21 soft rays; anal fin with II spines and 10-16 soft rays; caudal fin varying from slightly emarginate to forked or lunate. Colouration highly variable, some species very drab, others brilliantly hued. The young of many species, particularly those of the genera *Pomacentrus*, *Stegastes*, *Chrysiptera*, and *Neoglyphidodon*, are very different and generally much brighter in colour than adults. Most damselfishes occur in tropical seas, but some are restricted to temperate waters. Many are territorial and pugnacious, especially those feeding mainly on benthic algae, such as the species of the genus *Stegastes*. Unique among the damselfishes are the anemonefishes (Allen, 1975, 1978) which live symbiotically with sea anemones; they are able to hide among the anemone tentacles without being stung, hence gain the protection provided by the anemone nematocysts. In turn, they protect the anemone from being eaten by the few fishes which are able to prey upon stinging coelenterates. The damselfishes of the genera *Chromis*, *Dascyllus*, *Lepidozygus*, *Neopoma-* *centrus*, *Pristotis*, and *Teixeirichthys* are primarily zooplankton feeders and usually occur in aggregations. A few species such as *Cheiloprion labiatus* and *Plectroglyphidodon johnstonianus* feed predominantly on coral polyps. The eggs of damselfishes are elliptical and demersal; the male parent guards the nest until hatching. Several species of anemonefishes of the genus *Amphiprion* have been shown to begin mature life as males and later change sex to females. The anemonefishes have the shortest larval life of pomacentrids (7-22 days), whereas the species of *Chromis* include those with the longest stay in the pelagic realm (to 42 days) (Thresher et al., 1989; Wellington and Victor, 1989). Allen (1991) reviewed the family; he recognised 28 genera and 321 species. Eight species have been described in the family since Allen's review, including two discussed below.

679. Aggregation of *Abudefduf vaigiensis* (J. Randall)

680. *Dascyllus marginatus* in a coral colony (J. Hoover)

YELLOWTAIL SERGEANT
Abudefduf notatus (Day, 1869)

Dorsal rays XIII,12-14; anal rays II,13-14; pectoral rays 18-20; lateral-line scales 20-22; gill rakers 26-31; teeth uniserial and incisiform (true of other species of *Abudefduf*); margin of suborbital and preopercle smooth (also generic); body depth 1.7-2.0 in standard length; grey-brown, the edges of the scales darker, with five narrow greenish white bars on body; a small black spot above upper end of gill opening; upper opercular membrane blackish; caudal fin yellow; a black spot at upper base of pectoral fins. Reaches 17 cm. East coast of Africa to western Pacific; observed in Oman waters only along the Arabian Sea coast; occurs along exposed rocky shores.

681. *Abudefduf notatus*, about 13 cm (J. Randall)

SCISSORTAIL SERGEANT
Abudefduf sexfasciatus (Lacepède, 1801)

Dorsal rays XIII,11-14; anal rays II,11-13; pectoral rays 17-19; lateral-line scales 18-22; gill rakers 23-30; body depth 1.6-2.0 in standard length; caudal fin forked; blue-green dorsally, shading to white ventrally, with five black bars on body (broader dorsally than pale interspaces), the last across base of caudal fin linked with a black band in upper caudal-fin lobe; a separate black band in lower caudal lobe. Attains 19 cm. Red Sea south to Mozambique, east to the Marshall Islands and Rapa; in the western Pacific from southern Japan to New South Wales; observed in Oman only at Masirah Island and the vicinity of Barr al Hikman. Occurs on coral and rocky reefs, usually in aggregations, in the depth range of 1-15 m. *A. coelestinus* (Cuvier) is a synonym.

682. *A. sexfasciatus*, about 11 cm (J. Randall)

683. *Abudefduf sordidus* (J. Hoover)

BLACKSPOT SERGEANT
Abudefduf sordidus (Forsskål, 1775)

Dorsal rays XIII,15-16 (usually 15); anal rays II,14-15; pectoral rays 18-20; lateral-line scales 20-23; gill rakers 20-28; body depth 1.5-1.8 in standard length; caudal fin forked; pale brownish grey with six dark brown bars on body, broader than pale interspaces; a black spot about as large as eye on caudal peduncle at upper end of sixth dark bar; small blackish spots on head above and posterior to eye; a small black spot at upper base of pectoral fin. Reaches 23 cm. Indo-Pacific; generally found along exposed rocky shores in less than 3 m; the young are common residents of exposed tidepools. Feeds primarily on benthic algae.

INDO-PACIFIC SERGEANT
Abudefduf vaigiensis (Quoy and Gaimard, 1825)

Dorsal rays XIII,12-14; anal rays II,11-13; pectoral rays 16-20; lateral-line scales 19-23; gill rakers 23-33; body depth 1.5-1.8 in standard length; caudal fin forked; blue-green dorsally, shading to silvery white ventrally, with five broad bluish black bars on body, the first just behind head, the narrow fifths on caudal peduncle, the third to fifth extending into dorsal fin; dorsal part of body between first and third dark bars often yellow; no dark bands in caudal fin. Reaches 18 cm. Usually seen in aggregations feeding on zooplankton well above the substratum. Widely distributed in the Indo-Pacific region. *A. saxatilis* (Linnaeus) of the Atlantic and *A. troschelii* Gill of the eastern Pacific are so closely related to *A. vaigiensis* that some would prefer to regard them as subspecies.

684. *Abudefduf vaigiensis*, about 13 cm (J. Randall)

CLARK'S ANEMONEFISH
Amphiprion clarkii (Bennett, 1830)

Dorsal rays X-XI,14-17; anal rays II,12-15; pectoral rays 18-21; lateral-line scales 34-45; predorsal scales extending into interorbital space; gill rakers 18-20; bones

685. *Amphiprion clarkii*, juveniles (J. Hoover)

of head with free margins strongly serrate (true of all species of *Amphiprion*); teeth uniserial and conical (also generic); body depth 1.7-2.0 in standard length; caudal fin slightly forked, the corners rounded in ju-

veniles; colour variable, those in Oman usually dark brown with three bluish white bars, the anterior and ventral part of head orange (this colour sometimes extending onto abdomen); caudal and paired fins orange. Reported to 14 cm. The most widely distributed species of the genus, occurring from the Arabian Gulf and Gulf of Oman to the islands of Melanesia and Micronesia; in the Indian Ocean south to the Maldives, Chagos Archipelago, and Western Australia; in the western Pacific from Japan to Queensland. Reported from the depth range of 1-55 m. Lives with ten different host anemones (Fautin and Allen, 1992).

OMAN ANEMONEFISH
Amphiprion omanensis Allen and Mee, 1991

Dorsal rays X,16-17; anal rays II,14-15; pectoral rays 19-20; lateral-line scales 36-42; predorsal scales extending to rear of interorbital space; gill rakers 16-19; body depth 1.9-2.1 in standard length; caudal fin of adults deeply emarginate, the upper lobe longer than lower; orange to dark orangish brown (generally darker with age), with two narrow dark-edged bluish white bars, one on head enclosing posterior edge of preopercle and one in middle of body (this bar may be lost in individuals of 15 cm or larger); caudal fin whitish; pelvic and anal fins usually dark brown; pectoral fins with yellow-orange rays. Attains at least 15.5 cm. Known only from the Arabian Sea coast of Oman where it seems to replace *A. clarkii*. Symbiotic with the anemones *Entacmaea quadricolor* and *Heteractis crispa*.

688. *A. omanensis*, juvenile (J. Hoover)

686. *Amphiprion clarkii*, about 9.5 cm (J. Randall)

687. *Amphiprion omanensis* (J. Hoover)

SEBAE ANEMONEFISH
Amphiprion sebae Bleeker, 1853

Dorsal rays X-XI,14-17; anal rays II,13-14; pectoral rays 18-19; lateral-line scales 36-43; occiput scaled, but interorbital space naked; gill rakers 18-19; body depth 2.0-2.2 in standard length; caudal fin slightly rounded; dark brown, usually with a variable amount of yellow (generally front of head yellow, often the abdomen and caudal peduncle as well), and two very broad white bars, one on postorbital head and the other in middle of body, extending to edge of dorsal fin and often continuing posteriorly as a white margin; caudal fin yellow (juveniles may have a large black area submarginally in fin). Attains 12 cm. Occurs from Java (type locality) and Sumatra west to the Gulf of Oman and Gulf of Aden, including Andaman Islands, Sri Lanka, and Maldives. Symbiotic only with the sea anemone *Stichodactyla haddoni*.

HALF-AND-HALF CHROMIS
Chromis dimidiata (Klunzinger, 1871)

Dorsal rays XII,11-12 (usually 12); anal rays II,12; upper and lower spiniform caudal rays 2; pectoral rays 15-17; lateral-line scales 14-16; gill rakers 7-9 + 18-20; margin of preopercle smooth; this and other Oman *Chromis* with a row of conical teeth in jaws, largest anteriorly, and one or two irregular inner rows of small teeth at front of jaws; body depth 2.0-2.1 in standard length; caudal fin deeply forked, the lobes ending in two filamentous rays; head, body, pelvic fins, and dorsal fin anterior to a demarcation from base of ninth or tenth dorsal spine dark brown, white posteriorly; a large black spot at base of pectoral fins. Reaches 9 cm. Red Sea, south to Tanzania and Mascarene Islands, east to the Maldives and Sri Lanka; occasional on the Arabian Sea coast of Oman; not reported from the Gulf of Oman. Known from the depth range of 2 to 20 m.

ARABIAN CHROMIS
Chromis flavaxilla Randall, 1994

Dorsal rays XII,10-12; anal rays II,11; upper and lower spiniform caudal rays 3; pectoral rays 17-19; lateral-line scales 15-17; gill rakers 7-9 + 20-24; margin of preopercle smooth; body depth 1.9-2.0 in standard length; caudal fin moderately forked; membranes of spinous portion of dorsal fin not incised; olive brown, the scale edges darker, shading to pale grey ventrally; caudal fin light greenish grey with a broad black band in each lobe and a narrow blue upper and lower margin; margin of spinous portion

689. *Amphiprion sebae*, adult and juveniles (J. Hoover)

690. *Chromis dimidiata*, about 7 cm (J. Randall)

691. *Chromis flavaxilla*, about 5 cm (J. Randall)

of dorsal and anal fins and lateral edge of pelvic fins blue; axil of pectoral fins bright orange-yellow. Largest specimen, 7.2 cm. Shores of the Arabian Peninsula from the northern Red Sea to the Arabian Gulf. Forms zooplankton-feeding aggregations on reefs; retreats to the shelter of branching corals with the approach of danger. Closely related to *C. ternatensis* (Bleeker) from elsewhere in the Indo-Pacific region which differs from *C. flavaxilla* in having a more lunate caudal fin, steeper initial dorsal profile of the head, modally fewer lateral-line scales, modally more lower-limb gill rakers, and larger maximum size.

YELLOW-EDGE CHROMIS
Chromis pembae (Smith, 1960)

Dorsal rays XIII,11-12 (usually 12); anal rays II,11-12 (usually 11); upper and lower spiniform caudal rays 3; pectoral rays 18-20; lateral-line scales 15-17; gill rakers 7-8 + 20-23; margin of preopercle smooth; body depth 1.8-2.0 in standard length; caudal fin deeply forked, the lobe tips acute but not filamentous; yellowish brown, darker anteriorly and dorsally on head, dorsally on body, and basally in dorsal fin; outer part of spinous portion of dorsal fin bright orange, this colour continuing as a band in middle of soft portion of fin; outer part of soft portion with yellow rays and clear membranes; caudal fin abruptly white or pale yellow. Reaches 13 cm. Known from Tanzania (type locality) north to the Red Sea, and east to the Gulf of Oman, Seychelles (Randall and van Egmond, 1994), and the Chagos Archipelago (Winterbottom et al., 1989); generally found at depths greater than 25 m. A close relative of *C. analis* (Cuvier) from the western Pacific.

692. *Chromis pembae*, about 11 cm (J. Randall)

693. *Chromis weberi* (J. Randall)

WEBER'S CHROMIS
Chromis weberi Fowler and Bean, 1928

Dorsal rays XIII,10-11 (usually 11); anal rays II,10-11 (usually 11); upper and lower spiniform caudal rays 3; pectoral rays 17-20; lateral-line scales 17-19; gill rakers 8-9 + 19-23; preopercular margin smooth; body depth 2.1-2.5 in standard length; caudal fin deeply forked; olivaceous to bluish grey dorsally, the scale edges darker, shading to whitish ventrally; a narrow dark brown bar at posterior edge of preopercle and another at upper edge of opercle; caudal fin with a broad brown band on outer edge of each lobe, the lobe tips black; a blackish spot dorsally at base of pectoral fins. Attains 13.5 cm. Ranges from the Red Sea (Allen and Randall, 1980) south to Natal and east to the Marshall Islands and Pitcairn Group; in Oman, only from the southern coast, where not common.

YELLOWFIN CHROMIS
Chromis xanthopterygia Randall and McCarthy, 1988

Dorsal rays XIII,10-11(usually 11); anal rays II,10-11 (usually 11); upper and lower spiniform caudal rays 3; pectoral rays 18-20; lateral-line scales 16-18; gill rakers 9-10 + 23-26; margin of preopercle smooth to slightly irregular; body moderately elongate, the depth 2.2-2.55 in standard length; caudal fin deeply forked; body grey-brown with indistinct pale bluish stripes following scale rows; head with some yellow iridescence; outer part of spinous protion of dorsal fin yellow; basal part of anal fin yellow (broadest anteriorly); a broad yellow band at edge of each caudal lobe; a blackish bar at base of pectoral fins; pectoral axil black. Reaches 11.5 cm. Known only from the Arabian Gulf to central Oman; the most common species of the genus in the Arabian Gulf and Gulf of Oman; occasional at Masirah Island, but not observed farther south.

694. *Chromis xanthopterygia*, about 9.5 cm (J. Randall)

BLACKBARRED DAMSELFISH
Chrysiptera annulata (Peters, 1855)

Dorsal rays XIII,12-13; anal rays II,12-13; pectoral rays 17-18; lateral-line scales 17-18; preorbital and suborbital scaleless; gill rakers 5-6 + 10-12; margin of preopercle crenulate to finely serrate; teeth biserial, those in outer row columnar with rounded tips, the inner row buttressing the outer in spaces between; body moderately deep, the depth 1.9-2.0 in standard length; caudal fin slightly forked; white to pale yellow with five black bars, the first on head through eye, the last at caudal-fin base, the middle three extending into dorsal fin; pelvic fins black. Attains 7 cm. Western Indian Ocean from Red Sea to Natal, Madagascar, Mascarenes, and Seychelles; observed in Oman only on the southern and central coast. Not common; usually found in protected inshore waters.

695. *Chrysiptera annulata*, about 6 cm (J. Randall)

696. *Chrysiptera sheila*, adult (J. Hoover)

697. *Chrysiptera sheila*, subadult (J. Hoover)

SHEILA'S DAMSELFISH
Chrysiptera sheila Randall, 1994

Dorsal rays XIII,12-14 (rarely 12); anal rays II,12-13 (rarely 12); pectoral rays 18-19; lateral-line scales 17-19; preorbital and suborbital scaleless; gill rakers 6-8 + 12-14; preopercular margin smooth, the corner and ventral edge slightly scalloped; teeth biserial, slender, compressed, and bluntly pointed to truncate, the tips of inner series interdigitating with those of outer series; body depth 2.0-2.3 in standard length; caudal fin slightly forked with rounded lobes; adults brownish grey with whitish dots posteriorly on body and basally on median fins; a black spot dorsally on base of pectoral fins; juveniles yellow with small pale blue spots posteriorly on body and on base of median fins; a blue line from under eye across upper lip and a short one above it on side of snout; two blue-edged black spots posteriorly in dorsal fin, the second extending partly onto body. Largest specimen, 10.3 cm. Known thus far only from the Arabian Sea coast of Oman to the vicinity of Muscat in the Gulf of Oman; occurs along exposed rocky shores, generally in less than 3 m; a common resident of tidepools. Appears to be most closely related to *C. unimaculata* (see following account).

698. *Chrysiptera sheila*, juvenile (J. Hoover)

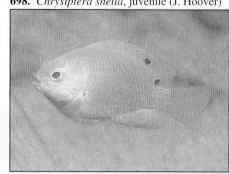

262

ONESPOT DAMSELFISH
Chrysiptera unimaculata (Cuvier, 1830)

Dorsal rays XIII,13-14 (rarely 14); anal rays II,12-14; pectoral rays 18-19 (usually 18); lateral-line scales 16-18; preorbital and suborbital scaleless; gill rakers 7-8 + 14-18; preopercular margin smooth; dentition as in preceding species; body depth 2.1-2.4 in standard length; caudal fin slightly forked with rounded lobes; colour variable, but adults usually grey-brown with a vertically elongate bluish spot on each scale of body; an oval black spot, generally edged in blue,

699. *Chrysiptera unimaculata*, juv. (J. Hoover)

700. *Chrysiptera unimaculata* (J. Randall)

701. *Dascyllus marginatus* (J. Hoover)

702. *Dascyllus trimaculatus* (J. Randall)

often at rear base of dorsal fin; pectoral fins usually yellow or yellowish; juveniles yellowish grey dorsally, shading to yellow or yellowish ventrally, with blue dots on scales and a blue band from snout over eye to end at a large blue-edged black spot at rear base of spinous portion of dorsal fin; a second small blue-edged black spot at rear base of soft part of fin, some of the blue extending dorsally onto caudal peduncle. Attains 8 cm. Red Sea south to Transkei, South Africa, east to Fiji; inhabits shallow exposed reefs and rocky shores, generally with mild to moderate wave action.

BLACKBORDERED DASCYLLUS
Dascyllus marginatus (Rüppell, 1829)

Dorsal rays XII,14-15; anal rays II,13-14 (usually 13); pectoral rays 17-19; lateral-line scales 15-19; preorbital and suborbital bones scaled; gill rakers 7-8 + 19-23; margin of suborbital and preopercle finely serrate; dentition typical of the genus, the teeth conical, moderately large anteriorly in jaws, with an inner band of small villiform teeth at front of jaws; body depth 1.4-1.5 in standard length; caudal fin slightly forked; pale yellowish, usually blackish over lower head, chest, and abdomen; with a light blue edge on scales of body; dorsal fin with a broad black margin, narrowing onto anterior soft portion of fin; anal fin with a broad black margin anteriorly; rays of caudal fin and soft portion of dorsal and anal fins yellowish grey, the membranes light blue; pectoral fins with a large black spot at base; pelvic fins black. Attains 6 cm. Red Sea to Gulf of Oman; closely associated with branching corals for shelter (mainly species of *Acropora* and *Stylophora*), generally several fish sharing the same coral head; depth range about 1-15 m.

DOMINO
Dascyllus trimaculatus (Rüppell, 1829)

Dorsal rays XII,14-16; anal rays II,14-15 (rarely 15); pectoral rays 19-21; lateral-line scales 18-19 (usually 19); preorbital and suborbital scaled; gill rakers 6-7 + 15-19; margin of suborbital and preopercle finely serrate; body depth 1.4-1.6 in standard length; caudal fin of juveniles slightly rounded, of adults slightly emarginate, the corners rounded; adults grey, the scale edges blackish, with a small white spot just above lateral line in middle of body; often a suffusion of yellow over head and chest; median and pelvic fins black; a black spot at upper base of pectoral fins; juveniles darker with a larger white to pale blue spot on body and another in middle of forehead. Reaches 14 cm. Indo-Pacific except Hawaii (where replaced by the close relative *D. albisella* Gill) and the Marquesas (another endemic replacement, *D. strasburgi* Klausewitz) (H. Randall and Allen, 1977). The young often commensal with large sea anemones (like anemonefishes, they enjoy immunity from the stinging cells of the tentacles); also they may seek shelter among branching corals or the spines of *Diadema*.

703. *D. trimaculatus*, juvs in gorgonian (J. Hoover)

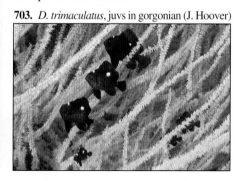

REGAL DAMSELFISH
Neopomacentrus cyanomos (Bleeker, 1856)

Dorsal rays XIII,11-12; anal rays II,11-12; pectoral rays 17-18; anterior lateral-line scales 17-18; preorbital scaled posteriorly; suborbital scaled, the lower margin scaled over; gill rakers 6-8 + 15-17; lower part of posterior margin of preopercle weakly serrate; teeth incisiform, close-set, in two rows anteriorly, those of second row buttressing the front row; body depth 2.3-2.6 in standard length; middle rays of soft portion of dorsal and anal fins prolonged; caudal fin lunate; dark brown, paler ventrally, the scales of nape and ventrally on body often with iridescent blue centres; a black spot larger than pupil and containing some green iridescence at origin of lateral line; dorsal fin dark brown, abruptly white to light yellow posteriorly, the brightest white or yellow at base; caudal fin dark brown with large centroposterior part abruptly white to pale yellow; pelvic fins dark brown with blue lateral edge. Reaches 9.5 cm. Red Sea and East Africa to western Pacific; usually found in protected waters such as harbours and bays; abundant in Musandam and the northern

704. *Neopomacentrus cyanomos* (J. Hoover)

Gulf of Oman, progressively less common to the south; occur in aggregations feeding on zooplankton over coral heads.

MIRY'S DAMSELFISH
Neopomacentrus miryae Dor and Allen, 1977

Dorsal rays XIII,11-13; anal rays II,11; pectoral rays 18-19; lateral-line scales 17-18; preorbital scaleless; suborbital scaled, its lower edge covered by scales; gill rakers 7-9 + 19-21; margin of preopercle smooth; teeth incisiform, close-set, in one row; body depth 2.2-2.6 in standard length; caudal fin deeply forked; olivaceous, the scales dorsally on body dark-edged; a white spot smaller than pupil dorsally on caudal peduncle just behind rear base of anal fin; a broad orange-yellow band dorsally on caudal peduncle extending submarginally into upper lobe of caudal fin; lower lobe of caudal fin with a less-developed orange-yellow submarginal band; upper edge of pectoral-fin base with a small black spot. Attains 11 cm. Red Sea to Gulf of Oman; abundant in southern Oman, especially off Dhofar, forming large aggregations feeding on zooplankton well above the substratum; occasional in the Gulf of Oman where it sometimes schools with *Chromis xanthopterygia*.

705. *Neopomacentrus miryae* (J. Hoover)

SIND DAMSELFISH
Neopomacentrus sindensis (Day, 1873)

Dorsal rays XIII,11-12; anal rays II,11-12; pectoral rays 18-19; lateral-line scales 18-19; preorbital scaled; suborbital scaled over; gill rakers 8-9 + 17-18; preopercular margin smooth; body depth 2.3-2.6 in standard length; caudal fin forked, the upper lobe more pointed and longer than lower; brownish to bluish grey, the scale edges dark, shading to yellow on caudal peduncle and fin; scales posteriorly on body with a small blue spot; posterior part of dorsal fin also yellow; margin of dorsal and anal fins bright blue except posteriorly; a black spot at upper base of pectoral fins; pelvic fins usually mostly black. Reaches 10 cm. Arabian Gulf to coast of Pakistan, the range here extended to Kovalam, southwest India by specimens collected by the author; not seen in Oman south of Masirah Island; common on protected inshore reefs where the bottom is silty sand or mud.

706. *Neopomacentrus sindensis*, about 6.5 cm (J. Randall)

JOHNSTON DAMSELFISH
Plectroglyphidodon johnstonianus Fowler and Ball, 1924

Dorsal rays XII,18-19; anal rays II,16-18; pectoral rays 19; lateral-line scales 21-22; suborbital and posterior preorbital scaled; gill rakers 0-2 + 11-13; margin of preopercle and suborbital smooth; teeth slender, close-set, and uniserial; lips fleshy and vertically furrowed; body depth 1.7-1.9 in standard length; dorsal profile of head nearly straight; caudal fin forked; yellowish grey to yellow, usually with a large, vertically elongate, blackish area just anterior to caudal peduncle which may extend into base of dorsal and anal fins; blue markings on head. Largest specimen, 12 cm. Indo-Pacific except the Red Sea, Arabian Gulf, and Gulf of Oman; occasional on the southern coast of Oman; closely associated with live corals, especially of the genera *Acropora* and *Pocillopora*; feeds heavily on coral polyps.

WHITEBAR DAMSELFISH
Plectroglyphidodon leucozonus (Bleeker, 1859)

Dorsal rays XII,15-16 (usually 15); anal rays II,12-13 (usually 12); pectoral rays 18-20; lateral-line scales 19-20; preorbital and suborbital scaled; gill rakers 3-4 + 12-14; margin of suborbital and preopercle smooth; teeth incisiform, slender, close-set, and uniserial; body depth 1.8-1.9 in standard length; caudal fin forked; brown, the edges of the scales darker, shading to yellow or yellowish on caudal peduncle and fin; a white bar on body centred on base of eighth dorsal spine; a blackish spot dorsoanteriorly on caudal peduncle; posterior dorsal and anal fins yellow or yellowish; a black spot at upper base of pectoral fins; juveniles more yellow than adults, with a large yellow-edged black spot basally in posterior spinous portion of dorsal fin and on adjacent back. Reported to 12 cm. Indo-Pacific; observed and photographed in

707. *Plectroglyphidodon johnstonianus* (J. Hoover)

708. *Plectroglyphidodon leucozonus,* about 10 cm (J. Randall)

Oman only at Masirah Island, but probably occurs along the south coast in its shallow habitat of rocky shore exposed to wave action. Feeds mainly on benthic algae. In the Red Sea the species has more yellow colour as an adult and a slightly higher gill-raker count; it has been regarded as a different subspecies, *P. leucozonus cingulus* Klunzinger. Based on colour, the Oman form is the same subspecies.

DARK DAMSELFISH
Pomacentrus aquilus Allen and Randall, 1980

Dorsal rays XIV,13-15; anal rays II,14-15; pectoral rays 17-19; lateral-line scales 17-19; preorbital scaleless; suborbital bones with few or no scales, the first with a posteriorly-directed spine; gill rakers 19-22; margin of preorbital, suborbital, and preopercle serrate; teeth incisiform with rounded tips, close-set, in two rows, the inner row smaller and buttressing the outer (dentition generally the same for other species of the genus); body depth 1.9-2.2 in standard length; caudal peduncle depth 2.0-2.2 in head length; caudal fin forked; large adults dark brown, the scale edges even darker; a black spot middorsally on caudal peduncle (difficult to see on dark individuals); a black spot at upper base of pectoral fins; juveniles yellow with two blue stripes dorsally on head which join shortly before linking with blue edge of large black spot at juncture of spinous and soft portions of dorsal fin; a small black spot partially edged in blue dorsally on caudal peduncle; subadults tan with brown edges on scales and blue dots on posterior half of body (one to three per scale). Attains about 12 cm. Red Sea to Arabian Gulf, south on east African coast at least to Kenya. Coral reefs and rocky bottom from 1-15 m.

709. *Pomacentrus aquilus* (J. Randall)

710. *Pomacentrus aquilus,* juv. (J. Hoover)

ARABIAN DAMSELFISH
Pomacentrus arabicus Allen, 1991

Dorsal rays XIV,14-15; anal rays II,14-15; pectoral rays 17-18; lateral-line scales 18-19; preorbital scaleless; suborbital scaled; gill rakers 19-22; margin of preorbital, suborbital, and preopercle serrate; body depth 1.6-1.8 in standard length; caudal peduncle depth 1.75-2.0 in head length; caudal fin slightly forked with rounded lobes; dark brown, the edges of the scales black; colour of juveniles unknown; it is suspected that it is similar to that of juvenile *P. aquilus* and has therefore gone unnoticed. Reaches 14.5 cm. Known only from the Gulf of Oman in the vicinity of Muscat; inhabits rocky inshore reefs in the depth range of 1-6 m. Differs from *P. aquilus* in its deeper body and in lacking blue spots on scales and a black spot at upper edge of caudal peduncle.

711. *Pomacentrus arabicus* (J. Hoover)

712. *Pomacentrus caeruleus*, about 6 cm (J. Hoover)

713. *Pomacentrus leptus*, about 6 cm (J. Randall)

CAERULEAN DAMSELFISH
Pomacentrus caeruleus Quoy and Gaimard, 1825

Dorsal rays XIII,14-15; anal rays II,15-16; pectoral rays 17-18; lateral-line scales 17-19; preorbital scaleless, ending in a short spine; suborbital largely scaleless; gill rakers 20-23; suborbital margin smooth or with a few small serrae; preopercular margin serrate; body depth 2.4-2.8 in standard length; caudal fin forked, the upper lobe more pointed and a little longer than lower; blue, becoming yellow ventrally and posteriorly on body; a small deep blue to black spot on opercle at upper end of gill opening; caudal fin, anal fin, pelvic fins, and posterior part of dorsal fin yellow, the anal with a blue margin and two blue lines in outer half of fin, the pelvics with a blue lateral edge; pectoral rays yellow, the membranes clear; a wedge-shaped black spot at pectoral-fin base. Reaches 8 cm. Red Sea and coast of East Africa south to Natal, east to Mauritius, Seychelles, and Maldives; observed in Oman only in the south; generally found on coral reefs or rubble bottoms in the depth range of 1 to 10 m. *P. pulcherrimus* Smith is a synonym.

SLENDER DAMSELFISH
Pomacentrus leptus Allen and Randall, 1980

Dorsal rays XIII,13-14; anal rays II,13-14; pectoral rays 16-17; lateral-line scales 15-17; preorbital and suborbital scaleless; gill rakers 17-20; margin of suborbital smooth or with a few weak serrae; margin of preopercle finely serrate; body slender for the genus, the depth 2.3-2.7 in standard length; caudal fin slightly forked; orangish brown, darker posteriorly, the scale edges dark brown, the scale centres with several tiny black dots; a small black spot on opercle at upper end of gill opening; caudal fin and distal third of soft portion of dorsal fin whitish to pale yellowish; a small black spot at upper base of pectoral fins; a blue colour form with the caudal fin and posterior dorsal fin more yellow occurs in the Gulf of Oman along with the more drab phase. Largest specimen, 6.8 cm. Red Sea to Arabian Gulf; occurs on coral reefs, generally in less than 10 m; more common in the Gulf of Oman than on the south coast.

714. *Pomacentrus trichourus*, juv. (J. Randall)

RETICULATED DAMSELFISH
Pomacentrus trichourus Playfair and Günther, 1867

715. *Pomacentrus trichourus*, about 7.5 cm (J. Randall)

Dorsal rays XIV,14-16; anal rays II,15-17; pectoral rays 16-17 (rarely 16); lateral-line scales 17-18; preorbital and suborbital scaleless; gill rakers 19-24; preorbital with a hook-like posterior spine; suborbital edge with a few small serrae; preopercular margin serrate; body depth 1.9-2.2 in standard length; caudal fin emarginate to slightly forked; adults dark brown, the scale centres paler, giving a reticulated effect; posterior part of caudal peduncle darker than rest of body (or there may be a large round black spot); a small black spot on opercle near upper end of gill opening; caudal fin abruptly white, the membranes transparent posteriorly; margin of dorsal fin black except posteriorly; axil and most of pectoral-fin base covered by a black spot; juveniles blue dorsally on head and on nape. Attains 11 cm. Red Sea, Arabian Gulf, and Gulf of Oman, south to Natal; not observed on the southern coast of Oman, and not known from oceanic islands of the Indian Ocean. Specimens collected by the author were taken in 2-15 m; Allen and Randall (1980) reported the species to depths as great as 43 m. Fishelson et al. (1974) documented the food habits as algae, ostracods, demersal fish eggs, small fishes, and sponges.

THREELINE DAMSELFISH
Pomacentrus trilineatus Cuvier, 1830

Dorsal rays XIII,14-16; anal rays II,14-16; pectoral rays 17-18; lateral-line scales 16-19 (modally 18); preorbital and suborbital scaleless; gill rakers 25-31; margins of preorbital, suborbital, and preopercle serrate; body depth 1.9-2.1 in standard length; caudal fin forked with rounded lobes; adults yellowish brown, dark brown, or bluish grey, the scale edges darker; posterior caudal peduncle and fin usually paler than body; a small blue-edged black spot dorsoanteriorly on caudal peduncle; a small deep blue spot on opercle in front of upper end of gill opening; blue dots may be present on scales posterior to tip of pectoral fins; large pale yellowish to pale bluish spots on operculum below level of eye; a black spot on upper base of pectoral fins, sometimes with a narrow ventral extension to lower edge; juveniles yellow with a blue dot on each scale of body except ventrally; two narrow bright blue bands dorsally on head (one from front of snout, the other from upper part of eye) extending along base of dorsal fin, ending in blue ring around a large black spot at junction of spinous and soft portions of dorsal fin; a short, sometimes broken, third blue line on side of snout through lower part of eye; a small blue and black spot dorsally on caudal peduncle. Reaches 10 cm. Red Sea south to Mozambique, Seychelles, and Madagascar; common on the shallow reefs at Barr al Hikman on the central coast of Oman; not known to the north. Often misidentified as *P. tripunctatus* Cuvier (as by Smith, 1960), a western Pacific species. Easily confused with *P. aquilus*, especially the juvenile; *aquilus* has XIV dorsal spines and lacks the pale caudal fin as an adult.

716. *Pomacentrus trilineatus*, about 10 cm (J. Randall)

717. *Pristotis obtusirostris*, 9.4 cm (J. Randall)

GULF DAMSELFISH
Pristotis obtusirostris (Günther, 1862)

Dorsal rays XIII,12-13; anal rays II,12-14; pectoral rays 17-18; lateral-line scales 19-20; preorbital and suborbital scaled; predorsal scales extending to mid-interorbital space; gill rakers 26-28; teeth incisiform, in one row, small along side of jaws; posterior margin of suborbital serrate; margin of preopercle and subopercle serrate; body elongate, the depth 2.5-2.9 in standard length; snout notably shorter than eye diameter; interspinous membranes of dorsal fin not incised; caudal fin forked; yellow dorsally, shading to whitish on sides and ventrally, with an iridescent blue spot on each scale; a bluish black spot at upper base of pectoral fins. Reaches 14 cm. Arabian Gulf to western Pacific where it ranges from the Ryukyu Islands to New South Wales. Inhabits open sand, mud, or rubble bottoms (hence often taken by trawling) in the depth range of 5-80 m. *P. jerdoni* (Day) from India is here reported as a junior synonym.

WRASSES
FAMILY LABRIDAE

The wrasse family is very diverse. The species vary greatly in size, from adults as small as 5 cm to the giant humphead wrasse recorded to 229 cm. They also vary greatly in shape, from moderately deep-bodied to slender, long to short-snouted, etc. The family can be defined collectively by the following characters: mouth usually terminal, protractile, and small to moderate in size, the maxilla not exposed on the cheek; lips often fleshy; teeth at front of jaws generally as well-developed canines which are usually protruding; teeth absent from roof of mouth (except for one or a few teeth on vomer of some species of *Bodianus*); a canine tooth often present at corner of mouth; pharygeal dentition well-developed on paired upper pharyngeal bones and single lower T- to Y-shaped pharyngeal plate, the teeth varying from stout and conical to molariform; scales cycloid; head naked or with just the cheek and/or opercle scaled; lateral line continuous or interrupted; a single dorsal fin of VIII-XXI spines, without a notch between spinous and soft portions (however, species of *Xyrichtys* have the anterior part of dorsal fin of two spines separated from or deeply notched from the rest of the fin), and 6-21 soft rays; anal spines usually III (a few species with II and two European genera with IV-VI), and 7-18 soft rays; pelvic rays I,5, the fins thoracic in position; branchiostegal rays 5 or 6; vertebrae 23-42 (the higher numbers in temperate species of Labrinae). The scleral cornea of the eye of the species of *Cirrhilabrus*, *Paracheilinus*, *Pteragogus* (*Duymaeria* is a synonym), and *Pseudocheilinus* is divided into two adjacent roundish parts. Most wrasses are very colourful, often with complex patterns. Juveniles frequently differ in colour from adults, and many species exhibit sexual dichromatism, generally associated with a change in sex from female to male. The first colour form of those species with sex reversal is termed the initial phase; it is usually less colourful than the second, the terminal male phase. In some species the initial phase may be either male or female, and spawning typically takes place in aggregations. Eggs and sperm are released at the peak of a sudden upward rush by a female and several males. Terminal males tend to establish sexual territories and maintain a harem of females; they spawn individually with females after courtship display. A few temperate labrid fishes build nests of seaweed, but the vast majority of the wrasses lay numerous tiny pelagic eggs. All wrasses are carnivorous, but their food habits vary enormously. Most species feed on a variety of hard-shelled invertebrates such as crabs, hermit crabs, molluscs, sea urchins, and brittle stars which they crush with their pharyngeal dentition. Some of the smaller species, such as those of the genera *Cirrhilabrus*, *Paracheilinus*, *Pseudocoris*, and some species of *Thalassoma*, feed in aggregations on zooplankton. The species of *Labroides* and the young of some other genera such as *Bodianus* and *Labropsis* feed primarily on the ectoparasites and mucus of other fishes. Adults of *Labropsis*, *Labrichthys*, and *Diproctacanthus* feed mainly on coral polyps (for which their very fleshy lips appear to be a specialisation). A few wrasses such as the species of *Hologymnosus* prey heavily on small fishes. The species

718. Cleaner wrasse (*Labroides dimidiatus*) and *Thalassoma lunare* (J. Hoover)

of *Anampses* forcefully strike the substratum with their mouths and projecting incisiform teeth, at the same time sucking in very small animals such as crustaceans, foramanifera, molluscs, and worms, along with sand and debris. The species of *Stethojulis* do the same but are more inclined to pick up sand. Those of the genus *Hemigymnus* ingest mouthfuls of sand, sort out the tiny animals within, and eject the inorganic material. Labrids are diurnal; they are among the first to retire to an inactive state on the bottom with the approach of darkness and the last to resume activity the following morning. Most of the smaller species bury in the sand at night; the larger ones hide deep within the cover of the reef. Wrasses are usually seen swimming with just their pectoral fins; they bring their caudal fin into action only when swift movement is needed. The wrasse family is the second largest of marine fishes with at least 60 genera and an estimated 500 species, exceeded only by the Gobiidae.

It is also second in the number of species for the Oman area, with 47.

BLUESPOTTED WRASSE
Anampses caeruleopunctatus Rüppell, 1829

Dorsal rays IX,12; anal rays III,12; lateral-line scales 27 (not including one beyond base of caudal fin); head scaleless (true of all species of the genus); gill rakers 18-21; body depth 2.3-3.0 in standard length; a single pair of forward-projecting teeth at front of jaws, the uppers somewhat flattened with pointed upcurved trips, the lowers nearly conical and curved downward; no remaining teeth in jaws or only a few minute ones (dentition generic); caudal fin truncate to slightly rounded; pelvic fins 2.1-2.5 in head length; females olive to brown dorsally, shading to orangish brown ventrally, with small dark-edged blue spots on body and fins and dark-edged narrow blue bands on head, many radiating from eye; males olive with a dark-edged vertical blue line on each scale of body; a broad light green bar often on body below base of sixth dorsal spine; head with narrow dark-edged blue lines and a broad blue band and across front of interorbital space. Largest specimen, 42 cm. Indo-Pacific; observed in Oman only on the Arabian Sea coast where not common. An inshore species, typically where exposed to surge, but may be seen as deep as 20 m. *A. diadematus* Rüppell is a synonym based on the male phase.

LINED WRASSE
Anampses lineatus Randall, 1972

Dorsal rays IX,12; anal rays III,12; pectoral rays 13; lateral-line scales 26; no median predorsal scales; gill rakers 14-16; body depth 3.15-3.4 in standard length; caudal fin rounded; pelvic fins 1.85-2.2 in head length; females orangish brown with dark-edged, light blue-green lines (some broken into series of dashes) following longitudinal scale rows; head and chest with pale blue-green spots and irregular narrow bands; a black spot on opercular flap; caudal fin white with a very large black area covering most of outer half of fin (leaving only a narrow white posterior margin); males develop a bright yellow patch beneath the pectoral fins, and the lines are more blue. Reaches 13 cm. Red Sea south to Natal and east to southern Indonesia, including the Seychelles and Maldives; observed only on the southern Oman coast where rare. A coral-reef species generally found at depths greater than 20 m. Originally described as a subspecies of the Pacific *A. melanurus* Bleeker.

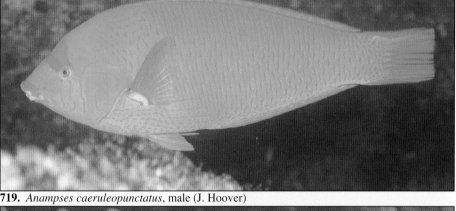

719. *Anampses caeruleopunctatus*, male (J. Hoover)

720. *Anampses caeruleopunctatus*, female, with small *Thalassoma lunare* (J. Hoover)

721. *Anampses lineatus*, female, about 10 cm (J. Randall)

SPOTTED WRASSE
Anampses meleagrides Valenciennes, 1840

Dorsal rays IX,12; anal rays III,12; lateral-line scales 26; no median predorsal scales; gill rakers 18-20; body depth 3.1-3.4 in standard length; caudal fin truncate to emarginate; pelvic fins 1.5-2.0 in head length; females dark brown with small round white spots on head, body, and dorsal and anal fins, those on body one per scale; caudal fin abruptly bright yellow; males dark reddish brown with a blue vertical line on scales of side of body, becoming blue spots on caudal peduncle; head and chest with irregular blue lines; dorsal and anal fins dull orange with blue lines; caudal fin orange with blue spots and a white posterior crescent edged anteriorly with blue. Reaches 21 cm. Indo-Pacific; observed in Oman only off the southern coast. *A. amboinensis* Bleeker is a synonym based on the male form.

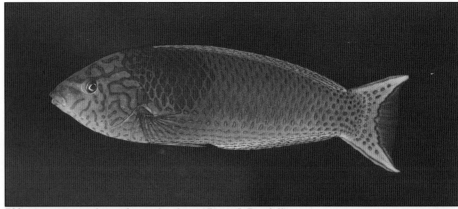

722. *Anampses meleagrides*, male, about 17 cm (J. Randall)

723. *A. meleagrides*, female, about 10 cm (J. Randall)

AXILSPOT HOGFISH
Bodianus axillaris (Bennett, 1831)

Dorsal rays XIII,9-10 (usually 10); anal rays III,11-12 (usually 12); pectoral rays 15-17; lateral line complete and smoothly curved (characteristic of the genus), the pored scales 30-31; scales dorsally on head reaching anterior to nostrils, those on cheek to below nostrils; a scaly sheath at base of dorsal and anal fins; gill rakers 15-18; body depth 2.8-3.1 in standard length; snout pointed, 2.9-3.2 in head; caudal fin slightly rounded to slightly double emarginate; adults dark reddish brown, shading to white posterior to a diagonal from front of abdomen to soft portion of dorsal fin; a large black spot at base of pectoral fins and in soft portion of dorsal and anal fins; a small black spot at front of dorsal fin; juveniles black with two series of four large white spots, one dorsal and one ventral; tip of snout white. Attains 20 cm. Red Sea south on east African coast to Natal, east to Samoa and the Marshall Islands; observed in Oman only in the south. The young are usually seen in caves; they, and occasional adults, are cleaners.

724. *Bodianus axillaris*, male, about 13 cm (J. Randall)

726. *Bodianus axillaris*, juvenile (J. Randall)

725. *Bodianus axillaris*, female, 18.5 cm (J. Randall)

DIANA'S HOGFISH
Bodianus diana (Lacepède, 1801)

Dorsal rays XII,9-10 (usually 10); anal rays III,10-12; pectoral rays 15-17; lateral-line scales 30-31; scales dorsally on head extending to middle of interorbital space; scales on cheek reaching to below nostrils; a broad sheath of scales basally on dorsal and anal fins; gill rakers 15-18; body depth 3.0-3.2 in standard length; snout pointed, 2.6-2.9 in head length; caudal slightly rounded in juveniles, truncate to slightly double emarginate in adults; head and dorsal part of body of adults reddish to purplish brown, shading to yellowish on rest of body, the scales rimmed with reddish brown; scales dorsoposteriorly on body with a small black spot; four small white to yellow spots in a row along back; median fins with red rays, the dorsal fin with a black spot at the front, the anal fin with two black spots, and the caudal with a small one at midbase; pelvic fins white with a large black area in middle of each fin; juveniles reddish brown with longitudinal rows of white blotches and small white spots; fins with the same black spots as adults except an additonal one posteriorly on dorsal. Reaches 25 cm. Red Sea and Gulf of Oman, south to Transkei, South Africa and east to the Marshall Islands and Samoa. The young and occasionally an adult may be seen picking at the bodies of other fishes. *Lepidaplois aldabrensis* Smith is a synonym based on the juvenile stage.

727. *Bodianus diana* (J. Hoover)

728. *Bodianus diana*, juvenile (J. Hoover)

GIANT HOGFISH
Bodianus macrognathos (Morris, 1974)

Dorsal rays XII,10; anal rays III,12-13; pectoral rays 16-17; lateral-line scales 40-42; scales dorsally on head extending to posterior interorbital space; small scales on cheek reaching to below eye; a scaly sheath at base of dorsal and anal fins; gill rakers 16-18; body depth 2.55-3.1 in standard length; snout length varying from 3.5 in head length in juveniles to 2.8 in large adults; dorsal profile of head progressively more convex with growth, the upper jaw protruding; lower jaw massive in adults; caudal fin of juveniles truncate, of large adults slightly rounded in middle, the lobes greatly prolonged; adults reddish, shading to whitish ventrally, the scale edges darker, with faint dark bars of unequal width on body; lower lip and chin light bluish grey; juveniles with a broad black stripe from front of snout (except lips which are white) and chin through eye, along upper side of body, and broadening on caudal peduncle and caudal fin; head and body above stripe red, the centres of scales whitish; a median black stripe on nape extending along upper back and including all of dorsal fin except last three or four rays and adjacent membranes; head and body below black lateral stripe white, the scale edges light red; pelvic fins and outer two-thirds of anal fin black. Attains at least 80 cm; one of 78 cm landed at Mutrah weighed 7.3 kg. Known from Kenya (type locality) north to the Gulf of Oman (but not the Red Sea); occurs from shallow water along exposed rocky coasts to depths of at least 65 m.

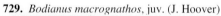
729. *Bodianus macrognathos*, juv. (J. Hoover)

730. *Bodianus macrognathos* (J. Hoover)

731. *Cheilinus lunulatus*, male, about 45 cm (J. Randall)

BROOMTAIL WRASSE
Cheilinus lunulatus (Forsskål, 1775)

Dorsal rays IX,10; anal rays III,8; pectoral rays 12; lateral line interrupted, the anterior pored scales 15-16 (usually 16); scales dorsally on head reaching to anterior interorbital space; gill rakers 10-12; body depth 2.4-2.7 in standard length; lower jaw slightly protruding; dorsal profile of head more convex in males; sixth and adjacent dorsal and anal soft rays prolonged in adults, two or more times longer than first and last rays; caudal fin slightly rounded, the rays of adults free of membranes posteriorly, the free part very long in males (hence the name Broomtail Wrasse); pelvic fins of adults very long; body of females greenish grey with a vertical orange-red line on each scale; body with four blackish bars, the second and third as double bars; a midlateral row of four or five blackish spots usually present; head and anterior body dull green with very small orange-red spots and a black spot on opercular flap containing an irregular bright yellow marking; males dark bluish grey on

732. *Cheilinus lunulatus*, female, about 23 cm (J. Randall)

body, the orange-red lines less evident, with a broad irregular greenish yellow bar across body below outer half of pectoral fin; head darker and brighter green. Reaches 50 cm. Occurs from the northern Red Sea to the Arabian Gulf.

733. *C. lunulatus*, juv., 9.8 cm (J. Randall)

272

CIGAR WRASSE
Cheilio inermis (Forsskål, 1775)

Dorsal rays IX,12-13; anal rays III,11-12; pectoral rays 12-13; lateral-line scales 45-47; head naked except for a few scales behind eye on preopercle and opercle; body very elongate, the depth 5.5-7.8 in standard length; width of body about 1.7 in depth; snout very long, 2.2-2.4 in head length; teeth conical, those at front of jaws recurved, the anterior pair of upper jaw as moderate canines; caudal fin rounded or rhomboid; ground colour variable – green, brown, orange-brown, or yellow; often with a narrow midlateral black stripe which may be broken into a series of dashes and spots; large males lack the stripe and develop an irregular orange to salmon pink area mixed with dark brown on upper side of body at tip of pectoral fin. Attains 50 cm. Indo-Pacific; occasional along the Oman south coast. Although may be seen on coral reefs, more common in seagrass beds or substrata with heavy algal growth. Feeds on gastropod and pelecypod molluscs, crabs, hermit crabs, sea urchins, and shrimps. M.F. Gomon and B.C. Russell noted that this species is allied with the Odacidae, hence may serve to link this family with the Labridae.

734. *Cheilio inermis*, female (J. Randall)

735. *Cheilio inermis*, male (J. Randall)

ROBUST TUSKFISH
Choerodon robustus (Günther, 1862)

Dorsal rays XIII,8; anal rays III,10; pectoral rays 16; lateral-line complete, the pored scales 29; scales dorsally on head not reaching interorbital space; cheek and opercle scaled; gill rakers 16-19; two pairs of stout canine teeth anteriorly in each jaw, the second pair in lower jaw directed laterally; body moderately deep, the depth 2.5-2.6 in standard length; dorsal fin nearly uniform in height, the interspinous membranes not incised; caudal fin truncate; females with a diagonal brown band from upper base of pectoral fin to rear base of dorsal fin; a broader white band below and adjacent to brown band; body above brown band orangish brown, becoming grey-brown dorsally and on head; body below white band yellowish, the scales with a pale blue vertical line except on caudal peduncle where they become spots or join to form longitudinal blue lines; head with blue markings around eye; upper lip and chin yellow, each with a blue stripe; lower edge of operculum blue; median fins yellow with longitudinal blue bands, the corners of caudal fin blue; males similar in color, the white band changing to orange, the blue markings on body and fins disappearing, and the ventral part of the head and chest becoming blue. Attains about 35 cm. Red Sea and Arabian Gulf south to Mozambique and Mauritius (type locality); also reported from Indonesia (Gloerfelt-Tarp and Kailola, 1984) and southern Japan; more common in the Arabian Gulf and northern Gulf of Oman than to the south.

736. *Choerodon robustus*, 25.2 cm (J. Randall)

SOCIAL WRASSE
Cirrhilabrus rubriventralis Springer and Randall, 1974

Dorsal rays XI,9; anal rays III,9; pectoral rays 15; lateral-line scales 15-17 + 5-7; median predorsal scales 4-5; horizontal scale rows on cheek below eye 1; gill rakers 14-16; body depth 3.1-3.4 in SL; head length 2.7-3.3 in SL; dorsal profile of head of males nearly straight; snout pointed, the snout length 3.2-3.7 in head; cirri of first two dorsal spines of male prolonged as long filaments, the second reaching nearly to rear base of dorsal fin when laid back; caudal fin rounded, the corners slightly prolonged in males; pelvic fins short in females, broad and very elongate in males, reaching beyond spinous portion of anal fin. Females red, shading to orange ventrally, with six dark-edged longitudinal blue lines or rows of spots or dashes; an irregular black spot smaller than pupil posteriorly on caudal peduncle above lateral line; a pinkish white spot medi-ally at front of snout; base of pectoral fins yellow. Males mainly red on head and body (but may be suffused with yellow) to level of lower edge of eye, abruptly white to pale yellow below, the demarcation a blue line on head and indistinct purplish line on body; dorsal filaments red; caudal fin, soft portion of dorsal fin, and base of anal fin with bright blue spots; pelvic fins bright red, black at base. Largest specimen, 6.4 cm. Known from the Red Sea, south coast of Oman, and Sri Lanka. Occurs in aggregations, usually over rubble bottoms, in the depth range of 3-40 m; feeds on zooplankton. Males maintain a harem; they display to females in courtship by elevating the dorsal fin, lowering the pelvic fins, and fluttering the caudal fin.

737. *Cirrhilabrus rubriventralis*, male, 6.5 cm (J. Randall)

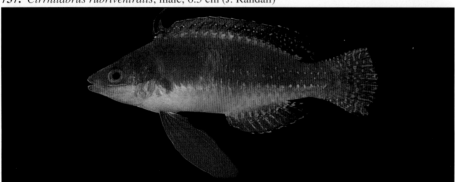

738. *C. rubriventralis*, juvenile (J. Hoover)

739. *Coris africana* (J. Randall)

AFRICAN CORIS
Coris africana Smith, 1957

Dorsal rays IX,12; anal rays III,12; pectoral rays 13; lateral-line complete, sharply deflected downward below posterior dorsal fin to straight peduncular part (true of other *Coris*), the pored scales 70-81; predorsal scales extending anteriorly to above eyes; no scales on cheek or opercle; gill rakers 16-19; two pairs of canine teeth at front of jaws, the more anterior pair distinctly larger, and one or two small canines at corner of mouth (also generic); body depth 3.2-3.8 in standard length; first two dorsal spines of adults flexible, close together, and elongate; space between second and third dorsal spines greater than spaces between remaining spines; caudal fin slightly rounded; adults reddish brown with green bands on head and small green spots (one per scale) on body (spots may be blue in small individuals); males with a pale green bar on body above origin of anal fin; juveniles orange-red with three black-edged white spots dorsally on body, the first two extending into dorsal fin; head with two similar but smaller middorsal spots. Reaches 38 cm. Western Indian Ocean, including Red Sea but not the Gulf of Oman or Arabian Gulf; only a single adult and a

740. *C. africana*, juv., about 8 cm (J. Randall)

few juveniles seen off Dhofar. Feeds mainly on molluscs, crabs, and hermit crabs; turns over rocks to prey upon the invertebrates hiding beneath. Closely related to *C. gaimard* (Quoy and Gaimard) of the eastern Indian Ocean and the Pacific.

741. *Coris aygula*, male (J. Randall)

742. *Coris aygula*, juv., about 8 cm (J. Randall)

CLOWN CORIS
Coris aygula Lacepède, 1801

Dorsal rays IX,12; anal rays III,12; pectoral rays 13-14 (rarely 13); lateral-line scales 59-67; head scaleless except nape; body depth 2.7-3.3 in standard length; gill rakers 18-21; a fleshy hump developing on forehead of large males; first two dorsal spines flexible, close together, and prolonged in males; space between second and third dorsal spines greater than spaces between remaining spines; caudal fin rounded in juveniles, slightly rounded in females, and truncate with rays prolonged and free of mem-

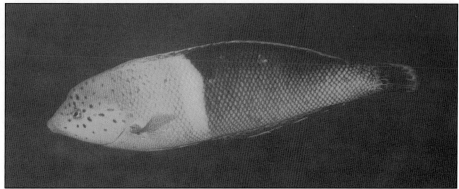

743. *Coris aygula*, female (J. Hoover)

brane in males; females light greenish anteriorly with small dark reddish spots; a pale bar across body above anus; body posterior to bar greenish, the scale edges blackish; median fins with dark reddish to black spots; males dark blue-green, often with a broad pale green bar above origin of anal fin; juveniles whitish with small black spots on head and anterior body and two large semi-

circular orange-red spots on back with a large ocellated black spot above each in dorsal fin. Reported to exceed 100 cm; however, the largest of 43 adults collected by the author measured 58.3 cm. Indo-Pacific; observed only in southern Oman where it is rare. Like *C. africana*, it often turns over rocks in search of its usual prey of shelled molluscs, hermit crabs, sea urchins, and crabs.

SPOTTAIL CORIS
Coris caudimacula (Quoy and Gaimard, 1834)

Dorsal rays IX,12; anal rays III,12; pectoral rays 13; lateral-line scales 47-52; head scaleless except nape; gill rakers 17-22; body depth 3.4-4.2 in standard length; dorsal spines somewhat sharp except first which is prolonged in males; second dorsal spine a little longer than third; caudal fin rounded; light green, shading ventrally to yellow, with four orange to salmon pink stripes on upper two-thirds of body, the lowermost breaking into a series of spots posteriorly; a small black spot on opercular flap, edged posteriorly with yellow; a large diffuse blackish spot often present on base of caudal fin; outer part of first two interspinous membranes of dorsal fin blackish. Reaches 20 cm. Indian Ocean from Red Sea to South Africa and east to Indonesia; occasional in southern Oman, rare in the Gulf of Oman.

744. *Coris caudimacula*, male (J. Hoover)

745. *Coris caudimacula*, female? (J. Hoover)

QUEEN CORIS
Coris frerei Playfair and Günther, 1867

Dorsal rays IX,12; anal rays III,12; pectoral rays 13; lateral-line scales 69-75; a narrow median scaleless zone on nape; also the anteroventral part of chest scaleless; gill rakers 16-19; body depth 2.7-3.5 in standard length; first two dorsal spines of adults flexible, very elongate (slightly prolonged on large juveniles) and close together, the space between second and third spines broader than spaces between remaining spines; caudal fin slightly rounded; body of females grey to greenish brown with numerous small black spots; head orange-yellow, shading to brown on operculum, with blue bands, the most prominent from near origin of dorsal fin passing just below eye and curving onto ventral part of head; outer scaleless part of caudal fin bright red with a broad white posterior border; body of males light reddish with a green or blue-green spot on each scale and about 11 dark purplish grey bars; head reddish grey with green bands similar in pattern to those of female; caudal fin purplish grey with blue spots, a narrow blue margin and broad red submarginal band;

juveniles similar in colour to the young of *C. africana*, differing in broader dark margins to the white spots, the first on body extending as a bar to ventral part of abdomen, the dorsal fin with a black spot. Reported to reach about 60 cm. Western Indian Ocean from the southern Red Sea (Randall, 1994) south to Natal, east to Sri Lanka; more common in southern Oman than in the Gulf of Oman.

746. *Coris frerei*, juvenile (J. Randall)

747. *Coris frerei*, female (J. Randall)

748. *Coris frerei*, male (J. Hoover)

749. *Coris nigrotaenia*, juv., 4.1 cm (J. Randall)

BLACKBAR CORIS
Coris nigrotaenia Mee and Hare, 1995

Dorsal rays IX,12; anal rays III,12; pectoral rays 13-14; lateral-line scales 47-50; predorsal scales extending to above preopercular margin; gill rakers 21-25; body depth 2.9-3.35 in standard length (males deeper bodied); head length 2.9-3.0 in standard length; dorsal spines sharp-tipped, the first spine shortest, 3.9-5.5 in head length (spines relatively shorter in larger fish); caudal fin slightly rounded; females mustard yellow, shading to whitish ventrally, with oblique light blue-green lines dorsally on body following scale rows, changing in about middle of body to rows of light blue spots, one per scale, which tend to merge to form longitudinal lines; a broad blackish bar on upper half of body centred at base of seventh dorsal spine; head with irregular light blue-

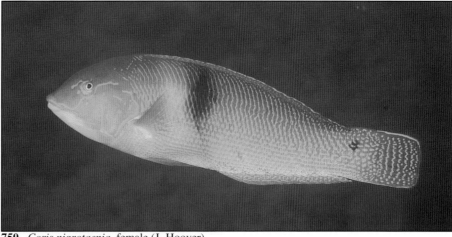

750. *Coris nigrotaenia*, female (J. Hoover)

green lines; median fins orangish brown with small blue-green spots and irregular lines; males with essentially the same pattern but more blue-green overall and with the blackish bar greatly reduced or absent; juveniles dark brown with four large irregular white blotches dorsally on body and another four ventrally; a black spot larger than pupil above and adjacent to lateral line at base of caudal fin; dorsal and anal fins dark brown and white, in alignment with white blotches and dark brown zones on body. Largest specimen, 43.5 cm. Known

only from the exposed rocky shores of Dhofar and Masirah Island, Oman; adults observed in the depth range of 1.5-20 m.

INDIAN OCEAN BIRD WRASSE
Gomphosus caeruleus Lacepède, 1801

Dorsal rays VIII,13; anal rays II,11; pectoral rays 15; lateral-line continuous, sharply deflected downward below posterior part of dorsal fin, the pored scales 25-26; head scaleless; teeth conical, those anteriorly in jaws incurved, the most anterior as moderate canines; body depth 3.7-4.0 in standard length; snout very elongate and tubular (except small juveniles), more than half head length in adults; caudal fin varying from slightly rounded in juveniles to lunate with filamentous lobes in large adult males; initial phase yellowish with a blackish spot on each scale except chest and lower abdomen; blackish spots also on postorbital head (some elongate ones in two rows behind eye) and interorbital space; a brown stripe on side of snout; caudal fin with a clear yellowish posterior margin and a broad blackish submarginal band; terminal males dark blue-green, this colour extending onto caudal fin except for a large semicircular light green area centroposteriorly in fin; outer part of dorsal and anal fins also light green. Attains 28 cm. Indian Ocean, including the Gulf of Oman (though rare there); the Red Sea population represents a different subspecies, *G. caeruleus klunzingeri* Klausewitz, 1962. Closely related to *G. varius* Lacepède of the Pacific. Uses its long slender snout to probe into crevices in the reef for small invertebrates.

753. *G. caeruleus*, juv., about 4 cm (J. Randall)

751. *Gomphosus caeruleus*, male, 24.3 cm (J. Randall)

752. *Gomphosus caeruleus*, females (J. Hoover)

BUBBLEFIN WRASSE
Halichoeres dussumieri (Valenciennes, 1839)

Dorsal rays IX,12; anal rays III,11-12 (rarely 11); pectoral rays 14-15 (rarely 14); lateral-line continuous, deflected sharply downward below posterior part of dorsal fin to straight peduncular part (true of all *Halichoeres*), the pored scales 27; anterior lateral-line scales with two to five pores; no scales on opercle; predorsal scales extending to interorbital space, without a naked mid-dorsal region; gill rakers 18-22; body depth 2.9-3.6 in standard length; ninth dorsal spine 2.7-2.85 in head length; membranes between second and fifth dorsal spines of males elevated above those of rest of fin; caudal fin rounded; females light greenish dorsally, shading to white ventrally, with six or seven irregular, interconnected, reddish brown bars, each forming a network, on upper two-thirds of body (bars resulting from a large dark spot on each scale); a series of four small white spots along side of body; irregular pink to light red bands on head; a triangular black spot at upper pectoral-fin base; dorsal and caudal fins with round green spots; males similar but the dark bars more red, a black and yellow spot in dorsal fin present between fifth and sixth spines, and a reddish crescent in caudal fin containing green spots. Reaches 14 cm. East coast of Africa south to Natal, east in continental waters to the Indo-Malayan region, north to

754. *Halichoeres dussumieri*, male, about 10 cm (J. Randall)

755. *Halichoeres dussumieri*, female (J. Hoover)

Hong Kong; not known from the Red Sea, but occurs in the Arabian Gulf and northern Gulf of Oman; a shallow-water species not generally seen on coral reefs. Often identified as *H. nigrescens* (Bloch and Schneider),

but as noted by Randall and Smith (1982), the type specimens are lost and the original description insufficiently detailed to link the name to any known species of the genus.

CHECKERBOARD WRASSE
Halichoeres hortulanus (Lacepède, 1801)

Dorsal rays IX,11; anal rays III,11; pectoral rays 13-14 (usually 14); lateral-line scales 26; anterior lateral-line scales with a single pore; a near-vertical band of small scales behind eye; scales dorsally on head extending to interorbital space; gill rakers 20-25; body of females with a pattern of small white squares edged broadly in black; a large yellow spot centred at base of fourth and fifth dorsal spines, followed by a large black blotch; head green with pink bands; caudal fin yellow; males similar but ground colour of body green, and caudal fin orange-red with yellow spots; juveniles broadly marked with white and black, with a large yellow-edged black spot in middle of dorsal fin. Reaches 26 cm. A coral-reef species wide-ranging in the Indo-Pacific; observed in Omani waters only off the southern coast.

758. *Halichoeres hortulanus*, juv. (J. Randall)

756. *Halichoeres hortulanus*, male (J. Hoover)

757. *Halichoeres hortulanus*, female (J. Randall)

RAINBOW WRASSE
Halichoeres iridis Randall and Smith, 1982

Dorsal rays IX,12-13 (rarely 13); anal rays III,12; pectoral rays 13-14 (rarely 14); lateral-line scales 27; scales of lateral line with three to five pores; head naked except a triangular area of scales dorsally on nape nearly reaching to above rear edge of eye; gill rakers 15-19; body depth 3.35-3.9 in standard length; caudal fin moderately rounded; body of females brown with a red band along back, this continuing around the extension of brown body colour into basal part of caudal fin; head and chest yellow-orange with green bands and a black spot behind eye; dorsal fin cream with a black spot at front and a bluish white margin; anal fin red basally, orange in outer part except for a bluish white margin and black submarginal line; males similar, but with less red on body, the head more yellow the green bands more distinct; outer part of caudal fin with a blue-edged red semicircular band. Largest specimen, 11 cm. Southern Red Sea (Randall, 1994) south to Natal, east to Oman (occasional on the south coast; rare in the Gulf of Oman); also known from Mauritius (type locality), Madagascar, Seychelles, Chagos Archipelago, and Maldive Islands. Recorded from the depth range of 6-43 m; usually found at depths greater than 20 m.

JEWELLED WRASSE
Halichoeres lapillus Smith, 1947

Dorsal rays IX,11; anal rays III,11; pectoral rays 13; lateral-line scales 27, the anterior scales with two to five pores; median dorsal zone of nape scaleless, the scales on side of nape extending to above preopercular margin; median ventral region of chest scaleless; gill rakers 17-21; body depth 2.8-3.3 in standard length; third and fourth dorsal spines slightly longer than fifth and sixth; third anal spine long, 3.2-3.5 in head length; caudal fin slightly rounded; females olive brown on back, shading to reddish brown, with small white spots dorsally and larger white spots ventrally which tend to join to form irregular stripes; dark brown spots in approximately three rows on lower two-thirds of body; head olive dorsally, soon shading to white, with five diagonal reddish bands; males dusky red-orange with rows of dark-edged green spots, those ventrally on body large and irregular; a large black spot flecked with yellow on side of body behind upper end of gill opening; head orange-red with diagonal green bands. Reaches 14 cm. Known from southern Mozambique (type locality), Natal, Madagascar, Mauritius, and southern Oman; usually found on rocky bot-

759. *Halichoeres iridis*, female?, about 6 cm (J. Randall)

760. *Halichoeres lapillus* (J. Hoover)

761. *Halichoeres leptotaenia* (J. Randall)

tom with a heavy cover of algae in the depth range of about 5-15 m.

THINSTRIPED WRASSE
Halichoeres leptotaenia Randall and Earle, 1994

Dorsal rays IX,11; anal rays III,11; pectoral rays 13; lateral-line scales 27, all with a single pore; no scales on head; predorsal scales extending to interorbital space; gill rakers 15-20; no canine tooth at corner of mouth (present on other species of *Halichoeres*, at least as adults; possibly present on males of this species, none of which were observed or collected); body depth 3.8-4.4 in standard length; caudal fin slightly rounded; adult females pale green with three narrow salmon pink stripes containing some brown pigment; midlateral stripe ending basally on caudal fin in a small dark brown spot; a black spot on side above tip of pectoral fin. Largest female specimen, 12.5 cm. Known only from the southern Arabian Gulf; type locality Jazirat Umm al Ghanam (Goat Island), Musandam; collected from the depth range of 1.5-15 m, generally from sand with isolated rocks.

762. *Halichoeres marginatus*, male (J. Hoover)

763. *Halichoeres marginatus*, female, with *Labroides dimidiatus* (J. Randall)

DUSKY WRASSE
Halichoeres marginatus (Rüppell, 1835)

Dorsal rays IX,13-14 (usually 13); anal rays III,12-13 (usually 13); pectoral rays 14-15 (rarely 15); lateral-line scales 27-28 (rarely 28), the anterior scales with two to four pores; predorsal scales extending to above rear edge of eyes; rest of head naked; gill rakers 17-20; body depth 2.6-3.35 in head; caudal fin rounded; initial phase (may be male or female) dark brown with faint pale stripes following scale rows; a small yellow-edged deep blue spot at front of dorsal fin and a large one in middle of fin; caudal fin whitish (larger fish developing a broad blackish crescent in fin); terminal males yellowish brown with a dark bluish spot on each scale, narrow oblique dark blue bands on head, and middle of caudal fin with a purple-edged red crescent containing small blue-edged green spots, the scaleless part of fin before crescent green, behind blue with a posterior yellow margin; juveniles with alternating broad dark brown and narrow pale yellow stripes. Attains 17 cm. Indo-Pacific; found throughout Oman, but most common in the Gulf of Oman.

764. *Halichoeres marginatus*, juv. (J. Randall)

BLACK WRASSE
Halichoeres melas Randall and Earle, 1994

Dorsal rays IX,11; anal rays III,11; pectoral rays 13; lateral line scales 27-28, each with two to four pores; no median predorsal scales, no median prepelvic scales; no scales on opercle or cheek; gill rakers 16-19; body moderately deep, the depth 2.75-2.95 in standard length; deep maroon, almost black (appears black underwater) with a dark green spot on a few scales posteriorly on body (green spots difficult to see unless light strikes the surface at a certain angle); iris yellow. Largest specimen, 15 cm. Known from only three specimens collected at the Juzor al Hallaniyat (Kuria Muria Islands) in the depth range of 9-10 m; all are males (no other fish of different colour were seen which might have been the female of this species).

765. *Halichoeres melas*, male, 15 cm (J. Randall)

NEBULOUS WRASSE
Halichoeres nebulosus (Valenciennes, 1839)

Dorsal rays IX,11-12 (rarely 12); anal rays III,11; pectoral rays 13-15 (usually 14); lateral-line scales 27, the anterior scales with one to three pores; median zone of nape naked except for a few embedded scales anterior to dorsal fin; scales on side of nape not reaching hind margin of eye; rest of head naked; body depth 3.0-3.6 in standard length; caudal fin slightly rounded; females with large, irregular, interconnected, diffuse blackish bars on body, darker dorsally; a large light red area on abdomen containing two or more white lines; a small black spot behind eye, one on opercular flap, a small one anteriorly in dorsal fin, and a large yellow-edged one anteriorly in outer soft portion of fin; males more green, the red area on abdomen reduced and less bright, the black spot behind eye and at front of dorsal fin absent, the black spot in middle of dorsal fin irregular and without a yellow edge, and vertical series of dark red spots in caudal fin. Largest specimen, 11.5 cm. Red Sea to South Africa at 32° S, east to the western Pacific where it ranges from the Ryukyu Islands to southern New South Wales; known from Oman only on the south coast. A common inshore species (often in less than 1 m) on exposed reefs and rocky bottom. Often

766. *Halichoeres nebulosus*, male, about 8.5 cm (J. Randall)

767. *Halichoeres nebulosus*, female, about 6 cm (J. Randall)

confused with the very similar *H. margaritaceus* (Valenciennes) which is distributed from the central and western Pacific to the eastern Indian Ocean (Kuiter and Randall, 1981).

ZIGZAG WRASSE
Halichoeres scapularis (Bennett, 1831)

Dorsal rays IX,11; anal rays III,11; pectoral rays 14; lateral-line scales 26, the anterior scales with one pore; a patch of small scales dorsally on opercle; predorsal scales extending forward to posterior interorbital space; gill rakers 17-21; body depth 2.4-3.9 in standard length; initial phase (may be male or female) with a dark brown stripe from eye to upper base of caudal fin (posteriorly as a series of contiguous spots; in larger size the stripe may form a zigzag pattern); body above stripe light greenish to pale yellowish brown, below whitish; a yellow stripe on side of snout, and edges of dark stripe on postorbital head yellow; body of terminal males lavender-pink with green spots on scales in a zigzag pattern on upper two-thirds of body, and vertical green lines ventrally; a large black blotch on upper side of body above pectoral fin; head pink with irregular green bands, shading to greenish yellow ventrally. Reaches 20 cm. Red Sea to Natal, east to the western Pacific; observed in Oman only at Juzor al Hallaniyat (Kuria Muria Islands); associated more with sand, rubble, or seagrass bottoms than coral reefs.

768. *Halichoeres scapularis*, male (J. Randall)

769. *Halichoeres scapularis*, female, 9.5 cm (J. Randall)

FLAG WRASSE

Halichoeres signifer Randall and Earle, 1994

Dorsal rays XI,12-13 (rarely 13); anal rays III,12-13 (rarely 13); pectoral rays 13-15 (usually 14); lateral-line scales 27-29 (usually 28), the anterior scales with three to five pores; a broad median naked zone on nape; scales on side of nape reaching forward nearly to a vertical at upper end of pre-opercular margin; no scales on opercle or cheek; gill rakers 17-21; body depth 4.0-4.3 in standard length; ninth dorsal spine 3.0-3.55 in standard length; caudal fin slightly rounded; females orangish brown, with a white stripe from chin, passing below eye, and reaching lower base of caudal fin; brown dots above and below posterior half of stripe; a white line from snout, passing above eye to below rear of dorsal fin; an irregular black spot about the size of pupil at upper base of caudal fin; a blackish spot behind upper part of eye; median fins largely light red; males with the same stripe as females but stripe pale greenish yellow and edged with blue on head; a broad orange zone above stripe with a blue spot on each scale; back above this mainly green; head above stripe orange with narrow pale blue bands; front of upper lip and median part of snout to level of upper edge of eye bright blue; a dusky spot behind eye; median fins light red with pale blue spots and bands; first two interspinous membranes of dorsal fin

770. *Halichoeres signifer*, male (J. Hoover)

771. *Halichoeres signifer*, female (J. Hoover)

largely covered by a blue-edged black spot, followed by yellow on most of the next membrane and part of the fourth. Attains 10 cm. Known from Masirah Island off the central coast of Oman to Rahah Bay on the south coast; collected from the depth range of 3-12 m; most often seen at the interface

of sand or rubble and low rocky reef, foraging in both areas. Males in courtship elevate the dorsal fin, thus displaying the colourful anterior part.

U-SPOT WRASSE

Halichoeres stigmaticus Randall and Smith, 1982

Dorsal rays IX,12; anal rays III,11-13 (usually 12); pectoral rays 14-16; lateral-line scales 27-29 (usually 28), the anterior scales with three to five pores; predorsal scales extending to above preopercular margin; a narrow median scaleless zone on nape or with a few embedded scales; gill rakers 18-21; body depth 3.35-3.8 in standard length; ninth dorsal spine 2.8-3.2 in head length; caudal fin slightly to moderately rounded; females whitish with two broad brownish red to yellowish brown stripes, one dorsally on body and the other lateral, ending in a black spot at base of caudal fin; males pale blue and yellow on dorsal half of body (above lateral line, scale centres yellow, the edges blue; the colours reversed below lateral line), gradually shading to whitish ventrally; a large U-shaped black mark within a pale blue area on upper side above tip of pectoral fin; a bright blue and yellow spot anteriorly on dorsal fin (first interspinous membrane mainly blue, the second mainly yellow). Largest specimen, 12.8 cm. Known only from the Arabian Gulf (where common) and Gulf of Oman (where rare); collected from the depth range of 3-25 m.

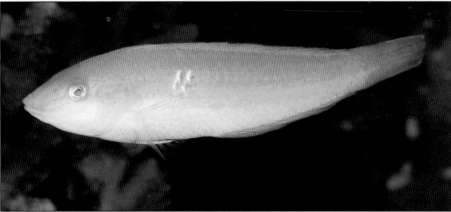

772. *Halichoeres stigmaticus*, male, about 11 cm (J. Randall)

773. *Halichoeres stigmaticus*, female, about 6 cm (J. Randall)

GOLDSTRIPE WRASSE
Halichoeres zeylonicus (Bennett, 1832)

Dorsal rays IX,11-12 (rarely 12); anal rays III,11; pectoral rays 13-15 (usually 14); lateral-line scales 27, the anterior scales with one to three pores; a median naked zone on nape (or only a few embedded scales in front of dorsal fin); small scales on side of nape not reaching posterior edge of eye; gill rakers 17-21; small canine tooth at corner of mouth usually present only in large adults; body depth 3.65-4.0 in standard length; ninth dorsal spine 2.85-3.3 in head length; caudal fin slightly rounded, becoming slightly double emarginate in males; females bluish, greenish, or pinkish grey dorsally, paler ventrally, with a broad bright orange-yellow stripe (may be orange-red in young) extending from eye to caudal-fin base (where it may contain a blackish spot); an orange-yellow stripe from upper lip to upper part of eye; a narrow irregular orange stripe from top of snout along back at base of dorsal fin to dorsal edge of caudal peduncle; a small black spot at upper base of pectoral fins; body of males blue-green dorsally and anteriorly, becoming whitish ventrally on abdomen and body between orange-yellow stripe and anal fin; stripe with irregular edges, narrowly bordered by blue; an irregular blue-edged black spot between stripe and base of eighth dorsal spine; head blue-green with irregular pink bands; a small blue-edged black spot at upper base of pectoral fins and an oblique pink band in front of base, extending onto anterior abdomen; median fins salmon pink with pale blue stripes and spots. Reaches 20 cm. Indian Ocean; *H. hartzfeldii* (Bleeker) of the western Pacific differs only in the colouration of the male; the large black spot on the body is just below the orange-yellow stripe instead of above, and there are usually one to three small black spots posteriorly on the upper edge of the stripe. This form might best be regarded as a subspecies of *H. zeylonicus*. Observed only in southern Oman, generally over sand near isolated rocks or reefs, usually at depths greater than 20 m.

774. *Halichoeres zeylonicus*, male, about 17 cm (J. Randall)

775. *Halichoeres zeylonicus*, female (J. Hoover)

776. *Hemigymnus fasciatus*, female (J. Hoover)

BARRED THICKLIP WRASSE
Hemigymnus fasciatus (Bloch, 1792)

Dorsal rays IX,11; anal rays III,11; pectoral rays 14; lateral-line scales 27; a few rows of small scales on cheek; a pair of protruding canine teeth at front of jaws and one at corner of mouth; lips very thick; gill opening restricted to side; body depth 2.3-2.6 in standard length; caudal fin slightly rounded to truncate; body white with five black bars much broader than pale interspaces; head yellowish green with irregular blue-edged pink bands; caudal fin dark dusky yellow to black; occasional large adults, presumed to be males in courtship colour, show a reversal of pattern, the narrow bars black and the broad zones white. Reaches about 50 cm. Indo-Pacific; occasionally sighted off the southern coast of Oman; occurs more often on protected rather than exposed reefs. Feeds in part by extracting small animals from mouthfuls of sand; also takes larger invertebrates such as molluscs and sea urchins.

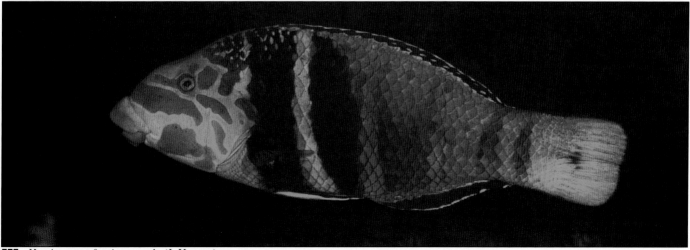

777. *Hemigymnus fasciatus*, male (J. Hoover)

PASTEL RINGWRASSE
Hologymnosus doliatus (Lacepède, 1801)

Dorsal rays IX,12; anal rays III,12; pectoral rays 13; lateral-line scales 97-112; head scaleless; gill rakers 18-22; two pairs of canine teeth anteriorly in jaws, but no tooth at corner of mouth; body elongate, 3.75-5.35 in standard length, and moderately compressed; caudal fin slightly rounded in juveniles and small initial-phase fish, becoming double emarginate in large males, the caudal concavity about 11 in head; pectoral fins of adults short, 1.9-2.1 in head; initial phase pale greenish to pinkish grey with 20-23 narrow orangish brown bars on body; a bluish black spot on opercular flap; terminal males pale blue-green with narrow lavender-blue bars and a broad pale yellowish zone in pectoral region bordered by purple bars; head blue-green with narrow pink bands; juveniles whitish with three narrow orange-red stripes. Largest specimen examined, 38 cm. Southern Red Sea (Randall, 1994) south to Natal, east to the Line Islands and Samoa; seen in Oman only in the south. Feeds mainly on fishes and crustaceans.

780. *H. doliatus*, juv., about 9 cm (J. Randall)

778. *Hologymnosus doliatus*, male (J. Hoover)

779. *Hologymnosus doliatus*, female (J. Hoover)

BICOLOUR CLEANER WRASSE
Labroides bicolor Fowler and Bean, 1928

Dorsal rays IX,11; anal rays III,10; pectoral rays 13; lateral-line scales 26; small scales on cheek, opercle, and nape; lips thick, the lower strongly bilobed; a single pair of canines anteriorly in jaws, a canine at corner of mouth, and several rows of small teeth on side of jaws; body depth 3.7-4.5 in standard length; caudal fin slightly rounded; females grey with a black lateral stripe anteriorly, the body becoming yellowish white posteriorly; a submarginal black crescent in caudal fin; males with a deep blue head, the body black anteriorly, yellow posteriorly; caudal fin green before black crescent and light blue behind; juveniles black with a bright yellow stripe dorsally. Reported to 14 cm. Indo-Pacific; only a few individuals seen on the Arabian Sea coast of Oman. Feeds on ectoparasites and mucus of fishes; ranges over a broader area in search of host fishes than the following species.

781. *Labroides bicolor* (J. Hoover)

782. *Labroides dimidiatus*, juv. (J. Hoover)

BLACK-AND-BLUE CLEANER WRASSE
Labroides dimidiatus (Valenciennes, 1839)

Dorsal rays IX,11; anal rays III,10; pectoral rays 13; lateral-line scales 50-52; small scales on cheek, opercle, and nape; lips and dentition as in *L. bicolor*; body depth 4.1-4.7 in standard length; caudal fin truncate to slightly rounded; bluish white, shading to light blue posteriorly, with a black stripe from mouth through eye, broadening as it passes posteriorly on body, and ending at posterior margin of caudal fin; juveniles black with a bright blue stripe dorsally on body and head. Largest specimen recorded, 11.5 cm. Indo-Pacific; found throughout Oman. Establishes "cleaning" stations on the reef which are visited by many different species of fishes which pose to have their ectoparasites removed (and mucus is also ingested); freely enters the mouth and gill chamber of larger fishes.

SHOULDERSPOT WRASSE
Leptojulis cyanopleura (Bleeker, 1853)

Dorsal rays IX,11; anal rays III,11; pectoral rays 13; lateral-line scales 27; front of jaws with two pairs of large canine teeth, the second pair strongly recurved and outflaring; a canine tooth at corner of mouth; no well-developed molariform pharyngeal teeth; body moderately elongate, the depth 4.0-4.55 in standard length; caudal fin slightly rounded in initial phase, double-emarginate in large terminal males; pelvic fins short; initial phase whitish with an orangish brown stripe from snout through eye to midbase of caudal fin; a second narrower stripe from top of head along base of dorsal fin to tip of caudal peduncle; terminal males bluish grey with a blue-edged orange-yellow stripe from front of snout through eye to middle of caudal fin; a group of blue-edged black scales forming a spot on stripe above pectoral fin; a blue-edge black spot middorsally on nape; caudal fin blue with three or four oblique orange-yellow bands in upper and lower halves of fin. Attains 13 cm. Arabian Gulf to the western Pacific. Feeds on zooplankton a meter or more above the substratum; reported from the depth range of 6-45 m.

783. *Labroides dimidiatus* cleaning *Gymnothorax favagineus* (J. Hoover)

784. *Leptojulis cyanopleura*, male (J. Randall)

785. *Leptojulis cyanopleura*, female (J. Randall)

TWOPART WRASSE
Macropharyngodon bipartitus Smith, 1957

Dorsal rays IX,11; anal rays III,11; pectoral rays 12; lateral-line scales 27, the anterior scales with two or three pores; head scaleless; no median predorsal scales; two pairs of canine teeth anteriorly in upper jaw, the first pair projecting forward, the second recurved; pharyngeal dentition dominated by a few very large molars; free margin of preopercle short, especially the lower edge; caudal fin rounded; initial phase orange on body with white spots, becoming black on abdomen and chest with irregular pale blue spots and bands; head yellow with black spots and irregular short bands; head and anterior body of terminal males with alternating diagonal bands of green and dusky red; rest of body dull orange-red, the dusky red bands of upper side breaking into a series of irregular, green-edged, blackish red spots, narrowing to a series of conjoined blue-edged spots posteriorly. Reaches 13 cm. Western Indian Ocean; the Red Sea population was described as a subspecies in a revision of the genus by Randall (1978); it is the subspecies from elsewhere in the Indian Ocean which occurs sporadically along the Arabian Sea coast of Oman. *M. varialvus* Smith is a synonym based on the initial phase.

786. *Macropharyngodon bipartitus*, male (J. Hoover)

787. *Macropharyngodon bipartitus*, female (J. Hoover)

788. *Novaculichthys taeniourus*, about 18.5 cm (J. Randall)

ROCKMOVER WRASSE
Novaculichthys taeniourus (Lacepède, 1801)

Dorsal rays IX,12, the origin of fin over preopercular margin, the first two spines flexible (very elongate in juveniles); anal rays III,12; pectoral rays 13; lateral line interrupted, the anterior pored scales 19-20; head naked except for two scales on upper part of opercle and a near-vertical row of small scales behind eye; a single pair of large canines anteriorly in jaws; body depth 2.65-3.0 in standard length; caudal fin rounded; body of females dark brown with a whitish spot on each scale, becoming reddish on chest and abdomen; head grey with narrow dark brown bands radiating from posterior half of eye; a whitish bar at base of caudal fin; a small yellow spot usually present at upper base of pectoral fins, and a pale-edged black band or large spots beneath basal part of these fins; males lose the bands on the head, the red on the chest and abdomen, and have a vertical pale yellowish line on each body scale instead of a spot; juveniles green, reddish, or brown, with narrow dark bars on body which extend into dorsal and anal fins and irregular white spots. Reaches 30 cm. Indo-Pacific; observed in Oman only on the south coast; not common. The adults are well known for turning over rocks to prey upon molluscs, crabs, sea urchins, worms, and brittle stars hiding beneath. The young mimic small drifting masses of algae.

789. *N. taeniourus*, juv., about 5 cm (J. Randall)

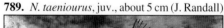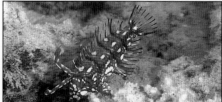

TWOSPOT WRASSE
Oxycheilinus bimaculatus (Valenciennes, 1840)

Dorsal rays IX,10; anal rays III,8; pectoral rays 12-13; lateral-line interrupted, 15-16 + 6-7; head scaled except snout, chin, and anterior interorbital space; scaly sheath at base of dorsal and anal fins; preopercular margin smooth; body depth 2.6-3.1 in standard length; caudal fin rounded in females, rhomboid with prolonged upper and central rays in males; females reddish to orangish brown finely flecked and blotched with whitish, shading to yellowish on abdomen and ventrally on head; a large blackish blotch on side between pectoral fin and lateral line, sometimes followed by three less distinct blackish blotches; a small dark bluish spot behind eye and one at front of dorsal fin; males variable in colour, but generally finely mottled orangish brown and light green on body, the blackish blotch on side usually evident; head mainly green with pink to orange-red lines radiating from eye; a bright red mark often present above and in front of dark blue spot on first interspinous membrane of dorsal fin. Maximum length about 15 cm. Indo-Pacific; common in the Gulf of Oman, less so to the south; usually found on weedy bottoms or seagrass beds. Formerly placed in the genus *Cheilinus*; reclassified in *Oxycheilinus* by Westneat (1993).

McCOSKER'S WRASSE
Paracheilinus mccoskeri Randall and Harmelin-Vivien, 1977

Dorsal rays IX,11; anal rays III,9; pectoral rays usually 14; lateral line interrupted, the pored scales 15-17 + 5-9; median predorsal scales 5; scale rows on cheek 2; gill rakers 13-15; posterior margin of preopercle finely serrate; body depth 3.0-3.55 in standard length; three pairs of laterally-projecting canine teeth anteriorly in jaws, the third pair largest and most strongly recurved; ninth dorsal spine 6.5-6.9 in standard length; first dorsal soft ray of males greatly prolonged; caudal fin rounded; orange-red, shading to whitish ventrally on head and abdomen, with three diverging narrow blue stripes on head, the upper and lower extending onto anterior body; body with four other blue stripes, the uppermost along base of dorsal fin, the second interrupted from posterior part of first head stripe, the third short, beneath pectoral fin, and the fourth from base of pectoral fin to caudal fin; males with bright blue bands in median fins, the anal fin largely red. Attains about 8 cm. Described from the Comoro Islands; range extended to the Maldives and Andaman Sea by Randall and Lubbock (1981), to the Chagos Archipelago (Winterbottom et al., 1989), and the

790. *Oxycheilinus bimaculatus*, two males fighting (J. Hoover)

791. *Oxycheilinus bimaculatus*, female? (J. Hoover)

792. *Paracheilinus mccoskeri*, male, 6.1 cm (J. Randall)

793. *Paracheilinus mccoskeri*, male and two females (J. Randall)

Arabian Gulf, Indonesia, and Fiji (Randall et al., 1994). Observed by John P. Hoover in the northern Gulf of Oman. Usually found over rubble substrata; feeds on zooplankton.

Males maintain a harem of at least several females; in courtship they exhibit a spectacular display with fins erect and the blue markings vivid and iridescent.

SIXSTRIPE WRASSE

Pseudocheilinus hexataenia (Bleeker, 1857)

Dorsal rays IX,11; anal rays III,9; pectoral rays 15-17 (rarely 17); lateral line interrupted, 16-18 + 4-6; median predorsal scales 5; cheek and opercle scaled; gill rakers 14-17; three pairs of canine teeth anteriorly in upper jaw, the lateral pair much the largest, curved outward and backward; a single pair of canines anteriorly in lower jaw; preopercle with a membranous flap at angle, the margin above it very finely serrate for about half its length; body depth 2.4-2.7 in standard length; caudal fin rounded; six purplish blue stripes on body alternating with narrow orange stripes, these extending narrowly onto postorbital head; lower part of head with orange dots; a pair of black spots at front of lower lip; caudal fin green with a small blue-edged black spot at upper base. Maximum length 7.5 cm. Indo-Pacific; common but usually hidden in reef. Observed only in southern Oman.

COCKTAIL WRASSE

Pteragogus flagellifer (Valenciennes, 1839)

Dorsal rays IX,10-12; anal rays III,9; pectoral rays 13-14 (rarelky 14); lateral-line sharply deflected downward beneath rear of dorsal fin, the pored scales 23-24; median predorsal scales 4; cheek and opercle scaled; gill rakers 12-15; two pairs of canine teeth anteriorly in jaws, the lateral pair larger and strongly recurved (outflaring in adults); posterior margin of preopercle finely serrate; body depth 2.5-3.1 in standard length; membranes from tips of dorsal spines prolonged to filaments, progressively longer anteriorly (very long in males); caudal fin rounded; pelvic fins extending slightly beyond anus; females greenish, finely mottled with white, usually with four large dusky blotches along midside of body, and another on opercle; lateral line with small white and black spots; an oblique white band on lower opercle; small black spots on postorbital head; a dark blue spot on first interspinous membrane of dorsal fin; males green, the dorsal filaments, soft dorsal, anal, and pelvic fins red. Reaches 20 cm. Arabian Gulf (Randall et al., 1994) south to Natal and east to Indo-Malayan region; rarely seen due to its cryptic habits.

BLUELINED WRASSE

Stethojulis albovittata (Bonnaterre, 1788)

Dorsal rays IX,11; anal rays III,11; pectoral rays 14-15 (usually 14); lateral line complete, bent downward below rear of dorsal

794. *Pseudocheilinus hexataenia*, about 4 cm (J. Randall)

795. *Pteragogus flagellifer*, 6.4 cm (L. McCarthy)

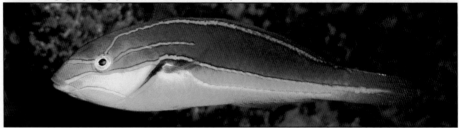

796. *Stethojulis albovittata*, terminal male (J. Randall)

797. *Stethojulis albovittata*, initial phase (J. Randall)

fin, the pored scales 25; head scaleless; gill rakers 25-30; no canine teeth except one at corner of mouth; teeth close-set and incisiform (characteristic of the genus); body depth 3.0-3.5 in standard length; caudal fin small, slightly rounded (generic); pectoral-fin base strongly oblique, nearer horizontal than vertical (also generic); initial phase (may be male or female) greenish to grey-brown, finely flecked with pale dots on upper half of body, whitish below, the two areas separated by a poorly defined reddish stripe; two small blue-edge black spots mid-laterally on caudal-fin base; a bright orange-red spot above pectoral-fin base; often exhibits two pale stripes on upper part of body; terminal males with three narrow blue stripes on body: one along base of dorsal fin extending dorsally onto snout, one midlateral from caudal fin to corner of mouth, and one from lower caudal peduncle to axil of pectoral fin, continuing along lower edge of gill opening, across cheek, and ending on chin. Reaches 12 cm. Western Indian Ocean; in Oman waters, only in the south. An inshore coral-reef species. Like other species of the genus, a rapid swimmer under pectoral-fin power. Feeds on a variety of very small invertebrates ingested from a rapid peck at rocky bottom or by intake of sand, sorting the food organisms while swimming away (sand then often expelled from the gill openings).

CUTRIBBON WRASSE
Stethojulis interrupta (Bleeker, 1851)

Dorsal rays IX,11; anal rays III,11; pectoral rays 12-13 (rarely 12); lateral-line scales 25; gill rakers 19-23; body depth 3.6-4.1 in standard length; initial phase yellowish brown to greenish or olive grey on dorsal half of body, whitish with blackish dots below, the two zones usually separated by a narrow diffuse blackish stripe; a narrow whitish stripe, sometime edged in black, from upper base of pectoral fin to corner of mouth; a second narrow whitish stripe from above eye across dorsal part of head, often extending onto body; terminal males greenish to olive grey on upper half of body, white below, the two zones separated by a narrow blue stripe, at least posteriorly; a narrow blue stripe from above eye, along back adjacent to dorsal fin, and ending in upper part of caudal fin; two horizontal narrow blue stripes on head, one above and one below eye; a bright orange spot above pectoral-fin base. To 13 cm. Red Sea and the coast of East Africa to the Mariana Islands and Samoa; common throughout Oman. *Stethojulis kalosoma* (Bleeker) is a synonym based on the initial phase.

798. *Stethojulis interrupta*, terminal male (J. Hoover)

799. *Stethojulis interrupta*, initial phase (J. Randall)

800. *Stethojulis interrupta*, juvenile (J. Randall)

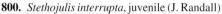

801. *Suezichthys caudovittatus* (after Steindachner, 1898)

TAILBAND WRASSE
Suezichthys caudovittatus (Steindachner, 1898)

Dorsal rays IX,11; anal rays III,10; pectoral rays 13; lateral-line scales 25; scale rows above lateral line 1.5; scales below lateral line 7.5; predorsal scales 5-6; cheek scale rows behind eye 2; cheek scale rows below eye 3; gill rakers 16-19; a pair of curved canines anteriorly in upper jaw, and two pairs of smaller canines anteriorly in lower jaw; a canine at corner of mouth; body depth about 3.9 in standard length; caudal fin rounded; life colour of initial phase not known; terminal males pinkish red, silvery white on abdomen; lower two-thirds of dorsal fin grey-violet, the upper third white; a black spot on first two membranes of dorsal fin; caudal fin with a diagonal black band in upper part of fin. Reaches at least 12 cm. Known from the northern Red Sea and Arabian Gulf to Somalia (Russell, 1985); the few specimens have been collected from the depth range of 50-130 m.

SLENDER WRASSE
Suezichthys gracilis (Steindachner and Döderlein, 1887)

Dorsal rays IX,11; anal rays III,10; pectoral rays 13-14; lateral-line scales 25-26; predorsal scales 4-5; scale rows above lateral line 1.5; scales below lateral line 7.5; cheek scale rows behind eye 2-3; cheek scale rows below eye 3; gill rakers 15-20; body slender, the depth 4.0-4.8 in standard length; caudal fin slightly rounded to trun-

cate; initial phase whitish with a brownish orange stripe along upper side of head and body (may be partially broken into segments and may be dark-edged), ending in an elliptical blackish spot at base of caudal fin; body above stripe orangish, below whitish; a narrower brownish orange stripe often present from above eye along base of dorsal fin to top of caudal peduncle (this stripe may also be broken into segments); terminal males with a darker stripe which contains a large blue and blackish spot above pectoral fin; no

black spot at base of caudal fin, but fin with a V-shaped blue-edged orange-yellow band. Largest specimen, 16 cm. Known in the western Pacific from Japan, Taiwan, Korea, Viet Nam, southern Great Barrier Reef, New South Wales, and New Caledonia (Russell, 1985). Kuiter (1993), however, regarded the southern form as a different species, *S. devisi* (Whitley). The only Indian Ocean record is that of Randall et al. (1994) from the Arabian Gulf.

802. *Suezichthys gracilis* (J. Randall)

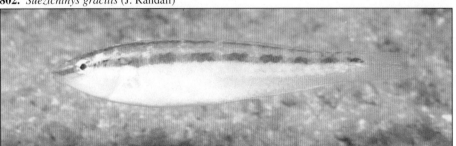

803. *S. gracilis*, subadult, about 5 cm (J. Randall)

SLANTBAND WRASSE
Thalassoma loxum Randall and Mee, 1994

Dorsal rays VIII,13; anal rays III,11; pectoral rays 14-15 (usually 15); lateral line complete, deflected downward beneath rear of dorsal fin, the pored scales 26; an isolated patch of 1-4 scales dorsally on opercle; gill

rakers 15-20; body depth 3.2-3.85 in standard length; head length 2.9-3.3 in standard length; snout short, 3.15-3.4 in head length; caudal fin truncate; body with alternating longitudinal series of vertically elongate green and salmon pink spots; a midlateral and a dorsal series of six blackish blotches; head green with three oblique salmon pink bands on cheek and opercle, the space be-

tween the upper two with a large blackish blotch. Attains about 18 cm. Known only from Oman; the most abundant inshore wrasse on the Arabian Sea coast, but rare and observed only as juveniles in the Gulf of Oman. Closely related to *T. cupido* (Temminck and Schlegel) of Japan and Taiwan.

804. *Thalassoma loxum*, male (J. Hoover)

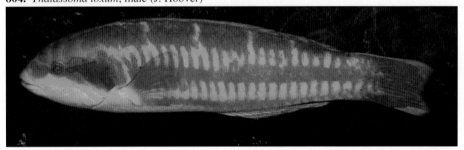

805. *T. loxum*, juv., about 4.5 cm (J. Randall)

MOON WRASSE
Thalassoma lunare (Linnaeus, 1758)

Dorsal rays VIII,13; anal rays III,11; pectoral rays 15; lateral-line scales 25; head naked except for a small patch of scales dorsally on opercle; gill rakers 18-20; body depth 3.1-3.7 in standard length; caudal fin varying from truncate in juveniles to strongly lunate in large terminal males; body of

initial phase green with vertical red lines on scales; head green with six rose pink bands radiating from eye except ventrally where there are two longitudinal rose pink bands; a blue-edged rose pink band in each lobe of caudal fin, the broad centroposterior part of fin yellow; pectoral fins blue with a large elongate rose pink centre; males similar but more blue (especially in courtship), the lines on scales and bands on head purplish red;

juveniles with a large black spot in middle of dorsal fin and a large diffuse blackish spot at caudal-fin base. Attains at least 25 cm. Indo-Pacific. Found throughout Oman; common in the Gulf of Oman, and the most abundant wrasse in the Arabian Gulf; not often seen in the south. A very active, relatively fearless fish; feeds mainly on benthic invertebrates, occasionally on small fishes.

806. *Thalassoma lunare*, male, about 12 cm (J. Randall)

807. *Thalassoma lunare*, juvenile (J. Hoover)

SUNSET WRASSE
Thalassoma lutescens (Lay and Bennett, 1839)

Dorsal rays VIII,13; anal rays III,11; pectoral rays 15-17 (usually 16); lateral-line scales 25; head naked except for a patch of small scales dorsally on opercle; gill rakers 20-23; body depth 3.0-3.5 in standard length; caudal fin slightly rounded to truncate, the lobes prolonged in terminal males; initial phase yellow to greenish yellow with vertical orange-red lines on body and faint light orange-red bands on head; head and anterior body of terminal males rose pink to purplish red with narrow curved green bands, followed in pectoral region by a broad zone of blue; rest of body greenish yellow with vertical orange-red lines; caudal fin yellow with a blue-edged salmon pink band in each lobe; juveniles with a black lateral stripe ending in a black spot at caudal-fin base; body above stripe yellow or green, white below. Attains 25 cm. Common throughout the tropical and subtropical central and western Pacific. The discovery of this species on the southern coast of Oman represents the first record for the western Indian Ocean.

TWOSPOT RAZORFISH
Xyrichtys bimaculatus Rüppell, 1828

Dorsal rays IX,12; anal rays III,12; pectoral rays 12; lateral line interrupted, the pored scales 19-20 + 4-5; two small scales on upper part of opercle; a column of small scales from below eye to corner of mouth, the first row of 7-9 scales curving up behind lower edge of eye; progressively fewer scales in lower rows; gill rakers 17-22; a pair of slender, long, incurved, and slightly outflaring canine teeth anteriorly in each jaw; body depth 2.65-3.1 in standard length (larger fish deeper bodied); body compressed, the width

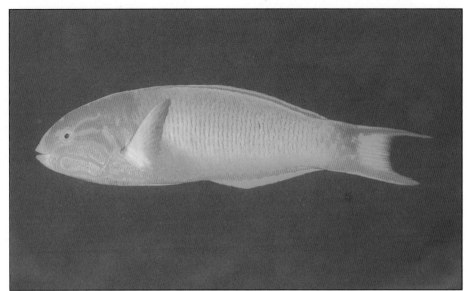

808. *Thalassoma lutescens*, terminal male (J. Hoover)

809. *Thalassoma lutescens*, initial phase, 12.5 cm (J. Randall)

3.3-4.0 in body depth; dorsal profile of head very steep, the anterior edge thin; first two dorsal spines flexible, two to three times longer than third spine; space between bases of second and third dorsal spines about twice that between the first two spines, and nearly twice that between third and fourth spines; membrane between second and third spines notched half or more length of third spine; caudal fin small, asymmetrically rounded; males pale grey, the scale edges a little darker, with a blackish spot on midside below tip of pectoral fin (spot covers three scales in fifth and sixth rows from top of body); scales around blackish spot with a small vertically elongate white spot; similar spots on caudal peduncle; a median blue line at front of head; fins translucent whitish, the dorsal with a series of bluish white dashes at base and a bluish white submarginal line; anal fin with a row of white spots along base and two wavy bluish white longitudinal lines; females lack the blackish spot on the side. Attains 18 cm. Described from the Red Sea; the author has obtained specimens from the Arabian Gulf as well as southwest and southeast India, and eastern Papua New Guinea. *X. hypsospilus* (Schultz) from Sulawesi is a synonym.

810. *Xyrichtys bimaculatus*, 15 cm (J. Randall)

PARROTFISHES
FAMILY SCARIDAE

Parrotfishes are well named for their bright colours and for the fusion of the teeth in their jaws to form beak-like plates; these plates have an obvious median suture (except in *Calotomus*); there may be one to three short conical teeth posteriorly on the side of the dental plates of adults. Also unique is the pharyngeal dentition; each of the interlocking upper pharyngeal bones has one to three longitudinal rows of molari-form teeth which form a convex surface that bears against the concave molar-studded surface of the single lower pharyngeal bone. All species of the family have a continuous un-notched dorsal fin of IX,10 dorsal rays and III,9 anal rays; the pectoral rays vary from 13-16. The scales are large and cycloid; the lateral line is

interrupted, the pored scales 17-20 + 5-7; median predorsal scales vary from 2-7, their number useful in classification; the opercle and cheek are scaled; the number of horizontal rows of scales on the cheek and the number of scales in these rows are also helpful in the identification of species. It seems clear that this family of fishes has evolved from a wrasse lineage. Indeed, some authors have classified the parrotfishes as a sub-family of the Labridae; however, Bellwood (1994) is followed in maintaining them in their own fami-ly, and his classification of the genera is accepted. The parrotfishes are dis-tinct in their dentition, loss of supra-neural (predorsal) bones, lack of a true stomach, very long intestine, and by being herbivorous. These

fishes feed mainly on benthic algae which they scrape from rock sur-faces; when the surface is dead coral, they usually scrape into the lime-stone with the algae. Some species take algae growing on the surface of sand, ingesting sand at the same time. A few of the larger species feed in part on live coral (leaving a char-acteristic mark showing the median suture). The algae, along with the bits of rock, coral, and sand, is tritu-rated in the pharyngeal mill, making it more digestible. In the process, limestone rock fragments and coral are ground into sand, and sand into finer sand. Parrotfishes, therefore, are a major producer of sand in coral-reef areas. Bellwood and Choat (1990) noted that there are two groups of parrotfishes based on jaw and tooth

811. *Scarus zufar*, terminal male (J. Hoover)

292

structure and their impact on the reef. One which includes the monotypic genera *Bolbometopon* and *Cetoscarus* and the newly recognised genus *Chlorurus* (for *C. sordidus* and allies) are termed excavators; with their more powerful jaws and stronger dental plates, the fishes of these genera remove part of the limestone or coral as they feed. The other group, called scrapers, take mainly the surface algae. Like the wrasses, juvenile parrotfishes are usually very different in colour from adults (there may be more than one juvenile pattern with growth; Bellwood and Choat, 1989), and there are often two strikingly different adult colour patterns. The first mature phase, sometimes only female (monandric) but more often both male and female (di-andric) is called the initial phase; it is generally drab, principally brown or grey; males in this colour form are termed primary males. Females of most species in this phase are able to alter their sex to male and undergo a change in colour to the terminal phase, and primary males may also change to the terminal colour form. This is more brightly – even gaudily – coloured, usually dominated by green or blue-green. Initial-phase fish may be seen spawning in large aggregations dominated by primary males. Terminal males tend to establish sexual territories, maintain a harem, and spawn individually with single females following courtship display. In both cases, eggs and sperm are released into the sea at the peak of a very rapid upward rush. Like the wrasses, normal swimming is achieved by the pectoral fins, but when speed is needed, as during the spawning rush, to chase a rival male, or to escape predation, the tail is brought into action. Scarid fishes sleep at night, usually well hidden in small caves or beneath ledges; some species often have an accumulation of mucus around them at night which is visible by the particulate matter that adheres to it. Two subfamilies are here recognised, the Sparisomatinae, characterised by a single row of scales on the cheek below the eye, a wide lower pharyngeal bone, and different structure of the dental plates, and the Scarinae. The western Indian Ocean species of Scarinae were reviewed by Randall and Bruce, 1983.

SUBFAMILY SPARISOMATINAE

STAREYE PARROTFISH
Calotomus carolinus (Valenciennes, 1840)

Pectoral rays 13; median predorsal scales 3-4 (usually 4); a single row of 4 or 5 rows of scales on cheek below eye; teeth not fully fused, the individual flattened teeth readily apparent on outer surface of dental plates, imbricate, the tips in outer row forming a jagged cutting edge; edges of dental plates not clearly overlapping; lips nearly covering dental plates; body depth 2.2-2.75 in standard length; dorsal spines flexible; caudal fin slightly rounded in juveniles, truncate in subadults, and deeply emarginate in adults; initial phase mottled dark orangish brown, shading to pale orangish ventrally; base of pectoral fins dark brown; posterior margin of caudal fin narrowly white; terminal males dull blue-green with a vertically elongate salmon pink spot on each body scale and salmon pink bands radiating from eye. Reported to 50 cm. Indo-Pacific and tropical eastern Pacific; observed in Oman only in the south. Often misidentified as *C. spinidens* (Quoy and Gaimard).

812. *Calotomus carolinus*, terminal male, 39 cm (J. Randall)

813. *Calotomus carolinus*, initial phase, about 23 cm (J. Randall)

814. *Calotomus carolinus*, juv., 5 cm (J. Randall)

SLENDER PARROTFISH

Leptoscarus vaigiensis (Quoy and
Gaimard, 1824)

Pectoral rays 14; median predorsal scales usually 4; a single row of scales on cheek below eye; oblique rows of teeth fused to form dental plates, the upper enclosed by lower when mouth closed (the reverse for Scarinae); lips covering dental plates; body elongate, the depth 2.9-3.8 in standard length; dorsal spines flexible, the interspinous membranes distinctly incised; caudal fin rounded; females mottled olive to brown, shading to dull yellow or pale greenish ventrally; fins mottled yellowish; males with small blue spots on head, body, anal, and caudal fins. Reaches 35 cm. Indo-Pacific, but not reported from many localities; known in Oman only from the Arabian sea coast. Occurs in seagrass beds or substrata with heavy algal growth (where it is well camouflaged).

SUBFAMILY SCARINAE

BULLETHEAD PARROTFISH

Chlorurus sordidus (Forsskål, 1775)

Pectoral rays 14-16 (nearly always 15); median predorsal scales 4, progressively larger anteriorly; two rows of scales on cheek; surface of dental plates smooth (true of species of *Chlorurus* and *Scarus*); no conical teeth on lower dental plate; large

815. *Leptoscarus vaigiensis*, male, about 19.5 cm (J. Randall)

816. *Leptoscarus vaigiensis*, female, 25.5 cm (J. Randall)

adults with one or two conical teeth on side of upper dental plate; lips covering less than half of dental plates; front of head strongly rounded, the dorsal and ventral profiles about equally convex; caudal fin usually truncate in adults (slightly emarginate in

some large terminal males); initial phase dark brown to reddish brown, becoming red around mouth and ventrally on head; two longitudinal rows of five or six small whitish spots often present on side of body; a broad whitish bar containing a large round dark brown spot may be seen midlaterally on caudal peduncle (this and the whitish spots can be quickly turned off and just as rapidly reinstated); body of terminal males usually green, the edges of scales pink to purple, except on caudal peduncle where solid green; postorbital head and interorbital green, the snout lavender with a broad green band from upper lip to eye (edge of lip narrowly pink); chin with two broad transverse green or blue-green bands; cheek usually greenish yellow; juveniles uniform dark brown or dark brown with four narrow yellowish white stripes. Attains 40 cm. Indo-Pacific; the most common parrotfish at many coral-reef localities. Occurs throughout Oman. Bellwood (1994) is followed in placing this species and the following in the genus *Chlorurus* (formerly in *Scarus*).

819. *C. sordidus*, juvs, about 5 cm (J. Randall)

817. *Chlorurus sordidus*, terminal male, about 27 cm (J. Randall)

818. *Chlorurus sordidus*, initial phase, about 22 cm (J. Randall)

ROUNDHEAD PARROTFISH
Chlorurus strongylocephalus (Bleeker, 1854)

Pectoral rays 15-17 (usually 16); median predorsal scales usually 4; three rows of scales on cheek, the lower row with 1-8 scales; one or two conical teeth on side of upper dental plate of large adults; one-fourth or less of dental plates covered by lips; dorsal profile of head steep and smoothly convex; caudal fin of adults lunate; initial phase yellowish green dorsally, becoming red on sides and ventrally; edge of lips with a broad blue-green band, the two bands not meeting at corner of mouth where pink; dental plates blue-green; body of terminal males green, the scales with a vertical lavender-pink bar, shading dorsoanteriorly to lavender-grey and to lavender-blue on snout; broad green band of upper lip continuing diffusely to eye; three narrow green bands diverging posteriorly from eye; cheek below lower green band yellow, shading ventrally to light green; juveniles dark brown, including caudal fin, with four narrow pale yellowish stripes, the third extending onto midbase of caudal fin. Maximum length about 70 cm. Western Indian Ocean, including the south coast of Oman but not the Red Sea or Gulf of Oman. Closely related to *C. gibbus* (Rüppell) of the Red Sea and *C. microrhinos* (Bleeker) of the central and western Pacific.

820. *Chlorurus strongylocephalus*, terminal male, about 40 cm (J. Randall)

821. *C. strongylocephalus*, initial phase (J. Hoover)

ARABIAN PARROTFISH
Scarus arabicus (Steindachner, 1902)

Pectoral rays 15; median predorsal scales 4; two rows of scales on cheek; no conical teeth posteriorly on side of dental plates; posterior margin of upper dental plate with four or five small blunt ventrally-projecting teeth; lips covering slightly less than half of dental plates; dorsal profile of head of terminal males steep; nostrils very small; caudal fin of initial phase truncate, of terminal males slightly emarginate; initial phase grey-brown, the scale edges orangish; lower part of head mainly turquoise blue; caudal fin dark grey-brown with a narrow white posterior margin; terminal males green, faintly suffused with yellow anteriorly, with a narrow pink bar on each scale; head greenish yellow, shading anteriorly to violet and ventrally to blue, with a broad irregular green band across interorbital space and enclosing eye; front of snout green, the edge of upper lip narrowly pink; pectoral fins purple, the upper edge broadly blue. Attains about 45 cm. Known only from the south coast of the Arabian Peninsula (type locality, Makalla, Yemen) to the Gulf of Oman (but not common there).

822. *Scarus arabicus*, terminal male, about 45 cm (J. Hoover)

823. *Scarus arabicus*, initial phase, about 22 cm (J. Randall)

824. *Scarus falcipinnis*, juv., 4.1 cm (J. Randall)

FALCATE-FIN PARROTFISH
Scarus falcipinnis (Playfair, 1867)

Pectoral rays 15-16 (usually 15); median predorsal scales 6 (on some a pair of small scales lateral and slightly anterior to first median scale), the fourth scale largest; three rows of scales on cheek, the lower row with 1-3 scales; terminal males with one or two conical teeth posteriorly on side of upper dental plate; lips covering about one-half to three-fourths of dental plates; dorsal profile of head of initial phase slightly convex, of terminal male nearly flat from before eye to dorsal fin; caudal fin of initial phase emarginate, of terminal male deeply lunate; body of initial phase olive grey, the scale edges orangish brown, with scattered small whitish spots, more numerous posteriorly; head orangish, shading to light red around mouth and ventrally; dental plates white; terminal males dull blue-green, the scale edges narrowly salmon pink, with a broad zone of blue-green on cheek which bifurcates anteriorly to a band to snout and one to chin, and continues posteriorly across side of chest and abdomen, extending broadly onto anal fin and ending on lower edge of caudal peduncle; dental plates blue-green. Largest initial phase, 48 cm; largest terminal male, 60 cm. Seychelles and Mauritius to coast of Africa at least as far south as 15°; a few individuals observed on the southern coast of Oman. Very closely related to *S. prasiognathos* Valenciennes which ranges from the Maldives east to the western Pacific.

RUSTY PARROTFISH
Scarus ferrugineus Forsskål, 1775

Pectoral rays 15; median predorsal scales 6-7 (usually 6); three rows of scales on cheek, the lower row with 2-4 scales; 0-2 conical teeth posteriorly on side of upper dental plate of terminal males; lips covering two thirds or more of dental plates; caudal fin of initial phase slightly rounded to truncate, of terminal males double emarginate; initial phase reddish brown to brown with dark brown bars, shading to yellow on caudal peduncle and fin; dental plates blue-green; body of terminal males blue-green, the scale edges pink, shading to greenish yellow anteriorly and on postorbital head, often with

825. *Scarus falcipinnis*, terminal male, 52.5 cm (J. Randall)

826. *Scarus falcipinnis*, initial phase, 20 cm (J. Randall)

827. *Scarus ferrugineus*, terminal male, about 35 cm (J. Hoover)

828. *Scarus ferrugineus*, initial phase, about 24 cm (J. Randall)

small green spots; edge of upper lip broadly pink, a broad green band above which extends to or below eye and may connect with a very broad green band on chin (except for a median pink spot at edge of lower lip); rest of snout and interorbital lavender with a variable number of green spots and irregular green lines; juveniles whitish with three brown stripes and a yellow caudal fin. Largest specimen, 41 cm. Known only from the seas of the Arabian Peninsula; more common in the Gulf of Oman than to the south.

BRIDLED PARROTFISH
Scarus frenatus Lacepède, 1802

Pectoral rays 14-15 (rarely 15); median predorsal scales 6-7 (usually 7), the fourth or fifth largest; rows of scales on cheek 3, the lower row with 2-4 scales; 0-2 canine teeth posteriorly on side of upper dental plate in both phases; lips covering three-fourths or more of dental plates; caudal fin truncate or slightly emarginate in initial phase, double emarginate or deeply emarginate in terminal males; initial phase yellowish grey to light reddish brown with six dark brown stripes on body following centres of scale rows (stripes sometimes obscure); head reddish brown; fins red; dental plates white; anterior two-thirds of body of terminal males green, densely marked with small dull orange-red spots and irregular lines, posterior third abruptly bright green; head above a demarcation at level of lower edge of eye lavendar pink with numerous small green spots and irregular lines; head below eye green, shading to pink with green markings below; upper lip broadly pink with a broader green band above; dental plates blue-green. Largest specimen, 47 cm. Indo-Pacific; observed in Oman only on the south coast. *S. sexvittatus* Rüppell is a synonym based on the initial phase, and *S. vermiculatus* (Fowler and Bean) a synonym based on the terminal male.

829. *S. frenatus*, juv., about 7 cm (J. Randall)

830. *Scarus frenatus*, terminal male (J. Randall)

831. *Scarus frenatus*, initial phase (J. Randall)

832. *Scarus fuscopurpureus*, terminal male, about 29 cm (J. Randall)

833. *Scarus fuscopurpureus*, initial phase, about 20 cm (J. Hoover)

PURPLE-BROWN PARROTFISH
Scarus fuscopurpureus (Klunzinger, 1871)

Pectoral rays 14-15 (usually 14); median predorsal scales 4; two rows of scales on cheek; large initial-phase fish with two small conical teeth posteriorly on upper dental plate; terminal males with one lower plate tooth and two upper plate teeth; lips covering about three-fourths of dental plates; caudal fin truncate in initial phase to lunate on large terminal males; initial phase reddish to purplish brown, the scale centres sometime dull greenish; a dull blue-green band at base of upper lip becoming submarginal to orange at side of lip and continuing to eye; three faint blue-green bands extending posteriorly from eye; chin orangish with two faint transverse dull blue-green bands; terminal males green, the scales edge reddish anteriorly on body (except ventrally); posteriorly the scale edges become salmon pink and broader until there is just a green spot on each scale of caudal peduncle; a pink to yellow bar often present on side of body in line with the first soft rays of dorsal and anal fins; head greenish, suffused with salmon pink, with the same blue-green bands as described for the initial phase, but much brighter. Attains 38 cm. Red Sea to the Arabian Gulf; less common in the Gulf of Oman than the south. Often seen grazing algae from compact sand substrata near reefs. The closely related *S. russelii* Valenciennes occurs elsewhere in the Indian Ocean from Sri Lanka to the west.

BLUEBARRED PARROTFISH
Scarus ghobban Forsskål, 1775

Pectoral rays 15-16 (rarely 16); median predorsal scales usually 6, the fourth usually largest; three rows of scales on cheek below eye, the lowermost with 1-2 scales; large adults with one to three (usually two) coni- cal teeth posteriorly on side of upper dental plate, best developed on large terminal males; lips covering one-half to four-fifths of dental plates; posterior nostril oval and large for the genus; caudal fin varying from slightly emarginate in small initial- phase fish to strongly lunate in large terminal males; initial phase with scale centres blu- ish, the edges orange-yellow; five blue bars on body the result of the intensification of the blue centres of scales; small initial phase often with a bluish white spot (sometimes two) on midside of body; head yellow with blue bands and spots, the lips salmon pink; terminal males green dorsally, the scales edged in salmon pink; side of body and ven- trally with progressively less green and more salmon pink; a faint blackish bar sometimes present in middle of body; head yellowish green with a broad irregular green band from corner of mouth across lower part of head linked with two blue-green bands on chin; edge of upper lips salmon pink with a broad green band above; dental plates pale salmon. Reaches at least 75 cm. Indo-Pacific and tropical eastern Pacific; found through- out Oman.

834. *Scarus ghobban*, initial phase, about 25 cm (J. Hoover)

835. *S. ghobban*, subadult, about 14 cm (J. Randall)

836. *Scarus ghobban*, terminal male, about 50 cm (J. Randall)

837. *S. niger*, juv., about 4.5 cm (J. Randall)

SWARTHY PARROTFISH
Scarus niger Forsskål, 1775

Pectoral rays 13-15 (usually 14); median predorsal scales 6-8 (usually 7); three rows of scales on cheek, the lower row with 2-5 scales; initial phase usually without conical teeth on upper dental plate (rarely one or two), usually two on terminal males; three-fourths or more of dental plates covered by lips; caudal fin of initial phase slightly rounded to truncate, double emarginate on terminal males with projecting lobes; initial phase brownish red to greenish grey, the scales crossed with dark brown lines, most of which are hoizontal, many joined to form narrow dark stripes; head brownish red, shading anteriorly to red-orange with two transverse green bands on chin, one above upper lip, one to below and behind eye, and two from behind eye; an irregular light green band sometimes present from upper edge of eye across dorsal part of operculum; dental plates blue-green; terminal males dark green, the scale edges dark reddish, with the same bands on head as initial phase; upper lip broadly salmon pink; a small yellow spot within a green band at upper end of gill opening; pectoral fins largely deep rose pink. Largest specimen, 39 cm. Indo-Pacific; observed in Oman only on the southern coast. Males display to females with the caudal fin held upward and the angular anal fin fully extended. *S. madagascariensis* (Steindachner) is a synonym based on the initial phase.

PERSIAN PARROTFISH
Scarus persicus Randall and Bruce, 1983

Pectoral rays 15; median predorsal scales 5-6, nearly equal in size; terminal males with two conical teeth posteriorly on upper dental plate; lips covering one-half to three-fourths of dental plates; nostrils very small; caudal fin of initial phase slightly rounded to slightly emarginate, of terminal male moderately emarginate; body of initial phase grey, the scale edges yellowish brown, shading ventrally to light red; head yellowish grey, shading to salmon pink on lips; dental plates blue-green; margins of dorsal and anal fins and upper and lower edges of caudal fin blue; terminal males lavender-pink to salmon pink with irregular green markings on scales of body and dorsally on head; a blackish bar in middle of body; chin salmon pink with a transverse green band; a square white spot at corner of mouth; dental plates deep blue-green. Attains about 50 cm. Known only from the Arabian Gulf to the southern coast of Oman, but not common in the south.

838. *Scarus niger*, terminal male, about 28 cm (J. Hoover)

839. *Scarus niger*, initial phase, about 22 cm (J. Hoover)

840. *Scarus persicus*, terminal male, about 50 cm (J. Randall)

841. *Scarus persicus*, initial phase, about 35 cm (J. Randall)

842. *S. persicus*, juv., about 5 cm (J. Randall)

PALENOSE PARROTFISH
Scarus psittacus Forsskål, 1775

Pectoral rays 13-14 (usually 14); median predorsal scales usually 4; two rows of scales on cheek; initial-phase fish usually with one conical tooth posteriorly on upper dental plate, and large terminal males usu- ally with one lower and two upper teeth on the plates; lips covering three-fourths or more of dental plates; caudal fin of adults in initial phase slightly emarginate, of termi- nal males deeply emarginate; initial phase usually reddish brown, shading to orange- red on chest and abdomen; snout paler than rest of head; a small black spot at upper base of pectoral fin, and a dark brown spot basal- ly on first membrane of dorsal fin; terminal males with scales of body half green and half salmon pink, the green merging to form three stripes on abdomen and partially merg- ing to form four or five stripes on caudal peduncle; head orangish suffused with green; snout lavender; a blue-green band from upper lip through lower part of eye, two ex- tending posteriorly from eye, and two across chin; dental plates white. A small species, the maximum length about 30 cm. Indo- Pacific; observed and photographed in Oman only at the Juzor al Hallaniyat (Kuria Muria Islands). *S. forsteri* Valenciennes is one of the 11 junior synonyms of this species.

EMBER PARROTFISH
Scarus rubroviolaceus Bleeker, 1847

Pectoral rays 14-16 (usually 15); median predorsal scales 5-7 (usually 6); three rows of scales on cheek, the lower row with 1-3 (usually 2) scales; females with at most a single conical tooth posteriorly on side of upper dental plate; males with one to three conical teeth on upper plate; lips covering about half of dental plates; body moderately elongate, the depth 2.75-3.1 in standard length; dorsal profile of head rising steeply from mouth to level of eye, then curving sharply, the remaining profile to dorsal fin nearly straight; caudal fin of females slightly emarginate, of males strongly lunate; body of females light reddish brown to yellowish grey, shading to light red ventrally, with small black spots and irregular lines on scales of body; head reddish brown, shading anteriorly and ventrally to red; dental plates pale red, becoming white on edges; fins red; terminal male green dorsally, the scales nar- rowly edged with salmon pink, shading to greenish yellow or pale salmon on side of body, and to light green ventrally; edge of upper lip salmon pink, with a broad green band above; rest of snout lavender-grey; two transverse green bands on chin separated by salmon pink, converging behind corner of mouth and continuing as a broad band to eye; dental plates deep blue-green. Reaches 70 cm. Indo-Pacific and tropical eastern Pacific; Gulf of Oman to southern coast of Oman. Limited data indicate this species is monandric (i.e. initial-phase fish only female).

843. *Scarus psittacus*, terminal male, about 22 cm (J. Randall)

844. *Scarus psittacus*, initial phase, about 19 cm (J. Randall)

845. *Scarus rubroviolaceus*, terminal male, about 50 cm (J. Hoover)

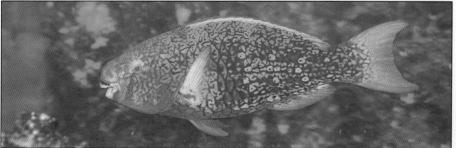

846. *Scarus rubroviolaceus*, initial phase, about 32 cm (J. Hoover)

847. *S. rubroviolaceus*, juv., 4 cm (J. Randall)

FIVESADDLE PARROTFISH
Scarus scaber Valenciennes, 1840

Pectoral rays 13-14 (rarely 13); median predorsal scales 4-7 (usually 6), the fourth or fifth largest; no conical teeth on side of dental plates; lips covering three-fourths to all of dental plates; nostrils small and close together; caudal fin of initial phase truncate to slightly emarginate, becoming deeply emarginate on terminal males; initial phase with five oblique dark grey bars dorsally on body separated by bright yellow zones of equal width; rest of body light grey to whitish, the scale edges darker; a dark grey stripe from side of snout through eye and across upper part of operculum; head above stripe light grey, below yellow, shading ventrally to whitish; terminal males with head above lower edge of eye and body at same level anterior to a demarcation from base of eighth dorsal spine purplish grey; rest of body green, the edges of scales broadly salmon pink, the green reduced to a central spot on each scale posteriorly on body; a broad blue-green band from front of snout, joined by one from chin, and continuing below eye across operculum; edge of upper lip pink; chin pink with a second blue-green band; behind this a longitudinal light blue-green band or series of spots; a narrow blue-green stripe through upper part of eye. Reaches about 37 cm. Smith (1956) recorded this species from Natal north on the coast of Africa. Observed by the author in Kenya,

848. *Scarus scaber*, terminal male, about 29 cm (J. Randall)

849. *Scarus scaber*, initial phase, about 23 cm (J. Hoover)

Gulf of Aden, the south coast of Oman (where it is rare), Seychelles, Mauritius, and the Maldive Islands.

DHOFAR PARROTFISH
Scarus zufar Randall and Hoover, 1995

Pectoral rays 14-15 (rarely 14); median predorsal scales 4; two rows of scales on cheek; no teeth on side of dental plates; upper dental plate about three-fourths covered by lip; lower plate about three-fourths exposed; caudal fin of adults truncate with moderately prolonged lobes; body of initial phase orange anteriorly with a submarginal green arc on each scale, the green becoming progressively broader posteriorly until it dominates the scale colour; snout and dorsal part of head greenish grey, becoming orange on cheek, with irregular green bands extending from eye, one passing to upper lip and another to chin, these two bands separated by a narrow orange band to corner of mouth and along edge of upper lip; pectoral fins orange with a narrow blue-green upper edge; terminal male similar, the snout and chin entirely green; a large orange to salmon pink area beneath and around pectoral fin, sometimes extending dorsally as a broad yellow zone. Attains at least 50 cm. Known only from the Juzor al Hallaniyat (Kuria Muria Islands) and the Dhofar coast of Oman where it is one of the four most common species of parrotfishes (the others *S. arabicus*, *S. fuscopurpureus*, and *S. ghobban*); usually seen along exposed rocky shores.

850. *Scarus zufar*, terminal male, about 42 cm (J. Hoover)

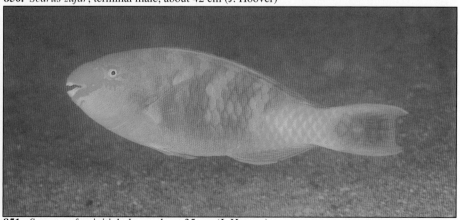

851. *Scarus zufar*, initial phase, about 35 cm (J. Hoover)

JAWFISHES
FAMILY OPISTOGNATHIDAE

The fishes of this family have a moderately elongate, strongly tapering body; the head is large, its dorsal profile steep; the eyes are set far forward, hence the snout is very short; the mouth is very large, the maxilla exposed on the cheek and usually extending well posterior to the eye; moderately large conical teeth in several rows in jaws, the teeth of outer row usually largest, narrowing to a single row posteriorly in jaws; no teeth on the palatines, and few or none on vomer. The scales are small and cycloid, often absent from the head; the lateral line is high on the body, ending beneath the soft portion of the dorsal fin. The dorsal fin is continuous, with X or XI usually flexible spines, 11-15 soft rays, and little or no notch between spinous and soft portions; anal fin with II or III slender spines and 10-16 soft rays; caudal fin rounded (lanceolate only in *Lonchopisthus*), with 12-14 branched rays in most species; pelvic fins I,5, anterior to pectorals, the first two rays thick and unbranched. Most jawfishes occur on open bottoms, often sand and rubble near reefs, and generally in less than 30 m (though some species have been taken from depths greater than 200 m). They live in vertical burrows of their own construction, typically lined with small stones, coral fragments, or shell. Longley (1941) poured plaster of Paris into the burrows of *Opistognathus maxillosus* at Tortugas, Florida, and determined that there is a chamber below the vertical shaft. These fishes usually have only the front of their head exposed from their burrows, but they may hover in a near-vertical stance above the burrow to feed on zooplankton; they may also make short excursions to prey on benthic invertebrates. Usually they enter their burrow tail first, but if threatened and hurried, they

852. *Opistognathus muscatensis*, 35.7 cm (J. Randall)

853. *Opistognathus nigromarginatus*, 12.6 cm (J. Randall)

may go in head first. Their large mouth serves them well in moving rocks and excavating sand, but also in the case of males, for the incubation of the eggs (Böhlke and Chaplin, 1957). There are three genera, *Opistognathus*, *Lonchopisthus*, and *Stalix* (this genus revised by Smith-Vaniz, 1989), with about 90 species, many still undescribed.

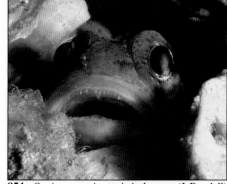

854. *O. nigromarginatus* in its burrow (J. Randall)

ROBUST JAWFISH
Opistognathus muscatensis Boulenger, 1887

Dorsal rays XI,15; anal rays III,15; pectoral rays 19; longitudinal scale series 103-142; gill rakers 13-17 + 23-29; body depth 3.4-4.0 in standard length; maxilla broadening posteriorly to its rounded end, not approaching margin of opercle, the upper jaw length 1.4-1.6 in head; anterior nostril a short tube without a cirrus; pale blue with irregular yellowish brown blotches of variable size on body, the three largest becoming black dorsally and extending into base of dorsal fin; an ocellated dark spot between third and eighth dorsal spines; a blackish streak on cheek behind upper edge of maxilla. Largest specimen, 41 cm. Known from the Arabian Gulf, Gulf of Oman, Kenya, Natal, and the Seychelles in the depth range of 30-50 m.

BRIDLED JAWFISH
Opistognathus nigromarginatus Rüppell, 1830

Dorsal rays XI,14-15; anal rays III,14-15; branched caudal rays 12; pectoral rays 19-21 (usually 20); longitudinal scale series 68-88; gill rakers 13-17 + 23-29; body depth 4.1-4.7 in standard length; maxilla widest at midlength, then slanting upward and tapering to extend almost to or beyond opercular edge, the upper-jaw length 1.0-1.2 in head length; anterior nostril a short tube with a small cirrus; whitish with irregular dark brown markings on body; dorsal fin grey-brown with small irregular bluish white spots and an ocellated black spot between fourth to eighth spines. Largest specimen, 18.6 cm. A shallow-water species known from the Red Sea south to Natal and east to India and Viet Nam; the only insular localities, Zanzibar and Aldabra.

OMAN JAWFISH
Stalix omanensis Norman, 1939

Dorsal rays XI,11; anal rays II,11; branched caudal rays 14; pectoral rays 23; longitudinal scale series about 43; lateral line ending beneath first and second soft rays of dorsal fin; gill rakers 10 + 19; body depth 5.1 in standard length; maxilla broader posteriorly, the end slightly rounded, the upper-jaw length 1.6 in head length; tips of first seven dorsal spines transversely forked (distally bifurcate dorsal spines characteristic of the genus); life colour unknown; colour from original description, brownish, darker on back; head with small dark spots; fins uniform; Smith-Vaniz, 1989 noted the lips as dark, and he illustrated a pair of dusky spots medially on chin. Known from one 4.2-cm specimen taken by trawl in 73 m in the northern Gulf of Oman. Closely related to *S. flavida* Smith-Vaniz from northwestern Australia.

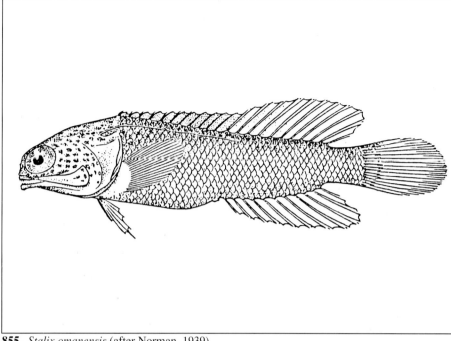

855. *Stalix omanensis* (after Norman, 1939)

BANDFISHES
FAMILY CEPOLIDAE

These distinctive fishes are moderately to very elongate with a tapering, highly compressed body and a lanceolate caudal fin; the mouth is large and strongly oblique, the maxilla extending to below the posterior part of eye; there is no supramaxilla; the teeth are slender, slightly curved, in a single row in jaws (some species with a cluster of small teeth at symphysis); there are no teeth on the vomer or palatines; the scales are cycloid; the lateral line passes close to the dorsal-fin base, ending below posterior part of fin. The dorsal fin is continuous with 0-4 flexible spines and 21-89 soft rays; anal fin with 0-1 spines and 13-102 soft rays; caudal fin with 9-15 branched rays; pelvic fins I,5, below or anterior to pectorals, the last ray not branched or only weakly branched. There are two subfamilies, the Owstoniinae (no species yet known from Oman) and the Cepolinae, each with two genera; the total number of species of the family is about 20. These fishes inhabit tropical to temperate seas, mostly at depths greater than 30 m, on mud or sand substrata where they live in burrows of their own construction.

YELLOWSPOTTED BANDFISH
Acanthocepola abbreviata (Valenciennes, 1834)

Dorsal rays 69-80 (all as unbranched soft rays); anal rays 0-II,70-84; pectoral rays 18-19 (branched except upper two and lowermost); branched caudal rays 10; longitudinal scale series about 167; scales with membranous crenulate edges (with three to six projections); opercle and cheek scaled except for outer flange of preopercle; predorsal scales to above preopercular margin; gill rakers 16 + 30; vertebrae 57-61; preopercle with five short spines, three on ventral margin, the largest at angle, and one above; front of upper jaw concave with no teeth at symphysis; body depth 7.5-8.1 in standard length; head length 6.3-7.6 in standard length; dorsal and anal fins joined to the short caudal fin; origin of dorsal fin slightly anterior to upper end of gill opening; origin of anal fin below eighth ray of dorsal fin; silvery white, the dorsal and anterior part of head pale orange-red, with a series of light yellow spots smaller than pupil along upper side of body anteriorly, on midside and vertically elongate posteriorly except the last a distinct round spot on base of caudal fin; dorsal fin translucent yellow; anal fin white with a broad yellow outer margin; median fins with a narrow blackish margin, most evident on anal fin. Attains at least 30 cm. Arabian Gulf and Gulf of Oman to Indo-Malayan region (type locality, Java), and Gulf of Carpentaria. The illustrated specimen was taken by trawling in the Arabian Gulf.

856. *Acanthocepola abbreviata*, 20.1 cm (J. Randall)

GAPERS
FAMILY CHAMPSODONTIDAE

This unique small Indo-Pacific fish family is characterised as follows: body elongate, little compressed; mouth large, oblique, the lower jaw strongly projecting; maxilla exposed on the cheek; upper jaw with two rows of depressible teeth, the inner row longer; lower jaw with three rows of teeth, the inner row of long and short depressible teeth, the long teeth with arrow-like tips; two patches of teeth on vomer; a long dagger-like spine at corner of pre-opercle; scales shark-like, consisting of a conical support embedded in skin capped by a flat plate with 2-9 spinules along the posterior margin; two indistinct lateral lines, each as a row of sensory papillae, joined by vertical rows of papillae which extend above and below to base of dorsal and anal fins; two dorsal fins, the first of IV-VI spines, the second with 18-23 soft rays; anal fin with 16-21 rays; caudal fin forked; pectoral fins short; pelvic fins long, the rays I,5, inserted before pectoral fins. The family consists of the single genus *Champsodon* with 13 species (revised by Nemeth, 1994).

OMAN GAPER
Champsodon omanensis Regan, 1908

Dorsal rays IV-V,18-20; anal rays 17-19; pectoral rays 12-14; gill rakers 1 + 10-12; chest fully scaled; abdomen scaled at least half way from anus to base of pelvic fins; five to seven pairs of sensory papillae dorsally on head from snout to interorbital space; maxilla extending posterior to a vertical at rear edge of eye; body depth 5.2-6.2 in standard length; head length 2.3-3.5 in standard length; colour in alcohol brown dorsally, shading on sides to silvery; chin dusky; a dark blotch at caudal-fin base continuing as a dark band in each lobe; remaining fins dark brown. Attains 15 cm. Described from three specimens taken in 260-365 m in the Gulf of Oman. Norman (1939) reported specimens from the Gulf of Oman, Arabian Sea, and Gulf of Aden in the depth range of 135-220 m. Klausewitz (1982) provided the first Red Sea record; his specimens were taken off Jeddah at depths of 360-1100 m.

SANDPERCHES
FAMILY PINGUIPEDIDAE

This family has often been called by the invalid names Parapercidae or Mugiloididae; Rosa and Rosa (1987) showed that the correct name is Pinguipedidae. These fishes have an elongate, near-cylindrical body anteriorly, becoming more compressed posteriorly; the eyes are oriented as much dorsally as laterally, the interorbital space very narrow; the mouth is moderately large, slightly oblique, and terminal or with the lower jaw slightly projecting; maxilla largely hidden beneath the preorbital when mouth closed; stout curved conical teeth in an outer row in jaws, largest anteriorly (three to five pairs at front of lower jaw the largest and termed canines); an inner band of villiform teeth anteriorly in jaws, narrowing and continuing posteriorly only on upper jaw; teeth present on vomer, present or absent on palatines; a stout spine on opercle; edge of preopercle smooth; gill membranes united, attached to isthmus, with a fold across; branchiostegal rays 6; scales small, ctenoid on body, those on cheek usually cycloid; lateral line complete; a long dorsal fin with IV-VII spines and 20-24 soft rays; anal fin with a slender spine and 14-22 soft rays; branched caudal rays 15, the fin varying from truncate to deeply emarginate; pelvic fins I,5, inserted below or in advance of the pectorals, the fourth soft ray longest. The family consists of four genera, of which *Parapercis* is the largest and the only one represented in the tropical Indo-Pacific region. Several species of this genus have been shown to be protogynous hermaphrodites (commencing mature life as females and changing sex to males later in life), and it is expected that this may be in effect for all the species. A significant change in colour pattern is generally associated with the sex reversal. The species of *Parapercis* are usually found on sand or sand and rubble bottoms, often in the vicinity of reefs; they reside on the substratum, propping themselves with their well-separated pelvic fins. Many species are surprisingly unafraid of divers. Cantwell (1964) revised *Parapercis*, recognising 26 species; he failed to notice the sexual dimorphism in colour pattern. The literature of the genus since Cantwell's revision was reviewed by Randall (1984), at which time the total number of species was 40. Four more valid species have since been described, and more remain to be named.

857. *Champsodon omanensis* (after Regan, 1908)

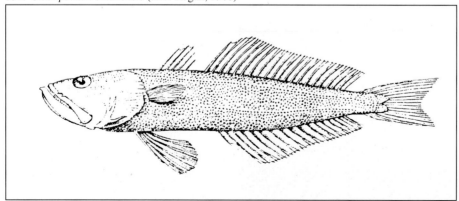

BLUENOSE SANDPERCH
Parapercis alboguttata (Günther, 1872)

Dorsal rays V,22; anal rays I,19; pectoral rays 17-19; lateral-line scales 58-60; three pairs of canine teeth in outer row at front of lower jaw; no palatine teeth; body depth 6.0-6.8 in standard length; caudal peduncle slender, the least depth 4.0-4.8 in head length; third and fourth dorsal spines longest; membrane from fifth dorsal spine connected to first dorsal soft ray near its base; caudal fin slightly emarginate; body light red dorsally, shading to white ventrally, the scale edges yellowish brown except ventrally; two longitudinal rows of indistinct light red blotches on body, ending in two distinct dark red spots on base of caudal fin; snout light blue with oblique yellow lines; fins largely white. Reaches about 27 cm. Ranges from the Arabian Gulf to the Indo-Malayan region and northwestern Australia. *P. smithii* (Regan), *P. tesselata* (Herre), and *P. cephalus* Kotthaus are synonyms.

858. *Parapercis alboguttata*, 20.5 cm (J. Randall)

859. *Parapercis hexophtalma*, male, about 22 cm (J. Randall)

860. *Parapercis hexophtalma*, female, about 19 cm (J. Randall)

SPECKLED SANDPERCH
Parapercis hexophtalma (Cuvier, 1829)

Dorsal rays V,21-22 (rarely 22); anal rays I,17-18 (rarely 18); pectoral rays 17-18; lateral-line scales 58-63; four pairs of canine teeth anteriorly in lower jaw; palatine teeth absent; body depth 4.8-5.8 in standard length; third and fourth dorsal spines longest; membrane from tip of last dorsal spine joining first soft ray at level of spine tip; caudal fin slightly rounded or rounded with the upper rays slightly prolonged; light greenish dorsally, speckled with dark brown, light grey on sides and white ventrally; a longitudinal series of large elliptical contiguous white spots along side of body with a small blackish spot or group of small spots in centre of each; lower side of body with a row of small black spots, most rimmed with bright yellow; head of females with small brown spots, of males with a series of oblique yellowish brown to yellow lines on cheek; caudal fin with a very large black blotch in centre; a black spot basally in dorsal fin between second and fourth spines; three or four rows of black spots in soft part of dorsal fin and one in anal fin. Reaches 28 cm. Red Sea south to Natal and east to the western Pacific as far as Fiji; a shallow-water species usually found on sand and rubble around protected reefs. *P. polyophtalma* (Cuvier) is a synonym based on the female phase.

HARLEQUIN SANDPERCH
Parapercis maculata (Bloch and Schneider, 1801)

Dorsal rays V,21-22 (usually 21); anal rays I,18-19 (usually 18); pectoral rays 16-17; lateral-line scales 57-64; four pairs of canine teeth anteriorly in lower jaw; palatine teeth absent; body depth 5.1-5.8 in standard length; fourth dorsal spine longest; membrane from tip of last dorsal spine joined a short distance (about one-fourth last spine length) from base of first dorsal soft ray; caudal fin of adults slightly rounded, the second to fourth branched rays somewhat prolonged; light brownish red to grey-brown dorsally, shading to whitish ventrally, with six large square dark brownish red blotches on ventral half of body linked through a narrow red bar to large irregular brownish red blotches on back; vertical curved blue lines on head; a blackish blotch in basal part of spinous dorsal fin; rows of orange spots in soft portion of dorsal fin and white spots in anal fin; lower third to fourth of caudal fin dark brownish red. Reaches 20 cm. Known from Japan, Taiwan, Hong Kong, India (type locality), Sri Lanka, and Zanzibar; the illustration herein from Musandam, Oman. *P. pulchella* (Temminck and Schlegel) is a synonym.

861. *Parapercis maculata*, about 10 cm (J. Randall)

SMALLSCALE SANDPERCH
Parapercis robinsoni Fowler, 1932

Dorsal rays V,21-23 (usually 22); anal rays I,18-19 (rarely 19); pectoral rays 16-17 (rarely 16); lateral-line scales 77-84; three pairs of canine teeth anteriorly in lower jaw; palatine teeth absent; three to five short stout teeth on vomer; body depth 5.1-6.5 in standard length; third and fourth dorsal spines longest; membrane from last dorsal spine attached to first dorsal soft ray at a height one-fourth to one-third length of last spine; caudal fin truncate to slightly emarginate; body with a midlateral dark-edged white stripe about as broad as eye; body below stripe white with seven narrow blackish bars which continue faintly across white stripe; body above stripe grey with eight large blackish blotches and small irregular blotches between the larger ones; snout brownish yellow with blue lines; caudal fin with a white stripe, in line with white stripe of body, containing small blackish spots; a large black spot above white stripe in basal part of caudal fin; remaining fins mainly whitish. Reaches at least 26 cm. This species was long misidentified as *P. nebulosa* (Quoy and Gaimard), described from Western Australia and wide-ranging in Australia. Randall and Stroud (1985) differentiated the two; they confirmed records for *P. robinsoni* from the Arabian Gulf, Gulf of Oman, Somalia, Natal, Aldabra, and Pakistan from the depth range of 6-55 m. Cantwell (1964) reported two specimens of *Parapercis clathrata* Ogilby from the Arabian Gulf; however, the specimens are *P. robinsoni*.

862. *Parapercis robinsoni*, about 10 cm (J. Randall)

SAND DIVERS
FAMILY TRICHONOTIDAE

This small Indo-Pacific family of a single genus, *Trichonotus*, is characterised by a very elongate, somewhat compressed body, a pointed head with a large slightly oblique mouth and a strongly projecting lower jaw; eyes oriented as much dorsally as laterally; a narrow fold of skin projecting as a rim over dorsoanterior part of eye; teeth in villiform bands in jaws and on vomer and palatines; gill membranes separate, not joined to isthmus; branchiostegal rays 7; scales cycloid; lateral line complete; dorsal fin long with III-VI spines and 39-46 soft rays; anal fin with a single spine and 34-42 soft rays; branched caudal rays 11-13; pelvic rays I,5, usually inserted slightly in advance of pectoral fins; vertebrae 49-56. These fishes live in small aggregations over sand substrata; they feed on zooplankton a short distance above the bottom; when alarmed they may dive into the sand, coming to rest with the upper part of the head just visible; if approached while in hiding, they erupt from the sand and dart a half meter or more away, generally taking refuge again in the sand. Shimada and Yoshino (1984) showed that *Trichonotus elegans* appears to be a protogynous hermaphrodite (i.e. it starts mature life as a female and changes later to a male). Males maintain a harem of females; they are larger and have higher fins, some with elongate anterior dorsal spines. In courtship they fully elevate their dorsal fins and lower their anal and pelvic fins. Seven species of *Trichonotus* have been described (key to species provided by Randall and Tarr, 1994), and two more await description.

ARABIAN SAND DIVER
Trichonotus arabicus Randall and Tarr, 1994

Dorsal rays III-IV,44-47; anal rays I,36-39; pectoral rays 13-15; branched caudal rays 11; lateral-line scales 57-58; body fully scaled; gill rakers 6-9 + 20-23; vertebrae 52-54; body depth 13-14 in standard length; head length 4.45-5.15 in standard length; edge of lower lip with a fringe of papillae which line the mouth opening when jaws closed; anterior dorsal spines not prolonged; caudal fin rounded, its length 4.15-6.75 in standard length; females with an indistinct narrow dark stripe on body above lateral line and no black anteriorly on dorsal fin; males with a longitudinal row of 14 brown spots (most larger than eye) and three rows of very small, dark-edged, pale blue spots; dorsal and anal fins with a row of yellow dots on each membrane. Largest specimen, 14.5 cm. A shallow-water species known only from the Arabian Gulf, Gulf of Oman, and southern Oman.

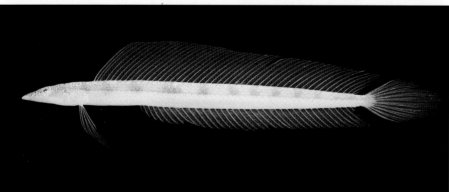

863. *Trichonotus arabicus*, male, 16.6 cm (L. McCarthy)

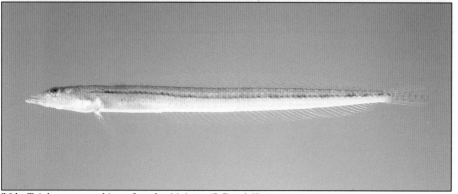

864. *Trichonotus arabicus*, female, 11.1 cm (J. Randall)

STARGAZERS
FAMILY URANOSCOPIDAE

This family is well named for its eyes which are oriented more dorsally than laterally; the head is large, flattened dorsally and ventrally, and partly covered with bony plates which may be granular or rugose; a stout venomous humeral spine at upper end of gill opening; mouth strongly oblique to vertical, the upper jaw protractile, the large lower jaw strongly projecting; small teeth in jaws and on vomer and palatines; lips fringed with papillae; gill openings very broad, the gill membranes separate and free from isthmus; branchiostegal rays 6; body moderately elongate and strongly tapering, naked or with small scales in oblique rows; lateral line high on body; spinous dorsal fin short or absent; soft dorsal and anal fins long; pectoral fins inserted on lower half of body; pelvic fins with I,5 rays, close together in throat region. These fishes are generally buried in sediment with just the eyes and fringed mouth barely exposed; many have a tentacle from inside the front of the lower jaw which can be wriggled, worm-like, to attract their prey of small fishes. There are eight genera and about 50 species in the family which inhabit tropical to warm temperate seas of the Indo-Pacific and Atlantic regions.

DOLLFUS' STARGAZER
Uranoscopas dollfusi Brüss, 1986

Dorsal rays IV,12-14; anal rays 13-14; pectoral rays 17-19; oblique scale rows from upper end of gill opening to rear base of caudal fin 47-54; no scales on abdomen, head, or nape except for a few embedded scales above anterior part of lateral line which extend forward about an eye diameter in front of spinous dorsal fin; surface of external bones of head rough from ridges around numerous tiny depressions; venomous humeral spine large, angling upward; a pair of suprascapular spines above opercle, the inner one triangular, about half length of the outer; five striated, ventrally-directed,

865. *Uranoscopas dollfusi* (O. Schlumberger)

bony ridges on preopercle ending in sharp spines; preorbital with three blunt spines which project obliquely downward, the middle one largest; a long ribbon-like tentacle from inside lower jaw; body moderately elongate and strongly tapering, the body depth 3.55-4.3 in standard length; spinous dorsal fin barely linked basally to soft dorsal; caudal fin slightly rounded; grey-brown, paler ventrally; fine reticulum of ridges on external bones of head reddish; outer three-fourths of spinous dorsal fin black, the basal fourth white; caudal fin grey-brown with a white posterior margin. Largest specimen, 23.7 cm. Reported previously only from the Gulf of Suez (type locality) and the Arabian Gulf (misidentified by Blegvad, 1944 as *U. guttatus*); here recorded from the Gulf of Oman from a specimen taken by trawl in 46 m.

TRIPLEFINS
FAMILY TRIPTERYGIIDAE

The triplefins are small (usually less than 6 cm) blennioid fishes of the order Perciformes that are found in tropical to temperate seas, but the

greatest number in the Indo-Pacific region. Their most distinctive feature is having three separate dorsal fins, the first with III-X spines, the second with VII-XXVI spines, and the third with 7-17 soft rays; the anal fin has 0-II (rarely IV) spines and 14-31 soft rays; the caudal fin has 9-11 branched rays; the pelvic fins have a spine and 2-3 soft rays, the fins inserted distinctly anterior to base of pectoral fins; the body is scaled, the scales usually ctenoid; there is either a single continuous lateral line (which may end beneath second dorsal fin or continue to caudal peduncle) or a discontinuous lateral line, with an anterodorsal part of pored scales and a midlateral posterior part of notched scales (the two may overlap broadly); there are bands of conical teeth in jaws, broadest anteriorly, the largest teeth in outer row at front of jaws; the gill membranes are broadly attached across the isthmus. There is a total of 30 genera in the family, of which the largest are *Enneapterygius* and *Helcogramma*, and at least 125

866. *Enneapterygius melanospilus* (J. Hoover)

species worldwide (Fricke, 1994). Triplefins are usually found on coral reefs or rocky substrata, often with good algal growth. Most species occur in shallow water, sometimes in rock pools of the intertidal zone. Males and females often have different colour patterns. Clark (1979) reviewed the Red Sea species of Tripterygiidae, Hansen (1986) revised *Helcogramma* (though two new species were described since her revision and more remain to be named), and Holleman (1991) revised *Norfolkia* (Fricke, 1994 added one more species).

HOLLEMAN'S TRIPLEFIN
Enneapterygius hollemani Randall, 1995

Dorsal rays III + XIII + 10; anal rays I,19; pectoral rays 15; lateral-line scales 16 + 23-24; longitudinal scale series 36; abdomen naked; nape scaled except for a narrow zone next to anterior part of first dorsal fin; mandibular pores 3 + 1 + 3; supratemporal sensory canal broadly U-shaped; first dorsal fin about equal in height to second dorsal fin; longest pectoral rays reaching to below base of tenth spine of second dorsal fin; pale in alcohol, the edges of scales with brown dots except ventrally; three very broad oblique dusky bars on body (as a result of darker edges of the scales) which branch ventrally; lower part of each branch still darker, thus forming a series of dark brown double bars on lower side of body; a large squarish dusky blotch posteriorly on caudal peduncle; anus of male edged in blackish, of female with a jet black spot just anterior to anus; chest, prepectoral region, and lower half of head of male dusky; anal fin with seven black spots along base which continue internally and expand distally as diagonal bands on fin; six series of dark brown spots on rays of pectoral fins, broader posteriorly, forming irregular transverse bands; pelvic fins a little dusky basally on males, entirely pale in females; in life pale green, the edges of the scales red with dark brown dots. Largest specimen, 3.9 cm. Known from only three specimens collected from rock pools on the central and southern coast of Oman.

SPOTFIN TRIPLEFIN
Enneapterygius melanospilus Randall, 1995

Dorsal rays III + XII + 10; anal rays I,18; pectoral rays 15-16; anterior lateral-line scales 14-15; posterior (notched) lateral-line

867. *Enneapterygius hollemani*, 3 cm (J. Randall)

868. *Enneapterygius melanospilus*, female, 3.2 cm (J. Randall)

869. *Enneapterygius pusillus*, male, about 3 cm (J. Randall)

870. *Enneapterygius pusillus*, female, about 3 cm (J. Randall)

scales 21-22; longitudinal scale series 34; abdomen scaleless; nape (below first dorsal fin) scaled; spinules on head along supratemporal sensory canal and sensory canal at dorsal and posterior edge of orbit; supraorbital tentacle a large bilobed or trilobed flap (simple in young); body with six vertical, unbranched, dark bars, the first two faint, the last four progressively darker posteriorly (bars a mixture of dark brown and orange); a large black spot basally in second dorsal fin between seventh and eleventh spines with an arc of bright orange above it; a curved, brown-edged, orange line below eye; rays of caudal fin pink. Largest specimen, 3.1 cm. Known from only three specimens (a juvenile and two females) taken off the south coast of Oman in 3-9 m.

PIXIE TRIPLEFIN
Enneapterygius pusillus Rüppell, 1835

Dorsal rays III + XII-XIII + 8-11; anal rays I,17-21; pectoral rays 13-14; anterior

lateral-line scales 9-12; posterior (notched) lateral-line scales 25-27; longitudinal scale series 29-30; abdomen not scaled; palatine teeth present (true of other species of the genus); supratemporal sensory canal a broad U-shape anterior to origin of first dorsal fin; first dorsal fin of adults usually as high or higher than second dorsal fin (always higher in males); longest pectoral ray reaching to below base of penultimate spine of second dorsal fin; four large, irregular, hourglass-shaped bars on body (the edges and lower part darker) and a fifth more straight-sided dark bar or triangle on caudal peduncle; males with lower half of head, chest, and anterior half of abdomen dark blackish red; females with an olive streak on side of snout, broadening onto lips; a preanal black spot present or absent; first dorsal fin variable in colour (may be white in females and pink or yellow in males); second dorsal crossed by three or four dusky bands; anal fin with six to nine oblique blackish bands; pectoral fins with three to five dusky bars, the longest rays distally yellow in males; males with basal third to more than half of pelvic fins black, the fins all white in females. Maximum length about 3 cm. Red Sea (type locality) east to India and south to Natal; in Oman from Musandam to the southern coast; generally found in less than 10 m.

BELLYSPOT TRIPLEFIN
Enneapterygius ventermaculus Holleman, 1982

Dorsal rays III + XI-XIII + 9-11 (usually 10); anal rays I,17-20 (usually 19); pectoral rays 13-14 (usually 14); anterior lateral-line scales 13-15 (usually 14); posterior (notched) lateral-line scales 21-22; longitudinal scale series 32-34; abdomen and nape below base of first dorsal fin scaleless; supratemporal sensory canal broadly U-shaped anterior to first dorsal fin; first dorsal fin about equal in height to second dorsal in females, slightly higher in males; longest pectoral rays reaching to below base of last spine of second dorsal fin; males greenish, the scales edged with blackish red; five double dark bars on lower side of body and a large triangular blackish mark covering posterior caudal peduncle; anal fin with five or six diagonal black bands which continue internally into body; a triangular or transversely crescentic black spot ventrally on abdomen before anus; chest, lower half of head, and base of pelvic fins blackish first dorsal fin pale pink to yellowish; females translucent with orange-red edges on the scales and less dark pigment. Largest specimen, 4 cm. Occurs from Natal (type locality) to the Arabian Gulf and coast of Pakistan (not yet known from the Red Sea); greatest depth of capture, 12 m; most often collected from rock pools at low tide.

SHORTSNOUT TRIPLEFIN
Helcogramma obtusirostre (Klunzinger, 1871)

Dorsal rays III + XII-XV (usually XIII or XIV) + 9-12 (usually 11-12 in Oman specimens); anal rays I,18-20; pectoral rays 17-18 (usually 17); lateral-line ending beneath anterior half of dorsal fin, the pored scales 18-27 (23-26 in Oman specimens); longitudinal scale series 40-41; no scales on head, nape (below first dorsal fin and anterior part of second dorsal), or abdomen; palatine teeth present (true of other species of the genus); head length 3.2-3.4 in standard length; a small orbital cirrus present at upper edge of eye above rear edge of pupil; 4 or 5 mandibular pores (ventrally on each side of lower jaw, not counting median pore); spines of first dorsal fin subequal, slightly more than half length of longest spine of

871. *Enneapterygius ventermaculus*, male, 3 cm (J. Randall)

872. *Helcogramma obtusirostre*, male (upper), 4.6 cm, female (lower), 4.2 cm (J. Randall)

second dorsal fin; body mottled pale greenish with interconnecting broad dark greenish grey bars dorsally which branch ventrally; head of males with an oblique blue streak from mouth across cheek, broadly edged above and below by black; base of pectoral fins with a red spot above and one below, the lower with a blue spot above and anterior; both sexes with a small black spot at rear base of membrane connecting first and second dorsal fins. Reaches 4 cm. Red Sea (type locality) south to Natal and east to the western Pacific; also reported from Ascension Island and St. Helena in the Atlantic. Specimens from Oman were collected only on the south coast in from 0.5-6 m. Hansen (1986) discussed the geographic variation.

873. *Helcogramma steinitzi*, male, 3.9 cm (J. Randall)

874. *Helcogramma steinitzi*, female, about 4.5 cm (J. Randall)

RED TRIPLEFIN
Helcogramma steinitzi Clark, 1979

Dorsal rays III + XII-XIV + 10-12; anal rays I,19-21; pectoral rays 15-17; lateral-line extending to below anterior half of third dorsal fin, the pored scales 21-27; longitudinal scale series 38-40; head and abdomen scaleless; nape (below first dorsal fin) scaled except adjacent to base of fin; head length 3.0-3.25 in standard length; a tiny orbital cirrus present on upper part of eye above posterior edge of pupil; 3 mandibular pores (ventrally on each side of lower jaw, not counting median pore); spines of first dorsal fin subequal in females, at most three-fourths length of longest spine of second dorsal fin; initial spine of first dorsal fin of males clearly longest, about as long as longest spine of second dorsal fin; upper two-thirds of body of males red with indistinct blackish blotches forming a reticulum (eight of these blotches in a longitudinal row on lower side of body alternating with white spots); scattered small white blotches and dots on upper half of body; head above level of lower edge of eye red, below dark bluish grey with a pale blue streak from above mouth across cheek; body of females translucent greenish, irregularly spotted with white, with large interconnected red blotches (from red and black pigment on scale edges) forming a coarse reticulum; head greenish with numerous dark red spots and short bands, the darkest a diagonal band on side of snout. Largest specimen, 5.6 cm. Occurs around the Arabian Peninsula from the northern Red Sea to the Arabian Gulf; collected from the depth range of 0.3-10 m.

SCALY-HEAD TRIPLEFIN
Norfolkia brachylepis (Schultz, 1960)

Dorsal rays IV + XII-XV + 9-11; anal rays II,18-20; pectoral rays 15-16 (usually 16); pelvic rays I,2, the soft rays not united by membrane; lateral-line scales 14-18 + 18-23; longitudinal scale series 31-34; abdomen, prepectoral region, dorsal part of head to interorbital space, cheek, and opercle scaled; palatine teeth absent; supraorbital tentacle a small flap with ragged distal edge; 3 mandibular pores (ventrally on each side of lower jaw, not counting 2 median pores); second dorsal fin usually higher than first dorsal (rarely the first dorsal equally high); whitish with six irregular brown bars on body, the scales within bars outlined in yellow; head mottled whitish and brown with a brown bar below eye; second and third dorsal fins of males red with three narrow irregular white bars. Largest specimen, 7.3 cm. Indo-Pacific from the Red Sea and South Africa to Fiji. The Oman record a single specimen collected in 7 m on the southern coast near Marbat.

875. *Norfolkia brachylepis*, male (upper), 4.1 cm, female (lower), 4 cm (J. Randall)

BLENNIES
FAMILY BLENNIIDAE

The blennies are small, agile, scaleless fishes. Most are blunt-headed; the head may have small tentacles, cirri or a fleshy crest. The mouth is low on the head and not protractile; the teeth in the jaws are numerous, slender, and close-set, either fixed or movable; the fangblennies (also called sabretooth blennies) have a formidable pair of large canine teeth in the lower jaw; vomer with or without teeth, the palatines toothless. There is a single dorsal fin with III-XVII flexible spines. All have II anal spines, but one or both of these spines may be reduced in size or embedded in females; in males they may be capped by fleshy tissue believed to secrete an attracting substance at spawning time; the last soft ray of the dorsal and anal fins may be joined by membrane to the caudal peduncle. The pectoral fin rays are unbranched; the pelvic fins, inserted anterior to the pectorals, have an embedded hidden spine and two to four unbranched soft rays. Springer (1993) has characterised the Blenniidae in detail and compared it with other blennioid families. Many blennies, such as those of the genera *Alticus*, *Entomacrodus*, and *Istiblennius*, live inshore on rocky substrata, sometimes in the surf-swept intertidal zone; most are able to leap from one pool to another (hence the common name rockskipper). Blennies tend to take refuge in small holes in the reef into which they enter tail-first. The majority of tropical blennies are herbivorous. The Shortbodied Blenny (*Exallias brevis*) feeds on coral polyps. Most unusual in their food habits are the fangblennies of the genus *Plagiotremus* (*Runula* is a synonym) which take scales, dermal tissue, and mucus from the skin of other fishes; their large fangs are not used for this feeding but for defence. The Mimic Blenny (*Aspidontus taeniatus*), in its guise of the Cleaner Wrasse (*Labroides dimidiatus*), feeds in part by biting pieces from the fins of other fishes. The species of one genus of fangblennies, *Meiacanthus*, have a venom gland associated with their large lower teeth. They are usually seen swimming a short distance above the bottom; no doubt their venomous canines enable them to be so fearlessly exposed to predation. Because they are avoided by predacious fishes, some other fishes, including species of the blenniid genera *Ecsenius*, *Plagiotremus*, and *Petroscirtes*, mimic them (Springer and Smith-Vaniz, 1972; Losey, 1972; Russell et al., 1976). The blennies for which the reproductive habits are known lay attached demersal eggs, guarded by the male parent. There are 53 genera and about 345 species of blennies in the world. No subfamilies other than the Blenniinae are currently recognised in the family; instead there are five tribes, four of which are represented by species in Oman seas: the Nemophini (fangblennies; revised by Smith-Vaniz, 1976; 1987); the Omobranchini (Springer, 1972; 1981); the Parablenniini (Bath, 1982, 1989), and the Salariini (Smith-Vaniz and Springer, 1971; Springer and Spreitzer, 1978).

876. *Alticus kirkii*, male, briefly exposed by a receding wave on a rocky shore (J. Hoover)

877. *Pereulixia kosiensis* guarding its eggs (dense white dots on stones around the fish) (J. Hoover)

BLACKTHROAT BLENNY

Alloblennius parvus Springer and Spreitzer, 1978

Dorsal rays XII-XIII,18-20; anal rays II,20-22; segmented caudal rays 13, the middle 8 or 9 branched; pectoral rays 13-14 (rarely 13); pelvic rays I,3, the third soft ray small and closely applied to second ray; teeth in jaws immovable, 30-35 in upper jaw and 25-28 in lower; no canines; margins of lips smooth; anterior nostril tubular with a slender cirrus at front and back; posterior nostril with a simple tentacle at front; a simple tentacle above eye (tentacles much longer in males); no cirri on nape; no crest on head; body elongate, the depth 6.0-7.8 in standard length; dorsal fin incised between spinous and soft portions; last dorsal and anal soft rays joined by membrane to caudal peduncle; yellowish grey with faint dark bars on body (more evident anteriorly where they bifurcate ventrally) and small maroon spots on upper half of body, the lowermost spots in a midlateral row, and scattered small iridescent pale blue spots; head with oblique dark red streaks on operculum and below eye, and pale blue-green dots extending onto nape; dorsal and caudal fins transparent, the rays with small dark reddish spots; a small black spot on upper half of first membrane of dorsal fin; anal fin dusky; males with a blackish area on gill membranes of throat, extending to prepectoral region. Largest specimen, 45 mm. Previously known only from the Comoro Islands and Sodwana Bay, Natal (Springer in Smith and Heemstra, 1986), the range here extended to southern Oman where specimens were collected from coral reefs in 6-10 m.

KIRK'S BLENNY

Alticus kirkii (Günther, 1868)

Dorsal rays XVII,20-22 (usually 21); anal rays II,25-28 (usually 26 or 27); caudal rays 11, all simple; pectoral rays 14; pelvic rays I,3; mouth distinctly inferior; teeth movable and very numerous; no canine teeth; a patch of small conical teeth on vomer; edge of upper lip crenulate, of lower lip smooth; a median, blade-like, fleshy crest on head commencing above eye; crest higher in male and posteriorly pointed with a small basal lobe behind; a fringed tentacle above eye about half to two-thirds orbit diameter; nasal cirrus also present; no cirri on nape; body elongate, the depth equal to or less than head length, 6.0-7.2 in standard length; dorsal fin slightly notched between spinous and soft portions, the spinous portion very elevated in male (as much as 1.3 times greater than body depth); tips of median fins free of membrane; last anal ray not attached to caudal peduncle by membrane; pale greenish grey with numerous curved grey bars on body; oblique white lines in dorsal fin; tips of anal rays white with a black submarginal band; a small black spot on pointed tip of crest of males. Attains about 11 cm. Mozambique east to India, including the Arabian Gulf but not the Red Sea (Jeffrey T. Williams, pers. comm.); lives high in the intertidal zone of exposed rocky shores, often out of water.

ADEN BLENNY

Antennablennius adenensis Fraser-Brunner, 1951

Dorsal rays XII,17-19; anal rays II,18-20; segmented caudal rays 13, the middle 7-9 branched (true of other species of the genus); pectoral rays 14; pelvic rays I,3; teeth in jaws incisiform, close-set, and immovable, 37-45 in upper jaw and 29-36 in lower; no canine teeth (also generic); margins of lips smooth (generic); no teeth on vomer (generic); a long cirrus posteriorly on anterior nostril; no supraorbital tentacle (generic); a pair of very small cirri on nape; no crest on head; body depth 5.1-5.8 in standard length; dorsal fin moderately notched (about half length of longest dorsal spine); first dorsal ray with a semicircular flap on anterior edge; last dorsal and anal rays bound by membrane to caudal peduncle (generic); grey, shading to whitish ventrally, with eight purplish grey bars, the last two reduced to lateral spots, and numerous white dots and small white spots; a large blackish blotch covering much of cheek and region behind eye, the cheek crossed by diagonal rows of pale blue dots; snout and dorsal part of head with pale blue dots; spinous portion of dorsal fin with a white margin and blackish submarginal band, the rest yellowish with dark brown blotches and small white spots; anal fin pale yellowish, every other soft ray dusky. Reaches 5 cm. Known from the Red Sea to the Arabian Gulf and Pakistan; Oman specimens were collected from 0.5-2 m on rocky bottom at Maqlab (Telegraph Island), Musandam.

878. *Alloblennius parvus*, about 4 cm (J. Randall)

879. *Alticus kirkii*, male, 10.7 cm (J. Randall)

880. *Antennablennius adenensis*, about 3.5 cm (J. Randall)

MOUSTACHE BLENNY

Antennablennius australis Fraser-Brunner, 1951

Dorsal rays XII-XIII,15-18; anal rays II,17-18; pectoral rays 14; pelvic rays I,3; teeth in jaws incisiform, close-set, and immovable, 26-30 in upper jaw and 23-28 in lower; tentacle on anterior nostril projecting downward, but not reaching mouth; a pair of cirri on nape; no crest on head; body depth about 4.0-5.0 in standard length; dorsal fin moderately notched; body pale yellowish anteriorly with brown bars containing pale vertical lines, the pale yellowish interspaces with yellowish brown lines; posterior part of body with a lateral row of irregular interconnected brown blotches with pale lines, the blotches and lines anastomosing dorsally; white dots postero-ventrally on body; dark blotches basally in dorsal fin in line with brown bars and blotches; head with some dark streaks and brownish orange dots before and below eye; margin of anal fin blackish anteriorly. Reported to 8.3 cm. Described from southern Mozambique and northern Natal; Bath (1983) extended the distribution to the southern Red Sea; Oman specimens were collected from tidepools on the south coast.

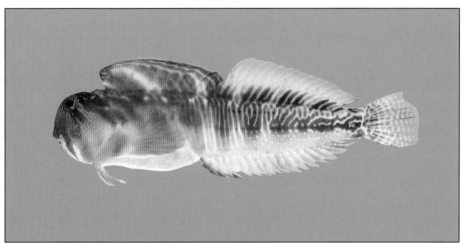

881. *Antennablennius australis*, 6.8 cm (J. Randall)

882. *Antennablennius bifilum*, 6.4 cm (J. Randall)

883. *Antennablennius hypenetes*, 4 cm (J. Randall)

HORNED BLENNY

Antennablennius bifilum (Günther, 1861)

Dorsal rays XI-XIII,18-20; anal rays II,17-21; pectoral rays 14; pelvic rays I,3; teeth in jaws incisiform, close-set, and immovable, 26-35 in upper jaw and 22-30 in lower; cirrus on anterior nostril small and downward-projecting; a close-set pair of very long cirri dorsally on nape; no crest on head; body depth 4.6-5.4 in standard length; dorsal fin moderately notched; body posterior to origin of anal fin light brown, shading to pale grey ventrally, with numerous small white spots and six dark brown spots which are progressively more vertically elongate anteriorly; anterior body with slightly diagonal, close-set, dark grey-brown bars which narrow onto abdomen, thus showing more white interspace; spinous portion of dorsal fin dark grey with diagonal rows of white blotches; soft portion of dorsal fin, anal fin, and caudal fin with small white spots on rays (only basally in anal fin). Reaches 8.5 cm. Known from South Africa (Smith, 1959b), Madagascar, Comoro Islands, Arabian Gulf, and northwestern India (the last record from Lal Mohan, 1968). *Blennius persicus* Regan, described from specimens taken in 18-37 m, is a synonym.

ARABIAN BLENNY

Antennablennius hypenetes (Klunzinger, 1871)

Dorsal rays XII-XIII,16-20; anal rays II,19-21; pectoral rays 14; pelvic rays I,3; teeth incisiform, close-set, and immovable, 33-39 in upper jaw and 21-34 in lower; a long downward-projecting tentacle on anterior nostril which may reach to or below mouth; a pair of small cirri on nape; a fleshy blade-like crest dorsally on head of male beginning above anterior edge of eye; body depth 5.0-6.2 in standard length; dorsal fin slightly notched; yellowish brown dorsally with small white spots and blotches, paler ventrally, with a midlateral series of dark brown spots (smaller and more horizontally elongate posteriorly) and small white to pale blue spots mostly in two longitudinal rows along side of body (those in dark spots more evident); a dark grey bar below front of eye to upper lip and another below posterior part of eye to chin, but interrupted above corner of mouth; dark reddish dots below eye and on pectoral-fin base, sometimes linked by dots across cheek; nasal tentacle yellow to orange; anal fin blackish with a broad median yellowish band in the middle and a row of small white spots along the outer edge of the basal blackish band. Attains 6.5 cm. Occurs around the entire Arabian Peninsula from the northern Red Sea to the Arabian Gulf; an inshore species of rocky substrata.

884. Head of *A. simonyi* (J. Hoover)

SIMONY'S BLENNY

Antennablennius simonyi (Steindachner, 1902)

Dorsal rays XII-18-20; anal rays II,19-21; pectoral rays 14; pelvic rays I,3; teeth incisiform, close-set, and immovable, 27-32 in upper jaw and 25-26 in lower; a tentacle on anterior nostril, small in female, but reaching to upper lip in male; male with a bilateral pair of crests on head, beginning above anterior part of eye; a pair of small cirri on nape, in the male just behind each part of the crest; body depth 5.2-5.8 in standard length; dorsal fin slightly notched; pale yellowish grey, the posterior half of body with a midlateral row of six dark brown spots which are progressively smaller and more elongate posteriorly, and numerous very small pale blue spots; anterior half of body with indistinct diagonal dark grey bars and elongate spots; opercle with a dark grey spot edged in orange and yellow; suborbital region with three dark grey bars and white and orange lines or rows of dots; posterior part of crest with small orange dots; margin of anal fin blackish except posteriorly; females with dark dots on dorsal and caudal

885. *Antennablennius simonyi*, 5.3 cm (J. Randall)

fins. Reaches 5.5 cm. Known from the Gulf of Aden (type locality) to the Arabian Gulf; found inshore on rocky bottom. *A. girad* Fraser-Brunner is a synonym.

ORANGEDOTTED BLENNY

Antennablennius variopunctatus (Jatzow and Lenz, 1898)

Dorsal rays XII-XIII,19-21; anal rays II,20-23; pectoral rays 14; pelvic rays I,3; teeth in jaws incisiform, close-set, and immovable, 32-39 in upper jaw and 26-34 in lower; nasal tentacle well developed (may reach to mouth in large adults); a small pair of cirri on nape; no crest on head; body depth 4.8-5.6 in standard length; greenish white with eight irregular dark brown spots along side of body, the three in middle vertically elongate; dorsal part of body with a fine dark reticulum dotted with orange; head

with dark grey bars and rows of orange dots extending from lower and posterior part of eye; spinous portion of dorsal fin with three broad oblique dark grey bands separated by a row of white spots; soft portion of dorsal fin with a few orange dots along base, the rays with alternating reddish orange and whitish spots; anal fin greenish white, every other soft ray and adjacent edge of membrane blackish. Attains 7.5 cm. Known from Mozambique to the coast of Pakistan, including the Gulf of Oman and Arabian Gulf but not the Red Sea; has been collected from the depth range of less than 1 to 7 m.

MIMIC BLENNY

Aspidontus taeniatus Quoy and Gaimard, 1834

Dorsal rays X-XII,26-29; anal rays II,25-28; pectoral rays 13-15; segmented caudal rays 11; body moderately elongate, the depth 5.0-6.5 in standard length; mouth ventral, the conical snout strongly overhanging; teeth in jaws close-set and slender except for a very large recurved canine on each side of lower jaw; origin of dorsal fin less than an eye diameter posterior to rear of eye, nearly uniform in height (except in late larval stage where it is elevated anteriorly); caudal fin truncate to slightly rounded; blue, shading to whitish or pale grey anteriorly, with a black stripe from front of snout to rear edge of caudal fin, the stripe progressively wider posteriorly. Indo-Pacific. Mimics the Cleaner Wrasse *Labroides dimidiatus* both in colour and swimming behaviour, thus gaining protection from predation and enabling it to closely approach fishes from which it bites pieces of the fins (Randall and Randall, 1960); also feeds in part on demersal fish eggs and tentacles of polychaete tubeworms.

888. Head of *Aspidontus taeniatus* (J. Randall)

886. *Antennablennius variopunctatus*, 5.1 cm (J. Randall)

887. *Aspidontus taeniatus*, about 9 cm (J. Randall)

BULLETHEAD ROCKSKIPPER
Blenniella periophthalmus (Valenciennes, 1836)

Dorsal rays XIII,19-21; anal rays II,20-22; segmented caudal rays 13; pectoral rays 14; pelvic rays I,3; lateral line rarely with any vertical pairs of pores; no scale-like flaps in continuous portion of lateral line; teeth slender, movable, and numerous (more than 100 in upper jaw and more than 75 in lower); a canine tooth present posteriorly in lower jaw; no vomerine teeth; edge of upper lip c renulate, of lower lip smooth ; a slender tentacle above eye, usually unbranched; a pair of small cirri on nape; no crest on head (a fleshy ridge or hump on head of male may be present); body depth 4.6-5.3 in standard length; dorsal fin notched between spinous and soft portions more than half length of first soft ray; last dorsal ray connected by membrane to caudal peduncle; last anal ray not attached by membrane to caudal peduncle; body of females light greenish grey with eight faint dusky H-shaped bars (lower part of each dark bar may be separated as a pair of spots), numerous orange-red to maroon dots, and two rows of small, elliptical, dark-edged, pale blue spots along side; head with orange-red dots, a dusky orange-red oblique spot behind eye, edged posteriorly in blue, and a small deep blue spot on opercle, edged in light blue and orange-red; dorsal and pectoral fins with orange-red to maroon dots; males with the same basic pattern but the ground colour dark purplish grey and with only a scattering of dark reddish dots on the body; spinous portion of dorsal fin dark purplish brown basally, the outer part a reticulum of yellow and purplish grey, the margin orange; soft portion of dorsal fin with oblique lines of purplish grey and dull yellow on basal half, becoming pale yellow on outer half with wavy orange lines; anal fin with dark purplish rays, the membranes dusky basally, shading to blackish distally; caudal fin yellow and orange-red, the lower rays purplish. Attains 15.5 cm. Western Pacific and Indian Ocean, including the Red Sea and Arabian Gulf; generally found at depths less than 1 m. Springer and Williams (1994) reclassified this species from *Istiblennius* to *Blenniella*, removed the closely related *B. paula* of the Pacific from synonymy, and discussed geographic variation.

FILAMENTOUS BLENNY
Cirripectes filamentosus (Alleyne and Macleay, 1877)

Dorsal rays XII (rarely XI or XIV),13-16 (usually 14 or 15); anal rays II,14-17 (usually 15 or 16); pectoral rays 15; pelvic rays I,3-4; lateral-line tubes 0-8, the lateral line

889. *Blenniella periophthalmus*, male (upper), 8.6 cm, female (lower), 9.8 cm (J. Randall)

890. *Cirripectes filamentosus*, 6 cm, aquarium photo (J. Randall)

891. *Ecsenius nalolo* (J. Hoover)

ending below second to sixth dorsal soft rays; cirri on nape in four groups, the total number generally 25-30; edge of lower lip crenulate laterally, smooth in middle; body depth 3.0-3.7 in standard length; dorsal fin notched before soft portion by a distance more than half length of first soft ray; most dorsal spines of adults filamentous, the anterior ones longest; dark brown with orange-red dots on snout and cheek; dorsal spines and rays primarily orange-red, this colour most evident distally on spines; caudal and lower pectoral rays usually orange-yellow. Attains 9 cm. Western Pacific from Taiwan to northern Queensland, west to the Arabian Gulf, Red Sea, and east coast of Africa; occurs on coral reefs or rocky substrata from the shallows to about 20 m. In his revision of *Cirripectes*, Williams (1988) recognised 19 species, all in the Indo-Pacific region. Two wide-ranging species, *C. castaneus* (Valenciennes) and *C. polyzona* (Bleeker), are recorded from the Yemen coast of the Gulf of Aden; therefore they might be expected from Oman waters.

NALOLO
Ecsenius nalolo Smith, 1959

Dorsal rays XII (rarely XI or XIII),12-15 (rarely 12 or 15); anal rays II,14-17 (rarely 14); segmented caudal rays 13-14 (rarely 14), none branched; pectoral rays 12-14;

pelvic rays I,3 (character of the genus; third soft ray may be difficult to detect); lateral line without vertical pairs of pores, extending posteriorly to below dorsal spines IX-XI; teeth in jaws numerous, close-set, slightly movable, and incisiform, about 130 in upper jaw and 41 to 54 in lower jaw; 0-1 small canines posteriorly in lower jaw; no vomerine teeth (also generic); a prominent tentacle on posterior rim of anterior nostril; no supraorbital tentacle and no nuchal cirri or crest (generic); body depth 4.0-5.7 in standard length; anterior profile of head vertical or beyond vertical, the snout and front edge of eye anterior to mouth (generic); dorsal fin deeply incised between spinous and soft portions; last dorsal and anal rays joined by membrane to caudal peduncle (generic); posterior part of body light brown with diffuse white spots about the size of pupil, the anterior part with four rows of horizontally elongate dark brown spots (the largest are two beneath pectoral fin); two rows of dark spots continue forward to end in eye; lower part of head and prepectoral area pale yellow with a black streak from below corner of mouth to lower opercle and another passing anteriorly from base of pectoral fin. Reaches 6.5 cm. Western Indian Ocean, including the Chagos Archipelago, Seychelles, Red Sea, and coast of East Africa to Natal (generic revision by Springer, 1988); observed in Oman only along the south coast.

GULF BLENNY
Ecsenius pulcher (Murray, 1887)

Dorsal rays XII (rarely XIII),18-20; anal rays II,19-23 (usually 21 or 22); segmented caudal rays 13 or 14 (rarely 14), none branched; pectoral rays 13-15 (rarely 13 or 15); lateral line without pairs of pores, terminating below dorsal spines VIII-XII; teeth in jaws close-set, somewhat movable, and incisiform, more than 100 in upper jaw and 44-53 in lower; 0-2 small canines posteriorly in lower jaw; a prominent tentacle on posterior rim of anterior nostril; body depth 3.7-4.6 in standard length; dorsal fin notched at end of spinous portion by a distance about equal to half length of first soft ray; posterior dorsal spines filamentous in adults; three colour patterns (apparently not related to sex or size): uniform dark grey-brown; dark brown dorsally on head and body to level of lower edge of eye, abruptly white below; and dark grey-brown on head and anterior three-fifths of body, the posterior two-fifths orange-yellow with narrow dark bars, the orange-yellow extending into middle of caudal fin; all three phases have the inner rim of the iris yellow with five spoke-like yellow lines radiating outward, the edge of the orbit with yellow spots or short lines (except ventrally). Attains about 11 cm. Known from the Arabian Gulf (where common) to the southern coast of Oman and east to the northwestern coast of India (Lal Mohan, 1968). The colour in the Arabian Sea is a little different from the fish of the Gulf of Oman and Arabian Gulf (compare the figure of the head of a bicoloured phase from the Arabian Gulf with that of the bicoloured fish from southern Oman).

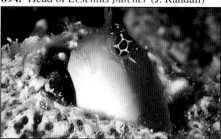

894. Head of *Ecsenius pulcher* (J. Randall)

892. *Ecsenius pulcher*, grey and yellow phase (J. Hoover)

893. *Ecsenius pulcher*, bicolour phase (J. Hoover)

HIGHBROW BLENNY
Hirculops cornifer (Rüppell, 1830)

Dorsal rays XII-XIII (rarely XIII),19-21; anal rays II,20-23; pectoral rays 14; segmented caudal rays 13, the middle 9 branched; pelvic rays I,3; lateral line angling down to midlateral position, ending beneath posterior spinous part of dorsal fin; teeth in jaws close-set, immovable, and incisiform, 34-44 in upper jaw and 22-26 in lower; one or two small canine teeth posteriorly in lower jaw; small conical teeth on vomer; a very long, ribbon-like, supraorbital tentacle; a short cirrus on anterior nostril; a pair of small cirri on nape; no crest on head; body depth 4.6-6.1 in standard length; dorsal fin moderately notched; last dorsal and anal rays joined by membrane to caudal peduncle; body yellowish grey with a lateral row of eight irregular grey blotches which bifurcate ventrally, these blotches containing small pale blue spots; head and body densely spotted with white dots and small white blotches; clusters of black dots along back below dorsal fin; median fins with numerous small white spots, the dorsal with a blackish spot on first membrane and to a lesser extent on second. Reported to 6 cm. Western Indian Ocean from Red Sea and Arabian Gulf south to South Africa, including the Seychelles; one record from northwestern India (Lal Mohan, 1968) and one from Indonesia (de Beaufort and Chapman, 1951).

895. *Hirculops cornifer*, 4.5 cm (J. Randall)

RIPPLED ROCKSKIPPER
Istiblennius edentulus (Bloch and Schneider, 1801)

Dorsal rays XIII (rarely XII or XIV),18-23; anal rays II,20-24; segmented caudal rays 12-13 (rarely 12); pectoral rays 13-14 (usually 14); pelvic rays I,3; lateral line ending in about middle of body, without vertical pairs of pores; incisiform teeth in jaws numerous and movable; no canine tooth posteriorly in lower jaw; edges of lips smooth; supraorbital tentacle slender, flattened, usually simple (may have one or two small branches); a pair of cirri on nape, relatively large for the genus; male with a blade-like fleshy crest on head; body depth 3.5-5.0 in standard length; dorsal fin incised more than half length of first dorsal soft ray; last dorsal ray bound by membrane to caudal peduncle or out on caudal fin, but last anal ray not attached to peduncle (true of all species of the genus); olivaceous, usually with six or seven dark brown double bars on body and an indistinct, irregular, narrow, dark bar in each pale interspace; males with diagonal white lines or rows of white spots in dorsal fin. Largest specimen, 18 cm. Known throughout the Indo-Pacific region except Hawaii and Easter Island; a common species found inshore on exposed rocky substrata.

SCARFACE ROCKSKIPPER
Istiblennius pox Springer and Williams, 1994

Dorsal rays XIII (rarely XII or XIV),20-23; anal rays II,22-24; segmented caudal rays 13; pectoral rays 14; pelvic rays I,3; continuous anterior part of lateral line of simple pores (no vertical pairs of pores), ending beneath the fourth to seventh dorsal spines, the lateral line continuing as 1-12 separated bi-pored tubes; body depth 4.5-5.3 in standard length; teeth in jaws numerous and incisi-

896. *Istiblennius edentulus*, male on intertidal oysters (J. Hoover)

897. *Istiblennius edentulus*, colour phase (J. Hoover)

form; no canine tooth posteriorly on lower jaw; edge of upper lip crenulate, of lower lip smooth; supraorbital tentacle branched; no cirri on nape; males with a blade-like fleshy crest; females without a crest or with a low ridge; dorsal fin deeply incised before soft portion; light yellowish grey with blackish longitudinal lines on body, some broken and irregular, especially posteriorly; irregular, near-vertical, black lines below eye and over preopercular region of cheek; males with small dark red spots on crest; soft portion of dorsal fin with diagonal black lines. Attains about 13 cm. Ranges from the southern Red Sea to the Arabian Gulf and coast of Pakistan; an inshore species; comes out of the water at night on rocks. Very closely related to *I. steindachneri* (Pfeffer) from East Africa south of the equator, Seychelles, and Mauritius, and to *I. lineatus* (Valenciennes) from the rest of the Indo-Pacific region; some might prefer to regard the three as subspecies.

898. *Istiblennius pox*, male (upper), 12.3 cm, female (lower), 10.6 cm (J. Randall)

SPOTTED ROCKSKIPPER
Istiblennius spilotus Springer and Williams, 1994

Dorsal rays XIII (rarely XIV),16-19 (rarely 16 or 19); anal rays II,17-19; segmented caudal rays 13; pectoral rays 13-14 (rarely 13); pelvic rays I,2-4; lateral line without vertical pairs of pores, ending beneath thirteenth dorsal spine and thirteenth dorsal soft ray; numerous incisiform teeth in jaws; no canine tooth posteriorly in lower jaw; margins of lips crenulate (the lower sometimes only partially); supraorbital tentacle pinnately branched; no cirri on nape; male with a blade-like fleshy crest on head; female without a crest or with a low ridge; body of females grey, shading to whitish ventrally, with numerous brown-edged white spots and a longitudinal row of elongate white blotches at level of upper edge of pectoral fin, the brown forming a reticulum of varying intensity; two short, irregular, black lines behind eye partly within a yellow spot; males yellowish grey with double dark grey bars on side of body and two longitudinal rows of small dark-edged blue spots; head with small dark-edged pale blue spots, mostly below eye and above mouth; two thick black lines or a black spot behind eye. Reaches 14 cm. Known from Pakistan and the Gulf of Oman to Natal and Madagascar; occurs along exposed rocky shores. Has been misidentified as the Red Sea species *I. flaviumbrinus* (Rüppell) and *I. unicolor* (Rüppell).

899. *Istiblennius spilotus*, male (upper), 7.8 cm, female (lower), 7.7 cm (J. Randall)

900. *Istiblennius spilotus*, male (J. Hoover)

901. *Mimoblennius cirrosus*, 4.4 cm (J. Randall)

FRINGED BLENNY
Mimoblennius cirrosus Smith-Vaniz and Springer, 1971

Dorsal rays XII-XIII,17-19; anal rays II,20-22; segmented caudal rays 13, the middle 9 branched; pectoral rays 13-14; lateral line consisting of bipored tubes that end beneath dorsal spines IV to VI; teeth in jaws close-set, incisiform, and relatively immovable, 30-34 in upper jaw and 24-30 in lower; a canine tooth posteriorly on lower jaw; edges of lips smooth; supraorbital tentacle usually with three to six branches; a pair of palmate flaps dorsally on nape, the edge with rounded lobes; a branched cirrus posteriorly on both anterior and posterior nostrils; body depth 5.1-5.6 in standard length; dorsal fin deeply incised between spinous and soft portions; body white with numerous small orange-red spots which tend to group to form indistinct bars; head with orange-red spots and short diagonal bands; median fins with orange-red spots basally; anal fin with orange-red rays. Largest specimen, 5.4 cm. Red Sea to Arabian Gulf; collected on coral reefs from 3-25 m.

902. Head of *M. cirrosus* (A. Woodward)

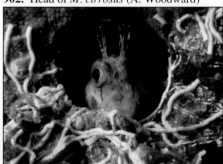

OMAN BLENNY
Oman ypsilon Springer, 1985

Dorsal rays X,25-26; anal rays II,23-24; segmented caudal rays 12-13; pectoral rays 13; pelvic fins I,2; lateral line consisting of 0-4 bipored tubes; teeth in jaws incisiform, close-set, and immovable, 23-24 in upper jaw and 23-26 in lower; a canine tooth posteriorly in jaws, the one on each side of lower jaw enormous; gill opening a small aperture above upper edge of pectoral-fin base; no supraorbital tentacle, nasal cirri, nuchal cirri, or crest; body depth 5.7-6.1 in standard length; dorsal fin very slightly incised; last dorsal and anal rays attached by membrane to caudal peduncle; body yellow, shading to whitish on abdomen; a dark brown band from front of upper lip through eye, ending on nape, edged below by a bluish white line; a white middorsal band on head separating ocular brown bands of each side; head below brown band white to pale orange, shading posteriorly on operculum to yellow; median fins yellow, the dorsal and anal with a pale blue margin; pectoral fins with slightly dusky rays and clear membranes; pelvic fins white. Reaches 4 cm. Known only from four specimens collected from rocky bottom in 2-6 m on the central coast of Oman, but observed in the south. Nearly always seen under ledges swimming upside down. At a glance the species might be mistaken for *Pseudochromis leucorhynchus*.

CLOISTER BLENNY
Omobranchus elongatus (Peters, 1855)

Dorsal rays XIII (rarely XII),17-20 (rarely 17); anal rays II,20-23 (rarely 20); segmented caudal rays 12-14 (almost always 13), none branched; pectoral rays 13 (modally 13 for all species); pelvic rays I,2 (also generic); lateral-line tubes 0-9; jaws with long, slender, incisiform, slightly movable teeth, 18-26 in upper jaw and 15-24 in lower; a canine tooth posteriorly in upper and lower jaws, the one in lower jaw enormous (applies to all species of the genus except the female of one Pacific species); edge of lips smooth; lower lip with a small, posterior, ventral-projecting flap; no cirri or tentacles on head (generic); no crest on head; gill opening restricted to area above fifth or sixth pectoral rays; body depth 4.9-6.1 in standard length; dorsal fin very slightly incised between spinous and soft portions; last dorsal and anal rays bound by membrane to caudal peduncle (generic); reddish grey with curved and oblique grey bars and white lines posterior to abdomen; a yellow-edged light red elliptical spot on opercle; a large dark grey blotch behind eye preceded by a bluish

903. *Oman ypsilon* (J. Hoover)

904. *Omobranchus elongatus*, 6.2 cm (J. Randall)

905. *Omobranchus fasciolatus*, about 7 cm (J. Randall)

white line; small dark spots sometimes present on ventral part of head and on chest (not seen on Oman specimens); males with a dusky spot in dorsal fin between ninth and thirteenth soft rays. Largest specimen, 6.6 cm. Indo-Malayan region to East Africa from Zanzibar to Mozambique; not known from the Red Sea or Arabian Gulf. Unpublished records from the Solomon Islands and Fiji (V.G. Springer, pers. comm.). Oman specimens were collected from a rocky bottom in 0.3 m at Barr al Hikman.

BARRED ARAB BLENNY
Omobranchus fasciolatus (Valenciennes, 1836)

Dorsal rays XII (rarely XI),18-19; anal rays II,20-22; segmented caudal rays 13, none branched; lateral-line tubes 3-8, the last below dorsal spines VII-X; jaws with long, slender, slightly movable, incisiform teeth, 18-25 in upper jaw and 18-26 in lower; edge of lips smooth; lower lips with a small ventral-projecting flap; no cirri on head (generic); males with a blade-like fleshy

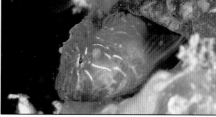

906. Head of *O. fasciolatus* (J. Randall)

crest dorsally on head (poorly developed or absent on females); gill opening restricted to area above first or second pectoral rays; body depth 5.0-6.1 in standard length; dorsal fin very slightly incised between spinous and soft portions; olive grey, shading to light tan on abdomen and lower head, the body with vertical white lines anteriorly and white dots posteriorly; a green spot as large as eye behind eye; bluish white lines radiating from eye; rows of dark brown dots in spaces between white lines on snout and below eye; males with a large oval dusky spot between ninth and fourteenth soft rays. Largest specimen, 6.8 cm. Occurs from northwestern India to the Arabian Gulf and Red Sea, south to Mozambique. Found in shallow water with rocky bottom, sometimes in tidepools.

MEKRAN BLENNY
Omobranchus mekranensis (Regan, 1905)

Dorsal rays XII (rarely XI),20-21; anal rays II,22-23; segmented caudal rays 13-14 (usually 14); lateral-line tubes 6-7, ending beneath dorsal spines IX-XI; teeth in jaws long, slender, and incisiform, 18-23 in upper jaw and 22-27 in lower; a fleshy blade-like crest dorsally on head of both sexes; gill opening restricted to area above upper base of pectoral fin; body depth about 5.0 in standard length; dorsal fin continuous, without indentation; body with seven pairs of dark bars on body which tend to broaden dorsally; narrow dark bands radiating from ventral half of eye; an oval dark spot nearly as large as eye on head behind eye. Attains 6 cm. Known from the coast of Pakistan, Gulf of Oman, and Arabian Gulf. No specimens of *O. mekranensis* collected for the present study; diagnosis and illustration from Springer and Gomon (1975) who revised the genus.

907. *Omobranchus mekranensis*, 5.6 cm (after Springer and Gomon, 1975)

MUZZLED BLENNY
Omobranchus punctatus (Valenciennes, 1836)

Dorsal rays XII (rarely XI or XIII),19-24; anal rays II,20-26; segmented caudal rays 12-14; lateral-line tubes 2-8, ending to below dorsal spines III-XII; jaws with long, slender, slightly movable, incisiform teeth, 21-33 in upper jaw and 22-38 in lower; edge of lips smooth; a small posterior ventral flap on lower lip; no crest on head; gill opening restricted to area above first pectoral ray; body depth 4.8-5.5 in standard length; dorsal fin very slightly incised between spinous and soft portions; translucent grey-brown with longitudinal rows of dark brown dashes and vertical rows of small pale greenish spots; a large transversely elongate black spot on nape in front of dorsal fin; head with slightly oblique dark brown bars. Reported to 11 cm. Western Pacific to Indian Ocean, the only previous western Indian localities: north-western India, Pakistan, Gulf of Oman, Arabian Gulf, Maldive Islands, southern Mozam-

908. *Omobranchus punctatus*, about 6 cm (J. Randall)

bique, and Suez Canal, the last locality from Bath (1980). Occurs on rocky shores; Ismail and Clayton (1990) reported the food habits as mainly algae, but small crustaceans (especially ostracods and copepods) and small gastropods are also eaten. From analysis of otoliths they determined that the population of this blenny ranges in age from 1-4 years.

CHEEKSPOT BLENNY
Parablennius opercularis (Murray, 1887)

Dorsal rays XII,16-17; anal rays II,18-19; segmented caudal rays 13, the middle 9 branched (applies to all species of the genus); pelvic rays I,3; dorsoanterior part of lateral line with 9-14 vertical pairs of pores, ending beneath dorsal spines VIII-IX; jaws with close-set, slightly movable, incisiform teeth, 23-35 in upper jaw and 21-28 in lower; a well developed canine tooth posteriorly in both upper and lower jaws (also generic); supraorbital tentacle large with one to five branches on one side; no cirri on nape; anterior nostril with a small cirrus on posterior rim; body depth 4.0-4.8 in standard length; dorsal fin incised to half length of first soft ray; last dorsal and anal rays linked by membrane to caudal peduncle (generic); olive brown with eight sets of four small blackish spots along back which form a square, the upper spots extending onto base of a dorsal ray (posterior sets of spots may be faint or absent); a midlateral row of small blackish spots usually present; a dark olive brown spot as large as eye on cheek behind eye; two dark bars below eye, one ending at upper lip, the other to behind corner of mouth; a greenish spot may be present on first membrane of dorsal fin. Attains 6 cm. Known from Pakistan (type locality) to the Arabian Gulf; Oman specimens taken in a tidepool at Masirah Island; also known to depths of 12 m.

909. *Parablennius opercularis*, 3.3 cm (J. Randall)

BUSHY-EYE BLENNY
Parablennius pilicornis (Cuvier, 1829)

Dorsal rays XII,19-21; anal rays II,22-23; pectoral rays 14; pelvic rays I,3; lateral line with 20-22 vertical pairs of pores, ending below dorsal spine XI and first ray of soft portion of fin; jaws with close-set, slightly movable, incisiform teeth, 16-20 in upper jaw and 14-18 in lower jaw; supraorbital tentacle with three to six cirri branching from a common base; dorsal fin notched between spinous and soft portions to two-thirds length of first soft ray; body whitish with two longitudinal rows of dark brown spots (as double spots anteriorly), broadly edged with orange-red, one midlateral, and the other just above (spots not in vertical alignment except posteriorly); numerous small dark brown spots edged in orange-red on ventral part of body; head with a large irregular red spot behind eye and numerous small brown-edged orange spots; two dark bars below eye as a result of denser brown pigment around spots within bars, one to corner of mouth and the other to the first of two transverse brown bands ventrally on head; dark brown spots and bars on opercle; rays of dorsal fin orange-red, most with a dark brown spot at base; anal fin with a small dark brown spot at the base of every other ray and an oblique orange streak across fin from each dark basal spot. Reported to 11 cm. Occurs in the western Mediterranean and eastern Atlantic from northern Spain to Western Sahara, reappearing in the Southern Hemisphere from Angola to South Africa; in the western Atlantic from southern Brazil to Patagonia; unknown on the coast of East Africa north of Natal except for one unpublished record from Somalia at the entrance to the Gulf of Aden (H. Bath, pers. comm.); Oman specimens were collected from Juzor al Hallaniyat (Kuria Muria Islands) and off Raysut, southern Oman on rocky substrata in 4-12 m.

TASSELED BLENNY
Parablennius thysanius (Jordan and Seale, 1907)

Dorsal rays XII,14-15; anal rays II,16-17; pectoral rays 14; pelvic rays I,3; lateral line with 9-11 vertical pairs of pores, ending posterior to eleventh dorsal spine; jaws with close-set, immovable, incisiform teeth, 22-34 in upper jaw and 20-26 in lower; supraorbital tentacle palmate with four or six cirri in females and as many as 22 in large males; body depth 3.4-5.1 in standard length; dorsal fin only slightly incised between spinous and soft portions; body brown with seven sets of four blackish spots along back; often a midlateral row of small blackish spots; head, nape, and chest with small orangish brown spots, many ventrally on head and thorax anastomosing into irregular lines; a dark bar dorsally on head behind eye; a dusky to blackish spot on first membrane of dorsal fin, and sometimes on second; anal fin with white-tipped rays and a blackish submarginal band (except posteriorly). Males reach 6.2 cm, females only about 5 cm. Bath (1989) listed the species from the Philippines (type locality), Gulf of Thailand, Sri Lanka, southwest India, Pakistan, central coast of Oman, and Arabian Gulf. Springer (1991) recorded it from the Hawaiian Islands, but indicated the possibility of unintentional introduction.

KOSI ROCKSKIPPER
Pereulixia kosiensis (Regan, 1908)

Dorsal rays XI-XIII,11-12; anal rays II,12-14; segmented caudal rays 13, the middle 9 branched; pectoral rays 15-16 (usually 15); pelvic rays I,4; lateral line complete, curving down below posterior half of spinous dorsal fin to midlateral posterior part, the first 10-12 pores double; scale-like flaps covering all but the posterior lateral-line pores; upper jaw with more than 150 slender, close-set, movable, incisiform teeth; lower jaw with 43-53 fairly rigid incisiform teeth and one posterior canine on each side; vomer with small curved conical teeth; edge of lips smooth; supraorbital tentacle long and tapering, little more than eye diameter

910. *Parablennius pilicornis* (J. Randall)

911. *Parablennius thysanius*, 4.9 cm (J. Randall)

912. *Pereulixia kosiensis*, male, 19.6 cm (J. Randall)

913. *Pereulixia kosiensis*, female, 15.7 cm (J. Randall)

in females, but may be three-fourths head length in males; two slightly overlapping transverse patches of cirri on each side of nape, separated by a gap middorsally; numerous cirri on anterior nostril; body depth 3.0-3.6 in standard length; dorsal fin deeply incised between spinous and soft portions; last dorsal ray joined by membrane to caudal peduncle; last anal ray free of peduncle; females brown, shading to white on abdomen, with large dark brown blotches and small spots, and numerous small white spots; males darker brown, hence dark brown blotches obscure, but small white spots very evident (those on the head may be blue). Reaches 20 cm. Known from Natal to Mozambique, and southern Oman to Pakistan (Shamsul Hoda, 1980). Occurs along exposed rocky shores, including deep tidepools.

ARABIAN FANGBLENNY
Petroscirtes ancylodon Rüppell, 1838

Dorsal rays X-XI (usually XI),17-19; anal rays II,17-19; segmented caudal rays 11, none branched (true of all species of the genus); pectoral rays 13-15; pelvic rays I,3 (also generic); lateral line passing close to base of dorsal fin to end of spinous portion where it arches downward as a few isolated tubes; jaws with close-set, little movable, incisiform teeth, 18-40 in upper jaw and 18-41 in lower (number of teeth increasing with growth); a canine laterally at front of upper jaw, and a huge one laterally at front of lower jaw (generic); a pair of small flap-like cirri on chin (one on each side), upper part of eye, posterior interorbital next to eye, posttemporal (in front of lateral line), and posteriorly on nape; gill opening small, not extending below level of upper edge of pectoral-fin base (generic); body depth 4.1-5.0 in standard length; no notch between spinous and soft portion of dorsal fin (characteristic of the tribe); last dorsal and anal rays bound by membrane to caudal peduncle (also a tribe character); a series of large, irregular, interconnected, dark olive brown blotches along upper side of body containing small blue spots; body above blotches finely flecked with white; below whitish with a dense fine reticulum of olive brown, becoming pale yellow on abdomen; a series of dark brown spots at base of dorsal fin paralleling rays, each edged anteriorly with a blue line; margin of dorsal fin white; anal ray tips white. Largest specimen, 11.5 cm. Known from the northern Red Sea to the Arabian Gulf; usually found in seagrass beds or substrata with heavy algal growth. Like other fangblennies, prone to bite with its big canines if handled.

HIGHFIN FANGBLENNY
Petroscirtes mitratus Rüppell, 1830

Dorsal rays X-XII,14-16; anal rays II,14-16; pectoral rays 13-16; lateral line as in *P. ancylodon*; incisiform teeth in upper jaw 20-33, in lower jaw 20-36; adults with a pair of flap-like cirri (may be fringed) on chin; other cirri on posterior nostril, upper part of eye, posterior interorbital (next to eye), three to five on lower preopercle, on nape (near origin of dorsal fin), and posttemporal (at anterior end of lateral line); body depth 2.9-4.3 in standard length; anterior part of dorsal fin elevated, much higher in males than females; finely mottled whitish and grey-brown with six irregular olive blotches along upper side of body, the second to fourth containing an oval black spot with a white spot in its upper part; a row of orange or yellow spots anteriorly on body below row of olive blotches. Largest specimen, 6.6 cm. Wide ranging from the Red Sea south to Mozambique, east to Tonga and Samoa. Usually found in weedy areas.

BLUESTRIPED FANGBLENNY
Plagiotremus rhinorhynchos (Bleeker, 1852)

Dorsal rays XI,31-37; anal rays II,29-33; segmented caudal rays 11, none branched (true of other species of the genus); pectoral rays 11-13; pelvic rays I,3 (generic except for two species which lack pelvic fins); mouth ventral, the snout strongly projecting; incisiform teeth in upper jaw 18-40; incisiform teeth in lower jaw 29-58, with chisel-shaped tips; an enormous canine tooth posteriorly in lower jaw; no cirri or tentacles on head (generic); body slender, the depth 6.2-7.9 in standard length; caudal fin forked; usual colour dark brown (may be yellow or yellowish brown) with two bright blue stripes, the first starting dorsally on snout and ending in upper part of caudal-fin base, the second from side of snout along lower side. Reaches 10 cm. Indo-Pacific except Hawaii where the closely related *P. ewaensis* (Brock) is found. Fishes of this genus feed by making rapid attacks on other fishes, removing mucus, epidermal tissue, and sometimes scales. The dark phase bears some resemblance to the Cleaner Wrasse (*Labroides dimidiatus*) in spite of its more slender body (partially offset by the blenny keeping its dorsal and anal fins erect); this resemblance seems to enable it to get closer to its prey fishes.

914. *Petroscirtes ancylodon*, about 9.5 cm (J. Randall)

915. *Petroscirtes mitratus*, about 6 cm (J. Randall)

916. *Plagiotremus rhinorhynchos* (J. Hoover)

TOWNSEND'S FANGBLENNY
Plagiotremus townsendi (Regan, 1905)

Dorsal rays VI-VIII,25-27 (lowest count for the genus); anal rays II,19-21; pectoral rays 11-13; mouth ventral, the snout strongly projecting; close-set incisiform teeth in jaws, 19-34 in upper jaw and 33-56 in lower; enormous curved canine tooth on each side of lower jaw typical of the genus; body slender, the depth 5.3-6.6 in standard length; height of dorsal fin when erect half or more body depth; caudal fin slightly forked; brown, shading to yellowish brown posteriorly; a bright yellow horizontal line across front of snout from eye to eye; spinous portion of dorsal fin with a very narrow white margin, a broad black submarginal band (about one-third height of fin), below this a light blue line; basal two-thirds of spinous portion of dorsal fin brown in females, bright orange in males; remainder of fin brown, gradually becoming hyaline posteriorly with brown rays. A small species; reaches only 4 cm. Known only from the Red Sea to the Gulf of Oman (type locality). Food habits presumably the same as described above for *P. rhinorhynchos*. In the Red Sea *P. townsendi* is grey-blue anteriorly, shading to yellow posteriorly; as noted by Smith-Vaniz (1976), it is a mimic there of the venomous fangblenny *Meiacanthus nigrolineatus* Smith-Vaniz.

MANED BLENNY
Scartella emarginata (Günther, 1861)

Dorsal rays XI-XIII,12-16; anal rays II,14-18; segmented caudal rays 13, the middle 9 branched; pectoral rays 14; pelvic rays I,4; lateral line of 13-18 vertical pairs of pores, then descending below last three dorsal spines as simple isolated tubes to straight posterior part and continuing to base of caudal fin; incisiform teeth in jaws close-set and immovable, about 22-32 in each jaw; vomer without teeth; margins of lips smooth; supraorbital tentacle a low base with a series of cirri; midline of nape with a fleshy ridge bearing a single row of cirri which extends into interorbital space (first appearing at a total length of about 2.5 cm; a 3-cm speci-

men has three); a small fringed flap on rear edge of anterior nostril; body depth 3.8-4.6 in standard length; dorsal fin notched to about half length of first dorsal soft ray; last dorsal and anal rays joined by membrane to caudal peduncle; head, body, and median fins whitish with numerous small black spots; six faint dark bars on upper third of body a little broader than pale interspaces (bars formed by broad dark grey edges around black spots); two dark smudges behind eye; two dusky bars below eye; throat and prepectoral area greyish yellow; cirri crossbanded with red; paired fins whitish, the pectoral rays with dark reddish dots basally which become longer distally on rays; lower pectoral rays yellow. Attains 10 cm. Known from southern Angola, Natal, southern Mozambique, Pakistan (type locality), and India. Oman specimens were collected from tidepools on the central coast near Duqm. *S. steindachneri* (Day) is a synonym.

SNAKEBLENNY
Xiphasia setifer Swainson, 1839

Dorsal rays XIII-XIV,105-119; anal rays II,107-117; segmented caudal rays 10, none branched, joined by membrane to dorsal and anal fins; pectoral rays 12-14; pelvic rays I,3; jaws with close-set, incisiform teeth, 12-30 in upper jaw and 10-34 in lower jaw; a pair of prominent canine teeth in both jaws, those in lower jaw much larger; no vomerine teeth; no cirri, tentacles, or crest on head; body extremely elongate, the depth about 30-40 in standard length, and compressed; origin of dorsal fin in adults over anterior part of eye; two middle rays of caudal fin of males greatly prolonged (the fin as much as 21% standard length); pale grey-brown with 26-28 indistinct broad dark bars on upper two-thirds of body which continue into dorsal fin; an ocellated black spot on outer part of dorsal fin between fifth and seventh spines; a broad submarginal blackish band in dorsal fin from tenth to fourteenth spines, edged below by a pale band which continues to front of fin; soft portion of dorsal fin with a narrow white margin and a broad, diffuse, blackish submarginal band. Reaches about 60 cm. Red Sea and Arabian Gulf to South Africa, east to the western Pacific. Occurs on mud or sand bottoms; takes refuge in tubes or burrows. The capture of a few adults at night-light stations might suggest nocturnal feeding near the surface (Smith-Vaniz, 1976). Kuthalingam and Menon (1965), however, found crustacean remains (including copepods), polychaete remains, foraminifera, fish scales, and considerable sand and mud in the stomachs of two specimens taken by trawl in 50-54 m off western India.

917. *Plagiotremus townsendi* (J. Hoover)

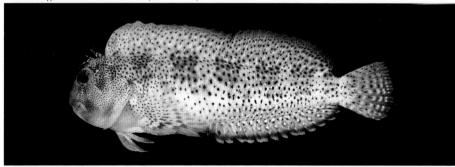

918. *Scartella emarginata*, 6.9 cm (J. Randall)

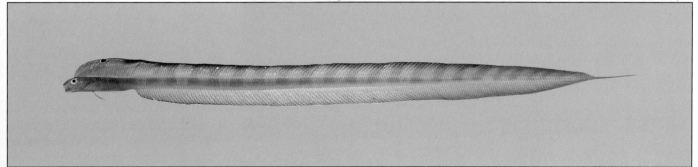

919. *Xiphasia setifer*, 57.3 cm (J. Randall)

GOBIES
FAMILY GOBIIDAE

The Gobiidae is represented by far more species in the marine environment than any other family, and many gobies are also known from freshwater. A total of 212 genera are recognised, with about 1,875 species. The definitive number of valid species will probably reach at least 2000. With so many species, it is difficult to find diagnostic characters which apply to all. One seemingly obvious one is small size; the goby *Trimmatom nanus* is the shortest fish in the world, females maturing as little as 8 mm in standard length; others of the same genus, *Trimma*, *Eviota*, *Pandaka*, and *Mistichthys* are nearly as small. Certainly the great majority of gobies are less than 10 cm in length, but lengths to 50 cm are recorded. The body of most species is scaled, the scales ctenoid or cycloid, but some are entirely naked; often the scales are relatively large posteriorly on the body and progressively smaller anteriorly. There is no lateral line, but the head is usually well supplied with sensory pores or papillae, and some species have barbels. Opercle without a spine; preopercle smooth except for a few species with one to a few short spines. Mouth typically moderately large and oblique; teeth in jaws conical, sometimes enlarged as small canines, in one to several rows; most species lack teeth on the palate. Branchiostegal rays 5; gill membranes often broadly attached to the isthmus, thus restricting the gill opening to the side of the body. Nearly all gobies have two dorsal fins, the first usually with II-VIII (frequently VI, but exceptionally to XVII in mudskippers) flexible spines, the second dorsal and the anal fins generally with a weak initial spine and 6-15 soft rays; caudal fin variable in shape, but commonly rounded, the segmented rays usually 16-17; pelvic fins close together, typically with a short spine and five soft rays, often fully united to form a sucking disc; when united there is frequently a transverse membrane (called the frenum) linking the spines. Gobiid fishes are carnivorous and bottom-dwelling; most rest directly on the substratum or live within burrows, but some hover a short distance above (these are more apt to have the pelvic fins divided). The famous mudskippers (*Periophthalmus* and allied genera; revised by Murdy, 1989) inhabit the mangrove habitat and mud flats; they spend more time out of the water than in it. Most gobies occur in shallow water, but some have been taken in depths greater than 200 m. Gobiids are associated with a variety of substrata such as coral reef, sand, mud, rubble, or seagrass. Many live in close association with other animals such as within sponges or on gorgonians. Species of several genera such as *Amblyeleotris*, *Cryptocentrus*, *Ctenogobiops*, and *Vanderhorstia* are symbiotic with snapping shrimps of the genus *Alpheus* (see Karplus, 1987). The shrimps (generally a pair) build and maintain a burrow in sand or mud, usually with an arch of coral or rock fragments or shell at the entrance; the gobies use the burrow as a refuge but earn their keep as sentinels by virtue of their superior vision and ability to monitor low frequency vibrations with the lateralis sensory system on the head. Nearly all of the gobies for which the reproductive habits are known lay demersal eggs which are guarded by the male parent. Some gobies have been shown to be protogynous hermaphrodites, i.e. they begin mature life as females and change sex later to males (Robertson and Justines, 1982; Cole and Robertson, 1988; Cole and Shapiro, 1990).

920. *Amblyeleotris triguttata* with the snapping shrimp *Alpheus bellulus* (J. Randall)

921. *Ego zebra* adults, about 4 cm (J. Hoover)

DAY'S GOBY
Acentrogobius dayi Koumans, 1944

Dorsal rays VI+I,10; anal rays I,9; pectoral rays 17-18; longitudinal scale series 38-41; scales large and ctenoid posteriorly, progressively smaller anteriorly, becoming cycloid below origin of first dorsal fin; predorsal scales reaching to within a half eye diameter of interorbital space; head naked except for small embedded scales on upper part of opercle; two longitudinal rows of papillae on lower cheek, originating together just above corner of mouth, connected with vertical rows of papillae; gill opening extending forward to below middle of opercle; teeth in villiform bands in jaws with an outer row of small canines, the largest tooth an incurved canine on side of lower jaw; body depth 4.2-4.8 in standard length; caudal fin rounded, a little shorter than head; pelvic fins with a well developed frenum; body light grey with a broken dark grey-brown stripe on lower side, a zigzag pattern of broad grey bars above, and small iridescent pale blue-green blotches along side of body; a blue-green to blue spot at upper base of caudal fin (persists as a dark brown spot in preservative); head with a dark streak behind eye following sensory canal and a few blue-green spots. Attains about 11 cm. Ranges from the Arabian Gulf to Pakistan; a shallow-water species of mud or silty sand bottoms; shelters in a burrow.

SLANTBAR SHRIMPGOBY
Amblyeleotris diagonalis Polunin and Lubbock, 1979

Dorsal rays VI+I,13; anal rays I,13; pectoral rays 19-20; longitudinal scale series 67-75; ctenoid scales dorsally on body extending forward to below base of sixth dorsal spine (more anterior on side); scales dorsally on nape reaching to above posterior margin of preopercle; head naked (true of all species of the genus); prepectoral area scaled; gill opening extending to below posterior margin of preopercle; villiform teeth in bands in jaws, narrowing to one to two rows posteriorly, the front of jaws with three or four pairs of small curved canines; lower jaw with one or two large recurved canines about half way back in jaw (dentition essentially the same for other species of the genus and many other gobies); body depth 5.2-6.7 in standard length; caudal fin longer than head, its length 2.8-3.6 in SL; pelvic fins divided, joined by membrane only basally; white with four diagonal dusky orange to dark reddish brown bars on body much narrower than pale interspaces; head with a comparable bar from nape to opercle, a dark reddish brown line parallel to dark bars from

922. *Acentrogobius dayi*, about 11 cm (J. Randall)

923. *Amblyeleotris diagonalis*, about 8 cm, and *Alpheus bellulus* (J. Randall)

924. *Amblyeleotris downingi*, about 12 cm, and *Alpheus ochrostriatus* (J. Randall)

occiput to corner of mouth, and a short dark brown line from upper lip to eye; a few small blackish blotches dorsally in pale interspaces on body. Attains about 9 cm. Described from specimens from the Great Barrier Reef, Sri Lanka, Madagascar, and Andaman Sea from the depth range of 6-30 m. Recorded by Randall and Goren (1993) from the Red Sea, Kenya, Seychelles, Maldive Islands, Indonesia, and the Solomon Islands, and by Randall et al. (1994) from the Arabian Gulf; occasional in the Gulf of Oman. Lives symbiotically with alpheid shrimps.

DOWNING'S SHRIMPGOBY
Amblyeleotris downingi Randall, 1994

Dorsal rays VI+I,16; anal rays I,17; pectoral rays 18-20; longitudinal scale series 116-129; no median predorsal scales; scales on side of nape extending about half distance from upper end of gill opening to posterior margin of preopercle; no prepectoral scales; gill opening reaching to below middle of preopercle (less than an orbit diameter behind eye); body depth 5.95-7.15 in standard length; caudal fin moderately long, 2.9-3.1 in standard length; pelvic fins united, with a frenum; three broad, faint, dusky orange bars on body and one at caudal-fin base, with a narrow dusky to blackish bar in each pale interspace on upper half of body; a blackish spot about as large as pupil above and behind upper end of gill opening; a larger blackish spot at base of first dorsal fin. Largest specimen, 13.5 cm. Known only from the Arabian Gulf from Kuwait to Musandam; specimens were collected from silty sand-rubble bottom in the depth range of 13-17 m. Lives in association with the snapping shrimps *Alpheus bellulus* Miya and Miyake and *A. ochrostriatus* Miya.

BLOTCHY SHRIMPGOBY
Amblyeleotris periophthalma (Bleeker, 1853)

Dorsal rays VI+I,12; anal rays I,11-12 (usually 12); pectoral rays 18-19; longitudinal scale series about 80; no predorsal scales or only a few embedded scales anterior to origin of first dorsal fin; scales dorsally on body ctenoid to below base of third or fourth dorsal soft rays; gill opening extending forward to below posterior edge of orbit; body depth 4.6-6.4 in standard length; caudal fin longer than head, 2.8-3.4 in standard length; pelvic fins separate, joined only basally by membrane; grey dorsally, shading to white ventrally, with four dark grey bars blotched with red or orange on body and one from nape onto opercle; pale interspaces of body with small irregular brown blotches; cheek and postorbital head with small, brown-edged yellow spots; two red spots at corner of mouth, one above the other. Attains 9 cm. Common in the western Pacific from southern Japan to the Great Barrier Reef, east to Samoa. Western Indian Ocean localities include Maldives, Seychelles, Mauritius, Zanzibar, Red Sea, Oman, and Arabian Gulf. Symbiotic with alpheid shrimps. *Cryptocentrops exilis* Smith and *A. maculata* Yanagisawa are synonyms.

925. *Amblyeleotris periophthalma*, about 7.5 cm, and *Alpheus ochrostriatus* (J. Randall)

926. *Amblyeleotris sungami*, about 10.5 cm (J. Randall)

927. *Amblyeleotris triguttata*, about 8 cm, and *Alpheus bellulus* (J. Randall)

MAGNUS' SHRIMPGOBY
Amblyeleotris sungami Klausewitz, 1969

Dorsal rays VI+I,13; anal rays I,13; pectoral rays 19; longitudinal scale series 100-106; scales ctenoid posteriorly, becoming cycloid on about anterior third of body; gill opening extending to below middle of opercle; body depth 5.6-6.2 in standard length; caudal fin distinctly longer than head, 2.25-2.6 in standard length; pelvic fins united only at base by a narrow membrane; pale yellowish grey with five orange bars, the first four slightly diagonal, the fifth on caudal peduncle vertical; head, pale interspaces of body, base of dorsal fins, and upper base of caudal fin with numerous small light blue blotches and irregular lines, some of the blotches containing a small bright orange-yellow spot. Reaches about 10 cm. Previously known only from the Red Sea, the range here extended to southern Oman. The scientific name is from the name of the first collector, Professor Magnus, spelled backwards.

TRIPLESPOT SHRIMPGOBY
Amblyeleotris triguttata Randall, 1994

Dorsal rays VI+I,13; anal rays I,14-15; pectoral rays 19-20 (usually 19); longitudinal scale series 96-104; no or only a few median predorsal scales; small embedded scales on side of nape extending slightly anterior to upper end of gill opening; gill opening reaching forward to within a half orbit diameter of posterior edge of eye; body depth 5.5-6.25 in standard length; caudal fin slightly longer than head, 2.75-3.25 in standard length; pelvic fins fully united; pelvic frenum present; white with four dark brownish orange bars on body, the first extending into base of first dorsal fin where it contains a black spot larger than pupil; a dark brownish orange bar from nape onto opercle, containing a black spot just above opercle; irregular dark lines usually present in pale spaces between bars on body; a narrow black bar extending ventrally from eye; scattered orange-yellow dots on body and dorsally on head; numerous orange-yellow dots in dorsal fins and upper basal part of caudal fin; a semicircular black or blackish orange spot anteriorly in first dorsal fin. Attains 9 cm. Known only from the Red Sea, Gulf of Oman, and Arabian Gulf; specimens collected from sand-rubble substrata in the depth range of 1.5-17 m; lives in symbiotic association with *Alpheus bellulus*.

WHEELER'S SHRIMPGOBY
Amblyeleotris wheeleri (Polunin and Lubbock, 1977)

Dorsal rays VI+I,12; anal rays I,12; pectoral rays 18-20; longitudinal scale series 50-58; predorsal scales extending to above posterior margin of preopercle; scales ctenoid on body to about base of sixth dorsal spine, cycloid anteriorly; gill opening extending forward to below middle of preopercle; body depth 4.5-5.2 in standard length; caudal fin rounded, only slightly longer than head; pelvic fins joined medially for nearly half length of fifth rays; head and body whitish to pale yellow with six slightly oblique dark reddish brown to red bars as broad or broader than pale interspaces, the first behind eye diffuse and containing bright red and orange spots, the second from nape to opercle also with red spots; a prominent red spot behind corner of mouth; numerous small pale blue spots on head, body, and fins except pectorals; dorsal fins with small red and/or yellow spots. Attains 8 cm. Red Sea south to Natal and east to the Marshall Islands and Fiji; in the western Pacific from southern Japan to the Great Barrier Reef; known from Oman only on the south coast. The most common shallow-water species of the genus in the coral reef environment, but it can occur at depths greater than 30 m. Lives in association with snapping shrimps, most often *Alpheus ochrostriatus*.

TAILSPOT GOBY
Amblygobius albimaculatus (Rüppell, 1830)

Dorsal rays VI+I,13-15; anal rays I,12-14; pectoral rays 19-21; longitudinal scale series 50-53; scales ctenoid posterior to an approximate line from upper base of pectoral fin to posterior base of first dorsal fin, the anterior scales cycloid; predorsal scales extending to interorbital space; small cycloid scales dorsally on opercle, the rest of head naked; prepectoral and prepelvic areas with cycloid scales; gill opening extending forward to below posterior half of opercle; an outer row of incurved canine teeth anteriorly in jaws; largest tooth a strongly recurved, outflaring canine on side of lower jaw; an inner row of slender conical teeth the length of jaws; body depth 3.4-4.6 in standard length; second to fifth spines of first dorsal fin filamentous (first and sixth spine tips may be slightly free of membrane); caudal fin rounded, longer than head, 3.2-3.7 in standard length; pelvic fins united; pelvic frenum present; light greenish grey to dark grey with five narrow dark grey to blackish bars on body and a black spot larger than pupil at base of caudal fin slightly above

928. *Amblyeleotris wheeleri*, about 7.5 cm (J. Randall)

929. *Amblygobius albimaculatus* (J. Hoover)

930. *Amblygobius albimaculatus*, dark phase (J. Randall)

midside; a dark red to black spot usually present above upper end of gill opening; a broad dark reddish brown band from upper lip to eye, dividing into two blue-edged dark reddish brown stripes from eye to upper anterior part of body; another blue-edged reddish brown band from behind corner of mouth to upper pectoral base, with a branch descending on lower edge of operculum; dorsal part of head with rows of dark-edged, red-orange spots; dorsal fins with numerous small pale blue spots. Reaches 18 cm. Ranges from the Red Sea and Arabian Gulf south to Natal. An inshore species living in protected waters; builds a burrow in sand or silty sand by moving out mouthfuls of sediment. Usually seen in pairs; tends to hover a short distance above the substratum.

ORANGESTRIPED GOBY
Amblygobius nocturnus (Herre, 1945)

Dorsal rays VI+I,13-15, the first dorsal fin linked to second by membrane near base; anal rays I,13-15; pectoral rays 19-20; longitudinal scale series 63-66; scales cycloid; no predorsal scales; small scales on side of nape extending a short distance in front of gill opening; gill opening reaching to below posterior third of opercle; dentition as in preceding species; body depth 4.7-6.4 in standard length; head length 3.5-4.2 in standard length; caudal fin slightly pointed, equal to or a little shorter than head length; pelvic fins joined, not reaching anus, with a weak frenum; light grey, shading to white on abdomen and lower head; a yellow to orange-red stripe, narrowly edged in black and pale blue from anterior nostril to eye, continuing from eye above opercle and gradually fading on anterior body; a similar band from corner of mouth (preceded by a black streak on upper lip), across cheek (containing a black spot on opercle) to pectoral base, continuing from beneath pectoral fin faintly (without black and blue margins) to middle of caudal fin; faint blue-edged orange bands at base of dorsal and anal fins, continuing onto last rays, and two converging orange bands in caudal fin; in the Pacific a series of small dusky spots along back at base of dorsal fins. Reaches 7 cm. Red Sea to French Polynesia (but with few records); in the western Pacific from southern Japan to northeastern Australia; reported from the Arabian Gulf by Ran-

931. *Amblygobius nocturnus*, 5.8 cm (J. Randall)

dall et al. (1994); occurs inshore in sheltered waters; usually seen hovering above its burrow entrance in sand or silty sand. *Ctenogobiops klausewitzi* Goren is a synonym.

HALFSPOTTED GOBY
Asterropteryx semipunctatus Rüppell, 1830

Dorsal rays VI+I,9-11 (usually 10); anal rays I,8-9 (usually 9); pectoral rays 16-18; longitudinal scale series 23-25; scales ctenoid; head scaled except for snout and interorbital space; gill opening ending below middle of opercle; three to nine close-set spines on edge of preopercle just above corner; body depth 3.0-3.6 in standard length; third dorsal spine greatly prolonged in adults; caudal fin rounded or truncate with broadly rounded corners, a little shorter than head, 3.35-3.8 in standard length; pelvic fins separate, joined by membrane only at extreme

base, reaching to or beyond origin of anal fin. Colour variable, dark to light grey, often with a broad blackish stripe from eye to caudal-fin base; numerous bright blue dots on head and body, mostly on ventral half. Attains 6.5 cm. Indo-Pacific; usually found in protected waters in silty dead-reef areas at depths of 1-15 m; takes refuge in a burrow or holes in reef.

MEGGITT'S GOBY
Bathygobius meggitti (Hora and Mukerji, 1936)

Dorsal rays VI+I,9; anal rays I,8; pectoral rays 20-22, the upper five or six with rays free of membranes, each with two to four branches; longitudinal scale series 38-40; scales ctenoid to below middle of first dorsal fin, cycloid anteriorly; embedded predorsal scales reaching to within a half-eye diameter of posterior edge of eye; anterior nostril with a small dorsoposterior flap; a small bump ventroposterior to nostril with a groove behind and below it; transverse fleshy lobe medially on chin (mental frenum), with a straight posterior margin and without long lateral lobes; body depth 4.1-4.3 in standard length; caudal fin rounded, shorter than head, 3.7-4.0 in standard length; pelvic fins united to form a circular disc; pelvic frenum fleshy with a pointed lobe on each side; females dark grey-brown dorsally, paler ventrally, with five large yellowish white blotches dorsally, the first on nape the last on caudal peduncle; a midlateral series of small, horizontally elongate dark brown blotches (more evident posteriorly) associated with indistinct pale blotches; one female specimen with dark-edged blue dots in rows on body (more distinct ventrally); head mottled with diffuse dark brown and pale spots; outer part of first dorsal fin broadly yellowish; males yellowish grey, densely and diffusely mottled with dusky, bluish white, and dull orange spots. Reaches 6 cm. Known from Burma (type locality) and specimens collected from tidepools of exposed coasts of southern and central Oman; a surprisingly large brachyuran crab (7.5 mm in carapace width) found in stomach of a 5.4-cm specimen.

932. *Asterropteryx semipunctatus*, about 4 cm (J. Randall)

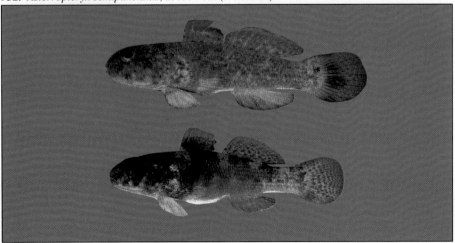

933. *Bathygobius meggitti*, male (upper), 5.9 cm, female (lower), 5.5 cm (J. Randall)

DUSSUMIER'S MUDSKIPPER
Boleophthalmus dussumieri Valenciennes, 1837

Dorsal rays V+I,24-28; anal rays I,25-26; pectoral rays 17-20; pelvic rays I,5; longitudinal scale series 103-105; predorsal scales 48-56; scales cycloid; conical teeth in jaws in one row, those at front of upper jaw as small canines, the lower teeth notched; body elongate, the depth 6.0-7.5 in standard length; head length 3.5-4.25 in standard length; eyes close together, movable to above dorsal profile of head; base of second dorsal fin 2.25-2.35 in standard length; caudal fin somewhat pointed, a little longer than head; pelvic fins united; grey, the scale centres paler than edges, with dark grey dots on head, anterior body, and pectoral-fin base; first dorsal fin with small black spots; second dorsal fin with rows of small white spots, the largest at base; anal fin whitish. Largest specimen, 18.7 cm. Arabian Gulf to west coast of India; lives on mud flats.

TIGER GOBY
Bryaninops tigris Larson, 1985

Dorsal rays VI+I,9; anal rays I,8-9; segmented caudal rays 16-17, the middle 10-11 branched; pectoral rays 12-14 (usually 13); longitudinal scale series 32-59; head,

934. *Boleophthalmus dussumieri*, 12.1 cm (J. Randall)

chest, and pectoral base scaleless; scales ctenoid; rows of different-sized sharp teeth in jaws; a curved canine tooth at midside of lower jaw; gill opening ending at level of lower edge of pectoral-fin base or a little lower; body elongate, the depth at anus 7.1-8.5 in standard length; head length 3.2-3.75 in standard length; caudal fin truncate with rounded corners, the fin length 5.1-9.1 in standard length; pelvic fins short and cup-like, the skin around the spines and frenum thickened and folded; transparent with a white line above vertebral column and six to nine narrow orange to red internal bars on dorsal half of body; lower half of body yellowish brown; a red to orange band from eye to front of snout. Reaches 3 cm. Known from

Hawaii (type locality), Great Barrier Reef, Solomon Islands, Viet Nam, and Chagos Archipelago; the Oman record is based on an underwater photograph taken by Bob Bedford off Muscat; identification of photo provided by Helen K. Larson who revised the genus (1985). Lives on the black coral *Antipathes dichotoma*; collected from the depth range of 15-53 m; darts out to feed on small animals of the plankton.

CLOWN GOBY
Callogobius amikami Goren, Miroz, and Baranes, 1991

Dorsal rays VI+I,10; anal rays I,8; pectoral rays 18; longitudinal scale series 24; predorsal scales 8; prepelvic area scaled; scales on cheek and opercle mostly embedded; scales posterior to base of fourth segmented dorsal ray ctenoid, those anterior cycloid; prominent black papillate ridges on head; two to three rows of conical teeth in jaws, the outer enlarged; no canine teeth; body depth about 4 in standard length; head length about 3.3 in standard length; caudal fin rounded, distinctly longer than head; pelvic fins united, with a well developed frenum; adult pale grey with narrow dark brown stripes following scale rows; a curved dark brown bar across caudal peduncle; head whitish with three dark brown bands radiating from eye, one to lower lip, one across cheek, and one across occiput; a broad irregular transverse dark brown bar across nape onto upper opercle; median fins mainly dark brown with a very narrow whitish margin, the dorsals with a few rows of white spots; juveniles white with narrow irregular black bars, one extending into each dorsal fin where broader and bright orange in the middle; caudal and pectoral fins with a broad black band containing a central orange region. Known from only one 3.9-cm specimen from the Gulf of Aqaba and a photograph of a juvenile from Muscat published by Debelius (1993).

935. *Bryaninops tigris*, about 3 cm (R. Bedford)

936. *Callogobius amikami*, 4 cm, aquarium photo (J. Randall)

329

DOUBLEBAR GOBY
Callogobius bifasciatus (Smith, 1958)

Dorsal rays VI+I,9-10 (usually 9); anal rays I,8-9 (usually 8); pectoral rays 16-18; longitudinal scale series 47-53; scales cycloid except for two or three rows of large scales posteriorly on caudal peduncle which are ctenoid; predorsal scales 21-23, extending forward to posterior interorbital space; cheek with small embedded scales; a few small embedded scales dorsally on opercle; prominent horizonal and vertical papillate ridges on head; gill opening ending at level of lower pectoral-fin base and extending forward to below middle of opercle; body depth 5.1-6.7 in standard length; head length 3.2-3.45 in standard length; head depressed, broader than high; caudal fin rounded, 3.7-4.0 in standard length; pelvic fins joined by membrane medially (easily torn), not reaching anus; a thin pelvic frenum present; finely mottled whitish and grey-brown with an irregular broad dark brown bar below first dorsal fin and extending into base of fin; a broad oblique dark bar passing from below second dorsal fin to base of posterior part of anal fin and adjacent caudal peduncle; a dark bar posteriorly on caudal peduncle; papillate ridges on head dark brown to black. Attains 7 cm. Known only from Mozambique (type locality) and Red Sea to Arabian Gulf; occurs on protected reefs or rubble bottoms; Oman and Arabian Gulf specimens were collected in from 1.5-17 m. Although common in collections, not seen while diving. *Drombus clarki* Goren is a synonym.

FEATHER GOBY
Callogobius plumatus (Smith, 1959)

Dorsal rays VI+I,9; anal rays I,7; pectoral rays 19; longitudinal scale series 31-32; scales cycloid, becoming ctenoid posterior to rear base of anal fin; scales dorsally on head to posterior interobital space; opercle and cheek with embedded scales; prominent black papillate ridges on head; gill opening extending forward to below middle of opercle; body depth 4.6-5.0 in standard length; head length 3.0-3.1 in standard length; head strongly depressed; second dorsal fin higher than first; caudal fin notably longer than head, 2.1-2.3 in standard length; pelvic fins joined to form a disc, with a frenum, the fins just reaching anus; white with a brown bar from beneath basal third of pectoral fin, curving broadly into first dorsal fin; a second dark brown bar in middle of body extending into anterior part of second dorsal fin; a diagonal dark brown bar from middle of ventral edge of caudal peduncle to tips of first three soft rays of second dorsal fin; a dark brown bar posteriorly on caudal peduncle; an irregular diagonal dark brown bar from eye across cheek. Attains at least 5 cm. Described from the coast of East Africa from Mozambique to Zanzibar and the Cosmoledo Group of the Seychelles; collected by the author at the islands of Jana and Jurayd in the Arabian Gulf in 5-6 m.

ADAMSON'S GOBY
Coryogalops adamsoni (Goren, 1985)

Dorsal rays VI+I,12-13; anal rays I,9-10; pectoral rays 19-22, all branched, the upper 5 or 6 free of membrane; longitudinal scale series 43-47; scales ctenoid except the two or three most anterior rows on body above pectoral base and ventrally on abdomen where cycloid; head, nape, prepectoral and prepelvic areas naked; gill opening restricted, ending slightly below lower edge of pectoral-fin base; body depth 4.3-4.5 in standard length; head length 3.0-3.15 in standard length; caudal fin rounded, 4.0-4.6 in standard length; pelvic fins joined medially, the fins not reaching anus; pelvic frenum present but not well developed. Whitish with five irregular, broad, dark brown bars on body which interconnect variously on lower side and contain pale spots; a midlateral line of dark brown dots in groups of two or three on body; two broad transverse dark brown bands across nape, one ending at upper pectoral base and the other narrowing and passing along posterior margin of preopercle; an irregular dark bar extending obliquely downward from posteroventral edge of orbit; a short bar extending downward from anteroventral edge of orbit; two diagonal dark bands in first dorsal fin which link with dark bars on body; base of caudal fin with a large dark brown arc; two small dark brown spots, one above the other on pectoral fin near base. Attains about 6.5 cm. Described in a revision of the genus *Monishia* (now a synonym of *Coryogalops*) by Goren (1985) from specimens from Pakistan; range extended to the Arabian Gulf by Randall et al. (1994) from specimens collected in 0.6-3 m. Two isopods and a hermit crab complete with 9-mm shell taken from gut of a 6-cm specimen.

937. *Callogobius bifasciatus*, 5.2 cm (J. Randall)

938. *Callogobius plumatus*, 5.2 cm (J. Randall)

939. *Coryogalops adamsoni*, 5.8 cm (L. McCarthy)

ANOMOLOUS GOBY
Coryogalops anomolus Smith, 1958

Dorsal rays VI+I,10-11 (usually 11); anal rays I,9-10 (usually 10); pectoral rays 16-19, all except the lowermost branched, the upper three free of membranes; longitudinal scale series 30-34, commencing slightly posterior to upper base of pectoral fins; scales ctenoid to below origin of second dorsal fin, cycloid ventrally on abdomen; no scales on thorax, prepectoral area, head, or nape; gill opening ending at lower base of pectoral fins; body depth 4.65-5.45 in standard length; head length 3.2-3.3 in standard length; caudal fin rounded, shorter than head, 3.5-4.0 in standard length; pelvic fins separate, joined only at extreme base, not reaching anus; yellowish, finely blotched with blackish and brownish yellow; nape and upper fourth of body with seven squarish pale bars alternating with dark bars of about equal width; a longitudinal series of about seven small dark brown spots on side a little below midlateral line; a dark brown spot above upper end of gill opening and another behind upper posterior end of preopercle; ventral part of head, including edge of branchiostegal membranes (but not isthmus) with small brown blotches; first dorsal fin with a dark-edged white band near base and a white submarginal band. Largest specimen, 5.8 cm. Recorded only from Zanzibar (type locality), Red Sea (*C. sufensis* Goren, a synonym), and Arabian Gulf (Randall et al., 1994). Occurs on silty sand, rubble, or seagrass from 1 to at least 16 m. The illustrated fish is from the south end of Masirah Island, Oman.

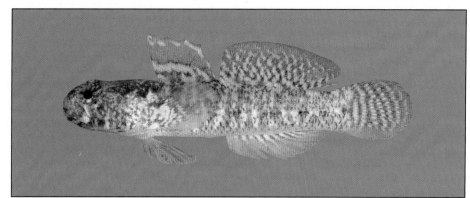

940. *Coryogalops anomolus*, 4.6 cm (J. Randall)

941. *Coryogalops bulejiensis*, 4 cm (J. Randall)

942. *Coryogalops monospilus*, 5 cm (J. Randall)

THINBARRED GOBY
Coryogalops bulejiensis (Hoda, 1983)

Dorsal rays VI+I,11; anal rays I,9; pectoral rays 21-22, the upper five or six branched rays free of membrane on outer half or more; longitudinal scale series 35-38; head, nape, prepectoral and prepelvic areas scaleless; scales ctenoid except for those on abdomen and a few of the small anterior scales dorsally on body; gill opening ending at level of lower edge of pectoral-fin base; a fleshy tentacle dorsally on eye about two-thirds pupil diameter; a prominent cirrus at rear edge of anterior nostril; posterior nostril with a distinct rim; body depth 4.3-5.7 in standard length; head length 3.2-3.5 in standard length; caudal fin rounded, shorter than head, 4.0-4.3 in standard length; pelvic fins united, with a thin frenum; body of females whitish with five large irregular brown blotches dorsally on body and a white midlateral line crossed by eight or nine narrow dark brown bars; a large triangular blackish

spot at base of caudal fin; head and nape yellowish brown with numerous small white spots and scattered small dark brown spots; first dorsal fin with two dark brown bands, the outer fourth white; pectoral fins with two dark brown spots, one above the other, in basal fourth of fin; males with the same basic colour pattern but darker brown, the bars on side of body narrower and more distinct, the fins darker, the head reddish brown grading to red anteriorly; outer part of first dorsal fin red. Attains 4.5 cm. Described from Pakistan, the range here extended to the coast of central Oman; all specimens were obtained from tidepools.

ONESPOT GOBY
Coryogalops monospilus Randall, 1994

Dorsal rays VI+I,11; anal rays I,10; pectoral rays 19, the upper three free of membrane; longitudinal scale series 41; head

naked; no scales on side of nape anterior to upper end of gill opening; a band of predorsal scales, narrowing to a single row which reaches half distance to interorbital space; no scales on chest or prepectoral region; scales dorsally on body ctenoid to origin of second dorsal fin, on side of body to axil of pectoral fins; gill opening ending at level of lower edge of pectoral-fin base; pelvic fins fully joined; a well-developed pelvic frenum present; body depth 5.0 in standard length; caudal fin broadly rounded and short, 4.4 in standard length; body brown, each scale with a whitish spot, shading to whitish ventrally; a narrow whitish stripe on lower side containing eight double dark brown spots; four faint diagonal whitish bars on back; a black spot as large as pupil on first two membranes of first dorsal fin; a large triangular dark brown spot on base of caudal fin; second dorsal and caudal fins with small brown spots. Known from a single 5-cm specimen taken in a rock pool at Kuwait.

TESSELLATED GOBY
Coryogalops tessellatus Randall, 1994

Dorsal rays VI+I,10-11 (usually 11); anal rays I,9-10 (usually 10); pectoral rays 16-19, the upper three free of membrane; longitudinal scale series 30-33; scales ctenoid except ventrally on abdomen; head naked; no predorsal scales; no scales on side of nape, prepectoral area, or ventrally on chest; gill opening ending at level of lower edge of pectoral-fin base; pelvic fins fully connected; pelvic frenum present; body depth 5.1-5.8 in standard length; caudal fin rounded and short, its length 3.85-4.35 in standard length; a narrow midlateral stripe composed of alternating double white and double black spots, ending in a triangular brown spot on base of caudal fin; body above stripe mottled brown and whitish; body below stripe white, the edges of scales dark brown; ventral part of head with a series of dark brown to black spots; first dorsal fin diagonally banded with blackish and white. Attains 4 cm. Known only from the Arabian Gulf to the central coast of Oman; specimens were collected from protected waters in 0.4-6 m on substrata that varied from sand and rubble, to rock with algae, and seagrass.

INNERSPOTTED GOBY
Coryphopterus inframaculatus Randall, 1994

Dorsal rays VI+I,9; anal rays I,7-8 (rarely 7); pectoral rays 19; longitudinal scale series 25-26; head naked except for scales which extend from side of nape nearly to eye; a narrow medial naked zone on nape; scales ctenoid; gill opening ending at level of lower edge of pectoral-fin base; body depth 4.8-5.15 in standard length; pelvic fins joined medially, reaching to or beyond anus; pelvic frenum present; first two dorsal spines prolonged, as long as 1.7 in standard length in males; second dorsal spine 70% or more length of first dorsal spine; caudal fin rounded, about equal to head length, 3.1-3.5 in standard length; translucent with small dusky-edged orange-yellow spots on head, body, and dorsal and caudal fins, the spots on head tending to lie in diagonal rows; some spots on body as close-set pairs, but rarely touching; an internal longitudinal series of five large, horizontally-elongate, black spots interspersed with white; an oval black spot at base of caudal fin, its length nearly equal to eye diameter; first interspinous membrane of first dorsal fin blackish. Reaches 6 cm. Described from specimens from the Arabian Gulf and Sur, Oman from rubble and sand of the coral reef environment in the depth range of 1.5-15 m. Specimens from Mauritius and Kenya appear to be the same

943. *Coryogalops tessellatus*, about 5 cm (J. Randall)

944. *Coryphopterus inframaculatus*, about 6 cm (J. Randall)

945. *Coryphopterus neophytus*, about 5.5 cm (J. Randall)

species. Closely related to *C. longispinus* (Goren) from the northern Red Sea.

NOVICE GOBY
Coryphopterus neophytus (Günther, 1877)

Dorsal rays VI+I,9; anal rays I,8; pectoral rays 18; longitudinal scale series 22-24; one scale on opercle; no median predorsal scales, but five or six scales extend anterior to first dorsal fin on side of nape; scales ctenoid except for those on chest, prepectoral area, and side of nape where cycloid; gill opening extending forward nearly to below posterior margin of preopercle; body depth 4.0-4.6 in standard length; head length 3.1-3.3 in standard length; snout pointed, its length about equal to orbit diameter; lower jaw slightly projecting; caudal fin rounded, about equal to head length; translucent with an internal row of black streaks alternating with white; numerous small dusky yellow spots externally; a black spot smaller than pupil at midbase of caudal fin; a short vertical blackish streak often present on lower midside of caudal peduncle; a U-shaped dark brown mark dorsally on snout, and a dark brown line on side of snout; a black spot anteriorly on first dorsal fin. Reaches 7 cm. Indo-Pacific. Typical habitat, sand and rubble next to coral reefs; known from the depth range of 0.5-25 m. Winterbottom and Emery (1986) reported the gut contents of a specimen from the Chagos Archipelago as harpacticoid copepods, amphipods, and a polychaete. Formerly classified in the genus *Fusigobius*, now shown to be a synonym of *Coryphopterus* (Randall, 1995).

ARABIAN GOBY
Cryptocentroides arabicus (Gmelin, 1789)

Dorsal rays VI+I,11-12 (rarely 11); anal rays I,11; pectoral rays 15-16; longitudinal scale series about 90; scales cycloid; no median predorsal scales; small embedded scales on side of nape extending forward to above posterior margin of preopercle; gill opening extending slightly below lower edge of pectoral-fin base; body depth 5.7-6.25 in standard length; head length 3.5-3.7 in standard length; second to fourth dorsal spines with filamentous tips, the third and fourth spines longest; caudal fin pointed, longer than head, 2.9-3.3 in standard length; pelvic fins joined to form a disc with a well developed frenum, the fins short, 4.3-4.8 in standard length; light greenish grey with numerous small red spots and bright blue dots on head and body; outer half of anal fin black with white dots. Reported to 13.5 cm. Occurs in very shallow water (specimens from less than 0.3 m); lives in a burrow in sediment, probably in association with an alpheid shrimp (but this not yet demonstrated). Previously known only from the Red Sea; Randall et al. (1994) extended the range to the Arabian Gulf. Illustrated specimen from Barr al Hikman, Oman. Only one other species in the genus, *C. insignis* (Seale), known from the Ryukyu Islands to Indonesia.

Y-BAR SHRIMPGOBY
Cryptocentrus fasciatus (Playfair and Günther, 1867)

Dorsal rays VI+I,10; anal rays I,9; pectoral rays 17-18; longitudinal scale series 77-92; scales cycloid; small embedded scales on prepectoral area, prepelvic area, isthmus, and nape nearly to interorbital space; head naked except for a few scales dorsally on opercle; gill opening extending forward to below posterior third of preopercle; body depth 4.4-5.2 in standard length; head length 3.0-3.3 in standard length; dorsal profile of snout steep; first dorsal fin higher than second; caudal fin rounded, 3.2-3.8 in standard length; pelvic fins joined medially, nearly reaching anus; pelvic frenum present but thin; whitish with five dark brown bars (sometimes with white flecks), the first on nape passing diagonally downward to cover most of opercle, the next three usually bifurcating dorsally, and the fifth posteriorly on caudal peduncle; head with a dark brown bar anteriorly, enclosing eye; small bright blue spots on head; membranes of anal fin with longitudinal bright blue lines. Attains 9.5 cm. Red Sea to Zanzibar (type locality), east to Melanesia and the Great Barrier Reef; reported from Musandam, Oman by Randall et al. (1994). Lives in symbiosis with snapping shrimps (most often *Alpheus bellulus*). Observed in the depth range of 6-20 m.

GAFFTOPSAIL SHRIMPGOBY
Cryptocentrus filifer (Valenciennes, 1837)

Dorsal rays VI+I,10; anal rays I,9; pectoral rays 18; longitudinal scale series 79-100; scales cycloid; no predorsal scales; scales on side of nape extending slightly anterior to first dorsal fin; body depth 5.5-5.8 in standard length; first dorsal fin very high, the second to fourth spines filamentous, the second longest, 2.3-3.0 in standard length; caudal fin rounded, 3.3-3.5 in standard length; pelvic fins united, about three-fourths head length; light orangish brown with six brown bars, the first from nape onto opercle, the last at base of caudal fin; pale blue dots on head and nape; a black spot near base of first membrane of first dorsal fin, and sometimes a small second spot behind it on next membrane. Reported to 13.2 cm. Southern Japan to Indo-Malayan region, west to Arabian Gulf (Kuronuma and Abe, 1972, 1986). Above diagnosis from the literature (no specimens examined).

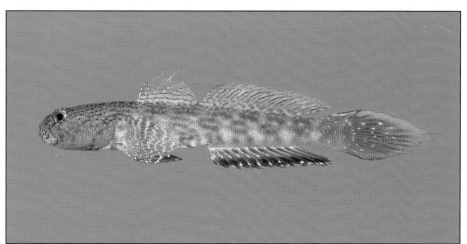

946. *Cryptocentroides arabicus*, 8.2 cm (J. Randall)

947. *Cryptocentrus fasciatus* and *Alpheus bellulus* (J. Randall)

948. *Cryptocentrus filifer* (Hajime Masuda)

LUTHER'S SHRIMPGOBY
Cryptocentrus lutheri (Rüppell, 1830)

Dorsal rays VI+I,11; anal rays I,10; pectoral rays 17-18; longitudinal scale series 95-101; scales cycloid; scales dorsally on head extending forward nearly to posterior edge of eyes; gill opening extending forward nearly to below posterior margin of preopercle; body depth 4.7-5.2 in standard length; head length 3.45-3.9 in standard length; first dorsal fin of adults higher than second; caudal fin rounded, about equal to head length; body of adults with eight dark brown bars (twice or more as broad as pale yellow interspaces) and numerous dark-edged blue dots, mainly dorsally and posteriorly; head and nape orangish tan with dark-edged bright blue spots; dorsal fins with blue-edged reddish brown bands paralleling rays and blue dots at base; body of juveniles white with four broad dark grey bars, the first with three ventral branches, the next two with two ventral branches; a midlateral row of eight black spots, the first larger than eye and edged in blue; head with blue spots, orange spots, and short, irregular, diagonal, orange bands. Largest specimen, 11 cm. Red Sea to Arabian Gulf; also collected by the author at Mafia Island, Tanzania. The most common shrimpgoby in the Arabian Gulf and Gulf of Oman.

TARGET SHRIMPGOBY
Cryptocentrus strigilliceps (Jordan and Seale, 1906)

Dorsal rays VI+I,9-10 (usually 10); anal rays I,9-10 (usually 9); pectoral rays 16-17; longitudinal scale series 54-63; scales dorsally on body ctenoid to below last dorsal spine, cycloid anteriorly; predorsal scales 11-17; no scales on head; a few small scales on prepectoral and prepelvic regions; gill opening extending forward to below posterior margin of preopercle; body depth 3.8-4.5 in standard length; head length 3.2-3.35 in standard length; second and third dorsal spines of adults prolonged; caudal fin rounded, about as long as head; pelvic fins united, usually reaching anus; five broad double

949. *Cryptocentrus lutheri*, about 7 cm, and alpheid shrimp (J. Randall)

950. *Cryptocentrus strigilliceps*, about 5 cm, and alpheid shrimp (J. Randall)

dark grey bars, the first from nape to above operculum, the second and third divided into three narrow bars ventrally, the fourth dividing to two; a series of five large black spots along midside of body, the first largest, edged in white or pale blue; head and body usually with small bright blue and orange-red spots, some on cheek and opercle large, irregular, elongate, oblique, and darker (may be black). Maximum length about 7 cm. East Africa to Samoa (type locality) and the Marshall Islands; shares a burrow in symbiotic association with snapping shrimps (*Alpheus* spp.). A shallow-water species often occurring in protected silty areas.

BIGHEAD GOBY
Ego zebra Randall, 1994

Dorsal rays VI+I,8; anal rays I,8; pectoral rays 18; longitudinal scale series 49-50; midlateral row of scales on body with large scales alternating with two smaller scales in vertical alignment; scales ctenoid except on prepectoral area, chest, and anteriorly on nape where cycloid; predorsal scales extending to mid-interorbital space; no scales on cheek or operculum; anterior and posterior nostrils surrounded by a fleshy rim, the anterior in a thin membranous tube, the posterior small, without a rim; no cephalic pores; sensory papillae of head reduced; head depth greater than maximum depth of body; body depth at origin of anal fin 1.3-1.4 in head depth; head narrow, its width 1.35-1.4 in head depth; gill opening extending anteriorly to below posterior margin of preopercle; second and third dorsal spines of male prolonged and filamentous; posterior dorsal and anal soft rays of male much longer than anterior; caudal fin slightly emarginate, shorter than head; pelvic fins joined medially, without a frenum; translucent with a black spot behind upper end of gill opening, followed by six black bars, the first and the last (at caudal-fin base) vertical, the second to fifth oblique. Described from three specimens 3.0-4.2 cm in total length collected from a cave in 21 m off Rahah Bay, southern Oman. Observed in aggregations of 10-20 or more individuals hovering above or away from the reef, but not far from shelter. Short darting movements suggest feeding on zooplankton; the two small specimens are fully mature females.

951. *Ego zebra*, 4.2 cm (J. Randall)

SPOTTED DWARFGOBY
Eviota guttata Lachner and Karnella, 1978

Dorsal rays VI+I,9; anal rays I,8; pectoral rays 17-18, the upper four or five unbranched; longitudinal scale series about 26; scales ctenoid; no scales on head, nape, or prepectoral area (true of all species of the genus); cephalic pore system complete; body depth 4.9-5.4 in standard length; caudal fin rounded to truncate with rounded corners, about equal to head length, 3.7-4.0 in standard length; pelvic fins separate, joined only at base by a thin membrane (no frenum), the fourth ray longest, usually with fringe-like lateral branching (also generic); fourth ray with 6-8 branches; fifth pelvic ray about one-tenth length of fourth ray; translucent green, flecked with irregular small red spots and blotches, with a series of ten red to maroon spots of progressively smaller size, the first about as large as eye beneath pectoral fin, the last seven at base of anal fin and lower edge of caudal peduncle; head with large red spots. Largest specimen, 2.2 cm; smallest gravid female 1.55 cm. Described from material from the Red Sea and Gulf of Oman. Randall et al. (1994) provided several more localities, extending the range to the Arabian Gulf and east to Fiji and Samoa. Oman specimens were obtained from coral reefs or rubble substrata in 1.5-10 m.

952. *Eviota guttata*, about 3 cm (J. Randall)

LEOPARD DWARFGOBY
Eviota pardalota Lachner and Karnella, 1978

Dorsal rays VI+I,8; anal rays I,7; pectoral rays 14-15 (usually 15), the upper five to eight unbranched; longitudinal scale series 25; scales ctenoid; cephalic pore system complete; body depth 5.0-5.5 in standard length; caudal fin rounded, slightly shorter than head, 3.75-4.0 in standard length; fourth pelvic ray with 6-9 branches; fifth pelvic ray one-tenth or less length of fourth ray; translucent with internal dark bars, the scales with a crescentic dusky orange line; a series of ten blackish orange spots (or double spots) along back from origin of first dorsal fin to base of caudal fin; a series of seven blackish spots ventrally on body (partly internal), the second and third above base of anal fin; head with orangish black spots, becoming smaller and more orange on snout and chin; three transverse orangish black bands on nape, ending at level of eye; two blackish orange spots at base of pectoral fins. Attains 2.2 cm. Lachner and Karnella (1980) reported this species as endemic to the Red Sea; Randall et al. (1994), however, extended the range to the Arabian Gulf; specimens were collected from coral reef or rubble bottoms in the depth range of 1.5-17 m.

REDSPOTTED DWARFGOBY
Eviota prasina (Klunzinger,1871)

Dorsal rays VI+I,8-10 (usually 9, rarely 8); anal rays I,8; pectoral rays 15-18, the eleventh to sixteenth usually branched; longitudinal scale series 23-25; scales ctenoid; cephalic pore system lacking the canal at top of preopercle and the intertemporal pore; body depth 4.0-5.0 in standard length; first dorsal spine of males filamentous; caudal fin rounded, a little shorter than head; fourth ray of pelvic fin with 4-14 branches (mean, 8); fifth pelvic ray absent or as a small rudiment; translucent greenish with two internal rows of dark spots; scales with a vertically elongate orange-red spot; a row of small irregular orange-red spots along back; a black spot larger than pupil posteriorly on side of caudal peduncle; five subcutaneous dark spots ventrally on body posterior to origin of anal fin; bright orange-red spots on head, those behind and below eye and on cheek overlaid with black dots; two red spots at pectoral-fin base with a horizontal white streak between. Reaches 3.7 cm. Western Pacific from southern Japan to Lord Howe Island and Norfolk Island, west to the Red Sea and East Africa; Oman record from Juzor al Hallaniyat (Kuria Muria Islands).

953. *Eviota pardalota*, 1.9 cm (J. Randall)

954. *Eviota prasina*, about 2.5 cm (J. Randall)

REDSTRIPE DWARFGOBY
Eviota sebreei Jordan and Seale, 1906

Dorsal rays VI+I,8-9 (usually 9); anal rays I,8-9; pectoral rays 16, none branched; longitudinal scale series 26-27; scales ctenoid; cephalic sensory pore system incomplete (Fig. 4 C of Lachner and Karnella, 1980); body elongate, the depth 5.5-6.3 in standard length; caudal fin rounded, as long or nearly as long as head, 3.6-3.95 in standard length; fourth pelvic ray with 19-24 branches; fifth pelvic ray slender, unbranched, and more than half length of fourth ray; translucent grey with a broad red stripe on head and body, beginning narrowly with anterior nostril and ending on caudal-fin base where it encloses a black spot larger than pupil which is rimmed above and behind by white and preceded by a small yellow spot; a series of white dashes along upper edge of stripe and a series of white spots on lower edge in abdominal region. Reaches 3 cm. Red Sea, Arabian Gulf and islands of western Indian Ocean east to Samoa (type locality) and the Marshall Islands; the photograph from Juzor al Hallaniyat (Kuria Muria Islands); known from the depth range of 6-33 m; often seen at rest on live coral.

FAN SHRIMPGOBY
Flabelligobius latruncularius (Klausewitz, 1974)

Dorsal rays VI+I,9-10; anal rays I,8-9; pectoral rays 16-18; longitudinal scale series 49-50; scales ctenoid on about posterior half of body, cycloid anteriorly; a few small embedded predorsal scales; head naked; gill opening extending forward nearly to a vertical at posterior edge of preopercle; body elongate, the depth 6.0-6.9 in standard length; head length 3.15-3.2 in standard length; first dorsal fin higher than second, the first to third spines prolonged and filamentous in males (the second and third longest); caudal fin asymmetrically rounded, about equal to head length, 3.05-3.2 in standard length; pelvic fins joined medially, the ray tips flaring outward, the fins nearly or just reaching anus, 3.95-4.05 in standard length; pelvic frenum well developed but thin; whitish with numerous, very small, brown-edged yellow spots and a series of four round blackish spots about as large as eye along side of body. Attains 5.5 cm. Described from the northern Red Sea; Randall and Goren (1993) extended the range to the Maldive Islands, and Randall et al. (1994) to the Arabian Gulf. Known from the depth range of 1.5-37 m; lives in association with snapping shrimps.

ANJER GOBY
Gnatholepis anjerensis (Bleeker, 1850)

Dorsal rays VI+I,11; anal rays I,11; pectoral rays 15-17 (usually 16); longitudinal scale series 28-30; scales on body ctenoid except small cycloid scales anterior to paired fins; median predorsal scales cycloid, extending to posterior interorbital space; scales posteriorly on side of nape, opercle, and posteriorly on preopercle ctenoid, those on cheek below eye cycloid; gill opening extending forward to below posterior half of opercle; body depth 3.5-4.7 in standard length; head length 3.1-3.6 in standard length; posterior part of lower lip with a prominent ventral-directed flap; caudal fin rounded, about equal to head length; pelvic fins united to form a disc, the fins reaching to or slightly posterior to anal-fin origin; pelvic frenum present but very thin; whitish with a longitudinal row of diffuse dark brown blotches on lower side of body and numerous orangish brown dots on head and body, some forming rows on body; a blackish blotch in shoulder region containing a yellow spot; a black line across interorbital, continuing below eye (orange below eye on some individuals); an oblique orange line on lower opercle, followed by a horizontal orange line to base of pectoral fin; small blue spots often present on cheek and lower opercle, and some may be scattered on lower half of body; dorsal fins with red to blackish red spots; anal fin whitish, often with two rows of elongate oblique reddish spots. Reaches 8 cm. Indo-Pacific; common on sand or sand and rubble adjacent to reefs; collected by the author in the depth range of 1-46 m. *Gobius cauerensis* Bleeker is a synonym.

955. *Eviota sebreei*, about 2.5 cm (J. Randall)

956. *Flabelligobius latruncularius* and *Alpheus bellulus* (J. Randall)

957. *Gnatholepis anjerensis*, about 4.5 cm (J. Randall)

CITRON GOBY
Gobiodon citrinus (Rüppell, 1838)

Dorsal rays VI+I,10-11 (usually 10); anal rays I,8-9; pectoral rays 18-19; no scales; ventral end of gill opening extending to level of twelfth pectoral ray; body deep, the depth 2.3-2.7 in standard length, and compressed; dorsal fins barely linked ventrally by membrane; caudal fin rounded, shorter than head; pelvic fins united to a small cup-like disc, the frenum lobate with two pointed posterior projections; ground colour variable, brown to bright yellow; a small black spot at upper end of opercular membrane; two blue lines extending ventrally from eye, another from nape across opercle, and a fourth across pectoral-fin base; a blue line at base of dorsal and anal fins. Largest specimen, 6.6 cm. Red Sea and East Africa to Samoa and the Marshall Islands; lives on branches of live coral (*Acropora*). Like others of the genus *Gobiodon*, this species produces copious thick mucus which has a strong bitter taste and probably serves to deter predators.

RETICULATE GOBY
Gobiodon reticulatus Playfair and Günther, 1867

Dorsal rays VI+I,10-12; anal rays I,9; pectoral rays 19-21; no scales; ventral end

958. *Gobiodon citrinus* (J. Hoover)

of gill opening reaching to level of last one or two pectoral rays; body deep, the depth 2.2-2.9 in standard length, and compressed, the width 2.0-2.2 in depth; head length 3.25-3.4 in standard length; dorsal profile of head nearly straight to above eye, then a distinct angularity; last membrane of first dorsal fin notched to about one-third length of initial spine of second dorsal; fifth dorsal spine longest, about 1.5 in head; longest dorsal soft ray about equal to head length; caudal fin rounded, 3.5-4.0 in head length; pelvic fins united and cup-like, the frenum not fleshy, with two pointed posterior projec-

tions; brownish orange to red with numerous, close-set, small, brown-edged pale grey to pale blue spots on body; five to six slightly oblique, pale bluish grey to pale blue lines on head, the first two passing ventrally from eye, and the last two extending onto base of pectoral fin; fins blackish, the dorsals and anal with a narrow, black or brown-edged, pale grey to blue band at base. Largest specimen, 2.1 cm. Reported from the Red Sea and Aden (type locality); range here extended to southern Oman, Gulf of Oman, and Arabian Gulf; generally found on live coral.

CHECKERED GOBY
Gobiopsis canalis Lachner and McKinney, 1978

Dorsal rays VI+I,10; anal rays I,9; segmented caudal rays 17, the upper and lower unbranched; pectoral rays 22-23; longitudinal scale series 50-55; predorsal scales 18-20; scales cycloid, small on abdomen, chest, and prepectoral area, none on cheek or opercle; gill opening to level of lower edge of pectoral-fin base; body elongate, the depth 5.8-8.0 in standard length; head length 2.9-3.1 in standard length; small barbels on chin, between nostrils, and along cheek; preopercular sensory canal joined to lateral cephalic canal; caudal fin rounded, shorter than head; pelvic fins united, with a frenum, not reaching anus; upper three-fourths of body dark grey with two longitudinal rows of large white spots not in vertical alignment; six white spots in upper row along back, the first above gill opening, the third below origin of second dorsal fin largest, and the sixth at upper edge of caudal-fin base smallest; a black band across pectoral fin near base. Reaches 6.3 cm. Described from a specimen taken by trawl in 13 m in the Arabian Gulf and one from southwest India. Oman record based on a juvenile collected by the author in 21 m at Juzor al Hallaniyat (Kuria Muria Islands) on rock and sand bottom.

959. *Gobiodon reticulatus*, 4.3 cm (J. Randall)

960. *Gobiopsis canalis*, male, 6.3 cm (after Lachner and McKinney, 1978)

COMMON GOBY
Hetereleotris vulgare (Klunzinger, 1871)

Dorsal rays VI+I,11; anal rays I,10; segmented caudal rays 17 (15 usually branched); pectoral rays 15-17 (rarely 17); no scales; gill opening not extending below pectoral-fin base; first gill slit closed by membrane for half or more length of lower limb of first gill arch (characteristic of the genus); anterior and posterior nostrils in tubes of about equal length; small mental frenum present (fleshy median lobe at tip of chin confluent with lower lip), followed by a slight groove and two longitudinal, slightly converging rows of about four small papillae; two lateral rows of small papillae ventrally on head paralleling lower jaw and extending posteriorly; body depth 4.2-5.3 in standard length; head length 2.9-3.2 in standard length; head broader than high; caudal fin rounded, longer than head, 3.8-4.2 in standard length; pelvic fins fully separated; white with six irregular dark brown bars on body, two to three times broader than pale interspaces (dark bars may contain irregular small white blotches); third and fourth dark bars may branch ventrally; first two dark bars extending into base of first dorsal fin and the next three into base of second dorsal fin; nape with an irregular dark brown bar that ends at upper base and axil of pectoral fin; a transverse dark bar on occiput. Attains 4 cm. Previously reported from the Red Sea (type locality), Mozambique, Pakistan, and one specimen from the eastern Mediterranean Sea (Hoese, 1986). Collected by the author in Djibouti and southern Oman in the depth range of 4-24 m.

BLACKBAR GOBY
Hetereleotris zonata (Fowler, 1934)

Dorsal rays VI+I,13-14; anal rays I,11; pectoral rays 16-19; scales cycloid, small, partially embedded, and difficult to count (about 50 in longitudinal series, ending at upper base of pectoral fin); gill opening ending at level of lower edge of pectoral-fin base; both nostrils tubular, subequal; body elongate, the depth 5.4-6.0 in standard length; head length 3.3-3.6 in standard length; head depressed, distinctly broader than high; mouth strongly oblique, the lower jaw projecting; pelvic fins well separated and short, 1.65-1.7 in head; dorsal fins connected by a low membrane; caudal fin rounded, shorter than head, 4.45-4.65 in standard length; light brown with a broad black bar below first dorsal fin, continuing into fin; six lesser, slightly diagonal, dark bars on rest of body, broader than pale interspaces; a dark band across interorbital space, continuing diagonally from eye to corner of preopercle. Larg-

961. *Hetereleotris vulgare*, 3.7 cm (J. Randall)

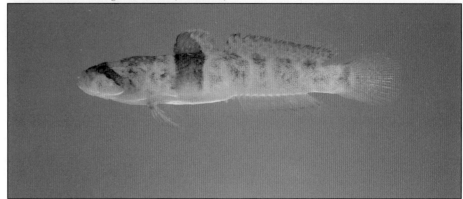

962. *Hetereleotris zonata*, 4.1 cm (J. Randall)

963. *Istigobius decoratus*, about 8.5 cm (J. Randall)

est, 6.5 cm. South Africa and southern Oman to northwest India, mostly from tidepools. South African specimens with one fewer dorsal, anal, and pectoral rays and longer paired fins (Hoese, 1986).

DECORATED GOBY
Istigobius decoratus (Herre, 1927)

Dorsal rays VI+I,10; anal rays I,9; pectoral rays 17-19; longitudinal scale series 27-28; scales on body ctenoid; scales on nape cycloid except for a few above opercle, the predorsal scales extending to posterior interorbital space; cheek and opercle naked; gill opening extending forward to below anterior third of opercle; body depth 4.9-6.1 in standard length; caudal fin rounded, 3.4-3.8 in standard length; pelvic fins joined to form a disc which reaches to or beyond anus (true

of other species of the genus); a series of four double black spots on midside of body and a fifth pair on base of caudal fin with white and black spots between; body above this series brown to grey with longitudinal rows of white spots, one per scale, and two or three longitudinal rows of small dark brown spots; body below midlateral row of spots white with one adjacent row of dark brown spots; head similar in colour to body but with irregular dark brown to reddish lines on lower half of head; small dark red spots in median and pectoral fins; a small black spot on at least first membrane of first dorsal fin. Largest specimen, 12.5 cm. The most wide-ranging species of the genus, Red Sea to Natal, east to Samoa (Murdy and Hoese, 1985); generally found in protected waters on clean sand near rocky areas or coral reefs; known from the depth range of less than 1 to 18 m.

ORNATE GOBY
Istigobius ornatus (Rüppell, 1830)

Dorsal rays VI+I,10-11 (usually 10); anal rays I,8-10 (usually 9); pectoral rays 17-20 (most often 19), the upper three or four free of membrane (unique for the genus); longitudinal scale series 28-29; scales on body ctenoid; scales dorsally on head extending to interorbital space; no scales on opercle or cheek; gill opening extending forward to below front of opercle; no large recurved canine tooth on side of lower jaw (present in other species of the genus); body depth 4.6-5.2 in standard length; caudal fin rounded, slightly longer than head; whitish with three or four longitudinal rows of broken dark brown lines on back, two longitudinal rows of deep blue spots, one on midside mostly as two or three spots together, and one row on lower side (mostly as double spots); small white or blue spots above and below rows of deep blue spots; orange-red and pale blue spots and short lines on cheek and opercle; median and pectoral fins finely spotted. Reaches 10 cm. Red Sea to Madagascar, east to Fiji; usually found in an estuarine environment.

OMAN GOBY
Lobulogobius omanensis (Koumans, 1944)

Dorsal rays VI+I,8; anal rays I,9; segmented caudal rays 17 (12 branched); pectoral rays 20-21 (all branched); longitudinal scale series 29-30; predorsal scales about 13, reaching anterior to a vertical at posterior margin of preopercle; scales ctenoid, large posteriorly, small on nape; bony ridge above eye; gill membranes forming a free fold across isthmus; body depth at anus 5.0-5.45 in standard length; head length 2.6-2.85 in standard length; eye small, 6.65-7.75 in head; caudal fin rounded, 4.3-4.6 in standard length; light grey-green. Reaches 5 cm. Known only from the Gulf of Aden, Gulf of Oman, and Viet Nam; depth of capture 35-45 m. Described by Koumans in Blegvad (1944); *Sicyodon albus* Fourmanoir from Viet Nam is a synonym (Larson and Hoese, 1980). Only species of the genus; related to *Pleurosicya*, hence *L. omanensis* might be expected to live in association with a sessile invertebrate.

SPINECHEEK GOBY
Oplopomus oplopomus (Valenciennes, 1837)

Dorsal rays VI+I,9-10 (usually 9); anal rays I,10; pectoral rays 18-19; longitudinal scale series 24-26; scales on nape extending to above middle of opercle; scales ctenoid except chest, prepectoral region, and anteriorly on nape; cheek and opercle naked; lower posterior margin of preopercle with one to three prominent spines; gill opening extending forward to below posterior margin of preopercle; body depth 4.1-4.7 in standard length; first spine of both dorsal fins thick and stiff; caudal fin rounded, about equal to head length; pelvic fins united, with a frenum; pale grey with a midlateral row of six elongate blackish spots; a few small blackish spots dorsally on body and one on head above opercle; numerous, small, iridescent pale blue spots and yellow dots on body, some yellow dots within and around blackish spots; head with iridescent pale blue spots and short lines; a median yellow streak in caudal fin. Reported to 8 cm. Indo-Pacific; lives in silty sand or seagrass beds; takes refuge in a burrow.

FROGFACE GOBY
Oxyurichthys papuensis (Valenciennes, 1837)

Dorsal rays VI+I,12; anal rays I,13; pectoral rays 21-23; longitudinal scale series 65-75; scales ctenoid to below origin of second dorsal fin, cycloid anteriorly; scales present on chest and side of nape, but not on prepectoral region, cheek, or opercle; a fleshy ridge medially on nape; no tentacle on eye; body elongate, the depth 5.6-6.5 in standard length; upper part of eye higher than dorsal profile of head; caudal fin long and pointed, nearly twice length of head; pelvic fins united, with a frenum; greenish dorsally, the scales edged in brown, shading to whitish ventrally, with a midlateral row of four large dark brown blotches on body and a large black spot at base of caudal fin; a dark brown spot at upper base of pectoral fins and one on opercle. Reported to 18 cm. Red Sea to Natal, east to the Indo-Malayan region; lives on mud substrata. Takes refuge in a burrow, but is able to dive into mud to escape predation.

964. *Istigobius ornatus*, about 7 cm (J. Randall)

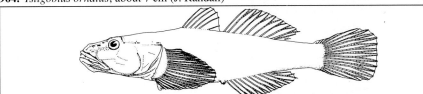

965. *Lobulogobius omanensis*, female, 4.4 cm (after Larson and Hoese, 1980)

966. *Oplopomus oplopomus*, about 8 cm (J. Randall)

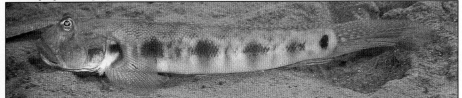

967. *Oxyurichthys papuensis*, about 25 cm (J. Randall)

METEOR GOBY
Palutrus meteori (Klausewitz and Zander, 1967)

Dorsal rays VII+I,8; anal rays I,7; pectoral rays 15-16; longitudinal scale series 26-29; predorsal scales 8; scales on body ctenoid, becoming cycloid on chest, prepelvic area, and nape; no scales on cheek or opercle; gill opening extending little below lower base of pectoral fin; body depth 5.1-5.5 in standard length; head length 3.25-3.55 in standard length; second dorsal spine longest; caudal fin rounded, about equal to head length; a round or slightly oblong black spot nearly as large as eye behind upper part of eye; a blackish blotch at base of caudal fin; a midlateral row of black dots on body; second dorsal and caudal fins with small dark spots. Largest specimen, 6.2 cm. Red Sea; one specimen from southern Oman in the collection of the Royal Ontario Museum. Lives inshore on reef flats.

BLACKTHROAT GOBY
Papillogobius melanobranchus (Fowler, 1934)

Dorsal rays VI+I,8-9 (usually 8); anal rays I,8; pectoral rays 13-15; longitudinal

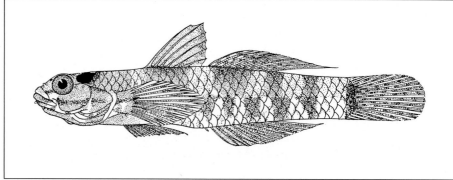

968. *Palutrus meteori*, 2.1 cm (after Klausewitz and Zander, 1967)

scale series 27-29; scales ctenoid except anteroventrally on abdomen, prepectoral and prepelvic areas, and a few scales above upper end of gill opening which are cycloid; no predorsal scales; head naked; gill opening extending forward to or anterior to middle of opercle; body depth 4.65-5.3 in standard length; head length 3.4-3.6 in standard length; caudal fin rounded, shorter than head, 3.8-4.25 in standard length; pelvic fins joined to form a disc, the fins reaching or extending slightly beyond anus; pelvic frenum well developed; females whitish, the upper two-thirds of body with small brown blotches on scales, mainly on edges; a midlateral row of blackish spots, mainly as double spots, the first beneath pectoral fin, the last

with half on either side of caudal-fin base; a blackish streak on side of snout from eye across lips; males pale greenish grey, more heavily mottled with brown, the midlateral blackish spots larger; vertical orange-yellow lines on ventral third of body; median part of branchiostegal membranes blackish; basal two-thirds of dorsal and caudal fins with small dusky yellow spots on a greenish white reticulum, the outer third of first dorsal black with a middle white band; caudal fin with a black spot on upper edge. Attains 5.5 cm. Known from Bali (type locality), Mozambique (Smith, 1959a), and the Arabian Gulf (Randall et al., 1994); Gulf specimens were collected from silty sand and seagrass in 0.3-5 m. Gill and Miller (1990) shifted this species from the genus *Favonigobius* Whitley to their new genus *Papillogobius* primarily on osteological characters and differences in the pattern of papillae of the cephalic sensory system.

OCELLUS-TAIL GOBY
Parachaeturichthys polynema (Bleeker, 1853)

Dorsal rays VI+I,9-11; anal rays I,9-10; pectoral rays 20-22; longitudinal scale series 25-30; predorsal scales 12-14; scales on body ctenoid; head with cycloid scales, those on cheek small; gill opening extending forward to below posterior margin of preopercle; two short barbels (may be branched) on chin of adults; also three rows of cirri ventrally below lower jaw; body depth 5.3-6.0 in standard length; head length 3.75-3.95 in standard length; caudal fin pointed, 3.0-3.05 in standard length; pelvic fins joined to form a disc with a frenum, not reaching anus; pale yellowish, the edges of the scales narrowly blackish; a white-edged black spot nearly as large as eye on upper part of caudal fin about one-third distance to posterior edge of fin; a black spot distally on first three membranes of first dorsal fin. Attains 15 cm. Coast of East Africa and Arabian Gulf to western Pacific; usually taken by trawls over mud bottom.

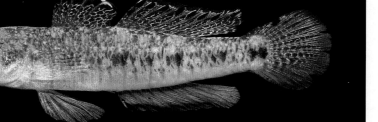

969. *Papillogobius melanobranchus*, male, 5.4 cm (L. McCarthy)

970. *Papillogobius melanobranchus*, female, 4 cm (L. McCarthy)

971. *Parachaeturichthys polynema*, 8 cm (J. Randall)

WALTON'S MUDSKIPPER
Periophthalmus waltoni Koumans, 1941

Dorsal rays X-XIII + 12-13; anal rays I,10-11; pectoral rays 13-15; longitudinal scale series 91-121; scales cycloid; conical teeth in jaws in a single row, those at front as small canines; eyes movable to above dorsal profile of head; body elongate, the depth 7.0-8.6 in standard length; head length 5.6-7.0 in standard length; dorsal fins well separated; base of second dorsal fin 3.7-4.3 in standard length; caudal fin asymmetrically rounded, the lower rays distally thickened; pelvic fins united for about half their length; pelvic frenum present; grey with black blotches dorsally on head and body, larger dark grey blotches along lower side of body, and diagonal white streaks on midside of anterior half of body; white dots on ventral half of head; first dorsal fin grey, the tips of spines yellow except posteriorly, with a large submarginal black spot on first six membranes; second dorsal with bands of grey, white, and black; remaining fins grey, paler near tips. Reaches 15 cm. Known from Pakistan to the Arabian Gulf; lives on mud flats.

MICHEL'S GOBY
Pleurosicya micheli Fourmanoir, 1971

Dorsal rays VI+I,8; anal rays I,8; segmented caudal rays 17, 11 as branched rays; pectoral rays 16-19 (rarely 19); longitudinal scale series 25; scales ctenoid; no scales on head, abdomen, chest, or prepectoral region; scales on side of nape extending a little anterior to upper end of posterior preopercular margin; gill opening extending forward to below rear edge of eye; body depth at anus 4.8-7.1 in standard length; head about one-third standard length; eyes large, dorsolateral; caudal fin slightly rounded, the upper half longer than lower; pelvic fins united with fleshy lobes on spines and forwardly-folded pelvic frenum; translucent with an internal red stripe which continues into lower half

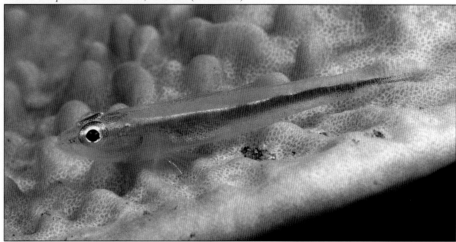

972. *Periophthalmus waltoni*, 12.3 cm (J. Randall)

973. *Pleurosicya micheli*, about 2.5 cm (J. Randall)

of caudal fin (stripe may be blackish posteriorly); a pinkish white line on top of red stripe, broken into segments posteriorly. Attains 2.5 cm. Indo-Pacific; commensal on coral. Larson (1990) revised the genus *Pleurosicya*.

CONVICT GOBY
Priolepis cincta (Regan, 1908)

Dorsal rays VI+I,10-11; anal rays I,9; pectoral rays 17-19; longitudinal scale series 34-37; scales on body ctenoid except abdomen, prepectoral and prepelvic areas where cycloid; scales on nape extending to mid-interorbital space; a patch of small scales, mostly cycloid, dorsally on opercle; no scales on cheek; gill rakers 3-4 + 12-14; gill opening extending forward to below posterior margin of preopercle; body depth 3.8-4.6 in standard length; head length 2.95-3.3 in standard length; caudal fin rounded, shorter than head; pelvic fins joined by membrane, not reaching anus; no pelvic frenum; body whitish with seven grey-brown bars with broad dark orangish brown edges, the pale interspaces much narrower than the dark bars; three orangish brown bars on nape, progressively narrower anteriorly, the most posterior extending onto posterior opercle and pectoral-fin base; four yellow bars on ventral part of head, the first on snout, the next two passing ventrally from eye, and the fourth on cheek linked to second brown bar on nape; dorsal and caudal fins with orange spots on rays. Attains 5 cm. Arabian Sea and Red Sea to Natal, east to the western Pacific. Like others of the genus, very cryptic and rarely seen by divers (generally in small holes within caves). Winterbottom and Burridge (1989) described a close relative, *P. squamogena*, from the islands of the Pacific Plate.

974. *Priolepis cincta*, 4.5 cm (J. Randall)

RANDALL'S GOBY
Priolepis randalli Winterbottom and Burridge, 1992

Dorsal rays VI+I,9; anal rays I,8; pectoral rays 17-19 (all branched or with uppermost and lowermost simple); longitudinal scale series 25-28; predorsal scales 14-16, just reaching interorbital space; scales ctenoid except for most anterior scales on nape, prepectoral area, and dorsally on opercle where cycloid (large adults with a few small scales posteriorly on cheek); gill rakers 3-5 + 15-17; gill opening extending forward to between verticals at posterior margin of preopercle and rear edge of eye; depth of body 3.5-4.1 in standard length; head length 2.7-2.9 in standard length; caudal fin rounded, shorter than head; pelvic fins united, without a frenum, reaching to or beyond anus; whitish with six orangish brown bars on body broader than pale interspaces; fourth bar broadest, centred at rear base of second dorsal fin, the last on caudal peduncle narrow; five brownish orange bars on head; a semicircular black spot at base of first dorsal fin between first and fifth spines; rays of dorsal and caudal fins banded with red and white. Largest specimen, 5.1 cm. Known from coral reefs of Jana Island in the Persian Gulf (type locality), southern Oman, and the Gulf of Aqaba, Red Sea in the depth range of 15-56 m.

SLENDER MUDSKIPPER
Scartelaos tenuis (Day, 1876)

Dorsal rays V+I,23-28; anal rays 24-27; pectoral rays 18-22; scales cycloid, small, and partially embedded, about 100 in longitudinal series; teeth in jaws in a single row, the front ten of upper jaw twice as long as posterior teeth, overlapping lower jaw; eyes movable to above dorsal profile of head; body very elongate, the depth 7.7-12.0 in standard length; head length 3.6-4.7 in standard length; first dorsal fin well separated from second dorsal; third dorsal spine may be prolonged; base of first dorsal fin 9.5-20 in standard length; second dorsal and anal fins not connected by membrane to caudal fin; base of second dorsal fin 1.8-2.25 in standard length; caudal fin lanceolate with rounded tip, 3.8-4.6 in standard length; pectoral fins united; pelvic frenum well developed; grey, shading ventrally to white, with numerous irregular bars of variable width on body; first dorsal fin black distally except for a white spot between first and third spines; second dorsal fin with a row of eight dark grey spots at base, the posterior margin black; dorsal edge and tip of caudal with a black margin. Reaches 15.5 cm. Ranges from the Arabian Gulf to Pakistan; lives on mud flats.

975. *Priolepis randalli*, 4.5 cm (J. Randall)

976. *Scartelaos tenuis*, 12.8 cm (N. Downing)

977. *Trimma winterbottomi*, 3 cm (J. Randall)

WINTERBOTTOM'S GOBY
Trimma winterbottomi Randall and Downing, 1994

Dorsal rays VI+I,10-11 (usually 10); anal rays I,9-10 (usually 9); pectoral rays 19-22 (usually 20); longitudinal scale series about 45; scales on body ctenoid; head, nape, prepectoral and prepelvic areas naked; gill rakers 3-4 + 14-16; gill opening extending to verticals between posterior margin of preopercle and eye; lower jaw projecting; prominent slender incurved teeth in outer row on anterior half of jaws, those laterally in lower jaw strongly recurved and outflaring; interorbital space a deep groove, continuing around orbit to behind middle of eye; body depth 3.9-4.4 in standard length; head length 3.6-3.8 in standard length; caudal fin rounded, shorter than head, 3.9-4.3 in standard length; pelvic fins joined by membrane only at base, the fourth ray longest, not reaching anus; light red with a row of red and white spots along back; head red with irregular white bars; a black spot just above upper end of gill opening. Reaches 3 cm. This species was named *Gobius townsendi* by Boulenger (1897) from the Mekran coast of Iran; however, this name is a junior homonym, hence a new name was needed. Randall et al. (1994) extended the range to islands in the Arabian Gulf; specimens were collected on coral reefs in 6-21 m.

BURROWING GOBY

Trypauchen vagina (Bloch and Schneider, 1801)

Dorsal rays VI,40-49; anal rays I,39-46; pectoral rays 15-18; longitudinal scale series 80-115; scales cycloid and partly embedded; no scales on head, nape, or chest; mouth strongly oblique, the chin projecting; eyes small and covered by skin (probably blind or nearly so); body elongate, the depth 7.9-10 in standard length; head length 5.7-6.5 in standard length; spinous and soft portions of dorsal fin continuous, without a notch; dorsal and anal fins confluent with caudal fin; caudal fin somewhat pointed, about equal to head length; pelvic fins united and short, 2.5-3 in head length; light red. Reported to 22.2 cm. Arabian Gulf to Indo-Malayan region, north to China and Taiwan; burrows in mud.

RAILWAY GOBY

Valenciennea helsdingenii (Bleeker, 1858)

Dorsal rays VI+I,11; anal rays I,11; pectoral rays 21-23 (rarely 21); longitudinal scale series 127-146; scales on body ctenoid, becoming cycloid anterior to middle of first dorsal fin and on abdomen; head and midline of nape naked (true of other species of the genus); side of nape scaled to above middle of operculum; prepectoral and prepelvic areas usually completely scaled in adults; gill opening extending forward only to below middle of opercle (applies also to other species of the genus herein); depth of body 4.5-6.3 in standard length; head length 3.1-3.6 in standard length; first dorsal fin not higher than second, its outer margin rounded; caudal fin of adults with the ray above and below the three central rays prolonged as a filament; pelvic fins I,5, completely

separate (also generic); light grey to tan, shading to white on sides and ventrally, with two parallel narrow stripes which vary in colour from dark reddish brown, to red, or orange-yellow, one commencing on front of snout above upper lip, the other from side of upper lip, each ending in one of prolonged filaments of caudal fin; first dorsal fin with a white margin and a large black submarginal spot on posterior half. Attains 16 cm. Gulf of Oman south to Natal, east to Marquesas (but with relatively few records between); known from the depth range of 1-40 m. Often seen in pairs, generally hovering just above the substratum; typically found in sand and rubble areas. Constructs a burrow in sand by carrying out mouthfuls of sand; feeds by sorting out the small fossorial animals after taking sand into the mouth (habits essentially the same for other species of the genus).

GULF GOBY

Valenciennea persica Hoese and Larson, 1994

Dorsal rays VI+I,13-14; anal rays I,13; pectoral rays 19-21 (rarely 19); longitudinal scale series 80-102; scales on body ctenoid posteriorly, becoming cycloid below first dorsal fin and on abdomen; prepectoral area naked; prepelvic area partly scaled; body depth 4.8-5.6 in standard length; head length 3.4-3.8 in standard length; first dorsal fin much higher than second and pointed, the third spine longest, 4.75-5.8 in standard length; caudal fin rounded, usually shorter than head, 3.65-4.7 in standard length; grey, paler ventrally, with a row of dark-edged light blue spots from behind eye along upper side of body to base of caudal fin; a blue stripe on lower side of body above anal fin; cheek with light blue spots and opercle with two light blue stripes; juveniles with the same blue spots, but with six orange spots in the same row as upper blue spots, the anterior ones linked with an orange stripe, the centres blackish; an orange stripe with five darker orange spots on lower side, the lower posterior edge blue; cheek and opercle suffused with orange. Largest specimen, 15.9 cm. Arabian Gulf to Masirah Island, central Oman; collected from the depth range of 2-12 m.

978. *Trypauchen vagina*, 14.7 cm (J. Randall)

979. *Valenciennea helsdingenii*, about 16.5 cm (J. Randall)

980. *Valenciennea persica*, largest about 9 cm (J. Randall)

981. *V. persica*, subadult, about 5.5 cm (J. Randall)

MAIDEN GOBY
Valenciennea puellaris (Tomiyama, 1956)

Dorsal rays VI+I,11-13 (usually 12); anal rays I,11-13 (rarely 11, usually 12); pectoral rays 19-22 (rarely 19); longitudinal scale series 72-91; scales ctenoid posteriorly, becoming cycloid anterior to first dorsal fin and on abdomen; side of nape scaled to above posterior half of operculum; prepectoral area naked; prepelvic area partly to fully scaled; body depth 4.5-5.8 in standard length; head length 2.9-3.5 in standard length; first dorsal fin pointed, the third spine longest, 4.6-6.4 in standard length; caudal fin rounded, 3.0-4.2 in standard length; white with oblique orange-yellow bars or elongate spots on back interspersed with small faint orange-yellow spots; an orange-yellow stripe, faintly edged in pale blue and usually containing more intense orange spots, on side of body from beneath pectoral fin to lower base of caudal fin; head with round to oblong, dark-edged, pale blue spots. Reaches 14 cm. Red Sea to Madagascar and Mauritius, east to Samoa; in Oman only on the south coast where rare. Usually found over moderately fine sand in the depth range of 10-30 m, but may occur in as little as 2 m in sheltered waters. Hoese and Larson (1994) documented the geographic variation.

SIXSPOT GOBY
Valenciennea sexguttata (Valenciennes, 1837)

Dorsal rays VI+I,11-13; anal rays I,11-13; pectoral rays 19-21; longitudinal scale series 71-99; scales ctenoid to a line from upper base of pectoral fin to origin of first dorsal fin, cycloid anterior to this and on abdomen; small embedded scales on nape extending a short distance in front of upper end of gill opening; prepectoral area naked to partly scaled; prepelvic area partly to fully scaled; body depth 5.0-6.2 in standard length; head length 3.2-3.6 in standard length; first dorsal fin pointed, the third ray longest (but not filamentous), 4.5-5.35 in head of adults; caudal fin pointed, longer in males, 2.9-3.6 in standard length, in females 3.3-3.9 in standard length; light grey, shading to white on sides and ventrally, with a light red to pink stripe on lower side, sometimes with four to seven pink to dusky bars extending upward from stripe which may link with a faint pink stripe on upper side; four to ten, round to elongate, iridescent pale blue spots on cheek and opercle; a black spot on tip of membrane between third and fourth dorsal spines; a blackish margin on anal fin of adults. Reaches 14 cm. Red Sea and Arabian Gulf south to Mozambique and east to the Line Islands in the central Pacific; a common shallow-water species of protected waters of lagoons and bays; usually found in male-female pairs which share the same burrow of their own construction (often in fine sand under a rock). Hoese and Larson (1994) discussed geographic variation of the species.

MERTENS' SHRIMPGOBY
Vanderhorstia mertensi Klausewitz, 1974

Dorsal rays VI+I,16; anal rays I,17-18; pectoral rays 18; longitudinal scale series 52-62; scales ctenoid posterior to origin of second dorsal fin, cycloid before; no median predorsal scales; small scales on side of nape extending a short distance anterior to origin of first dorsal fin; gill opening reaching to within an eye diameter of rear edge of orbit; body elongate, the depth 6.2-7.3 in standard length; head length 3.7-4.4 in standard length; third to fifth dorsal spines filamentous, the fourth longest, 1.7-3.1 in standard length; caudal fin lanceolate, 2.6-2.9 in standard length; pelvic fins united, the pelvic frenum well developed, the fins not reaching anus; whitish with a blue-green cast; scales on upper half of body with a dusky edge and submarginal yellow mark, this mark on posterior scales enlarged to a spot; five blackish spots in a longitudinal row on side of body; a small black spot behind upper end of gill opening and another the same size on upper part of opercle; head and nape with numerous dark-edged yellow spots; a black streak in groove above upper lip. Largest specimen, 9.8 cm. Known from only three specimens from the Gulf of Aqaba and one from Kalbuh, Gulf of Oman. Collected from silty sand in the depth range of 4-5 m. Lives in symbiotic association with a snapping shrimp.

982. *Valenciennea puellaris*, about 12.5 cm (J. Randall)

983. *Valenciennea sexguttata*, about 9.5 cm (J. Randall)

984. *Vanderhorstia mertensi*, 6.8 cm (J. Randall)

SHADOW GOBY
Yongeichthys nebulosus (Forsskål, 1775)

Dorsal rays VI+I,9; anal rays I,9; pectoral rays 18-19; longitudinal scale series 26-30; scales on body ctenoid except abdomen and prepelvic area where cycloid; no scales on head or nape except for a few ventrally on nape extending a short distance anterior to gill opening; gill opening ending at level of lower edge of pectoral-fin base; body depth 4.2-4.8 in standard length; head length 3.2-3.4 in standard length; several longitudinal rows of papillae on cheek; second dorsal spine filamentous, 3.4-4.0 in standard length; caudal fin rounded, a little shorter than head length; pelvic fins united; pelvic frenum present; whitish, the head and upper two-thirds of body mottled with brown; four large dark brown blotches in a row on side of body, the first under pectoral fin and the last on base of caudal fin; dorsal and caudal fins with numerous dark brown spots; anal fin with a dark brown margin. Reported to 18 cm. Red Sea south to Natal and east to the western Pacific; Oman specimens from inshore on west coast of Masirah Island. Usually found on mud bottoms. Said to have toxic skin.

985. *Yongeichthys nebulosus*, 8.2 cm (J. Randall)

WRIGGLERS
FAMILY XENISTHMIDAE

The fishes of this small Indo-Pacific family of fishes have been classified previously in the Eleotridae, Gobiidae, and Microdesmidae. Springer (1983) treated them as a subfamily of the Gobiidae; Hoese in Moser et al. (1984) elevated the group to family rank. The xenisthmids differ from the gobies in having a free ventral margin on the lower lip, six branchiostegal rays, the ascending process of the premaxilla absent or rudimentary, plus other osteological characters. They have an elongate body, a small depressed head, and a strongly oblique mouth with projecting lower jaw; the dorsal and anal fins are relatively low, the first dorsal with VI spines and the second with a spine and 10-13 rays. All are small (none exceeding 4.5 cm total length), sand-diving fishes that live in sand patches adjacent to coral reefs or reef rubble. The family consists of five genera and about 16 species.

FRECKLED WRIGGLER
Xenisthmus balius Gill and Randall, 1994

Dorsal rays VI+I,13; anal rays I,12-13 (usually 12); segmented caudal rays 17 (12-15 branched); pectoral rays 16-17; pelvic rays I,5, the fins not united; longitudinal scale series 60-70; scales cycloid (there may be a few ctenoid scales on caudal peduncle of some specimens); predorsal scales extending a little anterior to a vertical at posterior edge of preopercle; no scales on head; no teeth on vomer or palatines; body depth about 7 in standard length; head length 4.1-4.7 in standard length; caudal fin rounded and short, 5.3-5.9 in standard length; white, the upper two-thirds of body with dark brown dots and small, irregular, dark brown blotches; a black spot smaller than pupil on midside of base of caudal fin. Largest specimen, 3.8 cm. Presently known from nine specimens, all collected from Jana Island in the Arabian Gulf in the depth range of 1.5-17 m.

986. *Xenisthmus balius*, 3.8 cm (J. Randall)

DARTFISHES AND WORMFISHES
FAMILY MICRODESMIDAE

This gobioid family formerly included just the wormfishes. Hoese in Moser et al. (1984) reclassified the dartfishes (also known as hover gobies) from the Gobiidae to the Microdesmidae. The wormfishes and dartfishes certainly merit subfamily distinction, hence the division below to Microdesminae and Ptereleotrinae. These fishes have elongate compressed bodies with small, embedded, usually nonoverlapping, cycloid scales (may be weakly ctenoid and slightly imbricate posteriorly on body of some species of Ptereleotrinae); there is no lateral line. The mouth is oblique with a heavy protruding lower jaw; the gill opening is restricted to the side; there are five branchiostegal rays. The pelvic fins are separate, inserted below the pectorals, with I,2-4 rays. The wormfishes are extremely elongate with a long continuous dorsal fin having X-XXVIII flexible spines and 28-66 soft rays; anal fin with 28-61 soft rays. The dartfishes have two separate dorsal fins (except *Ptereleotris monoptera* where they are connected), the first with IV-VI flexible spines and the second with one spine and 9-39 soft rays; anal fin with one spine and 9-36 rays. The Microdesminae includes five genera and about 30 species; the Ptereleotrinae five genera and 43 species. The largest genus is *Ptereleotris* (*Ioglossus*, *Vireosa*, and *Pogonoculius* are among the six junior generic synonyms) with 16 species (revised by Randall and Hoese, 1985). Most microdesmid fishes live over sand or mud bottoms and take refuge in burrows. The dartfishes rise above the substratum to feed on zooplankton. Their name is derived from how swiftly they dart into their burrow with the approach of danger. Often a pair of adults will occupy the same burrow; aggregations of juveniles are sometimes seen, all using the same hole in the reef or burrow for shelter.

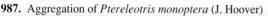

987. Aggregation of *Ptereleotris monoptera* (J. Hoover)

SUBFAMILY MICRODESMINAE

YELLOWSTRIPE WORMFISH
Gunnellichthys viridescens Dawson, 1968

Dorsal rays XX-XXI,38-41; anal rays 36-40; pectoral rays 12-13; pelvic rays I,4; vertebrae 59; body very elongate, the depth 11.5-17.5 in standard length; head length 6.2-7.2 in standard length; lower jaw massive and protruding; origin of dorsal fin slightly posterior to pectoral-fin base; caudal fin rounded, 9.2-11.5 in standard length; pectoral fins pointed, 11.5-14.9 in standard length; pelvic fins very small, 20.0-29.4 in standard length; white with a yellow stripe commencing on chin, crossing snout to eye, emerging wider behind eye, passing above pectoral-fin base, and continuing along side of body to end of caudal fin. Largest specimen 7.2 cm. Known from the Seychelles (type locality), Maldives, Great Barrier Reef, Palau, and the Marshall Islands; reported from Jurayd Island, Arabian Gulf by Randall et al. (1994) from one specimen taken on a rubble-sand bottom in 21 m.

SUBFAMILY PTERELEOTRINAE

RAO'S DARTFISH
Parioglossus raoi (Herre, 1939)

Dorsal rays VI+I,14-15; anal rays I,14-15; pectoral rays 15-17; branched caudal rays 13; scales small, cycloid, nonimbricate, and partially embedded; gill rakers 3 + 12-13; gill opening extending forward to below rear third of opercle; head and nape naked except for a few small cycloid scales above upper end of gill opening; no posterior nasal pore (just above posterior nostril); body depth 5.6-6.0 in standard length; head length 4.35-4.5 in standard length; a low median fleshy ridge on nape joined to front of dorsal fin; a similar but less developed ridge on isthmus; caudal fin of females truncate to slightly emarginate with broadly rounded corners, the fin length about 4.6 in standard length; caudal fin of males with fourth and fifth and ninth and tenth branched rays prolonged, the fin length 3.0-3.3 in standard length; pelvic fins completely separate, the fin length about 9.2 in standard length in females, up to 3.2 in standard length in males; translucent grey with an internal yellowish white line above vertebral column, the abdomen white; a black stripe of about pupil width from behind eye, gradually descending as it passes to lower edge of caudal peduncle ending in a large oval black spot at lower base of caudal fin (some dark pigment continuing from spot to end of fin); a diagonal blackish streak in upper part of caudal fin; a narrow middorsal black stripe on head and body; snout, interorbital, and chin blackish. Largest specimen, 3.4 cm. Recorded from the Andaman Islands (type locality), southern Japan, Philippines, Indonesia, Caroline Islands, and Fiji (Rennis and Hoese, 1985). Range extended to the Arabian Gulf and Gulf of Oman by Randall et al. (1994). Oman specimens were dipnetted from a small aggregation just below the surface at the edge of a rocky shore at Musandam.

ARABIAN DARTFISH
Ptereleotris arabica Randall and Hoese, 1985

Dorsal rays VI+I,26-29; anal rays I,25-28; pectoral rays 22-23; pelvic rays I,4 (true of all species of the genus); longitudinal scale series about 170; no scales on head (also generic); a few widely scattered small scales on side of nape; gill rakers 7-8 + 20-23; a median, broad-based, backward-directed barbel on chin, followed by a longitudinal fold; gill opening extending forward to below middle of postorbital head (about the same for other species of the genus); body elongate, the depth 6.75-8.3 in standard length; head length 4.5-5.5 in standard length; first dorsal fin lower than second, the fifth spine longest, 4.9-7.85 in standard length; second dorsal and anal fins not elevated anteriorly; caudal fin of adults with third and eleventh branched rays greatly prolonged as filaments; pelvic fins short, 1.25-1.5 in head; grey, faintly suffused with light blue-green; two pale blue-green stripes on opercle, the upper extending to eye; upper and lower edges of iris bright blue-green. Attains 13 cm (discounting caudal filaments). Known from the northern Red Sea and Arabian Gulf in the depth range of 1.5-15 m.

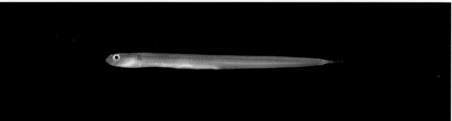

988. *Gunnellichthys viridescens*, 3.6 cm (J. Randall)

989. *Parioglossus raoi*, about 3.5 cm (J. Hoover)

990. *Ptereleotris arabica*, 12.5 cm (J. Randall)

347

SPOTTAIL DARTFISH
Ptereleotris heteroptera (Bleeker, 1855)

Dorsal rays VI+I,29-33; anal rays I,27-30; pectoral rays 21-24; gill rakers 5-6 + 17-20; scales very small, partially or completely embedded; scales present on nape, including dorsally, some scattered as far forward as rear margin of orbit; no barbel on chin; body depth 6.1-7.8 in standard length; head length 6.3-8.3 in standard length; first dorsal fin not as high as second, the third and fourth spines longest, 1.9-2.4 in head; second dorsal and anal fins not notably elevated anteriorly; caudal fin emarginate, the corners rounded; pelvic fins short, 1.2-1.4 in head; light blue to pale bluish grey, the caudal fin whitish to yellow with a large, oval, dusky to black spot (faint or absent in juveniles). Reaches 12.5 cm. Indo-Pacific, including the Hawaiian Islands; observed in Oman waters only in the south. Known from the depth range of 7-46 m; most often seen over rubble-sand substrata near reefs, sometimes in small aggregations.

991. *Ptereleotris heteroptera*, about 10.5 cm (J. Randall)

PALE DARTFISH
Ptereleotris microlepis (Bleeker, 1855)

Dorsal rays VI+I,25-29; anal rays I,24-27; pectoral rays 21-24; scales very small and embedded; no median predorsal scales, but scattered small embedded scales on side of nape extending forward nearly to posterior margin of preopercle; gill rakers 6-7 + 19-21; no barbel on chin, but a median fleshy ridge that narrows to a thin fold posteriorly; body depth 5.5-7.0 in standard length; head length 4.7-5.3 in standard length; first dorsal fin low, less than half height of second dorsal, the spines strongly curved posteriorly; fifth dorsal spine longest, 1.1-1.4 in head; second dorsal and anal fins a little elevated anteriorly; caudal fin slightly emarginate; pelvic fins slightly longer than head; pale grey to bluish grey, usually with two faint pale orange lines posteriorly on side of body which converge slightly as they pass onto caudal fin; a narrow black band edged in pale blue basally on lower half to two-thirds of pectoral fin; pale blue bands and spots on postorbital head. Attains 12 cm. Red Sea and Arabian Gulf south to Zanzibar and the Comoro Islands, east to the Line Islands and Tuamotu Archipelago; in the western Pacific from Japan to New South Wales. A shallow-water species usually found in sheltered waters over sand or sand-rubble substrata.

MONOFIN DARTFISH
Ptereleotris monoptera Randall and Hoese, 1985

Dorsal rays VII,35-39; anal rays I,33-37; pectoral rays 23-25; scales extremely small, embedded, and nonimbricate (even posteriorly); a few scattered tiny scales on side of nape a short distance anterior to upper end of gill opening; gill rakers 6-7 + 17-20; no barbel on chin; body depth 6.05-7.05 in standard length; head length 4.5-5.2 in standard length; dorsal fin low, continuous, with a slight notch between spinous and soft portions, the soft portion a little higher than spinous; caudal fin emarginate, the lobes narrowing to filaments in adults; pelvic fins of adults about equal to head length; pale greenish yellow with a large blue area on side of abdomen; a broad diffuse black bar below eye; iridescent blue-green markings on operculum; dorsal fin with an orange margin; anal fin with a blue margin and broad submarginal red band; lobes of caudal fin with a a narrow light orange-red band at edge. Reaches 15.5 cm. Seychelles to the Society Islands, and Japan to New South Wales, but from relatively few localities; Omani specimens from Juzor al Hallaniyat (Kuria Muria Islands). Takes refuge either in a burrow in sand or coral rock; sometimes seen in aggregations.

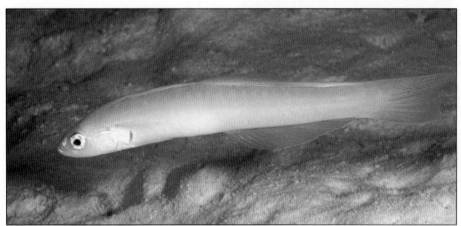

992. *Ptereleotris microlepis*, about 10 cm (J. Randall)

993. *Ptereleotris monoptera*, about 11 cm (J. Randall)

CLINGFISHES
FAMILY GOBIESOCIDAE

The clingfishes are aptly name for their ability to adhere firmly to the substratum, seaweed, or sessile invertebrates with their thoracic sucking disc (from specialised pelvic fins of a small spine and four soft rays); the disc is supported by highly modified pelvic and pectoral bones; the four pelvic rays form the lateral edge of the disc, the last ray attached by membrane to the lower part of the pectoral-fin base. These fishes have a single dorsal fin and anal fin without spines, the rays unbranched; pectoral fins with 16-31 rays. The head is usually broad, and the body tapering and slender; there are no scales. The dentition is highly variable. Some of the bones of the head have been lost (for example, no circumorbitals posterior to the lacrymal). Clingfishes are benthic, primarily shallow-water fishes of tropical to temperate seas; many occur in the intertidal zone exposed to wave action where they take advantage of their strong sucking disc. Most are less than 7 cm in length. When the family was revised by Briggs (1955), there were 33 genera and 93 species; there are now 36 genera and about 120 species. A skin toxin was discovered in two species by the author (reported by Hori et al., 1979); it may be expected in other species of the family.

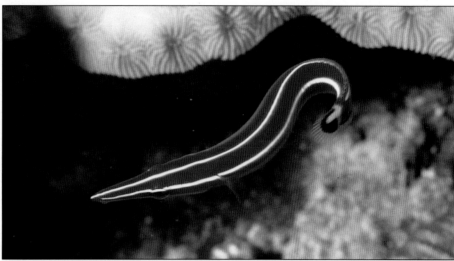

994. *Diademichthys lineatus*, about 5 cm (J. Randall)

995. *Discotrema lineatum*, about 2 cm (J. Randall)

URCHIN CLINGFISH
Diademichthys lineatus (Sauvage, 1883)

Dorsal rays 13-15; anal rays 12-14; pectoral rays 25-26; body elongate, the depth 9.7-12.9 in standard length; body broader than deep anteriorly and in abdominal region, becoming progressively more compressed posteriorly; head strongly tapering to the very long, slender, flat snout, the snout length 1.9-2.3 in head length; disc circular and small, 7.9-9.7 in standard length; dorsal and anal fins on posterior third of body; caudal fin small and rounded; dark red to almost black with two narrow pale yellow to white stripes, both originating on snout, one passing dorsally on body, the other along side; caudal fin with a large, dark, C-shaped mark containing and preceded by yellow. Attains 5 cm. Western Pacific to Mauritius; reported from Oman by Debelius (1993). Unusual for a clingfish in swimming freely above the bottom, though often sheltering among the spines of sea urchins or branches of coral.

LINED CLINGFISH
Discotrema lineatum (Briggs, 1966)

Dorsal rays 11; anal rays 8-9; caudal rays 12; pectoral rays 27; gill rakers on second gill arch 8; body slender, the depth about 5.8 in standard length; head length about 2.8 in standard length; head width about 4.1 in standard length; snout short, about 3.2 in head; disc length about 5.7 in standard length; upper jaw with a row of incisiform teeth, the tips of which are bent posteriorly; lower jaw with a row of small conical teeth; upper attachment of gill membrane anterior to pectoral fin opposite about twelfth pectoral ray; reddish brown with yellow lines as follows: one middorsal, two along side, and one ventral (connected on chin with line of other side); a longitudinal band of yellow dots often present in the two upper reddish brown zones between yellow lines; iris red. Attains about 45 cm. Described from the Gulf of Aqaba, Red Sea; ranges to the western Pacific; reported from Oman by Debelius (1993) as *Lepadichthys* sp. and from southeast Asia by Kuiter and Debelius (1994) as *Discotrema lineata*. Commensal with the crinoids *Capillaster multiradiata* and *Lamprometra klunzingeri* (see Fishelson, 1966).

DRAGONETS
FAMILY CALLIONYMIDAE

This large family of small benthic fishes is characterised by a strong spine, usually bearing barb-like spinules, on the corner of the preopercle, but none on the opercle or subopercle. The head is broad and depressed, often triangular when viewed from above; the body is elongate and moderately depressed; there are no scales. The mouth is small, the upper jaw very protrusible; jaws with villiform teeth; no teeth on roof of mouth. The gill opening is reduced to a small aperture on the upper posterior part of the head. There are two dorsal fins (except *Draculo* which has only the soft dorsal), the first usually with IV flexible spines, and the second with 6-11 soft rays; anal fin with 4-10 soft rays. The pelvic fins of I,5 rays are broadly separated, inserted anterior to the pectorals, the inner rays longer than the outer, the innermost broadly joined to pectoral-fin base by membrane. These fishes occur in all warm seas from the shallows to at least 400 m. They are usually found on sand or mud substrata,

996. *Callionymus marleyi*, female, about 6.5 cm (J. Randall)

but some occur in rocky or coral-reef areas. Those on sedimentary bottoms may be able to bury themselves quickly in the sand or mud. Dragonets feed mainly on small benthic invertebrates. Sexual dimorphism is usually evident, the males often with a higher first dorsal fin, and generally more colourful. Pair spawning has been observed; the eggs are pelagic. Fricke (1983) revised the Indo-Pacific species of the family; he recognised nine genera and 126 species. Worldwide, there are 11 genera and 155 species (R. Fricke, pers. comm.).

INDIAN DEEPWATER DRAGONET
Callionymus carebares Alcock, 1890

Dorsal rays IV + 9; anal rays 9; dorsal and anal rays not branched except last which is branched to base (true of all species of the genus); pectoral rays 19-23; lateral line from eye to end of fourth branched caudal ray or one of the two unbranched median rays; preopercular spine with a long, slightly upcurved tip, two (rarely one) spinules basally on dorsomedial margin, and a basal antrorse spine; body depth 6.5-8.5 in standard length; head large, 2.7-3.1 in standard length; first dorsal fin without filamentous spines, the first spine longest, about equal to or a little higher than first ray of second dorsal fin, 5.6-6.8 in standard length; caudal fin rounded to slightly pointed, 2.5-3.6 in standard length; colour in alcohol dark grey to dark brown, the abdomen pale; first dorsal fin of females with a large black spot on the third membrane; second dorsal fin distally dark, especially in males; anal fin distally black in both sexes; lower part of caudal fin often blackish. Reaches 18 cm. Gulf of Aden, Gulf of Oman, and Arabian Gulf to the coasts of India; found on sand or mud bottoms at depths of 135-330 m.

997. *Callionymus carebares*, male (upper), 15.7 cm, female (lower), 16.1 cm (after Fricke, 1983)

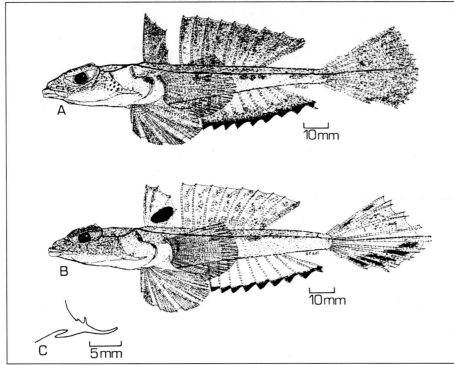

350

SMALLHEAD DRAGONET
Callionymus erythraeus Ninni, 1934

Dorsal rays IV + 9; anal rays 8; pectoral rays 17-21; lateral line from eye to end of third branched caudal ray, with a short transverse branch on occiput connecting the two sides, a connecting branch across top of caudal peduncle, a preopercular and often a suborbital branch; preopercular spine with lower edge strongly curved, the tip projecting slightly upward, the dorsomedial edge with three to five curved spinules; body depth 7.8-12.9 in standard length; head small, 4.0-5.0 in standard length; first dorsal fin of females low, without filaments, the second spine longest, 7.0-8.5 in standard length; second to fourth spines of first dorsal fin of males filamentous, the second longest, 1.6-2.1 in standard length; caudal fin rounded, 3.5-4.3 in standard length; tan with pale blue spots and brown dots; first dorsal fin of females largely white, of males translucent with pale blue spots; anal fin translucent whitish in females, the distal two-thirds black in males; caudal fin with an oblong black spot larger than pupil in outer lower part of fin. Reaches about 10 cm. Known from the Red Sea (type locality), Arabian Gulf, and southern India; collected from sand and mud bottoms with some rock in 1-10 m.

FILAMENTOUS DRAGONET
Callionymus filamentosus Valenciennes, 1837

Dorsal rays IV + 9 (female), I + III + 9 (male); anal rays 9; pectoral rays 18-20; lateral line from eye to end of third branched caudal ray, with two ventral branches on postorbital head, a connecting branch across occiput and another across caudal peduncle; preopercular spine with an antrorse spine on lower base and four to nine antrorse spinules on dorsomedial edge; body depth 7.4-10.8 in standard length; head length 4.0-4.9 in standard length; first dorsal spine of females about as long as second, 10.0-11.2 in standard length; first dorsal spine of males isolated and filamentous, 2.0-3.8 in standard length; caudal fin of females rounded, 3.1-3.9 in standard length; caudal fin of males with two prolonged median rays, the fin length 1.7-3.5 in standard length; light bluish grey, shading to white ventrally, with a midlateral row of small blackish blotches, the upper half of body and postorbital head with small brown to brownish yellow blotches, the cheek and suborbital region with small grey-edged yellow spots; first dorsal fin variously marked with black and white (variation shown by Fricke, 1983); caudal fin with blackish spots, the largest in median

998. *Callionymus erythraeus*, male, 10.6 cm (J. Randall)

999. *Callionymus erythraeus*, female, 7.2 cm (J. Randall)

1000. *Callionymus filamentosus*, male, 13.1 cm (J. Randall)

1001. *Callionymus hindsii*, male, 7 cm (J. Randall)

part of fin. Largest specimen, 16.5 cm. Red Sea and Arabian Gulf south to Natal, east to the Indo-Malayan region; found on mud or sand from the shore to 100 m.

HINDS' DRAGONET
Callionymus hindsii Richardson, 1844

Dorsal rays III + 9; anal rays 9; pectoral rays 16 -19; lateral line from eye to end of third branched caudal ray, with a preopercular branch, a transverse occipital branch and a transverse peduncular branch; preopercular spine with an upcurved tip, two to four curved spinules on dorsomedial edge,

and an antrorse spine at base; body depth 9.8-12.0 in standard length; head length 3.5-4.1 in standard length; first dorsal fin of females low, without filaments, the first spine 9.0-12.1 in standard length; first and second dorsal spines of males filamentous, the first 7.0-7.5 in standard length; caudal fin rounded, 3.5-4.3 in standard length; white with a row of thin dusky dashes on upper side; body above dashes and dorsal part of head with numerous, very small, yellowish brown blotches; first dorsal fin of females translucent, of the males white with diagonal black bands. Attains 9 cm. Arabian Gulf to Indo-Malayan region and China. Known from sand substrata at depths of a few to 40 m.

MARGARET'S DRAGONET
Callionymus margaretae Regan, 1906

Dorsal rays IV + 9; anal rays 8; pectoral rays 16-21; lateral line from eye to end of fourth branched caudal ray, with a branch across occiput and two across caudal peduncle; preopercular spine straight to slightly concave along base with a short straight tip, three to six short antrorse spinules on dorsomedial edge, and a strong antrorse lower spine; body depth 6.9-11.9 in standard length; head length 3.5-4.3 in standard length; first dorsal spine filamentous and elongate in both sexes, its length 2.1-2.9 in standard length; caudal fin long and pointed, its length 1.5-2.7 in standard length in females and 1.3-2.0 in males; a row of dark saddles on back and a row of elongate dark blotches just below lateral line; suborbital region of males with small dark spots; first dorsal fin of females with dark spots, in males these mostly joined to form diagonal bands; second dorsal fin with elongate dark spots; anal fin with a wide black outer margin, broader posteriorly; caudal fin with a broad black lower edge and vertical rows of black spots along central part of fin (fin may be plain dusky in females). Reaches 16 cm. Fricke (1983) recognised two subspecies, one from the southern Arabian Gulf and Gulf of Oman (type locality) to Pakistan, and the other from the western and southeastern coasts of India; depth range 22-107 m.

MARLEY'S DRAGONET
Callionymus marleyi Regan, 1919

Dorsal rays IV + 9; anal rays 8; pectoral rays 17-19; lateral line from eye to end of third or fourth caudal ray, with a suborbital branch, a divided preopercular branch, a branch across the occiput, and one across caudal peduncle; preopercular spine large, nearly straight ventrally with an upcurved tip, three to nine slightly curved spinules on dorsomedial edge, and a strong lower antrorse spine at base; body depth 8.8-10.8 in standard length; head length 3.6-5.0 in standard length; first dorsal fin about as high as first dorsal soft ray in males, the first spine longest, 4.8-5.7 in standard length (fourth spine usually nearly as long); first dorsal spine of females much longer than fourth, 7.5-9.1 in standard length; caudal fin rounded, 3.5-4.6 in standard length; brown dorsally, with numerous dark-edged pale blue spots and dark brown dots, shading to white ventrally; four or five faint dark saddles on back; first dorsal fin of females with a black spot covering last two membranes, the anterior membranes orange and white; first dorsal fin of males with dark lines; lower posterior edge of caudal fin of males black. Reaches 12.5 cm. Red Sea and Arabian Gulf to eastern India in the north and Mozambique, Madagascar, and Mauritius to Cape of Hope in the south. Fricke (1983) noted no records between 15°N and 13°S. Observed by the author in less than 2 m on silty sand bottom in the southern Arabian Gulf; known to depths of at least 20 m.

MUSCAT DRAGONET
Callionymus muscatensis Regan, 1906

Dorsal rays IV + 8; anal rays 8; pectoral rays 19-23; lateral line from eye to base or end of third branched caudal ray with a branch across occipital region; preopercular spine straight, including tip, with two to six small antrorse spinules on dorsomedial edge and one to three on ventral edge, with a large antrorse spine at base; a small preocular spine; occiput with a bifurate bony protuberance; a tentacle on upper edge of eye; body depth 5.8-7.1 in standard length; head length 3.5-4.0 in standard length; first dorsal fin of females without filaments, about as high as second dorsal, the first and second spines 3.8-4.2 in standard length; first dorsal fin of males with filamentous second and third spines, the second longest, 2.3-3.6 in standard length; caudal fin pointed, the fin length 1.3-2.4 in standard length of females and 1.1-1.4 in males; six to eight saddle-like blotches on back; side of head and body with irregular small brown blotches; first dorsal fin of males with irregular dark areas; first dorsal of females with a black margin and a black spot on outer part of third membrane; second dorsal of male with three oblique broad bands posteriorly; caudal fin with vertical rows of dark blotches. A small species, the largest specimen 7.5 cm. Southern Red Sea to Gulf of Oman, from the depth range of 40-70 m.

1002. *Callionymus margaretae*, female, 16.4 cm (J. Randall)

1003. *Callionymus marleyi*, female, 7.3 cm (J. Randall)

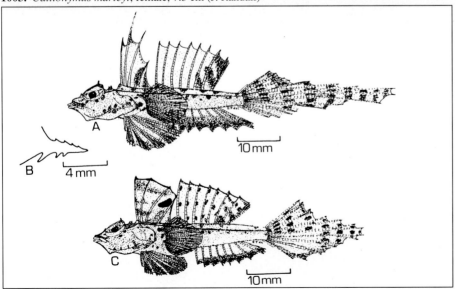

1004. *Callionymus muscatensis*, male (upper), 7.4 cm, female (lower), 6.3 cm (after Fricke, 1983)

PERSIAN DRAGONET
Callionymus persicus Regan, 1906

Dorsal rays IV + 9; anal rays 8; pectoral rays 18-21; lateral line from eye to end of third branched caudal ray, with occipital and peduncular transverse branches; preopercular spine nearly straight, including tip, with four to seven very small antrorse spinules on dorsoventral edge, and a lower antrorse spine at base; body depth 6.2-9.8 in standard length (males more elongate than females); head length 3.3-4.7 in standard length; first dorsal fin of females about equal in height to second dorsal, the first spine longest, 4.2-5.7 in standard length; first dorsal fin of males higher, the first to third spines in large males filamentous, their length as much as half standard length; caudal fin of females long and rounded, 2.3-2.9 in standard length, very long and pointed in males (may be longer than standard length); brown with small to very small, dark-edged bluish white spots, a row of four blackish blotches on back, the first at space between dorsal fins, and a lateral row of six blackish blotches; first dorsal fin of females dark yellowish brown with small white blotches; first dorsal fin of males white with oblique black lines and small black spots; caudal fin of both sexes with vertical rows of black blotches, the lower edge and that of anal fin broadly black. Largest specimen, the illustrated male, 25.8 cm. Arabian Gulf east to Mekran coast of Iran, west to Gulf of Aden and south to the Comoro Islands, Maldives, and Seychelles (Randall and van Egmond, 1994); depth range 15-55 m.

PYGMY DRAGONET
Diplogrammus pygmaeus Fricke, 1981

Dorsal rays IV + 8; anal rays 7; pectoral rays 16-20; lateral line extending to end of third branched caudal ray, with a branch across occiput; preopercular spine with an upcurved tip, three or four spinules on dorsomedial edge, and an antrorse spine ventrally on base; a longitudinal fold of skin along lower side of body; body depth 5.0-6.8 in standard length; head length 3.2-3.6 in standard length; second dorsal spine of adult males filamentous, 2.2-2.7 in standard length; first dorsal spine of females longest, 4.4-6.0 in standard length; caudal fin 3.35-4.7 in standard length; body of males pale lavendar-grey, finely mottled with white and pink, with a lateral row of five faint dusky blotches and a row of pink and grey saddle-like blotches along back; ventrolateral fold with white spots and blackish dots; head pale lavender-grey, becoming pink on occiput, and yellowish brown on opercle, with small white blotches; first dorsal spine banded with white and black; rest of fin translucent with small white blotches and orange-yellow dots; colour of female not recorded. Largest specimen, 3.7 cm. Known from six specimens: the holotype from 13.5 m off the southern Oman coast, the paratype from the Gulf of Oman, three from Jana Island, Arabian Gulf reported by Randall et al. (1994), and one from off Abu Dhabi; the Jana Island specimens were collected from rubble at base of a drop off in 16.8 m.

STELLATE DRAGONET
Synchiropus stellatus Smith, 1963

Dorsal rays IV + 8; anal rays 7; pectoral rays 19-24; lateral line from eye to middle or end of fourth branched caudal ray, with a branch across occiput; preopercular spine with a slightly upcurved tip and a single spinule on dorsomedial edge; body depth 4.4-5.8 in standard length; head length 3.0-4.4 in standard length; eyes elevated above dorsal profile of head; snout equal to or shorter than eye diameter; first dorsal fin of females equal in height or a little shorter than second dorsal, the first spine longest, 6.5-6.8 in standard length; first dorsal fin of males very high, the spines with or without short filaments, their length up to 1.8 in standard length; second dorsal and anal rays branched; caudal fin rounded, 3.0-3.5 in standard length; females light red to pale pink dorsally, with numerous, very small, white and dark red spots and large, stellate, dark red to dark reddish brown blotches; ventral part of body white with a row of dark red to dark reddish brown spots about size of pupil; dorsal fin dark brown to black with two white blotches on first membrane, abruptly white at distal edge; remaining median fins with large dark red blotches; males with dark blotches on body interconnected, the lower half of head with small blue spots; dorsal fin with blue lines and one or more ocellated black spots in outer part of fin. Attains 7.5 cm. East African coast south to Natal; also known from the Comoro Islands, Maldives, Seychelles, St. Brandon's Shoals, and Sri Lanka; Oman record based on an underwater photograph taken off southern Oman by John P. Hoover.

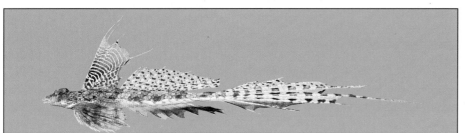

1005. *Callionymus persicus*, male, 25.8 cm (J. Randall)

1006. *Callionymus persicus*, female, 9.1 cm (J. Randall)

1007. *Diplogrammus pygmaeus*, male, 2.9 cm (J. Randall)

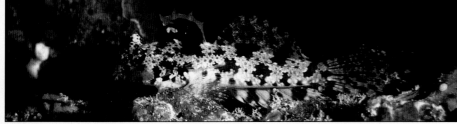

1008. *Synchirops stellatus*, about 4 cm (J. Randall)

SPINY TURBOTS
FAMILY PSETTODIDAE

This family is the most primitive of the flatfishes (order Pleuronectiformes). The fishes of this order are readily identified by having their eyes on one side of the head. In the larval stage there is an eye on each side, but before settlement to the bottom from the pelagic realm, one eye slowly migrates over the top of the head to the other side. Evidence of the primitive nature of this family is the presence of spines in the anterior part of the dorsal fin, the origin of this fin well behind the eyes, and the pelvic fins with a spine. Also they sometimes swim in an upright position. Other characteristics are a large mouth with large canine teeth in the jaws, some of which have barbed tips; minute teeth on vomer, palatines, and tongue; margin of the preopercle not covered by skin; cycloid scales; and lateral line developed on both sides of the body. There is a single genus with three species, two of which are restricted to tropical West Africa.

INDIAN SPINY TURBOT
Psettodes erumei (Bloch and Schneider, 1801)

Dorsal rays IX-XI,38-45; anal rays I,33-42; pectoral rays 14-16; pelvic rays I,5; lateral-line scales 68-75; no gill rakers (gill arches with teeth); maxilla extending well beyond lower eye; supramaxilla present; jaws with large canines in two to three rows, some with barbed tips; both eyes on left or right side; body depth 2.3-2.5 in standard length; head length 3.2-3.6 in standard

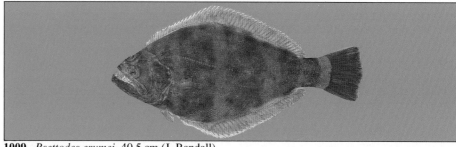

1009. *Psettodes erumei*, 40.5 cm (J. Randall)

length; caudal fin slightly rhomboid; grey-brown, often with five broad dark bars, the first from nape, across operculum to chest. Reaches 60 cm. Continental shelf waters from the Red Sea and Arabian Gulf south to southern Mozambique and Madagascar, east to the western Pacific where reported from southern Japan to Queensland. Known from the depth range of a few to about 100 m.

LARGESCALE FLATFISHES
FAMILY CITHARIDAE

This family of flatfishes was established by Hubbs (1945) for four genera previously classified in the Pleuronectidae and Bothidae. The pelvic fins of these fishes have a spine (although flexible) and five soft rays like the Psettodidae but unlike all the remaining flatfishes. Also their gill membranes are more widely separated than those of any other flatfishes except *Psettodes*. One character which separates them from all other flatfishes is the location of the anus on the eyed side of the midventral edge, rather than on the blind side. Other characters: a small supramaxilla may be present; palatines and tongue toothless, but teeth may be present on the vomer; scales large, ctenoid on eyed side; eyes on right or left side (but not either side in the same species); dorsal fin origin anterior to eyes; pectoral fins well developed; pelvic fins equally developed and short-based. Only five species are known in the family.

WIDEMOUTH LARGESCALE FLATFISH
Brachypleura novaezeelandiae Günther, 1862

Dorsal rays 65-74; anal rays 41-49; caudal rays 17-19 (13 branched); pectoral rays (ocular side) 10-12; lateral-line scales 29-32; scales deciduous, ctenoid on ocular side, cycloid or weakly ctenoid on blind side; no scales on anterior third of head; gill rakers long, 8-10 on lower limb; mouth large, the lower jaw projecting, the maxilla extending beyond middle of lower eye; cleft of mouth curved; teeth in two rows in jaws, those of outer row at front of upper jaw enlarged; a patch of small conical teeth on vomer; body depth 2.4-2.7 in standard length; head length 3.2-3.6 in standard length; eyes on right side; preopercular margin free; anterior dorsal rays of males prolonged; yellowish to greyish brown with faint irregular dark markings on body; small dark spots in dorsal and anal fins. Largest specimen, 12.2 cm. Arabian Gulf (Kuronuma and Abe, 1986) to India, Indo-Malayan region, and northwestern Australia; known from the depth range of 22-92 m. As noted by Norman (1934), the type locality of New Zealand appears to be an error.

1010. *Brachypleura novaezeelandiae* (after Norman, 1934)

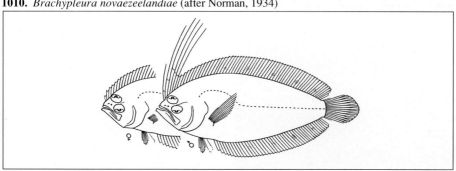

LEFTEYE FLOUNDERS
FAMILY BOTHIDAE

The species of this largest family of flatfishes, with few exceptions, have the eyes on the left side (sinistral). There are no spines in the fins; the dorsal fin originates above or before the upper eye; the dorsal and anal fins are not joined to the caudal fin; the pectoral and pelvic fin rays are not branched; pelvic fins with six or fewer rays, the fin of the blind side short-based, the fin of the ocular (eyed) side along the ventral edge with a long base, extending well anterior to fin of blind side; no supramaxilla; preopercle with a free margin; a single lateral line on ocular side, highly arched over pectoral fin (the one on blind side may be faint or absent); caudal fin often rhomboid; anus on the blind side. Males may have a spine or spines on the snout; also the eyes may be farther apart in males. Most species occur on open sand or mud substrata, but a few may be found in rocky or coral-reef areas. These fishes are masters of camouflage, closely matching the colour of the bottom; also they are able to quickly bury in the sediment. All are carnivorous, usually ambushing their prey of small fishes and crustaceans. The family is represented by 20 genera and at least 115 species.

1011. Male of *Bothus pantherinus* in courtship, about 17 cm (J. Randall)

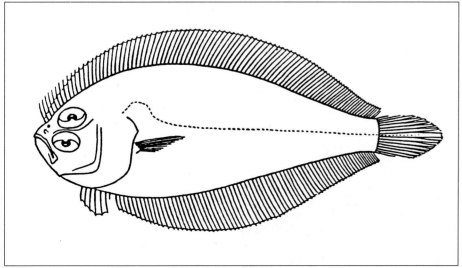

1012. *Arnoglossus arabicus*, 8.7 cm (after Norman, 1939)

ARABIAN FLOUNDER
Arnoglossus arabicus Norman, 1939

Dorsal rays 96-102; anal rays 75-78; pectoral rays of ocular side 12-13; scales in longitudinal series about 60; lower-limb gill rakers 11-12; maxilla ending anterior to middle of lower eye; no distinct canine teeth; body depth 2.5-2.75 in standard length; head length about 3.5 in standard length; snout shorter than eye; eyes close together, separated by a narrow bony ridge, the lower a little in advance of upper; origin of dorsal fin well anterior to upper eye, above posterior nostril of blind side; yellowish brown, without definite markings. Largest specimen, 10.5 cm. Gulf of Aden to southern Oman; recorded depth range, 83-220 m.

355

BROWN FLOUNDER
Arnoglossus aspilos (Bleeker, 1851)

Dorsal rays 80-84; anal rays 59-64; pectoral rays of ocular side 11-12; lateral-line scales 46-48; scales ctenoid on ocular side, cycloid on blind side; rays of median and pelvic fins with small scales; lower-limb gill rakers 7; body depth 2.1-2.4 in standard length; head length 3.7-4.1 in standard length; a notch in dorsal profile of head before eyes; eyes separated by a space less than half eye diameter, the lower eye a little in advance of upper; maxilla extending slightly posterior to a vertical at front edge of lower eye; teeth small, uniserial in jaws, not enlarged anteriorly; origin of dorsal fin at level of lower edge of upper eye; finely mottled brown with small blackish spots on rays of median fins, the largest one on each outer branched rays of caudal fin. Attains 8.5 cm. Indonesia, Singapore, and Arabian Gulf, the latter record from Blegvad (1944) and Kuronuma and Abe (1986) (no Gulf specimens examined by author). Bleeker (1875) gave the dorsal-ray counts as 80-84, and the anal-ray counts as 61-63; the illustrated specimen herein from Indonesia has 80 dorsal rays and 59 anal rays. Kuronuma and Abe recorded counts of 84-95 dorsal rays and 63-76 anal rays. The identification

1013. *Arnoglossus aspilos*, 7.9 cm (J. Randall)

of the Gulf specimens, therefore, may be regarded as provisional.

DRAB FLOUNDER
Arnoglossus tapeinosoma (Bleeker, 1866)

Dorsal rays 89-98; anal rays 67-72; pectoral rays (ocular side) 11-12; lateral-line scales 48-55; scales weakly ctenoid on ocular side, cycloid on blind side; lower-limb gill rakers 8-12; body depth 2.5-3.0 in standard length; head length 3.0-4.0 in standard length; snout shorter than eyes; eyes close together, separated by a sharp bony ridge, the lower eye slightly in advance of upper;

maxilla extending to below anterior third of lower eye; teeth small and close-set, none enlarged anteriorly; anterior dorsal rays of adult males greatly prolonged and filamentous; brown with indistinct dark blotches along dorsal and ventral edges of body, a large dark blotch at junction of curved and straight parts of lateral line and generally one or two blotches on straight part of line; a dark spot on outer part pectoral fin; distal edge of pelvic fins blackish. Reported to 12.7 cm. Arabian Gulf and Gulf of Oman (Norman, 1939) to Indonesia; depth range 46-100 m.

PANTHER FLOUNDER
Bothus pantherinus (Rüppell, 1830)

Dorsal rays 85-95; anal rays 66-72; pectoral rays of ocular side 9-11; lateral line scales 80-92; scales ctenoid on ocular side, cycloid on blind side; gill rakers short, 6-9 on lower limb; body depth 1.7-2.0 in standard length; head length 3.3-3.9 in standard length; interorbital width of male about equal to eye diameter, less in female; anterior edge of upper eye above or a little behind middle of lower eye; maxilla reaching to below anterior half of lower eye; mature males with one or more bony tubercles or short spines on snout and on edge of eye, and one or more short tentacles on eyes; origin of dorsal fin at level of upper edge of lower eye; pectoral fin of ocular side of males greater than about 15 cm very long with filamentous rays that may reach beyond base of caudal fin; light grey-brown, finely mottled with brown, with roseate dark-edged pale spots (may be partly pale blue), dark brown or brownish yellow spots nearly as large as eye, and numerous small yellow to brownish yellow spots (usually one in centre of each pale roseate spot); a large dusky blotch on straight part of lateral line; eyes finely spotted. Reported to 30 cm. Indo-Pacific; occurs from the shallows to depths of at least 60 m, generally on sand or silty sand, sometimes near reefs.

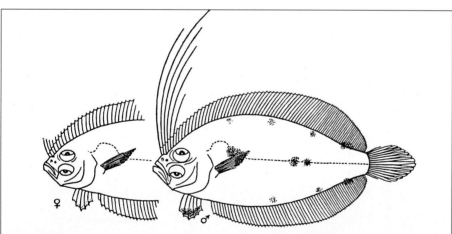

1014. *Arnoglossus tapeinosoma*, 7.2 cm (male) (after Norman, 1934)

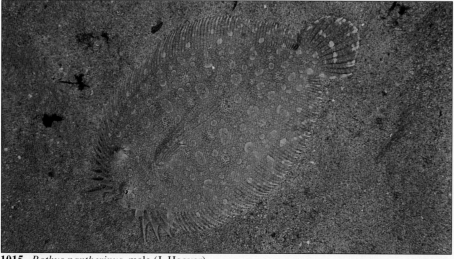

1015. *Bothus pantherinus*, male (J. Hoover)

BIGSCALE FLOUNDER
Engyprosopon grandisquama (Temminck and Schlegel, 1846)

Dorsal rays 79-89; anal rays 59-68; pectoral rays of ocular side 10-12; lateral-line scales 36-46; scales weakly ctenoid on ocular side, cycloid on blind side; gill rakers short, 5-7 on lower limb; body depth 1.6-2.1 in standard length; head length 3.6-4.2 in standard length; snout shorter than eye; interorbital space broad, 0.7-0.9 eye diameters in width in females and 0.7-1.7 in males; anterior edge of upper eye above about middle of lower eye; maxilla reaching to below anterior edge of lower eye, the upper-jaw length 3.0-3.5 in head length; lower-jaw teeth uniserial, upper-jaw teeth biserial and somewhat enlarged anteriorly; a spine on front of snout and on upper edge of eyes of males, small or absent on females; origin of dorsal fin slightly above level of upper edge of lower eye; light brown, finely mottled and spotted with dark brown, orange-yellow, and whitish; a prominent blackish spot centred on uppermost and lowermost branched caudal rays. Reaches 15 cm. Reported from Japan (type locality) south to New South Wales and west to the Nicobar Islands, Burma, Sri Lanka, Maldives, Natal, and the Gulf of Oman (Norman, 1934); depth range 7-100 m.

1016. *Engyprosopon grandisquama*, 8.6 cm (J. Randall)

1017. *Grammatobothus polyophthalmus* (after Bleeker, 1875)

TRIANGLE FLOUNDER
Grammatobothus polyophthalmus (Bleeker, 1866)

Dorsal rays 80-86; anal rays 64-67; pectoral rays of ocular side 13-15; lateral-line scales 77-82; scales ctenoid on ocular side, cycloid on blind side; lateral line equally developed on both sides; gill rakers short, 8-9 on lower limb; body depth 1.6-1.7 in standard length; head length 3.5-4.0 in standard length; dorsal profile of head notched in front of eyes; snout shorter than eyes; anterior edge of upper eye over middle or anterior to middle of lower eye; two or three blunt spines usually present in front of lower eye; maxilla extending to below anterior edge of lower eye; origin of dorsal fin at level of lower edge of upper eye, the second to fifth or sixth rays moderately prolonged; grey-brown with numerous dark brown blotches (may contain a yellow spot or spots), scattered small pale bluish spots, and three large ocellated black spots containing yellow dots, some in a ring which form a triangle in middle of body, one above and one below pectoral fin, and one on middle of straight part of lateral line. Attains 17 cm. Recorded from Indonesia, Queensland, northwestern Australia, Burma, South China Sea (Kyushin et al., 1982), and the Arabian Gulf (Kuronuma and Abe, 1986); known from the depth range of 35-55 m.

GÜNTHER'S FLOUNDER
Laeops guentheri Alcock, 1898

Dorsal rays 97-102; anal rays 77-81; pectoral rays of ocular side 14; lateral-line scales about 95; scales cycloid; lateral line developed only on ocular side; lower-limb gill rakers 6-8; body depth 2.5-3.0 in standard length; head length 4.3-5.0 in standard length; dorsal profile of head above and posterior to eyes slightly convex; upper eye projecting slightly above dorsal profile; lower eye in advance of upper; maxilla just reaching to below anterior edge of lower eye; small teeth in a narrow band on blind side of jaws; origin of dorsal fin above posterior nostril of blind side, the first two rays detached from rest of fin but not prolonged; dark grey-brown; dorsal and anal fins darker distally; caudal fin dusky. Reaches about 13 cm. Burma to Arabian Gulf; one recorded depth range, 28-46 m.

1018. *Laeops guentheri*, 10.2 cm (after Norman, 1934)

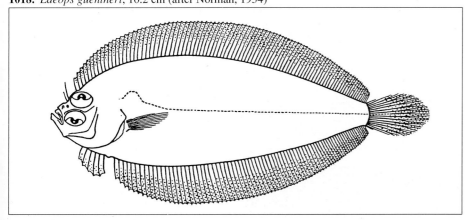

357

SHORTFIN FLOUNDERS
FAMILY PARALICHTHYIDAE

This family was regarded as a subfamily of the Bothidae by Norman (1934) and others. Hensley and Ahlstrom in Moser et al. (1984) elevated it to family rank. The principal difference from the Bothidae is in the structure of the pelvic fins; the paralichthyids have both of the fins short-based and nearly symmetrical. Also they have branched pectoral rays. Some species have a straight lateral line, while most have it highly arched over the pectoral fin. The other family characters given above for the Bothidae apply to this family. All the species of this family known from Oman waters belong to the large genus *Pseudorhombus*. The species from the Arabian Gulf identified as *P. javanicus* (Bleeker) by Blegvad (1944: 201, pl.12, fig. l) with a question mark, otherwise not known west of the east coast of India, may be *P. elevatus*.

RINGED FLOUNDER
Pseudorhombus annulatus Norman, 1928

Dorsal rays 67-70; anal rays 49-51; pectoral rays of ocular side 12 (8 branched); scales ctenoid on both sides of body; lateral line highly arched over pectoral fin with a branch on head passing to below lower eye, and a supratemporal branch to base of seventh to thirteenth dorsal rays (true of all species of the genus); gill rakers long and slender, 23-25 on lower limb; body depth 1.6-1.7 in standard length; head length 3.5-3.7 in standard length; snout shorter than eye diameter; eyes close together, separated by a bony ridge (also generic), the upper slightly in advance of lower; maxilla extending to or nearly to a vertical at centre of eye; teeth very small; origin of dorsal fin at level of middle of upper eye, the first two or three rays free of membrane, the succeeding rays with progressivly more membrane until the eleventh where fully membranous; anterior dorsal rays slightly prolonged, the first about half head length; caudal fin rhomboid (generic); light brown with numerous dark rings of about pupil size or larger; median fins with brown spots and blotches. Known from only five specimens collected off Muscat in 23-55 m, the largest 10.5 cm.

LARGETOOTH FLOUNDER
Pseudorhombus arsius (Hamilton, 1822)

Dorsal rays 72-80; anal rays 54-62; pectoral rays of ocular side 11-13; lateral-line scales 69-80; scales ctenoid on ocular side, cycloid on blind side; lower-limb gill rakers 8-15; body depth 1.75-2.25 in standard length; head length 3.3-3.75 in standard length; snout of adults longer than eye diameter; upper eye directly above or slightly in advance of lower; maxilla extending to below posterior half of lower eye, the upper jaw 2.3-2.7 in head length; upper jaw with two to four pairs of large canines at front, jaws with stout canines anteriorly, the teeth moderately large on side of lower jaw, especially on ocular side; no teeth with barbed tips; origin of dorsal fin in front of middle of upper eye; finely mottled brown, sometimes with small brownish yellow spots and small pale blue blotches; a large blackish blotch at junction of curved and straight part of lateral line and one in middle of straight part, the blotches often with small orange-yellow spots; other less distinct large blackish blotches or rings often present. Largest collected by author, 37.3 cm. Red Sea and Arabian Gulf to South Africa, east to the western Pacific where it ranges from Japan to New South Wales. A common species from shallow estuaries to 100 m.

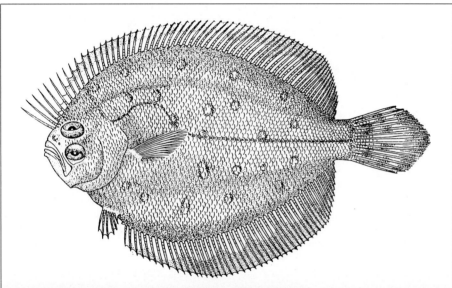

1019. *Pseudorhombus annulatus*, 10.2 cm (after Norman, 1928)

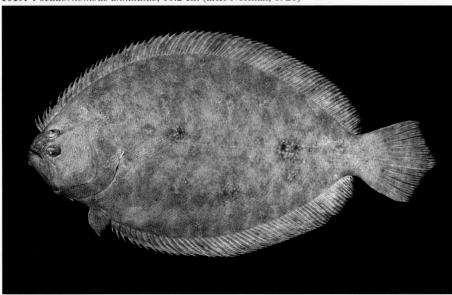

1020. *Pseudorhombus arsius*, 37.3 cm (J. Randall)

DEEP FLOUNDER
Pseudorhombus elevatus Ogilby, 1912

Dorsal rays 67-74; anal rays 52-58; pectoral rays of ocular side 11-19; lateral-line scales 65-74; scales ctenoid on ocular side, cycloid on blind side; gill rakers long and slender, 10-19 on lower-limb (see below); body relatively deep, the depth 1.8-2.0 in standard length; head length 3.2-3.45 in standard length; snout about equal to eye diameter; upper eye over or slightly posterior to lower; maxilla reaching to below about middle of lower eye; teeth small, only slightly larger anteriorly; origin of dorsal fin anterior to middle of upper eye; light brown with about five rows of inconspicuous dark rings the size of eye or smaller, smaller brown rings, blotches, and dots, a blackish blotch, with or without a ring of small white spots, at junction of curved and straight parts of lateral line, and one or two smaller ones on straight part; median fins with indistinct brown rings and small brown spots. Attains 18 cm. Arabian Gulf to South Africa and east along the continental shelf to Indonesia and northern Australia (Sainsbury et al., 1985); 7-200 m on clay, sand, or mud. Hensley in Smith and Heemstra (1986) noted that specimens from the Arabian Gulf and South Africa have longer and more numerous gill rakers (lower rakers 15-19) than elsewhere (10-15).

MALAY FLOUNDER
Pseudorhombus malayanus Bleeker, 1866

Dorsal rays 71-77; anal rays 55-61; pectoral rays of ocular side 12-13; lateral-line scales 70-78; scales ctenoid on both sides of body; gill rakers short, 8-10 on lower limb; body depth 1.75-2.0 in standard length; head length 3.2-3.5 in standard length; dorsal profile of head notched in front of upper eye; snout as long or a little longer than eye diameter; upper eye above or a little in advance of lower; maxilla extending to below posterior part of lower eye; teeth in jaws enlarged anteriorly, some with barbed tips; teeth of lower jaw stronger and more widely spaced than those of upper jaw; origin of dorsal fin anterior to middle of upper eye; olive to grey-brown with a blackish blotch at front of straight part of lateral line; scattered smaller dark blotches and small pale spots often present on head, body, and fins. Reaches 27 cm. Gulf of Oman (three small specimens reported by Blegvad, 1944); otherwise known from the east coast of India to the South China Sea (Kyushin et al., 1982); a species of shallow mud or sand substrata.

TRIOCELLATE FLOUNDER
Pseudorhombus triocellatus (Bloch and Schneider, 1801)

Dorsal rays 65-70; anal rays 49-52; pectoral rays of ocular side 12-13; lateral-line scales 63-69; scales ctenoid on ocular side, cycloid on blind side; gill rakers moderately long and slender, about 23 on lower limb; body subrhomboid and deep, the depth 1.5-1.75 in standard length; head length 3.3-3.55 in standard length; upper eye above or a little posterior to lower; maxilla not reaching posterior to middle of eye; teeth very small, slightly enlarged anteriorly; origin of dorsal fin anterior to upper part of eye, the anterior rays prolonged and free of membrane, the first ray more than half length of head; three black spots ringed in cream and often with an outer blackish ring (sometimes with a pale spot in centre), the spots forming a triangle on body, one above and one below lateral line posterior to pectoral-fin tip and one on lateral line about half way from pectoral tip to caudal-fin base. Reaches at least 17 cm. Indonesia to east coast of India (type locality); Blegvad (1944) recorded one specimen from the Gulf of Oman. The illustrated specimen was trawled from muddy sand in 17 m.

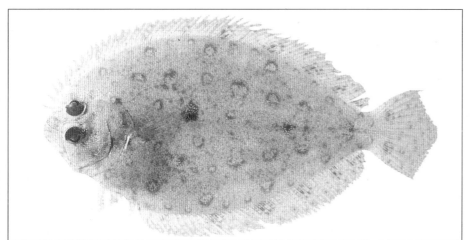

1021. *Pseudorhombus elevatus*, 16 cm (after Sainsbury et al., 1985)

1022. *Pseudorhombus malayanus* (after Bleeker, 1875)

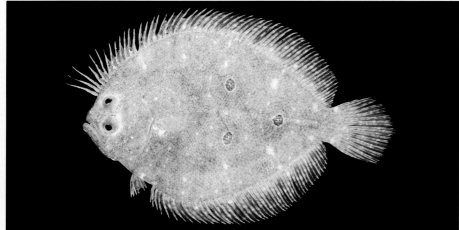

1023. *Pseudorhombus triocellatus*, 10.7 cm (J. Randall)

SOLES
FAMILY SOLEIDAE

This flatfish family is easily characterised by having the eyes on the right side (dextral), the edge of the preopercle covered by skin, the mouth slightly to strongly curved and usually inferior, no ribs, no fin spines, the dorsal-fin origin over or anterior to the eyes, and the pelvic fins free from the anal fin. The pectoral fins are sometimes absent (when present, the right is longer than the left); the dorsal and anal fins may be confluent with caudal fin. There is a single lateral line, straight on the body, but sometimes branched on head. Soles often bury in the sediment. The author has observed several species which were hidden by day to actively forage at night. The species of the genus *Pardachirus* and at least some of the genus *Aseraggodes* secrete a powerful toxin when under stress which is a deterent to predators (Clark and George, 1979; Randall and Melén-

dez, 1987). The family contains at least 20 genera and about 90 species, none in American waters. A second family of soles, the Achiridae, is restricted to the New World. An undescribed sole of the genus *Parachirus* represented by a single specimen, 81 mm in standard length, from Sur, Oman in the collection of the Royal Ontario Museum and specimens from South Africa misidentifed as *P. xenicus* Matsubara and Ochiai have been sent to Kazuo Sakamoto who is monographing the genus. The Oman specimen has 73 dorsal rays, 53 anal rays, and 85 lateral-line scales. Norman (1928) reviewed the Indian species of Soleidae. Menon in Fischer and Bianchi (1984) reported *Synaptura commersoniana* (Lacepède) from the Red Sea to the Arabian Gulf, but the author is unable to find any basis for this distribution.

ORIENTAL SOLE
Euryglossa orientalis (Bloch and Schneider, 1801)

Dorsal rays 61-65; anal rays 44-48; pectoral rays of ocular side 7-8; lateral-line scales 75-85; scales ctenoid on both sides, those on the blind side of the head modified into sensory filaments; body depth 1.8-2.2 in standard length; head length 4.2-5.3 in standard length; eyes separated by a scaly interorbital space; eyes small, 6.0-6.8 in head length, the upper slightly in advance of lower; mouth terminal and slightly curved; very small teeth in jaws on blind side; dorsal and anal fins scaled, confluent with caudal fin, the dorsal and anal rays extending posteriorly more than half length of caudal fin; origin of dorsal fin above front of upper eye; mottled olivaceous to grey-brown, the edges of scales dark, with scattered large dark blotches; vertical blackish lines extending above lateral line. Largest collected by author, 32.5 cm. Red Sea and Arabian Gulf south to Mozambique, Seychelles, Madagascar, and Mauritius, east to the Western Pacific where recorded from the Ryukyu Islands to New South Wales; a shallow-water species of mud or silty sand bottoms.

PIEBALD SOLE
Pardachirus balius Randall and Mee, 1994

Dorsal rays 73-82; anal rays 55-61; all rays of median fins branched except first dorsal, first anal, and upper and lower caudal rays; no pectoral fins; pelvic rays 5; lateral-line scales 85-101 (93-105 on blind side); scales ctenoid (except blind side of head); a basal band of small scales on dorsal and anal fins, but scales not extending farther out on rays; body depth 2.65-2.85 in standard length; head length 4.7-4.95 in standard length; upper eye anterior to lower; mouth strongly curved; a band of villiform teeth on blind side of jaws; origin of dorsal fin anterior to interorbital space; a large pore basally in unscaled part of dorsal and anal fins near most rays (pores lead medially to glands secreting a milky skin toxin); brown with large, well-spaced, round to elliptical, dark brown spots (the edges darker brown), and groups of small brown spots. Largest specimen, 22 cm. Southern Oman to Gulf of Oman; on sand in the depth range of 6-30 m. Closely related to *P. morrowi* (Chabanaud) from Kenya to Natal.

1024. *Euryglossus orientalis*, 32.5 cm (J. Randall)

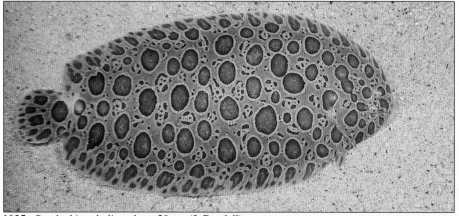

1025. *Pardachirus balius*, about 20 cm (J. Randall)

MOSES SOLE
Pardachirus marmoratus (Lacepède, 1802)

Dorsal rays 63-72; anal rays 48-55; no pectoral fins; pelvic rays 5; lateral-line scales 83-102; scales cycloid; body depth 2.2-2.5 in standard length; head length 4.2-4.65 in standard length; eyes small, the upper anterior to lower; a fringe of cirri from front of head to pelvic fins; origin of dorsal fin anterior to interorbital space; no caudal peduncle, but dorsal and anal fins not joined to caudal fin; caudal fin rounded; light brown to pale grey with scattered irregular dark brown rings and numerous, very small, dark brown dots on head, body, and fins; two dark brown spots containing yellow flecks and irregular lines often present on lateral line (a few other lesser dark brown spots may have yellow markings). Reaches 26 cm. Red Sea and Arabian Gulf south to Natal, Madagascar, and Mauritius, east to Sri Lanka; a shallow-water species usually buried in sand during the day except for eyes and tubular nostril. Well known for its powerful skin toxin.

ELONGATE SOLE
Solea elongata Day, 1877

Dorsal rays 72-77; anal rays 59-63; dorsal and anal rays branched except for last one or two; pectoral rays of ocular side 8-9; pelvic rays 4; lateral-line scales about 110; scales weakly ctenoid on both sides; body depth 2.6-3.0 in standard length; head length 4.0-4.75 in standard length; upper eye anterior to lower; mouth inferior and strongly curved, the maxilla extending to below middle of lower eye; fleshy cirri anteriorly on blind side of head well developed, extending well posterior to mouth dorsally and ventrally (see Norman, 1928: fig. 1); origin of dorsal fin anterior to upper eye; caudal fin rounded, not joined to dorsal and anal fins; light brown mottled with blackish to form a coarse reticulum; outer half of pectoral fin jet black; dorsal and anal fins pale with some dusky spots basally and dusky streaks paralleling rays; caudal fin with small dusky spots. Largest specimen, 11.5 cm. East coast of India to Arabian Gulf where taken in trawls in 8-28 m.

STANALAND'S SOLE
Solea stanalandi Randall and McCarthy, 1989

Dorsal rays 57-59; anal rays 46; dorsal and anal rays branched; pectoral rays 7-8, the middle four branched; pelvic rays 4-5; lateral-line scales 104-106; scales ctenoid

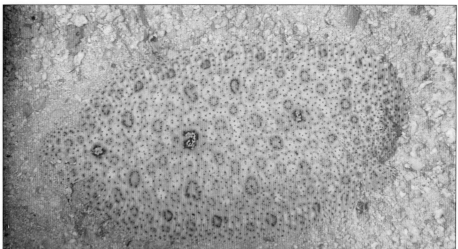

1026. *Pardachirus marmoratus*, about 26 cm (J. Randall)

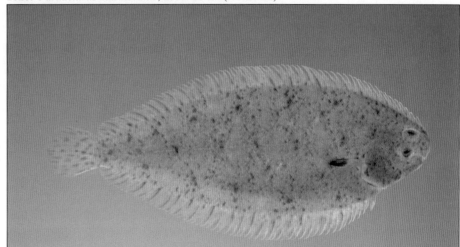

1027. *Solea elongata*, 9.8 cm (J. Randall)

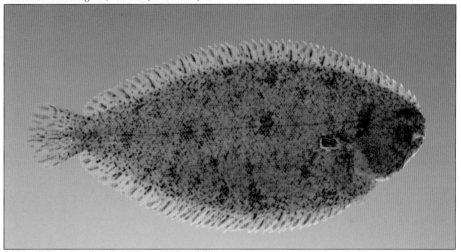

1028. *Solea stanalandi*, 12.3 cm (J. Randall)

on both sides except anterior part of head on blind side where fleshy cirri are well developed (similar to those of *S. elongata*); body depth 2.45-2.5 in standard length; head length 4.15-4.2 in standard length; upper eye anterior to lower; mouth anterior to lower eye, the cleft strongly curved, the maxilla ending below front of pupil of lower eye; origin of dorsal fin on a vertical between anterior nostril and front of mouth; caudal fin rounded; light brown, the scale edges blackish to a varying degree, the pigment concentrated to form large blackish blotches, especially on lateral line and along upper and lower edges of body; a white-edged black spot covering outer half of pectoral fin; median fins with blackish spots and streaks paralleling rays. Known from only two specimens taken on silty sand and sparse seagrass in 1-4 m in Half Moon Bay on the Saudi Arabian Gulf coast; largest specimen 12.3 cm.

CONVICT ZEBRA SOLE
Zebrias captivus Randall, 1995

Dorsal rays 62-65; anal rays 52-54; caudal rays 18; pectoral rays 7; pelvic rays 4; lateral-line scales 74-78; scales moderately ctenoid on both sides; anterior part of head on blind side to just behind mouth with small fleshy papillae; body depth 2.85 in standard length; head length 4.8-5.1 in standard length; eyes nearly contiguous, the diameter 3.2-4.0 in head length; upper eye anterior to lower; a small tentacle on upper part of both eyes; mouth slightly inferior and curved, the maxilla ending beneath anterior third of lower eye; dorsal and anal fins joined to caudal fin, the last dorsal and anal rays as long or nearly as long as adjacent caudal rays; pectoral fin of eye side 2.6-2.7 in head length; eye side light tan with nine dark-edged brown bars on body about equal in width to pale interspaces except the first (passes beneath pectoral fin) which is narrower, and the last which is 1.5 times broader than previous bar; three similar but narrower dark bars on head, the first two as double bars; dorsal and anal fins white, the dark brown edges of brown bars extending as double black bands into the fins; caudal fin black, the ray tips white, with a narrow irregular white bar near base and small pale yellow spots in outer part of fin near upper and lower edges; pectoral fin tipped with black. Known from only two specimen taken by trawling off Bahrain, the largest 9.7 cm.

INDIAN ZEBRA SOLE
Zebrias synapturoides (Jenkins, 1910)

Dorsal rays 69-76; anal rays 59-63; caudal rays 18, the middle 14-16 branched; dorsal and anal rays branched except for anteriormost anal ray and several anterior dorsal rays; pectoral rays 11; pelvic rays 4-5; lateral-line scales 66-71; scales strongly ctenoid on both sides of body; numerous fleshy cirri anteriorly on head on blind side to either side of jaws; body depth 2.7-2.9 in standard length; head length 4.2-5.1 in standard length; eyes close together, the upper in advance of lower; no tentacle on eyes; mouth slightly inferior and curved, the maxilla reaching at most to below middle of lower eye; dorsal and anal fins joined to caudal fin for about half its length; pectoral fins small, largely covered by opercular membrane; whitish with nine black-edged, dark brown bars on body wider than pale interspaces (posterior bars broader than anterior), extending into dorsal and anal fins; head and nape with three dark brown bars, the first covering snout and chin, the second behind eyes, and the third divided into two

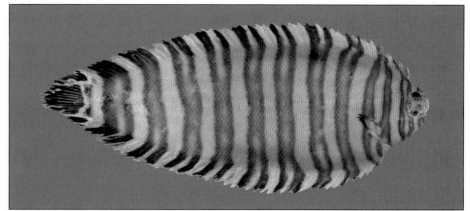

1029. *Zebrias captivus*, 9.1 cm (J. Randall)

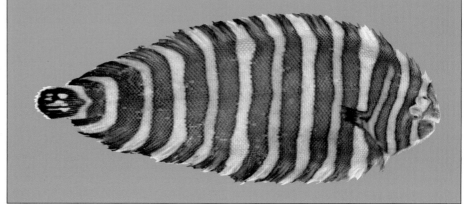

1030. *Zebrias synapturoides*, 9.7 cm (J. Randall)

bars over most of its length, half on opercle and half just behind eye (second bar on head may also be partially divided, as may several anterior bars on body); caudal fin black with yellow central spots and a white margin. Reaches at least 13 cm. Arabian Gulf to east coast of India; taken in trawls from 43-125 m. The specimen from the Arabian Gulf 62 mm in standard length tentatively identified by Kuronuma and Abe (1986) as *Z. quagga* is *Z. synapturoides* with an aberrant caudal region (appears to have regenerated after having the end of the tail removed).

TONGUESOLES
FAMILY CYNOGLOSSIDAE

This family of flatfishes is distinct in having the eyes on the left side (sinistral), the margin of the preopercle covered by skin, an elongate body, the dorsal and anal fins confluent with the caudal fin, the dorsal fin originating over or anterior to the eyes, and no pectoral fins. The pelvic fin of the blind side, of 4 rays, is on the midventral edge of the body, sometimes linked to the anal fin; the pelvic fin of the ocular side is often absent; the anus is on the blind side. The eyes are small and close together. The mouth is asymmetrical, the teeth minute and present only on the blind side. The scales are usually ctenoid on the ocular side. There are two subfamilies: the Symphurinae with a terminal, nearly straight mouth, no lateral line, and the pelvic fin free from the anal fin; and the Cynoglossinae with an inferior curved mouth, the snout overhanging the mouth and hook-like, two or three lateral lines (at least on the ocular side), and the pelvic fin connected to the anal fin. The Symphurinae consists of the single genus *Symphurus* with about 57 species; most occur in deep water (generally more than 300 m). The Cynoglossinae, confined to the Old World, contains two genera, *Cynoglossus* with about 50 species and *Paraplagusia* with five. Menon (1977) revised *Cynoglossus*, and Menon (1979) and Chapleau and Renaud (1993) revised *Paraplagusia*. Tonguesoles live on mud or sand substrata; they readily bury in the sediment.

LARGESCALE TONGUESOLE
Cynoglossus arel (Bloch and Schneider, 1801)

Dorsal rays 116-130; anal rays 85-98; caudal rays 10; two lateral lines on ocular side, none on blind side; midlateral line with 56-70 scales; scales between lateral lines 7-9; scales ctenoid on ocular side, cycloid on blind side; vertebrae 50-57; body depth 3.85-5.0 in standard length; head length 3.4-5.1 in standard length; eyes very small, 15-17 in head length, with a narrow scaly space between, the upper in advance of lower (usually true of other species of the genus); maxilla extending beyond lower eye; two nostrils on ocular side, the anterior tubular in front of lower eye, the posterior in front half of interorbital space; light brown. Attains 40 cm. Arabian Gulf (where it seems to be the most common tonguesole), along the continental shelf to the Indo-Malayan region, north to China and Taiwan; recorded from depths of 9-82 m. *C. macrolepidotus* (Bleeker) is a synonym.

FOURLINED TONGUESOLE
Cynoglossus bilineatus (Lacepède, 1802)

Dorsal rays 107-113; anal rays 80-88; caudal rays 12; two lateral lines on each side, the midlateral one of ocular side with 88-96 scales; scales between lateral lines 13-16; scales on ocular side ctenoid, of blind side cycloid; vertebrae 51-53; body depth 3.5-4.5 in standard length; head length 4.1-5.2 in standard length; eyes small, 8.5-11 in head length, slightly larger than interorbital space; maxilla extending beyond lower eye; tubular anterior nostril in front of lower eye, posterior nostril in anterior interorbital space; brown, the fins lighter than body, with a large blackish area over much of operculum. Attains 35 cm. Arabian Gulf (Blegvad, 1944) along continental shores to the Indo-Malayan region, northern Australia, and Queensland, north to Japan; reported on mud or sand from 13 to about 400 m. *C. quadrilineatus* (Bleeker) and *C. quinquelineatus* Day are synonyms.

CARPENTER'S TONGUESOLE
Cynoglossus carpenteri Alcock, 1889

Dorsal rays 101-110; anal rays 80-89; caudal rays 10; three lateral lines on ocular side, none on blind side; midlateral-line scales 75-96; scales cycloid on ocular side, becoming ctenoid posteriorly, cycloid on blind side; vertebrae 51-55; body depth 3.4-4.2 in standard length; head length 2.95-3.6 in standard length; eyes 9-12 in head length; maxilla extending well beyond lower eye;

1031. *Cynoglossus arel*, 16.4 cm (J. Randall)

1032. *Cynoglossus bilineatus*, 21.6 cm (J. Randall)

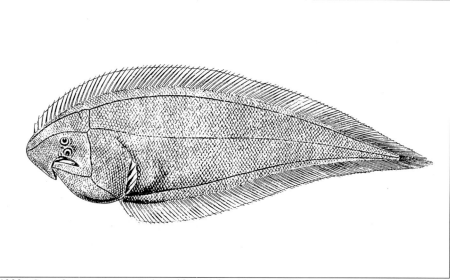

1033. *Cynoglossus carpenteri*, about 32 cm (after Alcock, 1889)

tubular anterior nostril in front of lower eye; posterior nostril in anterior interorbital space; uniform brown except blackish over opercular region. Largest specimen, 23 cm. Both coasts of India to Arabian Gulf and southern Oman; reported from the depth range of 27-400 m.

KOPS' TONGUESOLE
Cynoglossus kopsii (Bleeker, 1851)

Dorsal rays 103-115; anal rays 80-91; caudal rays 10; two, sometimes three, lateral lines on ocular side, the dorsal line often irregular, and may be incomplete; no lateral line on blind side; midlateral-line scales 57-72; scales between upper two lateral lines 7-12 (most often 9); scales ctenoid on both sides; vertebrae 50-55; body depth 2.95-4.45 in standard length; head length 4.1-5.3 in standard length; eyes 6-7.5 in head length, narrowly separated or contiguous; maxilla extending to below posterior half of lower eye; tubular anterior nostril before lower eye and posterior nostril at front of interorbital space; pale brown with dark brown blotches and short, irregular, transverse bands (dark pigment on edges of scales); median fins with blackish streaks paralleling rays. Largest specimen, 18.7 cm. Arabian Gulf to Indo-Malayan region and northwestern Australia, north to Hong Kong and Taiwan; also reported from the Maldives, Madagascar, and St. Brandon's Shoals in the Indian Ocean; depth range 24-90 m. *C. brachycephalus* Bleeker is a synonym.

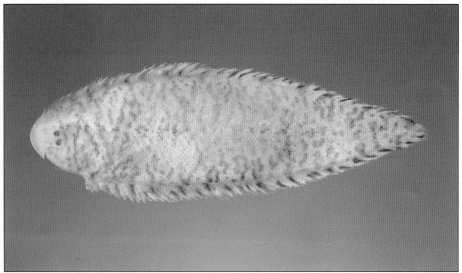

1034. *Cynoglossus kopsii*, 12.6 cm (J. Randall)

LACHNER'S TONGUESOLE
Cynoglossus lachneri Menon, 1977

Dorsal rays 113-121; anal rays 92-98; caudal rays 10; two lateral lines on each side, the scales of midlateral line on ocular side 100-111; scales between lateral lines 16-18; scales ctenoid on ocular side, cycloid on blind side; vertebrae 55-58; body depth 3.6-4.1 in standard length; head length 4.3-5.7 in standard length; eye diameter 7.5-11 in head length; eyes separated by a scaly space about half to two-thirds eye diameter; maxilla reaching to below or slightly posterior to rear edge of lower eye; tubular anterior nostril next to upper lip just in front of lower eye; posterior nostril in anterior interorbital space; brown or brown blotched with darker brown, the margin of median fins whitish. Reaches 46 cm. Known from Madagascar, Mozambique, Kenya (type locality), Zanzibar, Red Sea, Gulf of Oman, and Seychelles; the illustrated specimen was collected by the author from a small sand patch among rocks in 0.5 m.

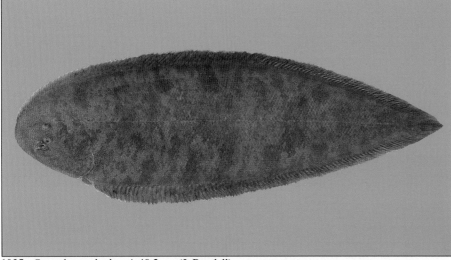

1035. *Cynoglossus lachneri*, 40.2 cm (J. Randall)

SPECKLED TONGUESOLE
Cynoglossus puncticeps (Richardson, 1846)

Dorsal rays 90-100; anal rays 72-78; caudal rays 10; two lateral lines on ocular side, none on blind side; midlateral line scales 78-99; scales between lateral lines 14-19; scales ctenoid on both sides; vertebrae 44-49; body depth 3.3-4.0 in standard length; head length 4.5-5.2 in standard length; eyes 8-10 in head length, separated by a narrow scaled zone of less than half eye diameter; maxilla reaching to below posterior half of lower eye; tubular anterior nostril at edge of upper lip in front of lower eye; posterior nostril in anterior interorbital space; brown, densely speckled with black dots, the fin membranes pale yellowish, the rays dark brown, becoming pale distally; young with very irregular dark bars. Largest specimen, 17.6 cm. Arabian Gulf (Blegvad, 1944) to the Indo-Malayan region, north to China (type locality); recorded from depths of 13-137 m.

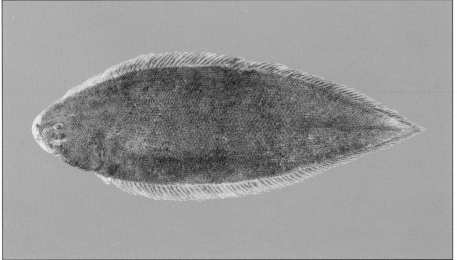

1036. *Cynoglossus puncticeps*, 16.6 cm (J. Randall)

BLOCH'S TONGUESOLE
Paraplagusia blochii (Bleeker, 1851)

Dorsal rays 99-105; anal rays 76-82; caudal rays 8; two lateral lines on ocular side, none on blind side; midlateral-line scales 75-83; scales between lateral lines 13-16; scales ctenoid on ocular side, weakly ctenoid on blind side; body depth 3.6-3.75 in standard length; head length 3.65-4.15 in standard length; lips with a fringe of arborescent tentacles; maxilla extending to below rear edge of lower eye; eyes small, 10-12 in head length, the upper distinctly in advance of lower; eyes separated by a scaly interorbital space about equal to eye diameter; brown, the scale centres paler than edges; postorbital head and abdomen dark grey; median fins pale yellowish, the rays light brown. Attains 22 cm. Known from southern Oman (illustrated specimen from Salalah market), India, Indonesia (Java the type locality), and the Philippines; recorded in India from 7-55 m.

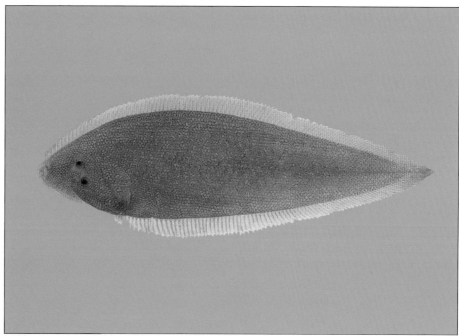

1037. *Paraplagusia blochii*, 21.1 cm (J. Randall)

DRIFTFISHES
FAMILY NOMEIDAE

The driftfishes are one of five families of the perciform suborder Stromateoidei. Unique to all except one monotypic family (for which adults remain unknown) are toothed pharyngeal sacs from the esophagus behind the last gill arch. Except for *Pampus*, all have a large preorbital (lacrymal) bone which covers most of the upper jaw which is scarcely, if at all protractile; the teeth are small; the eye is usually large, often rimmed with adipose tissue; scales are thin and easily shed, none on snout or dorsally on head; caudal fin with 15 principal rays; pelvic fins, when present, with I,5 rays. Some stromateoid fishes resemble carangids, but they lack the characteristic two detached anal spines of the jacks, as well as the scutes found on most carangids. The nomeids have IX-XII slender dorsal spines, the fin divided to the base before the last spine, this part folding into a groove in the back. The anal fin has I-III weak spines; the pelvic fins fold into a groove. The family includes the well known, pelagic Man-of-war Fish, *Nomeis gronovii* Gmelin, the young of which associate with the jellyfish *Physalia*; the genus *Psenes*, species of which may also be commensal with jellyfishes; and *Cubiceps*. The genus *Ariomma* is included in the Nomeidae, following Smith and Heemstra (1986). Some authors such as Haedrich (1967), who revised the suborder, prefer to treat *Ariomma* in a separate family, Ariommidae.

INDIAN DRIFTFISH
Ariomma indica (Day, 1870)

Dorsal rays X-XI+I,14-15; anal rays III,14-15; pectoral rays 21-24; lateral-line scales 39-49; scales cycloid, deciduous, not extending onto base of median fins; gill rakers 8 + 14-16; body depth 2.0-2.3 in standard length; caudal peduncle little compressed, nearly square in cross-section; head length 2.5-3.1 in standard length; a prominent ridge above eye; eye large and midlateral on head; snout blunt; mouth small and oblique, the maxilla not reaching eye; teeth in jaws unicuspid anteriorly, tricuspid posteriorly; no teeth on vomer or palatines; dorsal fins fully separated but contiguous, the spinous part about twice as high as soft; caudal fin deeply forked with two slightly covering fleshy keels on its base; silvery. Attains about 25 cm. A continental shelf species from South Africa to the Arabian Gulf (but not the Red Sea), east to the Indo-Malayan region, north to Japan; generally taken in trawls over mud bottom in 20-300 m. Occurs in small schools. Females are larger than males, maturing at a length of about 13.5 cm.

1038. *Ariomma indica*, 17.2 cm (J. Randall)

BUTTERFISHES
FAMILY STROMATEIDAE

Like the previous family, these fishes have tooth-bearing pharyngeal sacs off the esophagus and other characters of the stromateoid suborder. They are differentiated by their deep, compressed body; small head; small lateral eyes, surrounded by adipose tissue which extends forward around nostrils; small mouth, the maxilla joined to cheek and covered with skin; gill membranes broadly united to isthmus; small, cycloid, highly deciduous scales; dorsal and anal fins with numerous soft rays, elevated toward the front; and no pelvic fins (except in young of *Stromateus*). There are three genera, *Pampus*, *Peprilus*, and *Stromateus*, with about 13 species; of the three genera, only *Pampus* has Indo-Pacific species. Butterfishes are reported to feed primarily on ctenophores, salps, and medusae.

1039. *Pampas argenteus*, 15.7 cm (J. Randall)

fins with an elevated, pointed, anterior lobe; caudal fin strongly forked, the lower lobe longer than upper; no pelvic fins, even in juveniles; silvery (silvery grey when scales missing). Reaches about 60 cm. Arabian Gulf along the continental shelf to southern Japan (but not New Guinea or Australia). Generally found in schools over mud bottoms; known from the depth range of 5-80 m. Highly prized food fish; very important commercially in India and the Arabian Gulf.

SILVER POMFRET
Pampus argenteus (Euphrasen, 1788)

Dorsal rays 38-43; anal rays 34-43; dorsal and anal rays preceded by 5-10 very low, blade-like spines; scales very small, extending onto base of fins; gill rakers 2-3 + 8-10; body subrhomboid and deep, the depth 1.3-1.6 in standard length; head length 3.7-5.0 in standard length (head becoming shorter with growth); mouth inferior and oblique, the maxilla reaching to below posterior half of eye; teeth very small, uniserial, flat, and tricuspid; gill opening restricted to a vertical slit covered by a flap of skin; dorsal and anal

BARRACUDAS
FAMILY SPHYRAENIDAE

The barracudas were formerly believed to be allied with the threadfins (Polynemidae) and mullets (Mugilidae). They are currently classified in the perciform suborder Scombroidei, along with the cutlassfishes, snake mackerels, tunas, and billfishes (Johnson, 1986). The barracudas are

very distinctive with their very elongate, little-compressed bodies; large mouth with protruding, often pointed, lower jaw; very large, compressed teeth in jaws and on palatines, variable in size, some as long fangs; and widely separated dorsal fins, the first of V spines, and the second with I,9 rays. The anal fin has II,8-9 rays; the pectoral fins are on the ventral half of the body; the pelvic fins have I,5 rays, their base distinctly posterior to the pectoral-fin base; the caudal fin is forked or deeply double or triple emarginate. The scales are small and cycloid, the lateral line well developed and nearly straight. Gill rakers are absent or reduced to one or two. As the dentition would suggest, these fishes are carnivorous; they feed mostly on fishes. They may be diurnal or nocturnal, solitary or schooling. Although barracudas, in particular the Great Barracuda, have attacked man, this danger is exaggerated. In clear water without anything that might serve as an attractant, such as a wounded fish struggling on a spear or a metal object that flashes in the sun, there should be no reason to fear a barracuda. The family consists of a single genus and about 20 species. Barracudas occur in all tropical to temperate seas. Williams (1959) reviewed the East African species, and de Sylva and Williams in Smith and Heemstra (1986) the southern African species.

1040. School of *Sphyraena flavicauda*, about 18 cm (J. Randall)

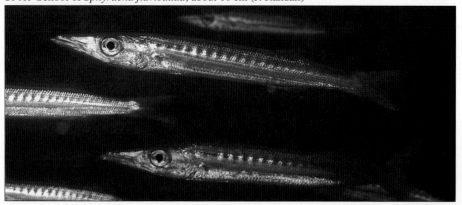

1041. *S. acutipinnis*, juv., 10 cm (P. Heemstra)

SHARPFIN BARRACUDA
Sphyraena acutipinnis Day, 1876

1042. *Sphyraena acutipinnis* (S. Chater)

Dorsal rays V + I,9; anal rays I,8; pectoral rays 14; lateral-line scales 120-128; a single gill raker at angle of first gill arch; body depth 6.5-8.5 in standard length; eye moderately large; preopercle without a large protruding membranous flap (but there is a narrow membranous edge on the ventral side of the corner); opercle with a single flexible flat spine; maxilla reaching to between nostrils and anterior edge of eye; front of lower jaw with a cartilaginous pointed knob; teeth in jaws erect and widely spaced; origin of first dorsal fin slightly anterior to origin of pelvic fins, both usually a little posterior to tip of pectoral fins; caudal fin forked; dark greenish dorsally, shading to silvery below; fins dusky. Attains 80 cm. India and Pakistan (type locality) to South Africa; occurrence in the western Pacific uncertain due to confusion with *S. helleri*

Jenkins, described from Hawaii, and *S. novaehollandiae* Günther, a temperate Australian species, both of which also have a single gill raker on the first gill arch. *S. africana* Gilchrist and Thompson is a synonym.

GREAT BARRACUDA
Sphyraena barracuda (Walbaum, 1792)

Dorsal rays V + I,9; anal rays II,8; pectoral rays 13-15; lateral-line scales 69-90; no gill rakers (rough platelets present on gill arch, but without spinules); body depth 6.0-8.2 in standard length; eye small (for the genus); cartilaginous knob at front of lower jaw not well developed; teeth erect and contiguous; origin of first dorsal fin slightly posterior to origin of pelvic fins; caudal fin triple emarginate (quadrilobed); tip of pec-

toral fins extending beyond base of pelvic fins; dark green to dark grey on back, shading to silvery on side, usually with a few scattered black blotches, mainly on lower posterior half of body; caudal fin with a large black area on upper and lower halves, the distal ends of the upper and lower lobes whitish; 18-22 slightly oblique dark bars on back, more evident on juveniles and subadults than adults. Reported to 1.7 m; world angling record, 38.5 kg. Indo-Pacific and tropical and subtropical Atlantic; juveniles usually found in estuaries or mangrove sloughs. Diurnal and usually solitary. Attacks on man nearly always a result of provocation (as by spearing) or in murky water when a limb might be mistaken for a fish. De Sylva (1963) studied the biology of *S. barracuda* in western Atlantic waters.

1043. *Sphyraena barracuda*, about 75 cm (J. Randall)

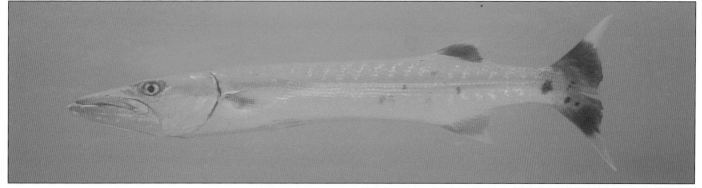

YELLOWTAIL BARRACUDA
Sphyraena flavicauda Rüppell, 1838

Dorsal rays V + I,9; anal rays II,9; pectoral rays 14; lateral-line scales 72-90; gill rakers 2; body depth 6.8-8.3 in standard length; eye large; corner of preopercle with a prominent membranous flap; opercle with a single flat flexible spine; maxilla ending about a pupil width before eye; origin of first dorsal fin behind a vertical at tip of pectoral fin; tip of lower jaw blunt, without a cartilaginous knob; teeth erect, separated by a space greater than tooth width; silvery green dorsally, shading to silvery on side, usually with a longitudinal series of short blackish bars along lateral line anteriorly but extending above it posteriorly; a narrow brownish yellow stripe may be visible on side of head

1044. *Sphyraena flavicauda*, 36.3 cm (J. Randall)

and lower side of body; lateral line yellowish brown; fins yellowish, especially the caudal which may be dark-edged; a blackish

blotch at base of pectoral fins. Attains about 40 cm. Often forms small aggregations by day; probably nocturnal.

BIGEYE BARRACUDA
Sphyraena forsteri Cuvier, 1829

Dorsal rays V + I,9; anal rays II,9; pectoral rays 14-15; lateral-line scales 112-123; no gill rakers, but spinules on 10-20 tubercles on lower limb of first gill arch; body depth 6.9-7.7 in standard length; eye very large; opercle with two flexible flat spines; corner of preopercle rounded, without a projecting flap; maxilla nearly reaching to below anterior edge of eye; teeth closely spaced, those posteriorly in lower jaw angling backward; origin of first dorsal fin slightly posterior to base of pelvic fins and tip of pectoral fins; caudal fin forked with a small inner lobe on each major lobe; bluish grey dorsally, silvery on sides and ventrally; a large blackish blotch in axil of pectoral fins and usually extending slightly above pectoral-fin base; median fins dusky, the tips of second dorsal and anal fins white. Attains 65 cm. Indo-Pacific. Nocturnal; may form schools by day. *S. toxeuma* Fowler is a synonym.

1045. *Sphyraena forsteri*, about 50 cm (J. Randall)

1046. *Sphyraena jello*, about 1.3 m (J. Randall)

PICKHANDLE BARRACUDA
Sphyraena jello Cuvier, 1829

Dorsal rays V + I,9; anal rays II,9; pectoral rays 14-15; lateral-line scales 130-140; no gill rakers (platelets on lower limb of gill arch rough, but without spinules); body depth 7.9-8.9 in standard length; eye not large (for the genus); corner of preopercle rounded, without a membranous flap; opercle with two flexible flat spines; no pointed cartilaginous knob at front of lower jaw;

maxilla reaching to below front edge of eye; teeth erect; origin of first dorsal fin slightly posterior to origin of pelvic fins and anterior to tip of pectoral fins; caudal fin deeply forked, without inner lobes; dusky blue-green on back, silvery on sides, with about 20 dark bars on body about equal in width to pale interspaces, those posterior to second dorsal and anal fins faint; caudal fin yellow. Reaches about 140 cm. Red Sea and coast of East Africa to the western Pacific. Diurnal; solitary or in small schools.

1047. *Sphyraena obtusata*, 16.8 cm (J. Randall)

OBTUSE BARRACUDA
Sphyraena obtusata Cuvier, 1829

Dorsal rays V + I,9; anal rays II,9; pectoral rays 13-15; lateral-line scales 80-91; gill rakers 2, one at angle and one on lower limb; body depth 5.5-7.5 in standard length; eye large; corner of preopercle with a protruding membranous flap; opercle with a single flat flexible spine; maxilla nearly reaching to below anterior edge of eye; no pointed cartilaginous knob at front of lower jaw; teeth erect and close-set; origin of first dorsal fin anterior to tip of pectoral fins and over rear base of pelvic fins; caudal fin forked; silvery yellow-green on back, silvery on side and ventrally; lateral line yellowish brown; caudal fin yellow, the posterior margin blackish; dorsal and pectoral fins yellowish. A small species; attains about 30 cm. Red Sea south to Seychelles and Mozambique, east to the western Pacific, ranging there from China to New South Wales. Juveniles form large shoals in midwater, the adults in smaller schools near the bottom.

SAWTOOTH BARRACUDA
Sphyraena putnamiae Jordan and Seale, 1905

Dorsal rays V + I,9; anal rays II,8; pectoral rays 14-16; lateral-line scales 120-133; no gill rakers, the first gill arch with spinules; body depth 6.9-8.5 in standard length; eye not large (for the genus); no membranous flap at corner of preopercle; two flexible flat spines on opercle; maxilla reaching to below anterior margin of eye; front of lower jaw with a pointed cartilaginous knob; teeth close-set, those in lower jaw angling backward; origin of first dorsal fin over tip of pectoral fins and over or slightly posterior to rear base of pelvic fins; caudal fin forked; bluish grey dorsally, shading to silvery on sides and ventrally, with wavy dark bars nearly the full depth of body in life, the darkest part of each on upper side as a slight chevron crossing lateral line. Reported to 87 cm. Indo-Pacific; occurs diurnally in schools. *S. bleekeri* Williams is a synonym.

1048. *Sphyraena putnamiae*, 26.7 cm (J. Randall)

BLACKTAIL BARRACUDA
Sphyraena qenie Klunzinger, 1870

Dorsal rays V + I,9; anal rays II,8; pectoral rays 15; lateral-line scales 120-130; no gill rakers, but gill arch with numerous spinules; body depth 6.0-7.9 in standard length; eye not large (for the genus); corner of preopercle without a membranous flap; front of lower jaw without a pointed cartilaginous knob; maxilla reaching to or beyond anterior edge of eye; teeth in jaws erect and close-set; origin of first dorsal fin above or slightly anterior to tip of pectoral fins and below or slightly posterior to rear base of pelvic fins; caudal fin forked, adults with a distinct small inner lobe to each side of middle of fin (hence fin is triple emarginate or quadrilobed); grey dorsally, silvery below, with 18-22 slightly curved black bars on body which extend below lateral line but not onto lower fourth of body; caudal fin dark grey with a black margin; a black spot at base of pectoral fins, broadest dorsally. Reaches 140 cm. Indo-Pacific; usually seen by day in large semistationary schools. Described from the Red Sea by Klunzinger; in 1884 he changed the spelling to *kenie*, but the original spelling must be followed.

1049. *Sphyraena qenie*, about 55 cm (J. Randall)

CUTLASSFISHES
FAMILY TRICHIURIDAE

The cutlassfishes are well named for their very long, extremely compressed, silvery bodies; the mouth is large, not protractile, the maxilla concealed by the preorbital bone; there are large compressed canine teeth in the jaws, those anteriorly in the upper jaw as huge fangs; very small teeth are present on the palatines, none on vomer; there is a single nostril (two in the related gempylids); scales are absent; there is a single lateral line; the dorsal fin is long and low, beginning above the postorbital head, the anterior spinous part shorter than the soft, with or without a notch between the two parts; the anal fin is low or reduced to a series of short spinules; the caudal fin is small and forked or absent, the posterior body tapering to a point; the pectoral fins are small low on the body; the pelvic fins are absent or reduced to a scale-like spine (or a rudimentary ray in *Benthodesmus*). As the awesome dentition would indicate, these fishes are voracious predators. They are found in coastal waters from inshore to moderate depths, those in shallow water often over mud bottoms. They are generally caught in seines or trawls. Nakamura and Parin (1993) revised the family and the Gempylidae; these two families are grouped with the Scombridae (tunas and mackerels) in the perciform suborder Scombroidei.

LONGTOOTH CUTLASSFISH

Eupleurogrammus glossodon (Bleeker, 1860)

Dorsal rays III,115-129; anal fin reduced to short, partially embedded spinules, its origin below base of 31st to 35th dorsal rays; no caudal fin; pectoral fins shorter than snout, with a spine and 13 soft rays; pelvic fins reduced to a scale-line spine below 11th to 14th dorsal rays; lateral line descending from upper end of gill opening to pass along lower part of body, the distance from lateral line to ventral edge of body at anus less than twice distance from base of dorsal fin; body elongate, the depth 13-17 in total length; body extremely compressed and tapering posteriorly to a very slender finless section (hence one common name, Hairtail; true of the following two species); head length 8.3-8.7 in total length; eye about 7-8 in head length; maxilla reaching to below anterior edge of eye; a pointed cartilaginous knob at tip of jaws (also present in the next two species); compressed canine teeth in one row in jaws, with two or three at front of upper jaw greatly enlarged; a pair of canines anteriorly in lower jaw also enlarged; silvery; front of jaws black; a black spot midventrally on chin; upper edge of pectoral fins black; spinous portion of dorsal fin blackish. Reaches 70 cm. Arabian Gulf to Indonesia; coastal waters to depths of 80 m; said to come to the surface at night; feeds on crustaceans, squids, and fishes.

SMALLHEAD CUTLASSFISH

Eupleurogrammus muticus (Gray, 1831)

Dorsal fin with III spines and about 140 soft rays; anal fin reduced to short embedded spinules, commencing below 41st to 43rd soft rays; pectoral fins about as large as snout, with a spine and 12 soft rays; pelvic fins reduced to a scale-like spine; lateral line passing near midside of body (slightly closer to ventral edge); body elongate, the depth 15-17 in total length, extremely compressed, and tapering posteriorly; head small, 10.2-10.9 in total length; eye about 6-8 in head length; maxilla reaching to below anterior edge of eye; compressed canine teeth in one row in jaws, two or three of fang proportions at front of upper jaw, but none greatly enlarged in lower jaw; silvery; front of jaws black; a small black spot at upper base of pectoral fins. Reaches 70 cm. Arabian Gulf east along continental shelf to Indonesia, north to Korea. Habits similar to *E. glossodon.*

LARGEHEAD CUTLASSFISH

Trichiurus lepturus Linnaeus, 1758

Dorsal rays III,130-135, the longest rays more than half maximum body depth; anal fin spine below 39th to 41st dorsal soft rays, the remaining 100-105 soft rays embedded or slightly breaking through skin; pectoral fins about as long as snout, with a spine and 11-13 soft rays; pelvic fins absent; lateral line descending below pectoral fin to pass along lower side of body (about one-fourth body depth from ventral edge of body); body elongate, the depth 13-16 in total length, extremely compressed, and tapering posteriorly; head large, 6.8-7.6 in total length; ventroposterior margin of operculum concave; eye moderately large, 5-7 in head length; maxilla reaching to below front edge of pupil; a row of sharp compressed teeth in jaws, with two or three pairs at front of upper jaw and one in lower jaw enlarged as fangs and bearing barbs; silvery. Reported to 120 cm. Cosmopolitan in tropical to temperate seas along continental shores and continental islands; in the western Pacific to New Caledonia and Fiji. Benthopelagic from inshore to depths as great as 350 m. Juveniles feed mainly on planktonic crustaceans, the adults principally on a wide variety of fishes, occasionally on squids and crustaceans. *T. haumela* (Forsskål) is a synonym.

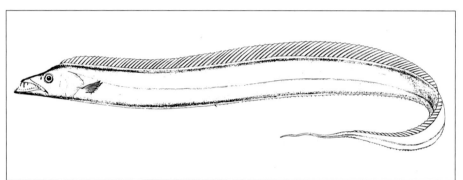

1050. *Eupleurogrammus glossodon* (after Bleeker, 1983)

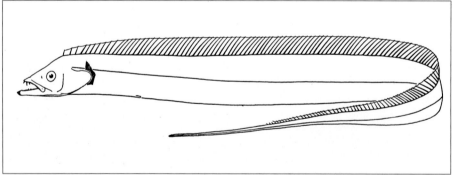

1051. *Eupleurogrammus muticus,* 61.7 cm (after Tucker, 1956)

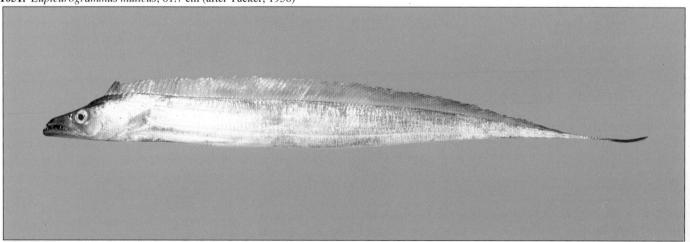

1052. *Trichiurus lepturus,* 70.5 cm (J. Randall)

TUNAS AND MACKERELS
FAMILY SCOMBRIDAE

This well known family of fishes includes species which form the basis for some of the world's most important commercial fisheries; many of these fishes are also highly prized by recreational fishermen and of great value to artisanal fisheries. As a family they are characterised by having a streamlined fusiform to elongate body with a narrow caudal peduncle that is reinforced by two or three keels on each side (the mackerels of the genera *Scomber* and *Rastrelliger* have two keels on the caudal-fin base; the remaining species have a large midlateral keel on the peduncle and fin base, in addition to the two on the fin base). The caudal fin is forked to lunate, and stiff; there are two dorsal fins, each depressible into a groove; the dorsal and anal fins are elevated anteriorly; five to twelve finlets are present behind the second dorsal and anal fins; the pelvic fins of 6 soft rays are inserted below the base of the pectoral fins. The scales are cycloid, and small to moderate in size; the body may be fully covered by scales, or naked except in some species with an anterior corselet of thick scales on the body. The gill membranes are free from the isthmus. The mouth is fairly large, the teeth variable in size, but none as true canines; the palate and tongue may have teeth. The mackerels (*Scomber* and *Rastrelliger*) have an adipose eyelid covering the anterior and posterior part of the eye. The colour is usually blue or green dorsally, becoming silvery on the sides and ventrally; often there is a distinctive pattern of dark bands or spots. The scombrids vary in size from the small mackerels to the huge Bluefin Tuna which attains a length of 4.2 m (the all-tackle world record 679 kg). The scombrids are among the swiftest-swimming of fishes. The four genera of tunas of the tribe Thunnini (*Thunnus*, *Katsuwonus*, *Euthynnus*, and *Auxis*) are unique among bony fishes in being able to maintain a body temperature a few degrees higher than the surrounding sea. All of the scombrid fishes are predaceous; the mackerels filter zooplankton from the sea with their long gill rakers; the tunas, Spanish mackerels, and bonitos feed mainly on small fishes, especially schooling species such as clupeoids, and squids. Scombrids, in general, are pelagic schooling fishes occurring at or near the surface. Many are migratory; tagging studies have revealed remarkable open ocean migratory patterns of some of the tunas. The Spanish mackerels (*Scomberomorus*) tend to move along coasts and may enter estuarine environments; one is unusual in swimming a considerable distance up the Mekong River. A total of 15 genera and 49 species are recognised in the family (Collette and Nauen, 1983; Collette et al., in Moser et al., 1984). They are divided into two subfamilies, the monotypic Gasterochismatinae, and the Scombrinae; the latter consists of four tribes: the tunas (Thunnini), the bonitos and Dogtooth Tuna (Sardini), Spanish mackerels (Scomberomorini), and the mackerels (Scombrini).

1053. Feeding school of *Rastrelliger kanagurta* (J. Randall)

WAHOO
Acanthocybium solandri (Cuvier, 1831)

Dorsal rays XXIII-XXVII + 12-16 + 8-9 finlets; anal rays 12-14 + 9 finlets; pectoral rays 22-24; body covered with small scales; a single lateral line curving abruptly downward below first dorsal fin; gill rakers absent; body very elongate, the depth 6.5-7.7 in fork length; snout pointed and long (about as long as rest of head); mouth large with a single series of compressed, close-set, triangular, finely serrate teeth; swim bladder present; most of posterior part of maxilla concealed under preorbital bone; median interpelvic process as two small flaps; blue-green on back, silvery on sides, with 24-30 deep blue to dark grey bars passing over most of body depth, a few Y-shaped. Attains 212 cm and a weight of 83 kg. The all-tackle angling record is 70.5 kg, from the Bahamas. A cosmopolitan surface-dwelling species of all warm seas; occasionally seen by divers in the blue water off steep drop-offs.

1054. *Acanthocybium solandri* (Illustration by R.A. Swainston)

BULLET TUNA
Auxis rochei (Risso, 1810)

Dorsal rays X-XI + 10-11 + 8 finlets; anal rays 13-15 + 6-7 finlets; pectoral rays 23-25; a well developed scaly corselet which extends in a band of six or more scales in width along lateral line to below origin of second dorsal fin; rest of body naked; gill rakers 9-10 + 33-37; body depth 4.1-4.7 in fork length; teeth small and conical, none on vomer or palatines; swimbladder absent; pectoral fins very short, not reaching a vertical at anterior margin of scaleless area above corselet; a large, single, pointed flap (interpelvic process) between pelvic fins; blue dorsally, silvery ventrally, with short, irregular, dark bars and elongate spots in scaleless area of back. Attains 42 cm. Circumglobal in warm seas, but exact distribution not known due to confusion with *A. thazard*. Feeds on small fishes, crustaceans, and cephalopods (Uchida, 1981).

1055. *Auxis rochei*, 28.8 cm (J. Randall)

FRIGATE TUNA
Auxis thazard (Lacepède, 1800)

Dorsal rays XI-XII + 10-12 + 8 finlets; anal rays 12-14 + 7-8 finlets; pectoral rays 22-25; a well developed scaly corselet which extends in a band of five or less scales in width along lateral line to below origin of second dorsal fin; rest of body naked; gill rakers 9-10 + 28-32; body depth 4.0-4.6 in fork length; teeth small and conical; no teeth on vomer or palatines; swim bladder absent; pectoral fins short, reaching a little posterior to a vertical at anterior margin of scaleless area above corselet; interpelvic process as in *A. rochei*; blue dorsally, silvery below, with irregular oblique dark bands and spots in scaleless area of back. Attains 60 cm. Cosmopolitan in tropical to warm temperate seas, typically occurring in schools in oceanic waters. Food habits as in *A. rochei*.

1056. *Auxis thazard*, 27.8 cm (J. Randall)

KAWAKAWA
Euthynnus affinis (Cantor, 1849)

Dorsal rays XV-XVII + 12-13 + 8 finlets; anal rays 13-14 + 7 finlets; pectoral rays 25-29; a corselet of thick scales present anteriorly on body, the rest of body scaleless; gill rakers 6-9 + 23-26; body depth 3.8-4.3 in fork length; teeth small and conical, 27-43 on each side of upper jaw and 27-37 on each side of lower; a patch of small teeth present on vomer, and elongate patches on palatines; no swimbladder; space between dorsal fins narrow; interpelvic process consisting of two small medial flaps; blue on back, silvery white below, with wavy oblique dark bands in naked area of body above lateral line; a few black spots between pectoral and pelvic fins. Attains about 100 cm and a weight of about 13.5 kg (all-tackle angling record

1057. *Euthynnus affinis*, 40.7 cm (J. Randall)

13.15 kg). Indo-Pacific, with a few records from the tropical eastern Pacific; the closely related *E. alletteratus* (Rafinesque) occurs in the Atlantic. Generally runs in small schools, sometimes with other scombrids; often seen in coastal waters.

1058. *Gymnosarda unicolor*, about 55 cm (J. Randall)

DOGTOOTH TUNA
Gymnosarda unicolor (Rüppell, 1836)

Dorsal rays XIII-XV+12-14 + 6-7 finlets; anal rays 12-13 + 6 finlets; pectoral rays 25-28; body with an anterior corselet of scales, the rest naked except for base of dorsal fin, lateral line, and middle keel of caudal peduncle; lateral line descending below dorsal fins to a low undulating posterior part; gill rakers 2-3 + 10-12; body depth 3.9-5.0 in fork length; mouth moderately large, the maxilla reaching to below middle of eye; teeth in jaws large and conical; two patches of tiny teeth on tongue, and numerous tiny teeth on palatines; swimbladder large; dorsal fins contiguous; pectoral fins short; inter-

pelvic process single and long; deep blue dorsally, silvery below; dorsoanterior part of first dorsal fin blackish; no other dark markings. All-tackle angling record, 131 kg, 206 cm fork length, hence about 220 cm total length, from Kwan-Tall Island, Korea. Indo-Pacific, but generally around oceanic islands or clear-water reef areas such as the Red Sea or Great Barrier Reef. Patrols the drop-offs of coral reefs, as solitary individuals or in small groups, preying mainly on schooling fishes in the vicinity of reefs such as fusiliers (Caesionidae), plankton-feeding surgeonfishes (*Naso* spp.) and wrasses (*Cirrhilabrus*), and mackerel scads (*Decapterus* spp.) (Randall, 1980). *G. nuda* (Günther) is a synonym.

SKIPJACK TUNA
Katsuwonus pelamis (Linnaeus, 1758)

Dorsal rays XIV-XVI + 12-14 + 7-9 finlets; anal rays 13-15 + 7-8 finlets; pectoral rays 26-28; an anterior corselet of thick scales; rest of body scaleless except for lateral line; gill rakers 16-21 + 34-41; body depth 3.7-4.1 in fork length; teeth small and conical, in one series, none on vomer or palatines; no swimbladder; dorsal fins narrowly separated; pectoral fins short; interpelvic process branched; blue on back (the corselet may be darker), shading to silvery on sides and ventrally, with four to six prominent dark stripes on lower half of body (in life, stripes may be interrupted by dark bars on midside of body). Reaches 115 cm and a weight of about 34 kg (all-tackle angling record, 18.9 kg, from Mauritius). Cosmopolitan in tropical and subtropical seas; usually occurs in large schools at or near the surface in offshore waters (recorded to depths of 260 m, but generally above the thermocline). Feeds on a wide variety of fishes and pelagic invertebrates. Matures at a fork length of about 45 cm. Biological data are summarised by Jones and Silas (1963) and Waldron (1963).

1059. *Katsuwonus pelamis*, 51.7 cm (J. Randall)

373

INDIAN MACKEREL
Rastrelliger kanagurta (Cuvier, 1817)

Dorsal rays IX-XI + 11-13 + 5 finlets; anal rays 11-12 (initial rudimentary spine not counted) + 5 finlets; pectoral rays 19-22; body entirely covered with scales, those anteriorly next to head and around pectoral fins larger, but not developed as a corselet; gill rakers very long (visible when mouth open), 30-46 on lower limb of first gill arch; longest gill rakers with numerous spinules; body depth 3.4-4.0 in fork length; body moderately compressed; mouth large, the maxilla extending to or posterior to rear edge of eye; teeth in jaws conical and very small, none on vomer or palatines; interpelvic process small and single; swimbladder present; silvery blue-green dorsally with two rows of blackish spots above lateral line, silvery on sides and below, sometimes with golden reflections; two or three narrow yellow stripes often visible on side of body. Reported to 38 cm, but any over 30 cm are exceptional. The most wide-ranging of the three species of the genus, known from the Red Sea (and via Suez Canal to the Mediterranean) south to Natal and east to Samoa. An inshore species that occurs in schools of variable size; feeds by swimming with mouth wide open through concentrations of zooplankton; the author once observed three individuals swim swiftly through the spawn of the wrasse *Thalassoma amblycephalum* to strain the ova (also reported by Colin, 1976). An important commercial fish in Asian waters. Jones and Rosa (1967) provided a synopsis of biological data of the species.

STRIPED BONITO
Sarda orientalis (Temminck and Schlegel, 1844)

Dorsal rays XVIII-XIX + 14-17 + 7-9 finlets; anal rays 14-16 + 6-7 finlets; pectoral rays 24-26; a well developed scaly corselet anteriorly, the rest of body with small scales; a single, gradually descending, wavy lateral line; gill rakers 2-3 + 7-10; body depth 4.2-4.9 in fork length; mouth large, the maxilla reaching to or posterior to rear edge of eye; teeth moderately large and conical, 12-20 on side of upper jaw and 10-17 on side of lower jaw; swimbladder absent; dorsal fins narrowly separated; pectoral fins short; interpelvic process consisting of two separate flaps; bluish grey with slightly oblique, narrow, dark stripes on upper third of body; variable bluish grey bars sometimes present in middle of body. Largest specimen reported, 107 cm; all-tackle angling record, 10.65 kg, from Seychelles. Indo-Pacific and tropical eastern Pacific, but spotty in distri-

1060. *Rastrelliger kanagurta*, 25.8 cm (J. Randall)

1061. *Sarda orientalis*, 41.3 cm (J. Randall)

1062. *Scomber japonicus*, 25.3 cm (J. Randall)

bution. Illustrated specimen taken by angling from shore at Mahallah, southern Oman.

CHUB MACKEREL
Scomber japonicus Houttuyn, 1782

Dorsal rays IX-X + 11-12 + 5 finlets; anal rays I,11-12 + 5 finlets; pectoral rays 19-21; body fully scaled, the scales anteriorly on body larger; a single, gradually descending lateral line; gill rakers 12-15 + 27-34; body slender and little compressed, the depth 4.8-6.8 in fork length; very small conical teeth in jaws, on vomer, and in a double row on palatines, narrowing to one row posteriorly; swimbladder present; dorsal fins well separated; interpelvic process single and small; green with oblique wavy dark bands on back and a midlateral zone of small dark spots. Reported to 54 cm; one of 51.5 cm weighed 1.1 kg. Wide-ranging in subtropical and temperate oceans of the world; absent from the Indian Ocean except for South Africa and the seas around the Arabian Peninsula; a coastal pelagic species which may occur from the surface to depths of 250-300 m. Forms schools by size; feeds on small fishes and the larger animals of the zooplankton.

NARROW-BARRED SPANISH MACKEREL
Scomberomorus commerson (Lacepède, 1800)

Dorsal rays XV-XVIII+15-20 (usually 16-17)+8-10 finlets; anal rays 16-21 (usually 18-19) + 7-12 finlets; pectoral rays 21-24; body fully scaled; lateral line single, bent downward below second dorsal fin and first finlet, wavy posteriorly; gill rakers 0-1 + 2-6; vertebrae 42-45; body elongate and compressed, the depth 5.0-6.4 in fork length; head pointed; mouth large, the maxilla exposed on cheek, reaching to below posterior edge of eye; teeth large, compressed, and triangular; teeth present on vomer and palatines; dorsal fins narrowly separated; second dorsal higher than anterior part of first dorsal; bluish grey dorsally, shading to silvery ventrally, with numerous, narrow, irregular, dark bars; median and pectoral fins grey to dark grey, the second dorsal and anal fins tipped with white. Reported to 245 cm; the all-tackle angling record is 44.9 kg, from Natal. Red Sea to South Africa, east to Fiji; in the western Pacific from Japan to Tasmania; a recent immigrant to the eastern Mediterranean via the Suez Canal; an inshore pelagic species capable of long migrations; feeds mainly on fishes, especially clupeoids. Observed by author only as solitary individuals. Probably the most important commercial fish in Oman where it is known by the English common name Kingfish.

1063. *Scomberomorus commerson*, about 80 cm (J. Randall)

SPOTTED SPANISH MACKEREL
Scomberomorus guttatus (Bloch and Schneider, 1801

Dorsal rays XV-XVIII+18-24 (usually 20-22) + 8-10 finlets; anal rays 19-23 + 7-10 (usually 8) finlets; pectoral rays 20-23; body fully scaled; lateral line single and irregular, angling downward below second dorsal fin and first two finlets, the anterior third with fine dorsal and ventral branches; gill rakers 1-2 + 7-12; vertebrae 47-52; body elongate and compressed, the depth 4.6-5.1 in fork length; head pointed, nearly equal to body depth; mouth moderately large, the maxilla exposed on cheek, nearly reaching posterior edge of eye; teeth large, compressed, and triangular, those in lower jaw larger; teeth present on vomer and palatines; dorsal fins narrowly separated; second dorsal fin higher than anterior part of first dorsal; bluish grey dorsally, shading to silvery white ventrally, with a broad zone of small dark spots on side of body; anterior part of first dorsal fin blackish to eighth spine. Attains 80 cm. Arabian Gulf along the continental shelf to Indonesia, north to Hong Kong and Sea of Japan.

YELLOWFIN TUNA
Thunnus albacares (Bonnaterre, 1788)

Dorsal rays XII-XIV+13-16 + 8-10 finlets; anal rays 12-15 + 7-10 finlets; pectoral rays 33-36; body with very small scales; an anterior corselet of larger scales present but not well developed (true of other species of *Thunnus*); gill rakers 7-9 + 20-23; body depth 3.8-4.5 in fork length; small conical teeth in one series in jaws, and villiform teeth in bands on vomer and palatines (also generic); dorsal fins contiguous; large individuals may have very elongate second dorsal and anal fins (up to 20% fork length); pectoral fins long, usually reaching beyond origin of second dorsal fin; interpelvic process bilobed (generic); swimbladder present; no striations on ventral surface of liver; dark blue dorsally, shading through brassy yellow on side to light silvery grey ventrally; lower third of body with near-vertical rows of small pale spots; second dorsal and anal fins bright yellow; finlets bright yellow with black edges. Reaches 220 cm; the all-tackle angling record, 176.4 kg (208 cm fork length). Worldwide in tropical to warm temperate seas (but not the Arabian Gulf); an offshore species, but occasionally encountered near shore where oceanic water is near. Schools by size, sometimes with other species, generally in the upper 100 m; large fish sometimes associated with porpoises. Feeds on a wide variety of pelagic fishes, crustaceans, and cephalopods. Grows rapidly, reaching 50 cm in a year and 1 m in two years. Schaefer et al. (1963) reviewed the biological data of the species in the Pacific.

1064. *Scomberomorus guttatus*, 52.4 cm (J. Randall)

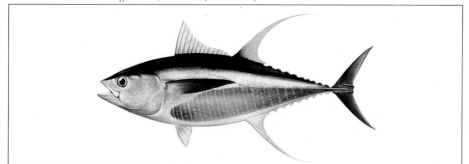

1065. *Thunnus albacares* (Illustration by R.A. Swainston)

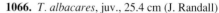
1066. *T. albacares*, juv., 25.4 cm (J. Randall)

BIGEYE TUNA
Thunnus obesus (Lowe, 1839)

Dorsal rays XIII-XIV+14-16 + 8-10 finlets; anal rays 11-15 + 7-10 finlets; pectoral rays 31-35; gill rakers 7-9 + 18-20; body deep, the depth 3.2-3.8 in fork length; eye large; dorsal fins separated by a very narrow space; second dorsal and anal fins not prolonged as in the Yellowfin Tuna; pectoral fins moderately long, 22-31% fork length; swimbladder present; ventral surface of liver of fish larger than 30 cm striated; dark blue on back, shading to silvery white below; in life an iridescent blue stripe along side; first dorsal fin deep yellow; second dorsal and anal fins light yellow; finlets bright yellow, edged in black. Attains 240 cm; the all-tackle angling record, 197.3 kg, from off Peru (236 cm long). Cosmopolitan in tropical to warm temperate seas (but not the Red Sea or Arabian Gulf); occurs from the surface to 250 m, but generally at the depth of the thermocline (optimal sea temperature for the species, 17-22°C). Food habits similar to that of other large tunas.

LONGTAIL TUNA
Thunnus tonggol (Bleeker, 1851)

Dorsal rays XII-XIV+14-15 + 8-9 finlets; anal rays 13-15 + 8-9 finlets; pectoral rays 30-35; gill rakers 5-8 + 14-17; body depth 3.8-4.3 in fork length, deepest below middle of first dorsal fin; dorsal fins separated by a very narrow space; second dorsal and anal fins not greatly prolonged; pectoral fins moderately long, 16-22% fork length in adults; swimbladder absent or rudimentary; ventral surface of liver not striated; dark blue dorsally, shading to light bluish grey ventrally, with rows of horizontally elongate pale spots on ventral third of body; dorsal, and paired fins blackish, the tip of seond dorsal and anal fins yellowish; anal fin silvery; finlets yellow with grey margins; caudal fin blackish with streaks of yellowish green. Reaches 140 cm; all-tackle angling record, 35.9 kg (fork length, 136 cm) from Montagne Island, New South Wales. Red Sea to the East Indies and Australia, north to Japan (where rare); not known from the Arabian Gulf of East Africa south of Somalia. A surface-dwelling, neritic species, but not found in turbid low-salinity waters.

BILLFISHES
FAMILY XIPHIIDAE

The billfishes have long been classified in two families, Xiphiidae for

1067. *Thunnus obesus* (Illustration by R.A. Swainston)

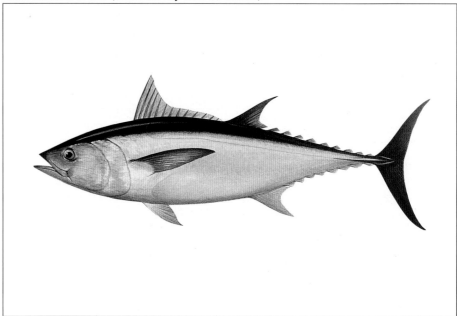

1068. *Thunnus tonggol* (Illustration by R.A. Swainston)

the Swordfish and the Istiophoridae for the marlins, sailfish, and spearfishes. Johnson (1986), however, united the two families and included them in the suborder Scombroidei with the barracudas, cutlassfishes, snake mackerels, and the tunas and mackerels. The most obvious family trait is the elongation of the anterior head bones (foremost, the premaxilla) to form the sword or bill. Other characters: gill membranes free from the isthmus; no gill rakers; origin of the dorsal fin over posterior part of head; no spines in the dorsal and anal fins; two anal fins; pectoral fins inserted low on the body, and pelvic fins absent or reduced to a spine and two rays. The Swordfish is now the sole species of the subfamily Xiphiinae; it is easily distinguished from the Istiophorinae as shown by the diagnoses below. The billfishes are pelagic in oceanic waters, though a few are known to penetrate coastal seas; most are very wide-ranging, some in all tropical to temperate seas. They are highly prized as gamefishes and very important commercial fishes. Females grow faster and reach larger size than the males. Nakamura (1985) revised the billfish family and summarised biological and fisheries data for all 12 species.

SUBFAMILY ISTIOPHORINAE

SAILFISH
Istiophorus platypterus (Shaw and Nodder, 1792)

Dorsal rays 39-48; anal rays 8-15 + 5-8; pectoral rays 17-20; pelvic rays I,2; body covered with elongate embedded scales; lateral line present, curved above pectoral fin; body elongate and slightly tapering, the greatest depth just behind head, 6.5-8.0 in fork length (measured to tip of bill); body moderately compressed; bill long, 3.9-4.5 in fork length, and round in cross-section; small, file-like teeth in jaws and on palatines (true of all species of the Istiophorinae); caudal peduncle and base of caudal fin reinforced by a pair of keels on each side (also applies to the subfamily); swimbladder consisting of many small bubble-like chambers (subfamily character); first dorsal, first anal, and pelvic fins fold into a groove when swimming rapidly (subfamily character); dorsal fin very elevated, the middle rays longest, twice or more body depth below these rays; pelvic fins long and slender, nearly reaching anus; deep blue on back, silvery below, with vertical rows of light blue spots on side of body (appearing pale on dark upper part of body); dorsal fin dark blue with numerous small black spots on membranes except distally and anteriorly. Reaches 340 cm; all-tackle angling record, 100.2 kg (length, 328 cm), from Ecuador; the angling record for the Atlantic is 61.4 kg, from Nigeria. Sailfish occur in all tropical to temperate seas, including the Red Sea and Arabian Gulf. Some authors, such as Nakamura (1985), prefer to regard the form in the Atlantic as a distinct species, hence *I. albidus* (Latreille). *I. platypterus* is the least pelagic of the billfishes, often venturing into nearshore waters. Tagging studies in the western Atlantic have shown extensive movements, the longest of 3,070 km from North Carolina to the Guianas. Preys on a wide variety of fishes and cephalopods; in feeding on schooling species such as sardines, anchovies, and mackerels, it is reported to lash with its bill and feed on those killed or stunned; cooperative predation by several sailfish on the same school has been observed. Females are mature at an age of three years and a length of 150 cm (van der Elst, 1981). Prince et al. (1986) reported the recapture of a tagged sailfish in Florida that weighed 24.6 kg and was 176.5 cm in lower-jaw fork length (hence about 223 cm total length); it was tagged 10 years and 10 months earlier at an estimated weight of 18.2 kg (probable age 2-4 years); therefore it is clear that the longevity of the sailfish is much greater than was formerly believed.

1069. *Istiophorus platypterus* (Illustration by R.A. Swainston)

BLACK MARLIN
Makaira indica (Cuvier, 1832)

Dorsal rays 34-43 + 5-7; anal rays 10-14 + 6-7; pectoral rays usually 19-20; body densely covered with elongate scales bearing one or two sharp posterior points; lateral line present, but obscure in large adults; body robust, tapering, and elongate, the depth 5.0-6.3 in fork length; nape of adults steep; snout 4.3-4.8 in fork length, the bill nearly round in cross-section; elevated anterior part of first dorsal fin less than body depth, the fin very long and low posteriorly, narrowly separated from the short second dorsal fin; caudal fin very large and lunate; pectoral fins project rigidly to the side and cannot be folded against the body; pelvic fins shorter than pectorals; dark blue dorsally, silvery white ventrally. Attains about 450 cm; all-tackle angling record, 707.6 kg (length, 442 cm), from off Peru. Widespread in the tropical and subtropical Indo-Pacific and eastern Pacific, occasional into temperature waters; also reported from the eastern Atlantic, probably as strays from around the Cape of Good Hope. Although an oceanic fish, it is most common near land masses. Usually occurs at or near the surface, but has been recorded as deep as 200 m. Feeds on a wide variety of fishes and cephalopods, but preys most often on tunas and bonitos. Prey from the stomach usually swallowed head-first and may bear slashes attributed to the bill.

1070. *Makaira indica* (Illustration by R.A. Swainston)

INDO-PACIFIC BLUE MARLIN
Makaira nigricans Lacepède, 1802

Dorsal rays 39-45 + 6-7; anal rays 12-17 + 6-7; pectoral rays 19-23; body densely covered with thick elongate scales bearing one to three posterior points; lateral line clearly evident in immature fish, becoming obscure in adults; body and fin shape similar to *M. indica*, but pectoral fins can be folded against side of body; dark blue dorsally, silvery white below, with about 15 narrow blue bars on body. Reaches about 500 cm; weights to 906 kg recorded from longline catches; all-tackle angling record, 624 kg. Occurs throughout most of the tropical and subtropical oceans of the world but ventures during warm months into temperate waters (unknown from the Red Sea, Arabian Gulf, and Mediterranean Sea). Nakamura (1985) is followed here in regarding the Indo-Pacific population as distinct at the species level, hence *M. mazara* (Jordan and Snyder), but most authors recognise only one worldwide species. More tropical and more oceanic than other marlins. Food habits vary with the availability of prey; mostly squids in the Philippine Sea; mostly scombrids off New Zealand and the Central Pacific (a 340-kg. specimen from Hawaii had a 27-kg Bigeye Tuna in its stomach). Nakamura (1985, after Radtke) gave the following estimates of age and growth from reading rings in otoliths: males 52.1 kg in six years, 96.9-114.2 kg in 11-12 years; female 135.4-147.4 kg in eight years, 336.5 kg in 17 years.

1071. *Makaira nigricans* (Illustration by R.A. Swainston)

SHORTBILL SPEARFISH
Tetrapturus angustirostris Tanaka, 1915

Dorsal rays 45-50 + 6-7; anal rays 12-15 + 6-8; pectoral rays 17-19; body densely covered with elongate scales, each ending posteriorly in 3-5 points; lateral line single and evident throughout life; body moderately compressed and elongate, the depth about 8-9 in fork length; bill very short, usually less than 15% of fork length; first dorsal fin a little higher than body depth anteriorly, soon decreasing to half body depth, then gradually increasing to three-fourths depth in middle of fin, followed by a gradual decrease in height, ending shortly before second dorsal fin; pectoral fins short, equal to length of postorbital head; pelvic fins about twice length of pectorals; deep blue dorsally, silvery white ventrally, without spots or bars. Maximum length about 200 cm; weight to 52 kg. Indo-Pacific and eastern Pacific in tropical to temperate seas, but rarely entering coastal waters (not known from the Red Sea or Arabian Gulf); a few records from the South Atlantic coast of Africa probably represent strays from the Indian Ocean. Analysis of the species of fishes in the stomach contents indicates that feeding does not occur at depths as great as that of the other billfishes, in general; in some areas, such as the eastern Pacific, squids may dominate the stomach contents.

1072. *Tetrapturus angustirostris* (Illustration by R.A. Swainston)

STRIPED MARLIN
Tetrapturus audax (Philippi, 1887)

Dorsal rays 37-42 + 5-6; anal rays 13-18 + 5-6; pectoral rays 18-22; body densely covered with embedded elongate scales ending posteriorly in one or two sharp points; a single lateral line with an arch above pectoral fin, then straight to caudal-fin base; body elongate and moderately compressed, the depth 6.2-7.5 in fork length; bill long for the genus, the snout length 4.2-5.0 in fork length, nearly round in cross-section; front of first dorsal fin equal to or slightly greater that body depth, decreasing sharply in height to about tenth ray, then gradually decreasing to terminate before short second dorsal fin; pectoral fins relatively long, about half head length; pelvic fins slightly shorter than pectorals; deep blue on back, silvery white ventrally, with about 15 narrow light blue bars or vertical rows of spots. Reaches about 350 cm; all-tackle angling record, 224 kg, from New Zealand. An oceanic species of the tropical to temperate Indo-Pacific and eastern Pacific; a few have been taken on the Atlantic side of South Africa, and one off Angola; penetrates the higher latitudes during the warm season; found more in temperate waters than other marlins and spearfishes; however, primarily surface-dwelling and not apt to swim below the thermocline. Like other billfishes, an opportunistic feeder on a wide variety of pelagic fishes and squids.

1073. *Tetrapturus audax* (Illustration by R.A. Swainston)

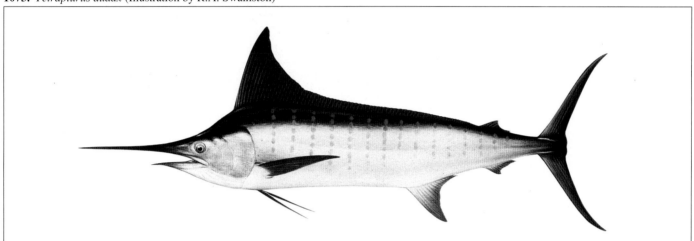

SUBFAMILY XIPHIINAE

SWORDFISH
Xiphias gladius Linnaeus, 1758

Dorsal rays 34-49 + 4-6; anal rays 13-14 + 3-4; pectoral rays 16; no pelvic fins; adults without scales and without lateral line (young to about 100 cm body length have spiny scales and a lateral line); no teeth in jaws of adults; eye large; body elongate, the depth about 6-7 in fork length, and nearly cylindrical; bill very long (the snout length about one-third fork length) and flat-oval in cross-section; caudal peduncle reinforced by a single large midlateral keel; swimbladder a single chamber; no grooves for fins; first dorsal fin of adults short-based, erect, and very broadly separated from tiny second dorsal fin; first anal fin also short-based and erect, well separated from tiny second anal fin; caudal fin very large and lunate; colour variously described as dark grey, bronze, brown, or bluish black dorsally, shading to whitish ventrally. Attains 445 cm; the all-tackle angling record, 536 kg, from off Chile. An open-ocean fish occurring in all tropical to temperate seas, including the Red Sea and Mediterranean Sea (but not the Arabian Gulf). It is known to 50°N in the Pacific, 60°N in the eastern Atlantic and 45-50°S; its optimum range of sea temperature is about 18-22°C, but it has been recorded from seas varying in temperature from 5-27°C. Occurs primarily at or near the surface, but is reported to reach depths as great as 650 m. Migratory; excursions to higher latitudes during the warm months of the year and tending to follow the warm currents. The young are very different from the adult; both jaws are elongate and bear teeth; there is a single, long, relatively high dorsal fin (suggestive of the sailfish) and a single long anal fin. With growth, the lower jaw shortens, the teeth, scales, and lateral line are lost, and the dorsal and anal fins broadly divide to two fins. Feeds on a wide variety of fishes and cephalopods. That it uses its bill by lashing laterally to stun or kill its prey seems evident from the slash marks found on stomach-content specimens.

1074. *Xiphias gladius* (Illustration by R.A. Swainston)

SICKLEFISHES
FAMILY DREPANIDAE

This small family of a single genus and two species is sometimes classified as a subfamily of the Ephippidae, but most current authors follow Johnson (1984) in recognising it at the family level. It is characterised by a very deep and compressed body (the depth can be as great as the standard length) and a small downward-protrusible mouth; maxilla exposed on cheek when mouth closed; jaws with villiform bands of teeth; no teeth on roof of mouth; lower edge of preopercle serrate; gill rakers small; two median rows of small slender barbels on chin, disappearing with growth; scales small and cycloid; opercle scaled only dorsally; dorsal fin with IX-X spines (including initial procumbent spine, visible only in young) and 19-22 rays, the fin deeply emarginate posterior to the longest (fourth) spine, and depressible into a scaly sheath; anal fin with III spines

1075. School of *Drepane longimana* (J. Hoover)

and 17-19 soft rays; caudal fin slightly rounded to rhomboid or slightly double emarginate, with 15 branched rays; pectoral fins very long and sickle-shaped, nearly reaching caudal-fin base; swimbladder bifurcate posteriorly, extending and tapering into tail; vertebrae 24. Indo-Pacific, one species extending range to West Africa; usually found in protected shallow (and often turbid) water over sand or mud bottoms.

BARRED SICKLEFISH
Drepane longimana (Bloch and Schneider, 1801)

Dorsal rays VIII-IX,19-23; anal rays III,17-19; pectoral rays 16-18; lateral-line scales 45-55; gill rakers 4-5 + 10-12; body nearly rhomboid in shape, the depth 1.0-1.3 in standard length (young more deep-bodied); posterior horns of swimbladder with 11 lateral branches; silvery grey dorsally, shading to silvery on sides and ventrally, usually with four to eight vertical dark bars on upper half to two-thirds of body; small dark spots. Reported to attain 50 cm. Red Sea (Randall, 1994) and Arabian Gulf south to South Africa and east to the western Pacific; also from West Africa; often found in estuaries. Some authors such as Weber and de Beaufort (1936) regarded *D. punctata* as a senior synonym of *D. longimana*; however, the structure of the swimbladder is very different in the two species (Kuronuma and Abe, 1986: table 48).

SPOTTED SICKLEFISH
Drepane punctata (Linnaeus, 1758)

Dorsal rays VIII-IX,19-22; anal rays III,19-22; pectoral rays 17-19; lateral-line scales 50-55; gill rakers 4 + 11-12; body depth 1.0-1.3 in standard length (the young deeper bodied); slender posterior horns of swimbladder without lateral branches; silvery with four to nine vertical rows of small blackish spots on upper half to two-thirds of body; two or three longitudinal rows of small black spots in soft portion of dorsal fin. Reported to 45 cm. Red Sea and Arabian Gulf (Blegvad, 1944: fig. 81) east to Samoa. Feeds on small crabs, shrimps, and worms, often ingesting mud with the prey (van der Elst, 1981). A 15-cm Bishop Museum specimen from the Arabian Gulf is a fully mature female.

1076. *Drepane longimana*, 15 cm (J. Randall)

1077. *Drepane punctata*, 20.3 cm (J. Randall)

SPADEFISHES
FAMILY EPHIPPIDAE

This family is represented by the genus *Chaetodipterus* in the Atlantic and eastern Pacific, the monotypic *Parapsettus* from the tropical eastern Pacific, and five Indo-Pacific genera, of which *Ephippus* and *Platax* have species in Oman waters. The fishes of the genus *Platax* have generally been given the common name of Batfish; however this name properly belongs to the Ogcocephalidae (Robins et al., 1991). It is here proposed that platax be used as a common name for the species of *Platax*, leaving the name spadefish for the species of *Chaetodipterus*. Ephippids are characterised by a deep compressed body; a small, terminal, near-horizontal, nonprotractile or slightly protractile mouth; maxilla partially slipping under preorbital when mouth closed; teeth small, in bands in jaws, none on palate; posterior nostril elongate; gill membranes broadly attached to isthmus, restricting gill openings to the side; upper-limb gill rakers comb-like; scales cycloid to ctenoid, small to moderate; base of median fins densely scaled; dorsal fin with V-IX spines and 18-39 soft rays; anal fin with III spines and 15-29 soft rays; caudal fin truncate to slightly double emarginate; pelvic fins I,5, their origin below pectoral-fin base, with a scaly axillary process; vertebrae 24. The five species of *Platax* were reviewed by Kishimoto et al. (1988), with emphasis on Japanese species. This and the following family have been reclassified from the suborder Percoidei to the Acanthuroidei (Tyler et al., 1989; Winterbottom, 1993).

ORBFISH
Ephippus orbis (Bloch, 1787)

Dorsal rays IX-X,19-20 (first spine procumbent, externally visible only in young); anal rays III,15-16; pectoral rays 18-19; lat-

1078. *Platax orbicularis*, subadults (J. Hoover)

eral-line scales 40-42; scales cycloid, the edges membraneous and irregular; top of head scaled to front of interorbital space; body orbicular, the depth 1.25-1.5 in standard length, and compressed; dorsal profile of head very steep, with a slight convexity before eyes; fourth dorsal spine longest, the first three and last three or four spines very short; pectoral fins short and rounded; silvery, often with five narrow dark bars on upper half or more of body. Attains 20 cm. Arabian Gulf along the southern continental Asian coast to Indonesia, north to China and Taiwan. Usually taken by trawling over mud bottoms.

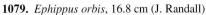

1079. *Ephippus orbis*, 16.8 cm (J. Randall)

381

CIRCULAR PLATAX
Platax orbicularis (Forsskål, 1775)

Dorsal rays V,34-39; anal rays III,25-29; pectoral rays 16-18; lateral-line scales 44-52; scales finely ctenoid; top of head not scaled; body of juveniles very deep, the depth greater than standard length (relative depth progressively less with growth, in large adults to 1.4 in standard length); snout of adults slightly protruding; teeth tricuspid, the middle cusp much the largest; chin with five sensory pores on each side; dorsal spines progressively longer, without a notch before spinous portion (true of other species of the genus); dorsal and anal fins of juveniles greatly elevated but broad, gradually shortening with growth; caudal fin of juveniles slightly rounded, of adults slightly double emarginate; pectoral fins short (also generic); pelvic fins greatly elongate in juveniles, becoming relatively shorter with growth (generic); juveniles light reddish brown to brownish yellow with a dark brown bar on head through eye; adults silvery grey, usually with a few scattered small black spots on body, a broad dark brown bar anteriorly on body, and a narrower one on head passing through eye. Reaches 40 cm. Indo-Pacific. The young are found inshore, sometimes lying on their side, resembling a drifting brownish yellow leaf (Randall and Randall, 1960). *P. vespertilio* (Bloch) is a synonym.

TEIRA
Platax teira (Forsskål, 1775)

Dorsal rays V,29-34; anal rays III,21-26; pectoral rays 16-18; lateral-line scales 56-66; scales finely ctenoid; top of head scaleless; body depth of juveniles more than standard length, of adults up to 1.4 in standard length; snout of adults not protruding, its dorsal profile nearly vertical, the steepness continuing to well above eye where there is a distinct angularity to nape; teeth tricuspid, the lateral cusps nearly as large as middle one; five sensory pores on each side of chin; dorsal and anal fins of juveniles enormously elevated; caudal fin of juveniles slightly rounded, of adults slightly double emarginate; juveniles silvery grey with a very broad dark brown bar posteriorly on body extending onto dorsal and anal fins, a broad dark brown bar anteriorly on body, and a narrower one on head through eye; adults with posterior half of body grey-brown, the anterior part darker to form a broad indistinct bar; head and body anterior to this bar pale grey with a broad dark grey-brown bar anteriorly on body and a narrower one on head through eye; a dark brown to black spot larger than eye on side of abdomen; median fins blackish posteriorly; pelvic fins varying from yel-

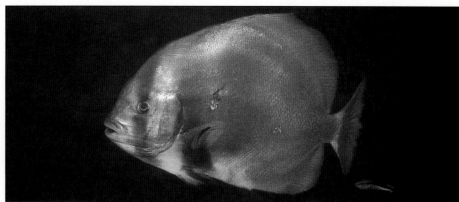

1080. *Platax orbicularis*, about 45 cm (J. Randall)

1081. *Platax teira*, about 40 cm (J. Randall)

low to yellowish brown. Reaches about 70 cm. Red Sea south to Natal and east to the western Pacific where it ranges from Hokkaido to Sydney, New South Wales; in Oceania, only to Palau. The young have been found drifting with masses of algae or objects on the sea surface far from land. The species identified as *P. pinnatus* by Basson et al. (1981: fig. 162) from Jana Island, Persian Gulf is *P. teira*.

SCATS
FAMILY SCATOPHAGIDAE

This small family of a single genus and four species is diagnosed by the following characters: a deep compressed body; head with a steep dorsal profile and a distinct concavity above eye; a very small, terminal, non-protractile, horizontal mouth; maxilla slipping under preorbital when mouth closed; teeth in several rows in jaws very small, and brush-like, none on roof of mouth; gill membranes joined, forming a narrow fold across isthmus; scales ctenoid, very small, and extending onto head and basally on soft portions of median fins; dorsal fin with XI-XII strong spines (the first procumbent) and 15 to 18 soft rays, deeply notched between spinous and soft portions; anal fin with IV stout spines and 13-16 soft rays; caudal fin rounded in juveniles, truncate to slightly double emarginate in adults, with 14 branched rays; pectoral fins short; pelvic fins I,5, their origin slightly posterior to pectoral-fin base, with a scaly axillary process; vertebrae 23; bones of head without spines or serrae, but the postlarva has a bony shield on the head with a suprascapular and a preopercular spine. Found in protected waters that vary from fully saline to fresh; at least one species can reproduce in freshwater. Often seen in small aggregations. The spines may inflict painful wounds and are believed to be venomous.

SPOTTED SCAT
Scatophagus argus (Bloch, 1788)

Dorsal rays XII (including procumbent spine),16-18; anal rays IV,14-15; pectoral rays 17; lateral-line scales about 95; body depth 1.5-1.7 in standard length; teeth in jaws multiserial, small, slender and compressed but sharp-tipped; fifth dorsal spine longest; penultimate dorsal spine shorter than last spine; ground colour variable, often greenish grey, with numerous dark grey spots on body, most of about pupil size or smaller on adults, but some may be as large or larger than eye; juveniles are more colourful, orange-red dorsally on the head and body, with dark bars which break up into spots with growth. Attains 30 cm. Western Pacific from Japan to New South Wales, west to the Arabian Gulf; usually found in estuaries or mangrove sloughs. The generic name means "dung-feeding", in reference to the feeding by this fish on sewage and offal, but it also ingests benthic algae and small invertebrates.

1082. *Scatophagus argus*, 14.2 cm (J. Randall)

RABBITFISHES
FAMILY SIGANIDAE

The rabbitfishes have long been classified with the surgeonfishes and *Zanclus* in the perciform suborder Acanthuroidei. Phylogentic studies by Tyler et al. (1989) and Winterbottom (1993) enlarged the suborder to include the Ephippidae, Scatophagidae, and *Luvarus*. The rabbitfish family consists of a single genus which is distinctive in having an ellipsoid, compressed body; a continuous dorsal fin with XIII spines and 10 soft rays; anal fin with VII spines and 9 soft rays; dorsal and anal spines alternating left and right of midline; pelvic fins of two spines with three soft rays between, the inner spine connected by membrane to the abdomen; very small, partly embedded, cycloid scales; a small, terminal to slightly inferior mouth with a broad upper lip and a single row of incisiform bicuspid teeth in jaws; no teeth on vomer and palatines; and 23 vertebrae. All the spines, including the procumbent one in front of the dorsal fin, are venomous; wounds from the spines are extremely painful but not lethal. All of the species are herbivorous, feeding primarily on benthic or detached algae. The family is confined to the Indo-Pacific region; 28 species are recognised. Fourteen of them are usually found in small schools in seagrass beds or over weedy bottoms. The others occur on coral reefs and are often seen in pairs. When they rest upon the bottom by day or when asleep at night, they assume a different colour pattern, generally a disruptive one of dark blotches. Woodland (1990) reviewed the classification and biology of the family; he recognised two subgenera, *Siganus* and *Lo*, the five species of the latter with a characteristic prolonged snout. Because of rapid growth, herbivorous food habits, and tasty flesh, some of the rabbitfishes have been candidates for aquaculture.

1083. School of *Siganus canaliculatus* (J. Hoover)

FORKTAIL RABBITFISH
Siganus argenteus (Quoy and Gaimard, 1825)

Dorsal rays XIII,10; anal rays VII,9; pectoral rays 17-19 (usually 18); pelvic rays I,3,I; scale rows above lateral line 16-22; midventral region of chest scaleless; body elongate for the genus, the depth 2.4-3.0 in standard length; head somewhat pointed; dorsal spines slender, the fourth to eighth longest 2.5-3.5 times longer than last dorsal spine; second to fourth dorsal soft rays longest, less than length of longest dorsal spines; second to fourth anal spines longest, 2.1-3.1 times longer than last anal spine; caudal fin strongly forked; blue to bluish grey or brown with numerous small yellow spots which may join to form narrow stripes, especially ventrally on body. Attains 45 mm. The most wide-ranging of the Siganidae, occurring from the Red Sea and east coast of Africa to Pitcairn Island in southeastern Oceania. Usually seen in small aggregations; moves in open water more than other rabbitfishes. The late postlarval stage up to 65 mm standard length may form dense schools offshore. *Amphacanthus rostratus* Valenciennes is a synonym.

PEARLSPOTTED RABBITFISH
Siganus canaliculatus (Park, 1797)

Dorsal rays XIII,10; anal rays VII,9; pectoral rays 15-18; pelvic rays I,3,I; scale rows above lateral line 21-27; no scales midventrally on chest; body depth 2.4-2.8 in standard length; dorsal spines slender, the fourth to seventh longest, about twice as long as last spine; dorsal soft rays short, the first to third longest, equal to or shorter than longest dorsal spine; caudal fin emarginate in young, slightly forked in adult; yellowish grey to light brown with scattered small whitish to pale blue spots (spots much smaller than interspaces); also capable of displaying small brown spots along with the pale spots; opercular membrane dark brown. Attains 30 cm. Arabian Gulf along continental shores to the Indo-Malayan region and Western Australia, north to Hong Kong and Taiwan. A schooling species occurring from inshore to at least 40 m. *Teuthis oramin* Günther is a synonym.

STREAKED RABBITFISH
Siganus javus (Linnaeus, 1766)

Dorsal rays XIII,10; anal rays VII,9; pectoral rays 17-18 (usually 18); pelvic rays I,3,I; scale rows above lateral line 30-38; midventral part of chest scaled; body moderately deep, the depth 2.0-2.3 in standard length; space between upper lip and eye less

1084. *Siganus argenteus*, about 15 cm (J. Randall)

1085. *Siganus canaliculatus*, night colouration, about 17 cm (J. Randall)

1086. *Siganus javus*, about 23 cm (J. Randall)

than eye diameter; fourth to sixth dorsal spines longest, 1.2-1.6 times longer than last spine; third or fourth dorsal soft ray longest, equal to or a little longer than longest dorsal spine; second to seventh anal spines subequal to longest dorsal spines; caudal fin slightly emarginate; brown to dark grey dorsally with very small white spots on head and body, becoming larger and more elongate on side of body and finally as alternating stripes of white and dark grey on ventral half; caudal fin blackish. The largest of the Siganidae; attains at least 53 cm (largest specimen recorded, from Gulf of Oman). Arabian Gulf along the coast of southern Asia to the western Pacific where ranging from southern China to northern Queensland and Vanuatu. Usually encountered in small schools on shallow coral reefs or rocky substrata; also occurs in estuaries.

SQUARETAIL RABBITFISH
Siganus luridus (Rüppell, 1829)

Dorsal rays XIII,10; anal rays VII,9; pectoral rays 16-17; pelvic rays I,3,I; scale rows above lateral line 15-20; midventral region of chest scaleless; body depth 2.4-2.8 in standard length (2.1-2.5 in Red Sea); dorsal spines slender, the third to seventh longest 1.3-1.7 times longer than last spine; second or third dorsal soft ray longest, as long or slightly longer than longest dorsal spines; third or fourth anal spines longest, equal to or a little shorter than longest dorsal spines; caudal fin truncate; two diurnal colour patterns, one greyish yellow with small, irregular, pale blue spots which tend to anastomose ventrally on body; the other dark greyish yellow dorsally on body with a narrow white stripe from nostrils, above eye, to below front of soft portion of dorsal fin, the body below level of lower edge of eye abruptly white. Reaches 24 cm. Red Sea and Arabian Gulf south to Mozambique, Aldabra, Mauritius, and Réunion; invaded the eastern Mediterranean via the Suez Canal. Adults solitary or in small groups, generally associated with hard substratum; juveniles may congregate in large numbers in shallow water. The record of *S. spinus* (Linnaeus) from the Arabian Gulf and Gulf of Oman by Woodland in Fischer and Bianchi (1984) was a misidentification of *S. luridus*.

1087. *Siganus luridus*, about 10 cm (J. Hoover)

1088. *Siganus luridus*, striped colour phase (J. Hoover)

MOORISH IDOL
FAMILY ZANCLIDAE

See discussion of the single species of the family below.

1089. *Zanclus cornutus* (J. Hoover)

MOORISH IDOL
Zanclus cornutus Linnaeus, 1758

Dorsal rays VII,40-43; anal rays III,33-35; pectoral rays 19; body very deep, 1.0-1.4 in standard length, and compressed; third dorsal spine extremely long and filamentous, usually longer than standard length; snout narrow and prolonged; mouth small, the teeth slender, slightly incurved, and uniserial; adults with a bony projection in front of each eye, larger in males; scales very small, each with a vertical row of erect ctenii which curve posteriorly, giving the skin a texture of fine sandpaper; two broad black bars, one from dorsal-fin origin to front of eye passing ventrally across head and anterior body, the second posteriorly on body before caudal peduncle, the broad interspace white at the front, continuing onto dorsal filament, and shading to yellow behind; snout white with a broad black-edged orange saddle; caudal peduncle yellow; caudal fin largely black. Attains 22 cm. Wide-ranging in the Indo-Pacific and the tropical eastern Pacific; occurs from the shallows to at least 180 m. Omnivorous, but feeds more on benthic animal life, such as sponges, than on algae. The unusually large late postlarval stage of this fish (which reaches 8 cm) has a stout, curved, preorbital spine on each side of the head which is shed during transformation. *Z. canescens* (Linnaeus) is a synonym based on this stage.

x

385

SURGEONFISHES
FAMILY ACANTHURIDAE

The surgeonfishes are named for the sharp spine or spines on the side of the caudal peduncle. The family is divisible into three subfamilies, the Acanthurinae in which the caudal spine is single and folds into a horizontal groove (includes the genera *Acanthurus, Ctenochaetus, Paracanthurus,* and *Zebrasoma*), the Nasinae in which one or two caudal spines are fixed and keel-like, and the Prionurinae with three to ten bony plates on the side of the caudal peduncle. The species of *Naso* are popularly known as unicornfishes because of the horn-like rostral projection on the forehead of many of the species; the species of *Ctenochaetus* are called bristletooths because of their numerous comb-like teeth; and those of the genus *Zebrasoma* are called tangs (perhaps from the German word for seaweed). As a group, the surgeonfishes have a deep compressed body; the eye high on the head; a long preorbital bone; a single unnotched dorsal fin with IV-IX spines and 19-33 rays; an anal fin with II or III spines (only *Naso* with II) and 18-28 rays; pelvic fins with I spine and 3 or 5 rays (*Naso* and *Paracanthurus* with 3); very small ctenoid scales; a small terminal mouth with a single row of close-set, incisiform teeth which may be spatulate with denticulate edges (*Acanthurus* and *Zebrasoma*), acute, with or without serrae (*Naso*), or numerous and comb-like with expanded, denticulate, incurved tips (*Ctenochaetus*); no teeth on the vomer or palatines. All of the surgeonfishes have a long intestine; the species of *Ctenochaetus* and some of the genus *Acanthurus* have a thick-walled, gizzard-like stomach. Most of the surgeonfishes graze on benthic algae, but a few species of *Acanthurus* and many of *Naso* feed mainly on zooplankton. The species of *Ctenochaetus* are detritus feeders. The author

has observed *Acanthurus xanthopterus* and *Naso vlamingii* mingling with schools of barracuda (*Sphyraena forsteri* and *S. qenie*) and jacks (*Caranx sexfasciatus*) well above the substratum; he wondered why until he saw them feed on the feces of these schooling fishes. Surgeonfishes have the capability of inflicting wounds on other fishes with their sharp caudal spines; this applies to humans as well if they attempt to grasp a live fish. Because of this ability, acanthurids are able to exert dominance over many other reef fishes. Some surgeonfishes have bright hues around their caudal spines, apparently serving as warning colouration. The eggs are pelagic. The spawning by species of *Acanthurus* and *Ctenochaetus* in large aggregations has been documented (Randall,1961a; Randall, 1961c; Myrberg et al., 1988). The late postlarval stage of acanthurids is orbicular, transparent with silvery over the abdomen, and scaleless with narrow vertical ridges on the body. This stage is called the acronurus for species of the Acanthurinae (proposed as a generic name for a postlarva of *Acanthurus*) and the keris (also proposed as a genus) for the species of *Naso* . Postlarval acanthurids have venomous second dorsal, second anal, and pelvic spines; the venom is lost in most species during transformation but retained in the adult of *Paracanthurus hepatus* and at least some species of *Naso*. The genera *Zebrasoma, Paracanthurus, Ctenochaetus,* and *Acanthurus* were revised by Randall (1955a, 1955b, and 1956). The family consists of 69 species, of which 61 are Indo-Pacific species, two are endemic to the eastern Pacific (both species of *Prionurus*), and six in the Atlantic (four species of *Acanthurus* in the western Atlantic and one of *Acanthurus* and one of *Prionurus* in the eastern Atlantic).

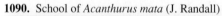

1090. School of *Acanthurus mata* (J. Randall)

SUBFAMILY ACANTHURINAE

EYESTRIPE SURGEONFISH
Acanthurus dussumieri Valenciennes, 1835

Dorsal rays IX,25-27; anal rays III,24-26; pectoral rays 16-17 (usually 17); pelvic rays I,5 (true also for other species of the genus); gill rakers 23-26; body depth 1.9-2.1 in standard length; large adults with a stongly convex forehead; total number of teeth in jaws vary from 14 in juveniles to 20-22 in large adults; caudal spine large, 3.0-5.0 in head; caudal fin lunate; stomach thick-walled; yellowish brown with irregular, longitudinal, blue lines on body; head yellow with blue lines and spots; a broad yellow band extending anteriorly from eye to eye, and an irregular yellow spot behind and adjacent to eye; opercular membrane blackish; sheath of caudal spine white, the socket rimmed with black; dorsal and anal fins yellow with a blue band at base and a blue margin (fins of young may be striped with blue); caudal fin blue with small blackish spots, yellow at base. Attains about 50 cm. East Africa (not the Red Sea) south to Natal and Mauritius (type locality), and east to the Hawaiian Islands and Line Islands in the central Pacific; in the western Pacific from southern Japan to New South Wales; observed in Oman only in the south. Sometimes misidentified as *A. bariene* Lesson.

POWDER BLUE SURGEONFISH
Acanthurus leucosternon Bennett, 1832

Dorsal rays IX,28-30; anal rays III,26-28; pectoral rays 15-16 (rarely 15); gill rakers 16-20; body depth 1.7-1.9 in standard length; snout length 4.0-4.35 in standard length; teeth in upper jaw of adults usually 10, in lower jaw usually 12; a single caudal spine on each side of caudal peduncle, folding into a groove (found on all species of *Acanthurus*, *Ctenochaetus*, and *Zebrasoma*), the spine length 2.1-3.3 in head length; caudal fin emarginate, the caudal concavity 10-16 in standard length; stomach thin-walled; blue with a broad white band crossing anterior chest from pectoral-fin base; caudal peduncle and spine yellow; head black; a white line extending from above corner of mouth around chin; dorsal fin yellow with a white margin and black submarginal line; anal fin grey with a white margin and narrow white band at base; caudal fin black with a large crescentic central white region and a white posterior margin. Reaches 23 cm. East Africa to southwestern Indonesia; common at islands of the western Indian Ocean; rare in Oman (one sighting in Gulf of Oman); a coral-reef species generally found in less than 15 m;

1091. *Acanthurus dussumieri*, about 33 cm (J. Randall)

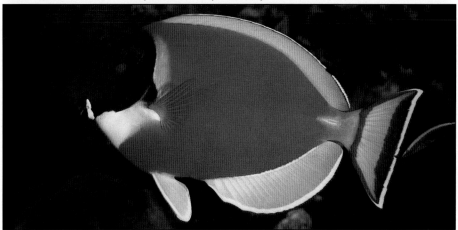

1092. *Acanthurus leucosternon*, about 14 cm (J. Randall)

1093. *Acanthurus mata*, about 38 cm (J. Randall)

may occur singly or in large feeding aggregations (which serve to overwhelm resident territorial fishes such as the damselfishes of the genera *Pomacentrus* and *Stegastes*).

BLUELINED SURGEONFISH
Acanthurus mata (Cuvier, 1829)

Dorsal rays IX,24-26; anal rays III,23-24; pectoral rays 16-17 (usually 17); gill rakers 13-17; body of adults elongate for the genus, about 2.5 in standard length (juveniles deeper bodied); dorsal profile of head sloping, forming an angle of about 45°; snout relatively short, 6.6-6.9 in standard length; caudal peduncle slender, the depth 10-12 in standard length (7.7-9.5 in other species of the genus); mouth small; teeth small, adults with 22-24 upper teeth and 24-26 lower; caudal fin of adults lunate; stomach large, U-shaped, and thin-walled with thorn-like papillae on inner surface; brown to dark brown with lengthwise blue lines on head and body; a yellow area behind eye, and two yellow bands extending anterior to eye; a blackish blotch at upper end of gill opening; a narrow blue stripe at base of dorsal fin with a black line below it that broadens posteriorly; capable of rapidly changing colour to pale blue (as in a cleaning station). Attains 50 cm. Indo-Pacific. Feeds on zooplankton; more inclined than other surgeonfishes to enter turbid water; may occur in aggregations. *A. bleekeri* Günther is a synonym.

SOHAL
Acanthurus sohal (Forsskål, 1775)

Dorsal rays IX,30-31; anal rays III,28-29 (usually 29); pectoral rays 17; gill rakers 15-17; body depth 2.0-2.2 in standard length;

1094. *A. sohal*, subadult, about 10 cm (J. Randall)

1095. *Acanthurus sohal*, about 35 cm (J. Hoover)

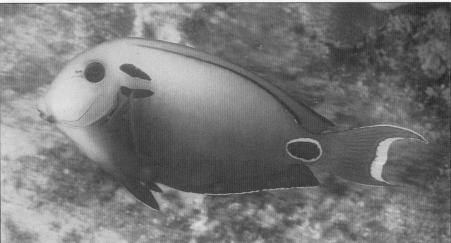

1096. *Acanthurus tennettii*, about 20 cm (J. Randall)

1097. *Ctenochaetus striatus*, about 15 cm (J. Randall)

caudal spine very long and slender, its length about 2 in head length; adults with as many as 16 upper and 18 lower teeth in jaws; caudal fin of adults strongly lunate, the lobes long and slender, the caudal concavity 3-4 in standard length; pale grey with narrow black stripes on head above level of lower edge of eye and along side of body; longitudinal black lines dorsally on body and in pectoral region; faint dark grey lines on head below eye and chest; an orange-yellow blotch midlaterally off tip of pectoral; sheath and socket of caudal spine bright orange; dorsal, anal, and pelvic fins black with blue margins, the dorsal with a blue line at base; caudal fin black with a blue margin and a large diffuse brown area in centre of fin. Attains 40 cm. Red Sea to Arabian Gulf; more common in the Arabian Gulf and Gulf of Oman than in southern Oman; usually seen in shallow water at the outer edge of reef flats where exposed to surge. A very aggressive and highly territory species, often seen chasing other fishes. Caudal spine reported as venomous.

DOUBLE-BAND SURGEONFISH
Acanthurus tennentii Günther, 1861

Dorsal rays IX,23-24; anal rays III,22-23; pectoral rays 16; gill rakers 23-25; body depth 2.0-2.35 in standard length; snout length 4.6-6.3 in standard length; adults with about 20 upper and 22 lower teeth; caudal spine 2.5-3.8 in head length; caudal fin emarginate in young to lunate in adults, the caudal concavity 5-10 in standard length; stomach thick-walled; brown with two black bands, one passing posteriorly from upper end of gill opening and the other above and parallel to it (the two joined posteriorly in juveniles and subadults); socket of caudal spine broadly bordered in black with an outer blue margin; caudal fin with a white border, very broad posteriorly in central part of fin; dorsal, anal, and pelvic fins with a light blue margin, the dorsal with a dark brown line at base; outer third of pectoral fins pale. Maximum length 31 cm. Known from Sri Lanka (type locality) west to the coast of Africa; fairly common at Mauritius, Seychelles, and Maldives; rare in Oman where observed only in the south. A coral-reef species observed at depths from 1-20 m; sometimes seen in small aggregations.

LINED BRISTLETOOTH
Ctenochaetus striatus (Quoy and Gaimard, 1825)

Dorsal rays VIII,27-31; anal rays III,24-28; pectoral rays 16-17 (usually 17); pelvic rays I,5 (applies to all six species of the genus); gill rakers 28-36; body depth 1.9-2.3 in standard length; teeth slender and flexible in jaws, the tips incurved and denticulate (5-7 denticulations on upper teeth and 4 on lower); adults with as many as 45 upper and 53 lower teeth; caudal fin of adults lunate, the caudal concavity 3.7-6.0 in standard length; stomach thick-walled (true of all species of the genus); brown to dark brown with numerous, longitudinal, light blue lines; nape and dorsal part of head with numerous orange-yellow dots; dorsal and anal fins with narrow blue stripes; a small black spot at rear base of dorsal fin. Attains 26 cm. Indo-Pacific on coral reefs; the most abundant of surgeonfishes at many localities within its range, but not common in Oman where observed only in the south. This and other species of *Ctenochaetus* feed on fine detrital and soft algal material by a combination of whisking with the movable comb-like teeth and suction.

GOLDRING BRISTLETOOTH
Ctenochaetus strigosus (Bennett, 1828)

Dorsal rays VIII,25-27; anal rays III,22-25; pectoral rays 15-16 (rarely 15); gill rakers 27-31; body depth 1.7-2.0 in standard length; dentition similar to that of *C. striatus*, the upper teeth with 5 denticulations on its incurved tips and the lower teeth with 3; adults with as many as 47 upper and 60 lower teeth; caudal fin slightly emarginate to truncate; reddish brown with light blue to yellow dots on head and body and a golden yellow ring around eye. Reaches 18 cm. Indo-Pacific; only one individual sighted in Oman, a juvenile on the Arabian Sea coast. In the Pacific the species has blue lines on the body instead of dots, and the caudal fin is deeply emarginate; insular populations within the Pacific also show differences (Randall, 1955b). Further study of *C. strigosus* over its range might result into its division into two or more species.

1099. *C. strigosus*, juv., about 4 cm (J. Randall)

1098. *Ctenochaetus strigosus*, about 18 cm (J. Randall)

YELLOWTAIL TANG
Zebrasoma xanthurum (Blyth, 1852)

Dorsal rays V,24-25; anal rays III,19-20; pectoral rays 15; pelvic rays I,5; teeth spatulate, close-set, denticulate, up to 20 in upper jaw and 22 in lower; adults with a velvet-like patch of setae anterior to caudal spine; body deep, the depth 1.7-1.85 in standard length; snout produced; dorsal and anal fins moderately elevated, the longest dorsal soft ray 3.4-3.7 in standard length; caudal fin slightly rounded; blue with dark dots on head, anterior body and abdomen; caudal fin and posterior part of pectoral fins bright yellow. Largest specimen, 22 cm. Red Sea to the Arabian Gulf; more common in the Arabian Gulf and Gulf of Oman than in the Arabian Sea. The type locality of Sri Lanka has been questioned; however, Randall and Anderson (1993) reported an adult of the species from the Maldives. The young appear in the Gulf of Oman during summer months.

1100. *Zebrasoma xanthurum*, about 20 cm (J. Hoover)

1101. *Z. xanthurum*, juv., about 4.5 cm (J. Randall)

FAGEN'S UNICORNFISH
Naso fageni Morrow, 1954

Dorsal rays V,24-26; anal rays II,23-25; pectoral rays 17; pelvic rays I,3 (characteristic of all species of *Naso*); gill rakers 13; body depth 2.4-3.2 in standard length (depth relative to length decreasing with growth); individuals of about 50 cm developing a slight bump in dorsal profile of snout just above upper lip, becoming more acute and projecting slightly anterior to mouth in larger fish; dorsal profile of large adults nearly straight; incisiform teeth small, acute, and finely serrate, about 40-60 in jaws; two keeled caudal plates midlaterally on each side of caudal peduncle, developing an antrorse point in adults; caudal fin emarginate, the upper lobe usually longer than lower; lobes of caudal fin of large adults slender and prolonged; grey to olive-grey dorsally, paler ventrally; large adults with numerous small dark spots; dorsal and anal fins with faint longitudinal bands. Believed to attain 100 m (Smith, 1966). Known previously only from the Philippines (type locality), New Caledonia, Mozambique, Kenya, and Seychelles; observed and photographed by the author and John P. Hoover at Juzor al Hallaniyat (Kuria Muria Islands), southern Oman. The individuals sighted were solitary, in shallow water, and difficult to approach. Subadults and juveniles of the species of *Naso* may be

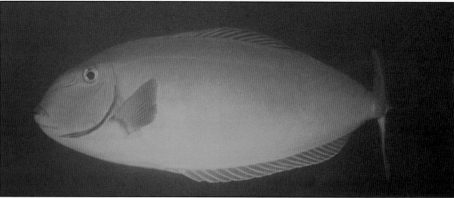

1102. *Naso fageni*, about 30 cm (J. Hoover)

difficult to differentiate, but *N. fageni* is easily distinguished, if specimens are in hand, by having the lowest dorsal and anal soft ray counts of the genus.

ORANGESPINE UNICORNFISH
Naso lituratus (Forster, 1801)

Dorsal rays VI,27-30; anal rays II,28-30; pectoral rays 16-17; body depth 2.0-2.4 in standard length (depth relative to length decreasing with growth); dorsal profile of head forming an angle of about 45° to the horizontal axis of body; no protuberance on forehead; teeth of adults incisiform, smooth-edged, with rounded ends, 30-35 in each jaw; two peduncular plates on side of caudal peduncle with a large, forward-curved, knife-like keel on each; caudal fin emarginate, the fin of adult males with a long filament from each corner; greyish brown, the peduncular plates bright orange; a diffuse yellow area behind and above eye; a narrow, curved, yellow band from eye to behind corner of mouth; snout in front of this band black; edge of lips broadly orange; dorsal fin orange-yellow with a broad black band near base, a blue line below, a white margin, and a black submarginal line; caudal fin with upper and lower edges (and filaments of male) black, the posterior margin white with a broad black submarginal band. Reaches 45 cm. Indo-Pacific; in the Pacific, the dorsal fin is mainly black; observed in Oman only on the southern coast. Feeds mainly on leafy brown algae such as *Sargassum*.

BLUESPINE UNICORNFISH
Naso unicornis (Forsskål, 1775)

Dorsal rays VI,27-30; anal rays II,27-30; pectoral rays 17-18; body depth 1.8 (in subadults) to 2.6 (large adults) in standard length; a tapering bony horn in adults projecting anteriorly at level of eye but not extending in front of mouth (horn first apparent as a protuberance at a length of about 12 cm); dorsal profile of snout to horn straight, forming an angle of about 45° to horizontal axis of body; 40-60 pointed incisiform teeth in jaws, the tips serrate (serrae may be absent on teeth of large adults); two bony plates on side of caudal peduncle, each with a well developed, forward-curving, knife-like spine in adults; caudal fin emarginate in young, truncate with filamentous lobes in adults; olivaceous with blue caudal peduncle plates and spines; lips bluish; dorsal and anal fins yellowish with narrow blue stripes. Reaches 70 cm. Indo-Pacific; in the western Indian Ocean from the Red Sea to Natal. Observed in Oman only on the Arabian Sea coast. An inshore species associated with coral reefs or rocky substrata; enters suprisingly shallow water for such a large fish in quest of its algal food (mainly leafy browns such as *Sargassum*).

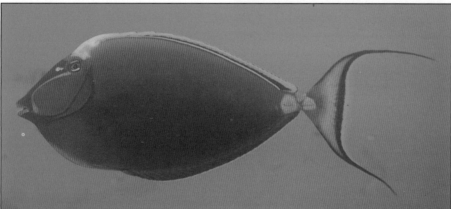

1103. *Naso lituratus*, about 40 cm (J. Hoover)

1104. *Naso unicornis*, about 50 cm (J. Randall)

TRIPODFISHES
FAMILY TRIACANTHIDAE

This family and the related Triacanthodidae are regarded as the most primitive of the nine families of the order Tetraodontiformes (formerly the Plectognathi). They are united by osteological characters such as the loss or fusion of bones of the head, along with other features such as a small gill opening and highly modified scales. The triacanthids are named for the long first dorsal spine and the two long pelvic spines. The pelvic spines can be locked in a fully extended position by a flange on the pelvis. With the dorsal fin erect, the fish would be able to discourage all but the largest of predators. The dorsal fin has VI spines, but usually only five are visible (the sixth being rudimentary); there are 20-26 dorsal soft rays, and 13-22 anal rays; the caudal fin is forked; the head is pointed, the dorsal profile straight except for a slight convexity before the eyes; the body is deepest anteriorly, then tapering both dorsally and ventrally to the slender and still tapering caudal peduncle; the gill opening is a short slit before the pectoral fin; the mouth is small and terminal with about ten strong incisiform teeth in each jaw in an outer series and an inner row of molariform teeth, generally two in upper jaw and two in lower. Tripodfishes are benthic on shallow, sedimentary bottoms; they feed on bottom-dwelling invertebrates. There are four genera and a total of seven species. Revision of the family and the Triacanthodidae by Tyler (1968).

1105. *Pseudotriacanthus strigilifer*, 9 cm (J. Randall)

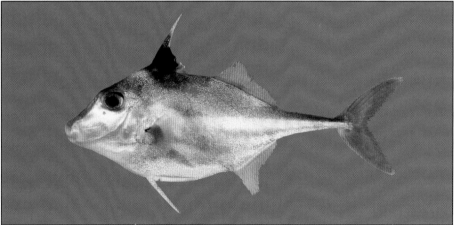

1106. *Triacanthus biaculeatus*, 21.2 cm (J. Randall)

LONGSPINE TRIPODFISH
Pseudotriacanthus strigilifer (Cantor, 1849)

Dorsal rays V + 20-24; anal rays 13-17; pectoral rays 12-14 (most often 13); pelvic fins I; ventral surface of pelvis (a median bone just beneath the ventral surface of the skin) tapering and ending in a point; body depth 2.7-3.5 in standard length; least depth of caudal peduncle 30-50 in standard length; first dorsal spine very long, 2.4-4.4 in standard length; second dorsal spine more than half length of first spine; base of anal fin about half base of soft dorsal fin; caudal fin forked; pelvic spine 3.6-5.1 in standard length; silvery with about seven horizontally elongate yellow spots as long as eye diameter on body; distal part of first interspinous membrane of dorsal fin black. Attains 25 cm. Arabian Gulf along the continental coast of southern Asia to the Indo-Malayan region; recorded to depths of 110 m. The only species of the genus.

SHORTNOSE TRIPODFISH
Triacanthus biaculeatus (Bloch, 1786)

Dorsal rays V + 21-26; anal rays 17-23; pectoral rays 12-16 (usually 14 or 15); pelvic rays I; pelvic bone not tapering to a point posteriorly; body depth 1.55-3.35 in standard length (juveniles deeper bodied); snout short, its length 4.95-6.4 in standard length; least depth of caudal peduncle 21-40 in standard length; first dorsal spine 1.9-5.8 in standard length (longest in juveniles); second dorsal spine less than half length of first dorsal spine; base of anal fin about three-fourths base of soft dorsal fin; caudal fin forked; pelvic spine 2.35-6.75 in standard length (relatively longer in smaller fish); silvery grey with an indistinct midlateral silver stripe which continues over pectoral-fin base onto head; a large dusky area on back beneath spinous dorsal fin; basal part of first dorsal spine and first three interspinous membranes black; caudal fin primarily yellow, the lobe tips white; pectoral fins yellow, the axil black. Reaches 30 cm. Arabian Gulf in continental waters to the western Pacific where ranging from southern Japan to Queensland. An inshore species of flat sand or mud bottoms; may be found in estuaries; maximum depth recorded, 60 m. Suzuki et al. (1983) studied the spawning and early life history in an aquarium. *T. brevirostris* Temminck and Schlegel is a synonym.

TRIGGERFISHES
FAMILY BALISTIDAE

The triggerfishes are named for the mechanism by which the first dorsal spine can be locked in erect postion by the small second spine; if one presses down on the second dorsal spine (the trigger), the first spine can be depressed. These fishes have moderately deep, compressed bodies; the eye set high on the head; a long snout, and a small, nonprotractile mouth with close-set, chisel-like teeth, eight in the outer row and six in an inner row which serve to buttress the outer teeth; the gill opening is a short slit anterior to the upper base of the pectoral fin; the skin is tough and rough to the touch, comprised of nonoverlapping scales, each with a broad area of small tubercles at the centre; most species have a patch of enlarged modified scales behind the gill opening; some have rows of small forward-curved spines posteriorly on the side of the body. There are two dorsal fins, the first of III spines (the third spine can be very small), the second dorsal and anal fins only of soft rays (nearly all branched); the caudal fin consists of twelve principal rays, the median 10 branched; there are no pelvic fins (they are replaced by the tip of the long depressible pelvic bone which is encased in four segments of modified scales). Triggerfishes are usually solitary; they swim by undulating the second dorsal and anal fins, using their tail only for rapid movement. When frightened, they often seek a hole in the reef with an entrance through which they can barely pass; once inside they erect their dorsal spine and depress their pelvic bone to lock themselves in position. At night they take refuge in this or a similar hole. Although their mouth is small, the jaws are powerful and the teeth strong; these fishes are able to reduce their prey to small pieces. Most feed primarily on benthic in-

vertebrates with hard skeletal parts such as crabs, molluscs, and sea urchins. Some such as *Odonus niger* and the species of *Canthidermis*, *Melichthys* and *Xanthichthys* feed heavily on zooplankton; an important part of the diet of *M. niger* (Bloch), however, is benthic algae. Triggerfishes lay demersal eggs which are aggressively guarded by the female parent. Some species excavate a shallow crater in sand and deposit the eggs in the centre. Divers should not venture close to guarding triggerfish because they may bite. Usually the fish will make a rush at the intruder but turn away before contact is made. If this threat is not heeded and the fish is approached more closely, the risk of being bitten is increased, particularly if the species is large, such as *Pseudobalistes viridescens* (Bloch and Schneider) (Randall and Millington, 1990). The family consists of 12 genera and 37 species. In the species accounts below, the rudimentary upper ray is included in the pectoral fin-ray count. Clark and Gohar (1953) reviewed the Red Sea species of the Tetraodontiformes which included eight species of trig-

gerfishes (two more later recorded); Matsuura (1980) reviewed the Japanese species of Balistidae, four of which range to Oman.

STARRY TRIGGERFISH
Abalistes stellatus (Lacepède, 1798)

Dorsal rays III + 25-27; anal rays 24-25; pectoral rays 15-16 (rarely 16); longitudinal scale series (from above upper end of gill opening) 33-41; enlarged osseous scales present behind gill opening; greatest body depth 2.0-2.5 in standard length; caudal peduncle depressed, the width greater than least depth, very slender and tapering, much longer than deep (as deep or deeper than long in other balistid fishes); an oblique groove before eye; first dorsal spine 1.6-1.9 in head length; third dorsal spine not short, about one-third length of first spine; front of soft dorsal and anal fins not elevated; caudal fin double emarginate, the lobes longer with growth; grey-brown to olivaceous dorsally with very small pale spots, becoming whitish ventrally with brownish yellow spots many of which anastomose into a reticulum; three large oval white spots along back and a small one dorsally on caudal peduncle; a broad white streak often present on side of body posterior to upper end of gill opening. Reported to 60 cm. Red Sea and Arabian Gulf to South Africa (also reported from West Africa), east to the western Pacific. Usually found on mud or silty sand bottoms.

1107. *Abalistes stellatus*, 28 cm (J. Randall)

LARGESCALE TRIGGERFISH
Canthidermis macrolepis (Boulenger, 1887)

Dorsal rays III + 23-26 (usually 25-26); anal rays 21-23 (rarely 21); pectoral rays 14-15 (usually 15); longitudinal scale series 35-40; no enlarged scales behind gill opening; scales of juveniles with a large central spine and one or two smaller spines above and below; some scales of juveniles with long, branched, dermal appendages; body elongate for a balistid, the greatest depth of adults 3.0-4.4 in standard length (depth about 1.8 in juveniles); an oblique groove before eye; first dorsal spine about 1.8 (juveniles)-2.5 (adults) in head length; third dorsal spine very small, not showing above dorsal profile of body; soft dorsal and anal fins greatly elevated anteriorly, the longest rays nearly as long as head; caudal fin of juveniles rounded, of adults double emarginate with produced lobes; grey, shading to pale grey ventrally; edges of second dorsal, anal, and caudal fins blackish; pectoral fins blackish. Attains 60 cm. Red Sea to Gulf of Oman; pelagic, but comes to the shallows to lay demersal eggs in a nest in sand. *C. longirostris* Tortonese and *C. villosus* Fedoryako are synonyms. Redescription by Gill and Randall (MS).

1108. *Canthidermis macrolepis*, about 35 cm (J. Randall)

INDIAN OCEAN DURGON
Melichthys indicus Randall and Klausewitz, 1973

Dorsal rays III + 30-35; anal rays 27-30; pectoral rays 14-16; longitudinal scale series 57-66; prominent longitudinal ridges on scales of caudal peduncle; a depressed circular zone of bony plates behind gill opening; an oblique groove anterior to eye; greatest body depth 1.8-1.95 in standard length; first dorsal spine 1.6-2.05 in head length; third dorsal spine short, but visible above dorsal profile of body when fin erected; soft dorsal and anal fins not very elevated anteriorly; caudal fin truncate to slightly rounded; black with six thin greenish lines radiating dorsally and anteriorly from eye; a thin, oblique, pale grey streak on lower side of head; a narrow bluish white band at base of soft dorsal and anal fins; caudal fin with a narrow white margin. Attains 25 cm. Red Sea to Natal and islands of the Indian Ocean to western Thailand and Sumatra; observed in Oman only on the Arabian Sea coast. Often seen well above the bottom where it appears to be feeding on zooplankton.

1109. *Melichthys indicus* (J. Hoover)

REDTOOTH TRIGGERFISH
Odonus niger (Rüppell, 1836)

Dorsal rays III + 33-36; anal rays 28-31; pectoral rays 15-16; longitudinal scale series 29-34; enlarged bony scales behind gill opening; about seven longitudinal rows of small spines on posterior half or more of body; greatest body depth 1.8-2.15 in standard length; mouth upturned, the chin protruding; tooth on each side of upper jaw long, protruding when mouth closed; a deep oblique groove before eye; first dorsal spine 1.75-2.25 in head length; third dorsal spine short but visible above dorsal profile of body when fin erect; front of soft dorsal and anal fins greatly elevated, the longest dorsal rays 1.1-1.7 in head; caudal fin lunate, the lobes greatly prolonged in adults; blue to dark purplish blue, the margins of soft dorsal, anal, and caudal fins light blue; head can be altered to dull yellowish green; teeth red. Reaches 40 cm. Indo-Pacific; the most abundant triggerfish in the Gulf of Oman; also very common in the Arabian Sea; generally found on steep outer reef slopes. Feeds mainly on zooplankton, often well above the substratum.

1110. *Odonus niger*, about 35 cm (J. Randall)

PICASSO TRIGGERFISH
Rhinecanthus assasi (Forsskål, 1775)

Dorsal rays III + 25-27 (usually 25 or 26); anal rays 22-24; pectoral rays 15; longitudinal scale series 36-43; three rows of small, forward-curved spines posteriorly on side of body, the upper row short; greatest body depth 2.0-2.25 in standard length; snout long and pointed; no groove anterior to eye; first dorsal spine 2.5-2.9 in head length; third dorsal spine very short, not extending above dorsal profile of body; soft dorsal and anal fins not elevated anteriorly; caudal fin slightly rounded to slightly double emarginate; tan, shading to white ventrally; a tapering blue-edged brown bar from eye to gill opening, preceded by a yellow band and a blue line; four narrow blue bands separated by black across interorbital space; lips yellow, a narrow blue zone adjacent to upper lip; above this a dark reddish brown streak which extends to lower pectoral-fin base; anus in a large black spot broadly surrounded by orange; spines posteriorly on body in narrow black stripes within an elliptical bluish white area; membrane of spinous dorsal fin black. Reaches 30 cm. Red Sea to Arabian Gulf, but not seen on southern coast of Oman south of Masirah Island. Difficult to approach underwater.

1111. *Rhinecanthus assasi*, about 18 cm (J. Hoover)

FLAGTAIL TRIGGERFISH
Sufflamen chrysopterus (Bloch and Schneider, 1801)

Dorsal rays III + 26-28; anal rays 23-26; pectoral rays 13-15; longitudinal scale series 41-47; scales in rows posterior to middle of soft dorsal fin with a small antrorse spine; greatest body depth 1.9-2.2 in standard length; snout moderately long, its dorsal profile straight; a deep oblique groove before eye; first dorsal spine 1.9-2.3 in head length; third dorsal spine short, but visible above dorsal profile of body when fin is erect; soft dorsal and anal fins not elevated anteriorly; caudal fin truncate to slightly rounded with acute corners; yellowish grey to dark brown with a pale yellow streak from below pectoral-fin base to posterior edge of eye; lower

1112. *Sufflamen chrysopterus*, about 17 cm (J. Hoover)

head and abdomen often deep purplish blue; caudal fin yellowish brown with a pure white border on all edges. Reaches 22 cm. Coast of East Africa to Micronesia and Samoa. *S. albicaudatus* (Rüppell) in the Red Sea has a white bar across the caudal-fin base connecting the white margins of the caudal fin; in other respects it seems identical to *S. chrysopterus*, hence it might best be regarded as a subspecies.

BRIDLED TRIGGERFISH
Sufflamen fraenatus (Latreille, 1804)

Dorsal rays III + 27-31; anal rays 24-28; pectoral rays 14-16; longitudinal scale series

43-54; longitudinal rows of scales on side of body posterior to origin of soft dorsal fin with a small spine on each scale; body depth 1.8-2.1 in standard length; first dorsal spine 1.9-2.1 in head length; third dorsal spine small, but visible above dorsal profile of body when fin is erect; anterior part of soft dorsal and anal fins not elevated; caudal fin slightly rounded to slightly double emarginate; grey-brown with a narrow yellow band on base of lower lip; males with a pale yellow to pink band under chin linking behind corner of mouth to a narrow band of the same colour which continues across lower cheek; a broad whitish bar often present at base of caudal fin; juveniles dark brown on back and dorsally on head, abruptly whitish below with irregular, longitudinal, yellowish brown lines. Reported to 38 cm. Indo-Pacific. The most common triggerfish on the Arabian Sea coast of Oman; in some year present in huge numbers in southern Oman, with many dying and washing up on beaches; rare in the Gulf of Oman. Known from the depth range of 8 to over 100 m. Feeds mainly on sea urchins, heart urchins, fishes, molluscs, tunicates, brittle stars, crabs, and other crustaceans; occasionally ingests small amounts of algae. *Balistes capistratus* Shaw is a synonym.

1113. *Sufflamen fraenatus*, about 23 cm (J. Hoover)

FILEFISHES
FAMILY MONACANTHIDAE

The filefishes are named for their tough, shagreen-like skin. The family is very closely related to the triggerfishes, and some authors have combined the two as subfamilies of a single family. They differ from triggerfishes in having a longer and more slender first dorsal spine (also capable of being locked in an erect position), a very small second spine (absent in a few species), and no third dorsal spine; the body is more compressed; there are six outer teeth in the jaws, reinforced by four inner teeth; there are nonoverlapping scales as in the Balistidae, but instead of nodules in the centre, there is a cluster of spinules which gives the skin its sandpaper-like texture and tends to obscure the scale margins; the spinous knob at the end of the pelvic bone is encased in three or fewer pairs of modified scales or is absent; the body depth can be increased by depressing the pelvic bone, and stretching the loose skin of the pelvic flap above it; the rays of the soft dorsal and anal fins are unbranched. The uppermost pectoral ray is rudimentary, but it is included in the counts of pectoral rays below. Because the greatest depth of the body of filefishes may vary depending on how much the pelvic bone is lowered (and hence the pelvic flap stretched), the depth generally used is vertically from the origin of the anal fin. Filefishes are more secretive than triggerfishes, and with few exceptions, they tend to match the colour of their surroundings; many have cutaneous flaps or cirri that augment their protective colouration. They are omnivorous, in general, feeding on a wide variety of benthic animal and plant life, including for some species noxious sponges and coelenterates which are avoided by most fishes. Some filefishes are sexually dimorphic, especially with respect to the spines or setae on the side of the caudal peduncle (usually larger in males). There are about 31 genera and approximately 95 species of monacanthid fishes in the world. Australia has 28 of the genera (Hutchins, 1977) and 54 of the species. Filefishes are called leatherjackets in Australia.

UNICORN FILEFISH
Aluterus monoceros (Linnaeus, 1758)

Dorsal rays II + 45-51; anal rays 47-53; pectoral rays 15; body moderately elongate, the depth at origin of anal fin 2.6-3.0 in standard length, and highly compressed; dorsal profile of head slightly convex, the ventral profile initially concave, then strongly convex; mouth slightly upturned; gill opening nearly twice orbit diameter and highly oblique, its lower end extending anterior to a vertical at front of eye and anterior to pectoral-fin base; eye an eye diameter or more below top of head; first dorsal spine long and slender (easily broken), originating above front of eye, and not followed by a deep groove; caudal fin rounded in young, emarginate or double emarginate in large adults, the fin short, 1.5-1.8 in head length; spinous pelvic knob rudimentary (absent in large adults); light grey to brown, often faintly mottled and spotted with darker grey or brown. Attains 75 cm. Worldwide in tropical and subtropical seas, but nowhere abundant; rare in Oman waters. A 29-cm specimen was obtained by the author in Bahrain from a trap fisherman.

SCRAWLED FILEFISH
Aluterus scriptus (Osbeck, 1765)

Dorsal rays II + 43-49; anal rays 46-52; pectoral rays 14-16; body depth at anal-fin origin 2.7-3.1 in standard length; dorsal and ventral profiles of head concave; mouth slightly upturned, the lower jaw projecting; gill opening oblique; eye about half an eye diameter from top of head; first dorsal spine long and slender, originating over eye, and not followed by a deep groove; caudal fin rounded and very long, its length 1.6-3.0 in standard length; spinous pelvic knob rudimentary or absent; light bluish grey to olive or brown with blue or blue-green spots and short irregular bands as well as scattered small black spots; capable of rapid changes in colour. Attains 75 cm. Cosmopolitan in all warm seas; common in some years in the Gulf of Oman, rare in others. Stomach and intestinal contents vary greatly from fish to fish; some contain only plant material (algae or seagrasses); others hydrozoans (including the stinging coral *Millepora*), gorgonians, tunicates, toxic zoantharians such as *Palythoa*, gastropods, sponges, etc.

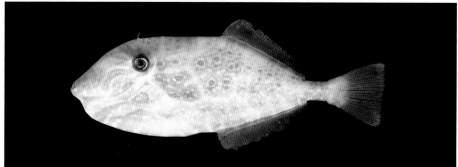

1114. *Aluterus monoceros*, 38.2 cm (J. Randall)

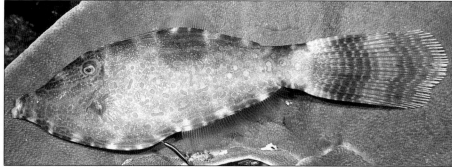

1115. *Aluterus scriptus*, about 45 cm (J. Hoover)

BARRED FILEFISH
Cantherhines dumerilii (Hollard, 1854)

Dorsal rays II + 34-39; anal rays 28-35; pectoral rays 15-16 (rarely 15); body depth at origin of anal fin 2.2-2.4 in standard length; dorsal and ventral profiles of head straight; mouth terminal; two pairs of prominent, forward-curved spines on side of caudal peduncle (larger in males); first dorsal spine without long spinules or barbs, its origin over eye, and folding into a deep groove in back when depressed (applies to all species of the genus), the spine length 1.0-1.8 in snout length; longest dorsal soft ray 1.9-2.2 in snout length; caudal fin rounded; pelvic knob not movable (also generic); greyish brown, usually with about 12 narrow dark brown bars on posterior two-thirds of body; caudal peduncular spine bases bright orange; lips flesh-coloured to whitish, edged with blackish; soft dorsal, anal, and pectoral rays yellow; caudal fin orange, the rays sometimes dusky basally; juveniles and subadults may have small white spots. Largest collected by author, 37.5 cm. Indo-Pacific and tropical eastern Pacific; rare in Oman waters. Limited data indicate the principal food is branching corals; echinoids, bryozoans, molluscs, sponges, and algae are also eaten. *C. carolae* Jordan and McGregor and *C. albopunctatus* (Seale) are synonyms. The genus *Cantherhines* and the related monotypic genus *Amanses* were revised by Randall (1964).

HONEYCOMB FILEFISH
Cantherhines pardalis (Rüppell, 1837)

Dorsal rays II + 32-36; anal rays 29-32; pectoral rays 13-15; body depth at origin of anal fin 2.1-2.3 in standard length; dorsal and ventral profiles of head slightly concave; mouth terminal; adult males with a dense patch of brush-like setae on side of caudal peduncle and extending a short distance anterior to it; first dorsal spine varying from slightly shorter to slightly longer than snout length; longest dorsal soft ray 1.8-2.4 in snout length; caudal fin not long, 4.4-5.0 in standard length, and rounded; colour can be altered to any of three basic patterns; dark brown, light grey-brown mottled with dark brown, and grey with numerous orange-brown spots which may be so close together as to give a honeycomb effect; all three phases have in common a small white spot at rear base of soft dorsal fin. Largest specimen, 20.6 cm. Indo-Pacific; in Oman only on the southern coast. Absent from the Hawaiian Islands where replaced by the related *C. sandwichiensis* (Quoy and Gaimard). The Atlantic *C. pullus* (Ranzani) is also a close relative.

1116. *Cantherhines dumerilii*, 31.7 cm (J. Randall)

1117. *Cantherhines pardalis*, about 12 cm (J. Randall)

1118. *Paraluteres prionurus*, about 8 cm (J. Hoover)

MIMIC FILEFISH
Paraluteres prionurus (Bleeker, 1851)

Dorsal rays II + 25-28; anal rays 22-25; pectoral rays 11-12 (usually 12); body depth at anal-fin origin 2.0-2.4 in standard length; dorsal profile of head straight, the ventral profile slightly concave to straight; mouth terminal; gill opening vertical, directly above pectoral-fin base; adult males with a broad, elliptical, dense patch of setae on posterior half of body, ending in two pairs of strong antrorse spines at caudal-fin base; first dorsal spine over rear edge of eye, connected by membrane from tip of spine nearly to origin of soft dorsal fin, this membrane preventing spine from being elevated to more than about 45°; pelvic knob rudimentary; no ventral flap; whitish with small brown spots and blotches except on about ventral fourth of head and body; four black bars, one above posterior half of eye, the second below membrane of first dorsal fin, narrowing to pass below pectoral fin onto abdomen, the third from below anterior half of second dorsal fin, narrowing to above origin of anal fin, and the fourth triangular from posterior third of soft dorsal fin; caudal fin yellow. Reaches 10 cm. Coast of East Africa to the islands of Micronesia; in the western Pacific from Japan to the Great Barrier Reef; rare in Oman. As first noted by Clark and Gohar (1953), this filefish is an obvious mimic of the toby *Canthigaster valentini* (Bleeker), a poisonous species rarely bothered by predators. The first dorsal spine of *P. prionurus* is usually not raised (as that would reveal it as a filefish).

GULF FILEFISH
Paramonacanthus sp.

Dorsal rays II + 27-29; anal rays 27-30; pectoral rays 12-14; scales with a single multi-branched spinule (usually four to six slender branches which project outwardly and posteriorly); no cutaneous flaps or cirri on body; body depth at anal-fin origin 2.25-2.7 in standard length; dorsal profile of head slightly concave to straight, the ventral profile straight; mouth terminal; gill opening slightly oblique, centred below rear margin of eye, its lower end in front of middle of pectoral-fin base; no spines or setae on caudal peduncle; first dorsal spine over posterior edge of eye, its length varying from slightly shorter to slightly longer than snout length; each posterolateral edge of dorsal spine with six to nine large, barb-like, down-curved spinules; soft dorsal and anal fins somewhat elevated anteriorly, the longest dorsal ray 1.3-1.7 in snout length; caudal fin rounded, the uppermost branched ray prolonged in males, the fin length 1.1-1.3 in head length; pelvic fin rudiment of moderate size, movably articulated with posterior end of pelvis; body pale yellowish grey with large blackish blotches, the darkest on back centred below eighth and ninth dorsal soft rays; head with small blackish blotches and diagonal lines; caudal fin with two broad dusky bars paralleling curve of posterior margin and a triangular dusky spot at base. Largest specimen, 6.7 cm. Presently known only from the Arabian Gulf where taken by trawling. Closely related to *P. horae* Fraser-Brunner; currently under study by J. Barry Hutchins.

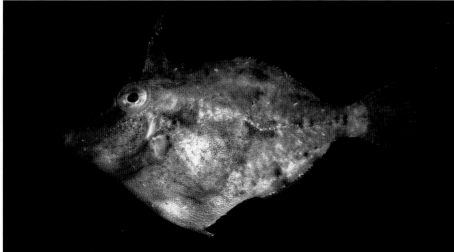

1119. *Paramonacanthus* sp., about 6.9 cm (J. Randall)

1120. *Paramonacanthus* sp., night colouration, 9 cm (J. Randall)

LOZENGE FILEFISH
Stephanolepis diaspros Fraser-Brunner, 1940

Dorsal rays II + 32-34; anal rays 32-33; pectoral rays 15-16; greatest body depth 1.8-1.95 in standard length; dorsal profile of head slightly concave, the ventral profile a sinuous curve; dorsal profile of body with a hump centred at origin of soft dorsal fin; mouth terminal; gill opening about equal to eye diameter, centred below posterior edge of eye, the lower end anterior to midbase of pectoral fin or a little above it; first dorsal spine over posterior fourth of eye, with barb-like, down-curved spinules along each posterolateral edge, its length 1.1-1.6 in snout length; soft dorsal and anal fins elevated anteriorly, the anterior rays about three times longer than posterior rays, 1.5-1.7 in snout; adult males with second dorsal soft ray prolonged to a filament, and a patch of forward-curving bristles on side of caudal peduncle; caudal fin rounded, about 1.2 in head length; pelvic fin rudiment movable; body whitish with numerous, large, elliptical, brown spots (Fraser-Brunner described them as lozenge-shaped), so close-set that the intervening pale space forms a reticulum. Reported to 25 cm. Arabian Gulf to the Red Sea and as an immigrant via the Suez Canal to the Mediterranean Sea; often caught in trawls. The author dipnetted juveniles of 2.5-4 cm in length at the surface off Musandam that were associated with jellyfishes. Very similar in morphology and colour to *S. cirrhifer* (Temminck and Schlegel), but the scale structure is different (as noted by Kuronuma and Abe, 1986).

1121. *Stephanolepis diaspros*, about 22 cm (J. Hoover)

1122. *Stephanolepis diaspros*, juv. (J. Hoover)

BLACKVENT FILEFISH
Thamnaconus melanoproctes (Boulenger, 1889)

Dorsal rays II + 32-34; anal rays 32-34; body depth at anal-fin origin about 2.7 in standard length; dorsal profile of head straight to slightly concave; mouth terminal; gill opening oblique, larger than eye diameter, below posterior half of eye, the lower end below level of midbase of pectoral fin; no spines or setae on caudal peduncle; origin of first dorsal spine above centre of eye, its length about 1.2-1.6 in snout length, each posterolateral edge with about 20 small barbs; soft dorsal and anal fins higher anteriorly, the longest dorsal ray about 2.5 times longer than posterior rays; caudal fin slightly rounded; pale brown with two slightly irregular, dark brown stripes dorsally on body, one from above eye and the other from lower half of eye; a narrow dark brown streak below first 12 rays of soft dorsal fin; a broad zone of horizontal dark brown lines on lower side of body except ventrally; head and chest with numerous irregular brown lines and dots; anus in a large dark brown spot. Attains 20 cm. Described from specimens from the Gulf of Oman; known otherwise only from one juvenile taken by trawling in 73-200 m in the Gulf of Aden (Norman, 1939). No specimens examined; above diagnosis from the Boulenger's description and underwater photographs taken by the author in 30 m at Fahl Island off Muscat.

TRUNKFISHES
FAMILY OSTRACIIDAE

This family, also popularly known as boxfishes, is unique in possessing a bony carapace of polygonal plates with gaps for the mouth, gill opening, anus, caudal peduncle, and fins. The carapace may be triangular, quadrangular, pentagonal, hexagonal, or nearly round in cross-section; its surface is usually rough due to the presence of small bony tubercles on the plates. Some trunkfishes possess large spines which project from the carapace; the species of the genus *Lactoria* have a pair of such projections from the front of the head, hence their common name cowfishes. Other characteristics for the family are a small mouth which is low on the head; thick lips; teeth uniserial in

1123. *Thamnaconus melanoproctes*, about 19 cm (J. Randall)

jaws, conical to incisiform with rounded tips; no teeth on the palate (as in other tetraodontiform fishes); gill opening a near-vertical slit extending dorsally from in front of pectoral-fin base; no spines in the fins; a single dorsal fin posterior in position; and no pelvic fins. As would be expected from their bony armour and boxy shape, trunkfishes are slow swimmers; their usual propulsion is by a sculling action of the dorsal and anal fins; the caudal fin is brought into action when they want to move faster. They feed on a wide variety of benthic animals, particularly sessile forms such as tunicates, sponges, and alcyonarians; many also ingest large amounts of algae. Although the bony carapace alone would seem to be enough to discourage a predator, particularly in those species with spines on the carapace, some trunkfishes, at least, have another defence; they secrete a skin poison called ostracitoxin when the fish is under stress (Thomson, 1964; Boylan and Scheuer, 1967). If a trunkfish is placed in a

small volume of water with other fishes and harrassed, the other fishes will die; if the level of the toxin is high enough, the trunkfish will die as well. The family is divisible into two subfamilies, the Aracaninae (some authors prefer to regard this as a separate family) with an open carapace posterior to the dorsal and anal fins and usually 11 principal caudal rays (no species recorded for Oman) and the Ostraciinae with a closed carapace and usually 10 principal caudal rays. A total of 14 genera and 34 species are known for the family (review by Trubschenck, 1981). Counts given for the pectoral rays below include the rudimentary upper ray.

LONGHORN COWFISH
Lactoria cornuta (Linnaeus, 1758)

Dorsal rays 8-9; anal rays 9; pectoral rays 10-11; a pair of sharp horns about twice eye diameter in length extending anteriorly and often slightly upward from front of head at level of upper part of eye; a second pair of spines extending posteriorly, one from each

1124. *Lactoria cornuta*, 14.3 cm (J. Randall)

side of rear of carapace; dorsal profile of head nearly vertical; caudal fin very long, 1.5-2.0 in standard length, and truncate (though often ragged on the trailing edge); colour variable but usually olive to yellowish grey with pale blue spots on side; ventral part of carapace may be orange-yellow; caudal fin often with pale spots and sometimes indistinct dusky spots. Reported to 46 cm. Indo-Pacific; generally found in seagrass beds or substrata with heavy algal cover; reported to depths of 100 m.

1125. *Ostracion cubicus*, male, about 28 cm (J. Randall)

1126. *Ostracion cubicus*, female, about 25 cm (J. Hoover)

1128. *Ostracion cyanurus*, male, about 9 cm (J. Randall)

1129. *Ostracion cyanurus*, females, about 12 cm (J. Hoover)

YELLOW TRUNKFISH
Ostracion cubicus Linnaeus, 1758

Dorsal rays 9; anal rays 9; pectoral rays 11; carapace quadrangular in cross-section, the sides concave, broader at base than top, without spines, and without a median dorsal ridge (applies to all species of the genus); body becoming more elongate with growth (carapace depth of small juveniles about 1.5 in standard length, of large adults about 3); large adults with a bump anteriorly on snout; caudal fin rounded; small juveniles yellow with round black spots nearly as large as pupil; with growth, black spots more numerous and relatively smaller; still larger fish with one black-edged white or pale blue spot on each polygonal plate; large adults purplish brown, the spots on carapace faint or absent, the grooves between polygonal plates yellow; fins with small black spots. Reported to attain 45 cm. Indo-Pacific; not common in the Gulf of Oman, but the most common trunkfish in the south.

1127. *O. cubicus*, juv., about 3 cm (J. Hoover)

BLUETAIL TRUNKFISH
Ostracion cyanurus Rüppell, 1828

Dorsal rays 9; anal rays 9; pectoral rays 11; carapace quadrangular in cross-section, broader at base; dorsal profile of snout of female slightly concave, of males slightly convex; jaws with ten upper and eight lower teeth; lips fleshy; chin fleshy and protuberant; caudal fin slightly rounded; females dull yellow with numerous small black spots on carapace, caudal peduncle, caudal fin and lips, the spots close-set (yellow interspaces generally not greater than spot diameters); males greenish yellow dorsally on carapace, blue on the sides with small black spots (which may have brown edges) and a large irregular brownish orange blotch in region covered by pectoral fin; caudal peduncle and caudal fin blue with small black spots except for a broad posterior whitish border of fin. Reaches 15 cm. Red Sea to Arabian Gulf; common in the Gulf of Oman but not seen on the Arabian Sea coast of Oman. No very small males have been observed, so they evidently change colour from yellow with black spots with the onset of sexual maturity.

THORNBACK TRUNKFISH
Tetrosomus gibbosus (Linneus, 1758)

Dorsal rays 9; anal rays 9; pectoral rays 11; carapace triangular in cross-section; a large blade-like ridge middorsally on carapace, elevated above middle of body to a broad-based spine; ventral ridge of carapace with a series of five posteriorly-directed spines (the first below gill opening small); ridge over eye bearing a spine; jaws with ten upper and eight lower teeth; caudal peduncle slender; caudal fin rounded; yellowish grey to olive brown with pale blue spots; a blackish spot on side of broad middorsal spine; a broad, irregular, dusky bar across middle of body; a few other obscure dark blotches; caudal peduncle with small dark spots. Reaches 30 cm. Red Sea south to Natal and east to the western Pacific, ranging there from southern Japan to Queensland; usually found on seagrass or sand bottoms; maximum depth recorded, 110 m. Sometimes classified in *Rhinesomus*, but this is a synonym of the Atlantic genus *Lactophrys*.

1130. *Tetrosomus gibbosus*, about 18 cm (J. Randall)

PUFFERS
FAMILY TETRAODONTIDAE

The puffers, also known as blowfishes, are named for their ability, when provoked, to inflate themselves by drawing water (or air if taken out of water) into a highly distensible ventral diverticulum of the stomach. They are characterised further by having the teeth of the jaws fused to beak-like dental plates (with a median suture); a slit-like gill opening in front of the pectoral-fin base; tough skin without typical scales (small spinules are often present, especially ventrally, and their pattern may be important in classification); no spines in the fins; a single, short-based dorsal fin posterior in position; a comparable anal fin below or behind the dorsal; caudal fin with 10 principal rays and no procurrent rays; no pelvic fins; and no ribs. Puffers are found in all tropical to warm temperate seas, usually in shallow water, but some occur at moderate depths; a few are pelagic. Most species are solitary, but some form small aggregations. Puffers are well known for producing a powerful poison, tetradotoxin, in their tissues, especially in the liver and ovaries (Halstead, 1967). The toxin varies greatly in the different species, some being safe to eat, others potentially lethal, and it can vary with geographical area and the reproductive season. The family is divisible into two subfamilies, the Tetraodontinae and the Canthigasterinae. Species of the former have rounded bodies, a conspicuous lateral line, gill opening usually extending below midbase of pectoral fin, and 17-29 vertebrae. This subfamily consists of about 18 genera and 95 species. The Canthigasterinae, popularly known as tobies or sharpnose puffers, have laterally compressed bodies; an elongate pointed snout; an inconspicuous lateral line; a small gill opening, the lower end generally at or above midbase of pectoral fin; an erectile ridge of skin middorsally and midventrally; and usually 17 vertebrae. It consists of a single genus, *Canthigaster*, with 26 brightly coloured species, of which 25 occur in the Indo-Pacific region (reviewed by Allen and Randall, 1977 and Randall and Cea Egaña, 1989). The species of *Canthigaster* have a repelling skin toxin and are rarely eaten by predators. Counts of fin rays below include the rudimentary ray anteriorly in the dorsal and anal fins and dorsally in the pectoral fins.

1131. Head of *Arothron stellatus* (J. Randall)

SUBFAMILY TETRAODONTINAE

WHITESPOTTED PUFFER
Arothron hispidus (Linnaeus, 1758)

Dorsal rays 10-11; anal rays 10-11; pectoral rays 17-19; small spinules on head and body except snout and posterior caudal peduncle; snout short and obtuse; bony ridge over eye extending above level of interorbital space; nasal organ consisting of two fleshy flaps from a common base (characteristic of the genus); caudal fin rounded; grey to olivaceous or brown, with numerous small white spots, shading to white below with some dark bars extending into white ventral part of head and body; region around pectoral-fin base and gill opening black with a circle and arcs of white (often also yellow). Largest specimen, 48 cm. Indo-Pacific and tropical eastern Pacific; occurs in the Gulf of Oman and the Arabian Sea coast of Oman, but not common. Feeds on algae and detritus, molluscs, tunicates, sponges, corals, zoanthids, crabs, tube worms, sea urchins, brittle stars, starfishes (including the crown-of-thorns), hermit crabs, and hydroids.

1132. *Arothron hispidus* (J. Hoover)

IMMACULATE PUFFER
Arothron immaculatus (Bloch and Schneider, 1801)

Dorsal rays 9-11 (usually 10); anal rays 9-10 (usually 10); pectoral rays 16-19; skin with small slender spinules except posteriorly on caudal peduncle and regions around mouth, eye, dorsal, anal, and pectoral fins, and gill opening; snout short, its length 2.25-2.4 in head length; interorbital space flat except at edges, 2.65-3.1 in head; caudal fin large and rounded, its length 2.6-3.6 in standard length; light olivaceous dorsally, shading to whitish on sides and ventrally, without any spots or bands on head and body; lips yellowish; a dark area often present around pectoral-fin base and gill opening; fins usually yellowish, the caudal broadly edged with blackish. Reaches 30 cm. Red Sea to South Africa, east to the Indo-Malayan region, north to the Ryukyu Islands; in Oman from the Gulf of Oman south to Masirah Island. Occurs in seagrass beds and mangrove areas in as little as 1 m of water; also taken by trawling over mud bottoms as deep as 17 m. *A. manilensis* de Procé of the central and western Pacific was considered a synonym until Randall (1985) showed that it is distinct on the basis of its dark stripes and longer caudal fin.

1133. *Arothron immaculatus* (J. Hoover)

GUINEAFOWL PUFFER
Arothron meleagris (Bloch and Schneider, 1801)

Dorsal rays 10-13 (usually 11 or 12); anal rays 11-13; pectoral rays 17-21 (modally 19); small spinules on head and body except for most of snout and chin, caudal peduncle, and an area of variable size on back (spinules best developed on ventral half of body); gill rakers 5-19; bony interorbital width 6.1-9.2 in standard length; caudal fin rounded; dark brown to black dorsally, usually a little lighter ventrally, with numerous small white spots on head, body, and fins (fins of some individuals show pale outer margins). A second, much less common, colour phase is bright yellow with a few widely scattered small black spots; the illustrated specimen in intermediate colour was photographed at Juzor al Hallaniyat (Kuria Muria Islands). Attains 32 cm. Indo-Pacific and tropical eastern Pacific; usually found on or near coral reefs. Stomach and gut contents of six specimens consisted of corals (77% by volume), sponges, molluscs, bryozoans, tunicates, foraminifera, algae, and detritus.

1134. *Arothron meleagris*, about 19 cm (J. Randall)

BLACKSPOTTED PUFFER
Arothron nigropunctatus (Bloch and Schneider, 1801)

Dorsal rays 9-12 (modally 10, rarely 9 or 12); anal rays 10-12 (usually 11, rarely 12); pectoral rays 16-20 (modally 18); spinules on head and body similar to those of *A. meleagris*; gill rakers 11-40; bony interorbital width 8.1-12.0 in standard length; colour variable, grey to dark brown dorsally, whitish to bright yellow ventrally, but always with scattered black spots of different size and usually with a transverse pale band dorsally on snout separating dark areas around eye and mouth; anus black. Largest specimen, 29.5 cm. East coast of Africa to the islands of Micronesia and Samoa ; in the western Pacific from southern Japan to New South Wales; the Oman record is based on an underwater photograph by Bob Bedford taken in the Gulf of Oman. Su and Tyler (1986) were followed in part in the diagnoses of this species and *A. meleagris*.

1135. *Arothron nigropunctatus*, 19.1 cm (J. Randall)

1136. *Arothron stellatus*, resting colouration (J. Hoover)

STELLATE PUFFER
Arothron stellatus (Bloch and Schneider, 1801)

Dorsal rays 11-12; anal rays 11; pectoral rays 17 -20; small spinules on head and body except top of snout, base of fins, and side of caudal peduncle, the spinules most evident ventrally; caudal fin slightly rounded; adults white with small black spots on head, body, and median fins, those on pectoral-fin base and around gill opening largest (spots more numerous and relatively smaller with growth); juveniles yellow to orange with small black spots, the abdomen with broad, irregular, oblique, black bands. Reaches at least 90 cm. Indo-Pacific. Limited food habit data indicate a highy varied diet including sea urchins, sponges, coral, stinging coral (*Millepora*), starfishes, crabs, hermit crabs, and algae. *A. alboreticulatus* (Tanaka) is a probable synonym (Matsuura in Masuda et al., 1984).

1137. *A. stellatus*, juv., about 10 cm (J. Randall)

MILKSPOTTED PUFFER
Chelonodon patoca (Hamilton, 1822)

Dorsal rays 10; anal rays 8; pectoral rays 15-16; a patch of spinules on back from behind interorbital space nearly to dorsal fin and another on throat and abdomen; nasal organ a depression with a low rim and anterior and posterior flaps; origin of anal fin below midbase of dorsal fin; caudal fin slightly rounded; grey to brown dorsally with large round to ovate white spots (sometimes with dark centres), shading to white ventrally; a broad streak of yellow on lower side within the white region; irregular dark bars often present on body. Recorded to 33 cm. Arabian Gulf to western Pacific; generally found inshore, frequently in brackish areas.

1138. *Chelonodon patoca*, 15 cm (J. Randall)

DIAMONDBACK PUFFER
Lagocephalus guentheri Ribeiro, 1915

Dorsal rays 13-14 (usually 14); anal rays 12-13 (usually 13); pectoral rays 18; lateral-line system very similar to that of *L. lunaris*; patch of small spinules dorsally on body approximately diamond-shaped, commencing above a point half way beween eye and nostrils and ending nearly half distance from hind edge of eye to origin of dorsal fin; broad patch of spinules ventrally on body commencing below nostrils and ending a half to two-thirds eye diameter anterior to anus; body depth 3.2-3.6 in standard length; caudal peduncle tapering, deeper than long at any point; dorsal and anal fins pointed and slightly falcate; origin of anal fin a little anterior to a vertical at midbase of dorsal fin; caudal fin moderately emarginate; grey to olive brown dorsally with three broad, short, blackish bars dorsally on body, one above outer half of pectoral fin, one below dorsal fin, and one posteriorly on caudal peduncle; a dark blotch next to dorsoposterior edge of eye; side of head and body broadly silvery; ventral part of body silvery white; leading edge of dorsal fin dusky; caudal fin dusky, the lobe tips white. Attains at least 26 cm. Arabian Gulf, southern Oman, India, Indonesia, northwestern Australia, and the South China Sea. Sometimes misidentified as *L. spadiceus* (Richardson), as by Gloerfelt-Tarp and Kailola (1984), Sainsbury et al. (1985), and Kuronuma and Abe (1986), but the patch of spinules on the back of *L. spadiceus* narrows

1139. *Lagocephalus guentheri*, 11.8 cm (J. Randall)

to a thin middorsal band which nearly reaches the dorsal fin (this feature confirmed on the type specimen in the Natural History Museum, London by A.C. Gill; he also examined the holotype of *L. guentheri*, allegedly from Brazil, and found the pattern of spinules dorsally and ventrally as described above).

1140. *Lagocephalus lunaris*, 15.7 cm (J. Randall)

LUNARTAIL PUFFER
Lagocephalus lunaris (Bloch and Schneider, 1801)

Dorsal rays 12-14; anal rays 11-13; pectoral rays 16-19; two lateral lines, the lower in a ventrolateral ridge from front of chin to lower base of caudal fin (applies to all species of the genus); upper lateral line forming a quadrangle dorsoposterior to eye and continuing around eye, with a branch across occiput and another across front of snout; a broad patch of spinules dorsally on head and body from above posterior edge of nostrils to origin of dorsal fin, the spinous patch within the upper lateral lines (except for a few anterior spinules just below the lines); patch of spinules ventrally on body from below anterior edge of eyes to below tip of pectoral fins; body depth 2.9-3.5 in standard length; caudal peduncle tapering, deeper than wide at any point; gill opening anterior to pectoral-fin base and extending a short distance above (also generic); nasal organ a tubular papilla set in a depression with a nostril at each end (generic); dorsal and anal fins pointed, the anal a little posterior; caudal fin deeply emarginate; grey dorsally without obvious dark markings, silvery on side and ventrally, sometimes with a golden sheen on lower side; caudal fin often yellowish grey on upper half, the lower half bluish. Reported to 30 cm. Red Sea and Arabian Gulf to South Africa, east along continental shores to the western Pacific, ranging there from southern Japan to Australia; generally taken by trawling over mud bottoms.

ELONGATE PUFFER
Lagocephalus sceleratus (Gmelin, 1788)

Dorsal rays 11-13; anal rays 9-12; pectoral rays 16-18; two lateral lines essentially as in *L. lunaris*; small spinules on dorsal part of head and body nearly to caudal fin, and on ventral part of head and body to anus; body elongate, the depth 4.5-6.0 in standard length; caudal peduncle long and tapering, broader than deep; dorsal and anal fins narrow-based, slightly falcate, and pointed, the anal approximately below the dorsal; caudal fin deeply emarginate; greenish grey dorsally with small dark spots (variable in size in young), silvery white ventrally; a bright silver stripe on side. Reported to over 100 cm. Indo-Pacific; an Arabian Gulf specimen from 18 m; Wass (1984) recorded a specimen from Samoa taken in 100 m. Said to be very poisonous to eat. Sometimes classified in the genus *Gastrophysus*, now considered a synonym of *Lagocephalus*.

1141. *Lagocephalus sceleratus*, 49.5 cm (J. Randall)

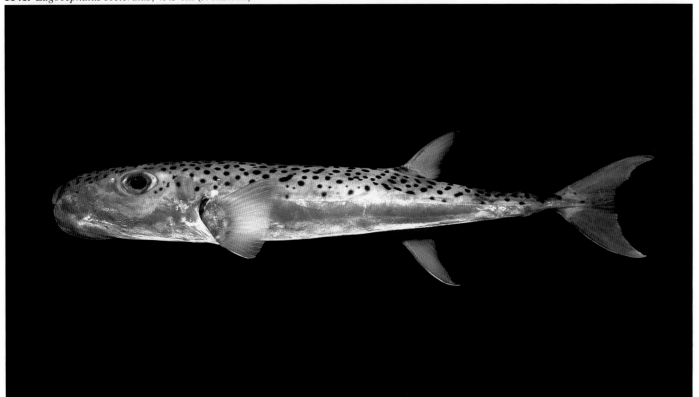

YELLOWSPOTTED PUFFER
Torquigener flavimaculosus Hardy and Randall, 1983

Dorsal rays 9; anal rays 7-8; caudal rays 11; pectoral rays 15-16; dorsal lateral line encircling eye, with a ventral branch from behind eye, another across occiput, then gradually descending along side of body to middle of caudal fin; ventral lateral line passing downward from behind corner of mouth and thence along ventral part of body to lower base of caudal fin; ventrolateral skin fold extending posteriorly from the prominent bulbous chin; spinules only on ventral part of head and abdomen, in about 20-21 approximate rows between pectoral-fin bases; body depth between origins of dorsal and anal fins 5..2-6.8 in standard length; caudal peduncle length 3.4-4.4 in standard length; eye diameter 3.3-4.4 in head length; dorsal and anal fins short-based and pointed; caudal fin truncate; a row of yellow to brownish yellow spots on body from upper axil of pectoral fin to midbase of caudal fin; dorsal part of head and body densely dotted with dark reddish brown except where outlining numerous, round to elliptical, white spots on body and irregular white bars on side of head; ventral part of head and body white. Attains 13 cm. Northern Red Sea (type locality) and Kenya; a recent emigrant to the Mediterranean Sea via the Suez Canal. Recorded from the Arabian Gulf by Kuronuma and Abe (1986) as *Lagocephalus hypselogeneion* (Bleeker) (their specimen of 81 mm standard length mistakenly listed as 181 mm SL) and from Seychelles by Randall and van Egmond (1994). Known from the depth range of 3-57 m.

1142. *Torquigener flavimaculosus*, about 10 cm (J. Randall)

SUBFAMILY CANTHIGASTERINAE

CROWN TOBY
Canthigaster coronata (Vaillant and Sauvage, 1875)

Dorsal rays 9-10 (usually 10); anal rays 9-10 (usually 9); pectoral rays 16-17 (usually 17); caudal fin slightly rounded (true, in general, for all species of the genus); white with small blue spots (and often short lines); four broad dark brown bars dorsally on head and body, the first across top of head, centred on posterior edge of eye; the second with its lower anterior corner ending at upper end of gill opening, the last two triangular; a yellow area around eye (except dorsoposteriorly where transverse dark brown bar is adjacent to eye), with radiating short blue lines; caudal fin yellowish. Reaches 14 cm. Red Sea to Natal, east to Hawaii and islands of Micronesia, north to Japan and south to New South Wales; observed only in southern Oman where rare. The species in the Pacific differs in having numerous bright yellow spots and short lines. Usually found at depths greater than 15 m; occurs to at least 100 m. Generally found on sand bottoms, often near reefs. Stomach and gut contents of 12 specimens from Hawaii consisted of algae and detritus, gastropods, crabs, pelecypods, polychaetes, sponges, sipunculids, ophiuroids, bryozoans, tunicates, echinoids, foraminifera, amphipods, shrimps, and isopods (in the order of volume of the food material). Tyler (1967) showed that *C. cincta* Jordan and Evermann is a synonym.

RIVULATED TOBY
Canthigaster rivulata (Temminck and Schlegel, 1850)

Dorsal rays 9-10 (usually 10); anal rays 9-10 (usually 10); pectoral rays 16-18; two parallel dark brown stripes flecked with yellow on side of body (about as wide as eye diameter in adults, the upper stripe more evident; stripes may be indistinct on large adults); stripes connected by an arc of brown in front of gill opening, the upper stripe continuing a short distance anterior to arc; body and postorbital head above upper stripe with a reticulum of brownish yellow and blue lines; body below lower stripe white; bright blue and orange-yellow lines radiating ventrally and anteriorly from eye, the anterior lines continuing less brightly to front of snout; lower part of head white with faint blue lines and yellow spots; caudal fin yellow with longitudinal blue lines, the base of fin and adjacent caudal peduncle yellow with irregular vertical blue lines. Attains 18 cm. Indo-Pacific from scattered localities, including Japan (type locality), Hawaii, Western Australia, Seychelles, Somalia, and South Africa; one pair seen in southern Oman, and a 12.5-cm specimen collected in 20 m; known to depths of 350 m. *C. caudofasciata* (Günther) is a synonym.

SOLANDER'S TOBY
Canthigaster solandri (Richardson, 1844)

Dorsal rays 8-10 (usually 9, rarely 8); anal rays 8-9 (rarely 8); pectoral rays 16-17 (usually 17); body orangish brown dorsally with irregular, mainly longitudinal, blue lines; side of body with numerous small white spots, grading to white ventrally; a double black spot edged in blue at base of dorsal fin; blue lines radiating from eye; a series of oblique blue lines passing from below eye along dorsal part of snout; lower part of head with brown-edged white spots; caudal fin brown with small white spots basally, becoming orange with vertical blue lines distally. Reaches 11.5 cm. Indo-Pacific; replaced by *C. papua* (Bleeker) in the Indo-Malayan region and by *C. margaritata* (Rüppell) in the Red Sea; illustrated specimen photographed at Fahl Island off Muscat.

1143. *Canthigaster coronata*, about 12 cm (J. Randall)

1144. *Canthigaster rivulata* (J. Hoover)

1145. *Canthigaster solandri*, about 9 cm (J. Hoover)

MODEL TOBY
Canthigaster valentini (Bleeker, 1853)

Dorsal rays 9; anal rays 9; pectoral rays 16-17 (usually 16); white with small brownish orange spots (except ventrally on abdomen where spots are pale yellow, and faint) and four black bars, one on nape, two in middle of body which become narrow on abdomen, and a short triangular one dorsally on caudal peduncle; an orange area with bright blue lines behind and below eye; caudal fin yellow with some brownish orange spots basally, the upper and lower edges blackish (most evident toward base of fin). Attains 9 cm. Indo-Pacific. A shallow-water, coral-reef species; common in the Gulf of Oman and in the south. Serves as the model for the mimicking filefish *Paraluteres prionurus* (see account of this species above).

1146. *Canthigaster valentini*, about 8 cm (J. Hoover)

PORCUPINEFISHES AND BURRFISHES
FAMILY DIODONTIDAE

The porcupinefishes share with the puffers the ability to inflate themselves by drawing water into a highly distensible ventral diverticulum of the stomach. They have the added protection of formidable sharp spines; these may be three- or four-rooted, hence fixed, and relatively short, as seen on species of *Chilomycterus* and *Cyclichthys* (called burrfishes), or two-rooted, movable, and long as in *Diodon*. Normally the spines of *Diodon* are directed posteriorly and lie against the body, but when the fishes expand their bodies, the spines are elevated perpendicular to the skin surface or nearly so. Like the puffers, the porcupine fishes have the teeth fused to beak-like dental plates, a short vertical gill opening anterior to the pectoral-fin base, no spines in the fins, a single dorsal fin posterior in position, and no pelvic fins. In addition to having large spines on the head and body, diodontids differ from the puffers in lacking a median suture in their stout dental plates, having large eyes, and broader pectoral fins (often with the posterior margin emarginate). Most species are nocturnal, generally hiding in caves or beneath ledges during the day. Their strong dental plates and powerful jaws enable them to crush the hard tests of sea urchins, the shells of gastropod molluscs and hermit crabs, and the exoskeletons of crabs and other crustaceans. These prey animals, which are mostly active at night, are the principal food of diodontids. Care should be taken handling porcupinefishes, not only because of their sharp spines, but because they are capable of inflicting a severe bite. There have been reports of persons poisoned eating diodontid fishes (Halstead, 1967), presumably from tetradontoxin, but they also have the potential to cause ciguatera. Diodontids occur worldwide in tropical to warm temperate seas; most species are benthic on coral reefs or rocky substrata, but a few range over sedimentary bottoms, and *Diodon eydouxii* Brissout de Barneville is pelagic as an adult. Porcupinefishes do not form schools as adults. The family consists of six genera and 19 species. The genus *Diodon* was revised by Leis (1978).

1147. *Diodon liturosus* (inflated), about 25 cm (J. Randall)

ORBICULAR BURRFISH
Cyclichthys orbicularis (Bloch, 1785)

Dorsal rays 11-13; anal rays 10-12; pectoral rays 18-21; spines short, slightly recurved, and three-rooted, hence not erectile; a small movable spine below and behind corner of mouth, and another in axil of pectoral fin; about eight spines in an approximate row anterior to origin of dorsal fin; no spine on caudal peduncle (i.e. posterior to rear base of anal fin); no fleshy tentacles; dental plates not as strong as those of *Diodon*; distance between nostrils less than an eye diameter; dorsal, anal, and caudal fins rounded (true of other species herein; pointed in *D. eydouxii*); anal fin posterior to a vertical at midbase of dorsal fin; brown to grey dorsally, shading to white ventrally, with black spots which tend to cluster to form a dark bar on side of body anterior to dorsal fin, another usually beneath pectoral fin and extending above, and a few spots may form a bar on head behind eye; base of spines often in a white or yellow spot; no distinct dark spots on fins. Reaches 15 cm. Red Sea and Arabian Gulf to South Africa, east to the Indo-Malayan region, north to Japan (Matsuura et al., 1993), and south to Queensland. Usually found on sand or rubble substrata.

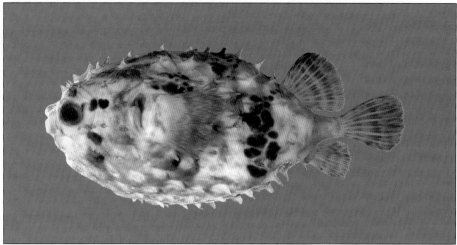

1148. *Cyclichthys orbicularis*, 12.3 cm (J. Randall)

YELLOWSPOTTED BURRFISH
Cyclichthys spilostylus Leis and Randall, 1982

Dorsal rays 12-13; anal rays 10-12; pectoral rays 20-22; spines short and three-rooted except some dorsally on head with four roots; 11-12 spines in an approximate row anterior to dorsal fin, the most anterior medial between nostrils; three spines above eye; no spines on caudal peduncle; origin of anal fin behind a vertical at midbase of dorsal fin; greyish brown, each spine in a white or yellow spot, shading to white ventrally where the spines are in a black spot (some spines on side of body in a yellow and black spot); fins pale grey without spots. Largest specimen, 34 cm. Recorded from the Red Sea (type locality), Gulf of Oman, South Africa and Mozambique (Leis in Smith and Heemstra, 1986), west coast of India, Indonesia, Philippines, northwestern Australia (Gloerfelt-Tarp and Kailola, 1984), Hong Kong, and Japan (Matsuura et al., 1993); surprisingly, it was recently discovered in the Galapagos Islands (Humann, 1993). Known from the depth range of 3 to at least 90 m.

SPINY PUFFER
Diodon holocanthus Linnaeus, 1758

Dorsal rays 13-15; anal rays 13-14; pectoral rays 21-25; spines two-rooted and erectile (characteristic of the genus); 12-16 spines in an approximate row from front of snout to dorsal fin; spines very long, those medially on forehead usually longer than longest spines posterior to pectoral fins; no spines on caudal peduncle; a pair of short tentacles on chin and a few elsewhere on head and body; head broad, the width 2.6-4.6 in standard length; posterior rays of anal fin nearly reaching base of caudal fin; light olive to light brown dorsally with a few to numerous small black spots, white ventrally; a dark bar from above to below eye; a broad transverse dark band on occipital region of head and another on back; a large oval dark spot above pectoral fin, and one around base of dorsal fin; fins without black spots or with a few basally on caudal fin. Reaches 29 cm. Cosmopolitan, but mainly in subtropical and warm temperate seas; illustrated fish from the Gulf of Oman. Known from the shallows to depths of at least 100 m; more inclined than the following species to occur far from the shelter of reefs.

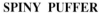

1149. *Cyclichthys spilostylus*, about 35 cm (J. Randall)

1150. *Diodon holocanthus* (J. Hoover)

PORCUPINEFISH
Diodon hystrix Linnaeus 1758

Dorsal rays 14-17; anal rays 14-16; pectoral rays 21-25; 16-20 spines in an approximate row from front of snout to dorsal fin; spines on forehead shorter than longest spines posterior to pectoral fins; one or more small spines dorsally on caudal peduncle; no small spine pointing downward below eye; no small tentacles on chin; head very broad, the width 2.4-3.3 in standard length; posterior rays of anal fin reaching to about midlength of caudal peduncle; olive to light grey-brown dorsally with numerous small black spots, shading to white ventrally; fins yellowish with small black spots. Largest specimen collected, 71 cm. Circumglobal in tropical to warm temperate seas; illustrated fish from the Gulf of Oman. Nocturnal; feeds mainly on molluscs (especially gastropods), sea urchins, heart urchins, crabs, and hermit crabs.

BLACKBLOTCHED PORCUPINEFISH
Diodon liturosus Shaw, 1804

Dorsal rays 14-16; anal rays 14-16; pectoral rays 21-25; 16-21 spines in an approximate row from front of snout to dorsal fin; spines on forehead much shorter than those behind pectoral fins; a short, downward-pointing spine below front of eye; no spines on caudal peduncle; a pair of short tentacles usually present on chin; a short tentacle may be present above eye; head broad, its width 3.3-4.2 in standard length; posterior rays of anal fin nearly reaching base of caudal fin; light brown dorsally, shading to white ventrally; small black spots associated with spines on side of body; a broad, white-edged, black band across occipital region of head; an oval white-edged black blotch on middle of back, another above pectoral fins, and one around base of dorsal fin; a dark brown to black bar, sometimes white-edged, below eye, another in front of gill opening and continuing ventrally; a dark brown to black transverse band at front of chin, continuing posteriorly on each side of throat; fins yellowish, without spots. Attains 50 cm. Indo-Pacific. *D. maculatus* Dumeril and *D. bleekeri* Günther are synonyms.

BLACKLIP PORCUPINEFISH
Lophodiodon calori (Bianconi, 1855)

Dorsal rays 10-12; anal rays 10-11; pectoral rays 21-23; spines short, most on head and abdomen two-rooted and erectile, those on sides and back three-rooted and fixed; about 16 spines from front of snout to dorsal

1151. *Diodon histrix*, about 25 cm (J. Randall)

1152. *Diodon liturosus*, about 35 cm, night (J. Randall)

1153. *Lophodiodon calori*, about 29 cm (J. Randall)

fin; two prominent spines dorsally on caudal peduncle about half way from rear base of dorsal fin to caudal fin; two to four short, forward-projecting spines medially in front of nostrils; posterior rays of anal fin nearly reaching caudal-fin base; light brown dorsally, whitish ventrally; some short spines on back in a black spot; lips broadly black; a black bar below eye; a large dusky blotch in front of gill opening, the spines within in a black spot (some spines yellow); a comparable large blotch beneath pectoral fins; a small blackish blotch associated with a few yellow spines on side of body in front of dorsal fin; fins pale grey without markings. Attains 30 cm. Known from South Africa and Mozambique (type locality), southern Oman (illustrated fish from Juzor al Hallaniyat), southern Indonesia and northwestern Australia (Gloerfelt-Tarp and Kailola, 1984), and the South China Sea.

NOTE ON PHOTOGRAPHY

When good photographs taken of fishes in Oman or near-Oman waters were not available, illustrations were prepared from photographs taken outside Arabian seas. These photographs are listed below by figure number and locality.

1. Southern Mozambique; **8**. Hawaii; **11**. New South Wales, Australia; **12**. Hawaii; **26**. Philippines; **28**. Taiwan; **30**. India; **35**. Hawaii; **37**. Marshall Islands; **39**. Coral Sea; **42**. California; **44**. Indonesia; **46, 48**. Hawaii; **70**. Marshall Islands; **78**. South Africa; **79**. India; **81**. Mauritius; **94**. Hawaii; **105**. Flores, Indonesia; **107**; Maldives; **119, 122, 126**. Cochin, India; **135**. Madras, India; **137**. Cochin, India; **138, 141**. Lombok, Indonesia; **144, 148**. Cochin, India; **153**. Seychelles; **158**. Mauritius; **161**. South Africa; **162**. Hawaii; **169**. Seychelles; **171**. Hawaii; **177, 178**. Cochin, India; **179**. Sipadan Island, Borneo; **181**. Maldives; **182**. Papua New Guinea; **197**. Maldives; **203**. Madras, India; **209**. Flores, Indonesia; **211**. Maldives; **218**. New Britain; **226**. Japan; **231**. Western India; **247**. Mauritius; **249**. Gulf of Suez; **255**. Java, Indonesia; **256**. Cochin, India; **257**. Madras, India; **260**. Seychelles; **261**. Cochin, India; **265**. Papua New Guinea; **266**. Sulawesi, Indonesia; **267**. Mauritius; **268**. Society Islands; **269**. Cochin, India; **270A**. Okinawa; **277**. Japan; **280**. Marshall Islands; **281**. Indonesia; **286**. Mauritius; **292**. Maldives; **293**. Natal, South Africa; **302**. Somalia; **303**. Red Sea; **304**. India; **312**. Maldives; **313**. Natal, South Africa; **315**. Okinawa; **317**. Taiwan; **318**; Mauritius; **319**. Natal, South Africa; **323**. India; **326**. Papua New Guinea; **352**. Easter Island; **356**. Negros, Philippines; **388**. Madras, India; **417**. Cochin, India; **421**. Bahamas; **422**. Hawaii; **426**. Lombok, Indonesia; **438**. Seychelles; **447**. Maldives; **451, 454**. Hawaii; **458**. Gulf of Mexico; **467**. Madras, India; **472**. Natal, South Africa; **473, 474**. Cochin, India; **479**. Bali, Indonesia; **480**. Lombok, Indonesia; **482**. Kovalam, India; **484**. Natal, South Africa; **485**. New Caledonia; **487**. Cochin, India; **488**. Natal, South Africa; **489**. Cochin, India; **493**. Okinawa; **504**. Cochin, India; **506**. Sri Lanka; **516**. Seychelles; **521**. Japan; **525**. Seychelles; **570**. Maldives; **581**. Madras, India; **602**. Lombok, Indonesia; **603**. Java, Indonesia; **615**. Cochin, India; **630**. Maldives; **717**. Lombok, Indonesia; **724**. Maldives; **734**. Bali, Indonesia; **746, 754**. Sri Lanka; **757**. Seychelles; **763**. Maldives; **767**. Mauritius; **768**. Kenya; **769**; Tanzania; **774, 788**. Maldives; **809**. Minami Tori Shima (Marcus Island); **812, 813**. Hawaii; **814**. Marshall Islands; **818**. Maldives; **815, 816, 824, 825**. Mauritius; **826**. Seychelles; **829**. Line Islands; **847**. Indonesia; **848**. Seychelles; **859**. Kenya; **860**. Maldives; **875**. Ogasawara Islands; **887, 888**. Maldives; **911**. Hawaii; **948**. Southern Japan; **950**. Flores, Indonesia; **966**. Papua New Guinea; **967**. Sulawesi, Indonesia; **973**. Papua New Guinea; **978**. Cochin, India; **993**. Bali, Indonesia; **994**. Papua New Guinea; **995**. Flores, Indonesia; **998, 999**. Mandapam, India; **1002**. Cochin, India; **1006**. Seychelles; **1008**. Maldives; **1011**. Guam; **1016**. Kovalam, India; **1023**. Madras, India; **1030, 1032**. Cochin, India; **1035**. Seychelles; **1036**. Cochin, India; **1041**. South Africa; **1045**. Solomon Islands; **1055**. Taiwan; **1056**. Hawaii; **1058**. Maldives; **1059**. Easter Island; **1060**. Cochin, India; **1066**. Hawaii; **1077, 1082**. Cochin, India; **1086**. Sri Lanka; **1090, 1092**. Maldives; **1096**. Sri Lanka; **1098**. Seychelles; **1099**. Maldives; **1106**. Cochin, India; **1114**. Hawaii; **1116**. Johnston Island; **1124**. Java, Indonesia; **1135**. Maldives; **1147**. Sulawesi, Indonesia; **Page 16**: Hawaii.

GLOSSARY

Adipose eyelid: immovable transparent outer covering or partial covering of the eye of some groups of bony fishes, such as mullets and trevallies, which performs protective and streamlining functions.

Adipose fin: a small fleshy fin without rays found on the back behind the dorsal fin of some primitive teleost fishes such as the lizardfishes.

Alcyonarian: animal of Subclass Anthozoa (corals, sea anemones) of Phylum Coelenterata; polyps with eight tentacles; includes soft corals and gorgonians.

Allopatric: in reference to species with different geographical distributions; the opposite of sympatric.

Amphipod: a crustacean animal of the Order Amphipoda, most of which are small and aquatic; the body is usually laterally compressed.

Antrorse spine: a small bony projection directed anteriorly (present on the lower preopercular margin of some serranids).

Anus: the posterior external opening of the digestive tract from which wastes are voided; sometimes called the vent.

Artisanal fishery: a fishery of which the catch is locally consumed.

Axil: the acute angular region between a fin and the body; usually used in reference to the underside of the pectoral fin toward the base. Equivalent to the armpit of man.

Band: an oblique or irregular marking (compare *bar*, below).

Bar: an elongate colour marking of vertical orientation, the sides of which are usually more-or-less straight (although they need not be parallel).

Barbel: a slender tentacle-like protuberance of sensory function which is often seen on the chin of some fishes such as goatfishes and some of the croakers.

Benthic: referring to the benthos, the fauna and flora of the sea bottom.

Bifurcate: divided into two branches.

Biserial: arranged in two separate rows.

Branched tubules: refers to lateral-line scale tubules which divide into two or more branches.

Branchiostegal rays: the slender bony supports of the gill membranes.

Bryozoan: an aquatic, plant-like or encrusting animal of the Phylum Bryozoa, commonly called moss animals; they are sessile, colonial, with a complete digestive tract and ciliated tentacles around the mouth.

Canine: a prominent slender sharp-pointed tooth.

Carapace: a rigid shield encasing the body.

Carnivore: a flesh-eating animal.

Caudal fin: the tail fin. The term tail alone generally refers to that part of a fish posterior to the anus.

Caudal peduncle: the part of the body between the posterior basal parts of the dorsal and anal fins and the base of the caudal fin. The usual vertical measurement is the least depth; the length measurement herein is horizontal, generally from the rear base of the anal fin.

Cephalic: referring to the head.

Cephalic flaps: the forward-directed projections on either side of the mouth of manta or devil rays (Mobulidae).

Cephalopod: a marine animal of the Phylum Mollusca, Class Cephalopoda. The class includes the squids, octopuses and nautiluses.

Ciguatera: an illness resulting from eating a fresh fish with ciguatoxin in its tissues.

Circumnarial groove: a cleft or groove around the nostril openings found in some sharks.

Circumpeduncular scales: the transverse series of scales that completely encircle the caudal peduncle.

Cirrus: a small slender flexible fleshy protuberance; the plural is cirri.

Claspers: rod-like grooved processes attached to the pelvic fins of male sharks, skates, rays and guitarfishes. Used to transmit sperm during copulation.

Cloaca: cavity into which the intestinal, urinary and reproductive canals open.

Coelenterate: an aquatic animal of the Phylum Coelenterata which is characterised by a central mouth usually surrounded by tentacles bearing stinging cells, and no anus; includes sea anemones, corals and jellyfishes.

Commensal: refers to an association of two different organisms whereby one gains benefit by living with, on or within the other, but without harm or benefit to the other.

Community: the assemblage of animals and plants living in one habitat.

Compressed: laterally flattened; often used in reference to the shape of the body – in this case deeper than wide.

Copepod: a small to microscopic aquatic animal of the Subclass Copepoda, Class Crustacea. May be free-living (benthic or pelagic), commensal, or parasitic. A major component of the zooplankton.

Corselet: a zone of thickened scales that covers the anterior part of the body of tunas and bonitos.

Crenulate: wavy or scalloped, in reference to the shape of an edge (as of a lip).

Crustacean: an animal of Class Crustacea, Phylum Arthropoda; includes crabs, lobsters, shrimps and copepods.

Cryptic: in reference to an animal that tends to remain hidden.

Ctenoid scales: scales of bony fishes which have tiny tooth-like projections along the posterior margin and part of the exposed portion. Collectively these little teeth (or ctenii) impart a rough texture to the surface of the scales.

Cuspidate: bearing a pointed projection (cusp); generally used in reference to sharks' teeth with more than one cusp.

Cycloid scales: scales of bony fishes, the exposed surfaces and edges of which lack any small tooth-like projections; they are, therefore, smooth to the touch.

Deciduous: in reference to scales which are easily dislodged.

Demersal: living on the sea bottom.

Denticles: tooth-like projections such as the scales which cover the bodies of cartilaginous fishes.

Depressed: dorsoventrally flattened. The opposite in body shape of compressed.

Depth: vertical measurement of the body of a fish; most often employed for maximum height of body excluding fins.

Distal: outward from the point of attachment; the opposite of proximal.

Dorsal: toward the back or upper part of the body; the opposite of ventral.

Dorsal fin: a median fin along the back which is supported by rays. When there are two or more dorsal fins the most anterior one is designated the first.

Echinoderm: an aquatic marine animal of the Phylum Echinodermata; radially symmetrical with a skeleton composed of calcareous plates (may be reduced to spicules); many move via their numerous tube feet; includes starfishes, brittle stars, sea urchins and sea cucumbers.

Elasmobranch: a subclass of cartilaginous fishes including sharks, skates and rays.

Elongate: extended or drawn out.

Emarginate: concave; used to describe the posterior border of a caudal fin which is inwardly curved.

Endemic: native; in reference to an animal or plant restricted to a certain area.

Epipelagic: pertaining to the surface layer of the open sea.

Esca: the bait or lure of lophiiform fishes (see illicium).

Euryhaline: capable of withstanding a wide range of salinity.

Eurythermal: capable of withstanding a wide range of temperature.

Falcate: sickle-shaped; used to describe the shape of fins.

Family: a major entity in the classification of animals and plants which consists of a group of related genera. Family words end in "idae", such as Gobiidae for the goby family; when used as an adjective, the "ae" is dropped, thus gobiid fish.

Finlet: a small median fin, usually occurring in a series, posterior to the second dorsal and anal fins of scombrid fishes (tunas and mackerels) and some carangids (jacks).

Foramanifera: an order of single-cell animals of the Phylum Protozoa, mostly tiny, which are covered by a shell; they may be benthic, pelagic or commensal.

Fork length: the straight-line distance from the front of the snout to the distal end of the shortest middle caudal fin ray.

Forked: inwardly angular; used in describing the shape of a caudal fin which is divided into two equal lobes, the posterior border of each of which is relatively straight.

Fossorial: fitted for digging; generally refers to an animal which lives beneath the surface of sediment.

Fusiform: spindle-shaped; used in reference to the body shape of a fish which is cylindrical or nearly so and tapers toward both ends.

Gas bladder: a tough-walled gas-filled sac lying in the upper part of the body cavity of many bony fishes just beneath the vertebral column, the prinicipal function of which is to offset the weight of the heavier tissues, particularly bone. The organ is also called the swim bladder.

Genus: a group of closely related species; the first part of the scientific name of an animal or plant. The plural is genera.

Gill arch: the bony and cartilaginous support for the gill filaments and gill rakers. Normally there are four pairs of gill arches in bony fishes.

Gill opening: the opening posteriorly and often also ventrally on the head of fishes where the water of respiration is expelled. Bony fishes have a single such opening on each side whereas cartilaginous fishes (sharks and rays) have five to seven. The gill openings of sharks and rays are called gill slits.

Gill rakers: stout protuberances of the gill arch on the opposite side from the red gill filaments; they function in retaining food organisms. Gill rakers vary greatly in number and length and are important in the classification of fishes.

Gonads: reproductive organs.

Gorgonian: a sessile animal of the Subclass Alcyonaria, Class Anthozoa, Phylum Coelenterata; includes sea fans and sea whips.

Head length: the straight-line measurement of the head taken from the front of the upper lip to the membranous posterior end of the operculum.

Herbivore: a plant-feeding animal.

Homonym: the scientific name of an organism which is the same as that given to another organism; the second of these two identical names is invalid.

Hydrozoan: an aquatic, radially symmetrical animal of the Class Hydrozoa, Phylum Coelentera, which may occur as free-living medusae or as benthic colonies, the polyps of which have a ring of tentacles around the mouth. The tentacles bear stinging capsules termed nematocysts.

Illicium: the "fishing pole" and "lure" of lophiiform (pediculate) fishes which is used to attract prey close to the mouth.

Imbricate: overlapping, typical of most fish scales.

Incisiform: chisel-like; used to describe teeth which are flattened and truncate with sharp edges like the front teeth of some mammals such as man.

Inferior tail ridge: a bony ridge along the lower edge of the tail in pipefishes.

Inferior trunk ridge: a bony ridge along the lower edge of the trunk of the body in pipefishes.

Interdorsal ridge: a tough fold of skin that runs along the middle of the back between the dorsal fins of some sharks.

Interopercle: one of the bones comprising the operculum; bordered anterodorsally by the preopercle and posterodorsally by the opercle and subopercle.

Interorbital space: the region on the top of the head between the eyes; measurements may be taken of the least width, either fleshy (to the edges of the orbits) or bony (between the edges of the frontal bones which rim the orbits).

Interradial membrane: the membrane between fin rays.

Invertebrate: an animal lacking a vertebral column; includes the vast majority of animals on earth such as the corals, the worms and the insects.

Isthmus: the throat region of a fish which extends forward from the ventral part of the chest (thorax) and narrows anteriorly.

Keel: a lateral strengthening ridge posteriorly on the caudal peduncle or base of the caudal fin; typically found on swift-swimming fishes with a narrow caudal peduncle and a broadly lunate caudal fin.

Labial furrows: grooves around the outer edges of the lips that are prominent in some sharks.

Lacrymal (also spelt *lachrymal*): the most anterior of the series of suborbital bones which rim the lower part of the orbit. Also called the *preorbital* (see below).

Lanceolate: lance-shaped, hence gradually tapering to a point; used to describe a caudal fin with very long middle rays. An unusual fin shape most often seen among the gobies.

Lateral: referring to the side or directed toward the side; the opposite of medial.

Lateral line: a sensory organ of fishes which consists of a canal running along the side of the body and communicating via pores through scales to the exterior; functions in perceiving low frequency vibrations, hence provides a sense which might be termed "touch at a distance".

Lateral-line scales: the pored scales of the lateral line between the upper end of the gill opening and the base of the caudal fin. The count of this series of scales is of value in the description of fishes. Also of value at times is the number of scales above the lateral line (to the origin of the dorsal fin) and the number below the lateral line (to the origin of the anal fin).

Lateral trunk ridge: a bony ridge along the middle part of the anterior body of pipefishes.

Leptocephalus: the elongate, highly compressed, transparent larval stage of some primitive teleost fishes such as the tarpon, bonefish and eels.

Lower limb: refers either to the horizontal

margin of the preopercle or to the ventral part of the gill arch.

Lunate: sickle-shaped; used to describe a caudal fin which is deeply emarginate with narrow lobes.

Maxilla: a dermal bone of the upper jaw which lies posterior to the premaxilla. On the higher fishes the maxilla is excluded from the gape, and the premaxilla bears the teeth.

Medial: toward the middle or median plane of the body; opposite of lateral.

Median fins: the fins in the median plane, hence the dorsal, anal and caudal fins.

Midlateral scales: refers to the longitudinal series of scales from the upper edge of the operculum to the base of the caudal fin. Generally used for fishes without a lateral line.

Molariform: shaped like a molar, hence low, broad and rounded.

Mollusc: an animal of the Phylum Mollusca; unsegmented with a muscular "foot" and visceral mass; often protected by one or two shells; includes gastropods (snails and nudibranchs), pelecypods (bivalves such as clams and oysters), cephalopods (such as squids and octopuses) and amphineurans (chitons).

Nape: the dorsal region of the head posterior to the occiput.

Nasal barbel: tentacle-like protuberance located close to the nasal opening.

Nasal fossa: cavity or pit containing the nasal organ.

Nasoral groove: a cleft or furrow between the nostril and mouth in some sharks.

Neritic: refers to that part of the ocean over the continental shelf (from the low-tide mark to a depth of 200 metres); the more offshore part of the pelagic environment is termed the oceanic zone.

Nictitating eyelid: a movable transparent membrane which serves to protect the eye of elasmobranch fishes.

Occipital: refers to the occiput, the dorsal posterior part of the cranium.

Ocellus: eye-like marking with ring of one colour surrounding spot of another.

Omnivore: an animal which feeds on both plant and animal material.

Opercle: the large bone which forms the upper posterior part of the operculum; often bears one to three backward-directed spines in the higher fishes.

Operculum: gill cover; comprised of the following four bones; opercle, preopercle, interopercle and subopercle.

Ophiuroid: a radially symmetrical, benthic, marine animal of the Class Ophiuroidea, Phylum Echinodermata. Includes the brittle stars, serpent stars and basket stars.

Orbital: referring to the orbit or eye.

Order: a major unit in the classification of organisms; an assemblage of related families. The ordinal word ending in the Animal Kingdom is "iformes".

Origin: the beginning; often used for the anterior end of the dorsal or anal fin at the base. Also used in zoology to denote the more fixed attachment of a muscle.

Osseous: composed of bone.

Osteological: in reference to a study of the bony skeletal parts of an animal.

Oviparous: producing ova (eggs) that hatch after leaving the body of the mother; the mode of reproduction of the great majority of bony fishes.

Ovoviviparous: producing eggs which hatch within body of mother; mode of reproduction of most sharks and rays.

Paired fins: collective term for the pectoral and pelvic fins.

Palatine: a paired lateral bone on the roof of the mouth lying between the vomer and the upper jaw; the presence or absence of teeth on this bone is of significance in the classification of fishes.

Papilla: a small fleshy protuberance.

Pectoral fin: the fin usually found on each side of the body behind the gill opening; in primitive fishes such as herrings, this pair of fins is lower on the body than in more advanced forms.

Pelagic: pertaining to the open sea (hence not living inshore or on the bottom); oceanic.

Pelecypod: a bivalve aquatic animal of the

Class Pelecypoda, Phylum Mollusca; includes clams, oysters, mussels, and so on.

Pelvic fin: one of a pair of juxtaposed fins ventrally on the body in front of the anus; varies from abdominal in position in primitive fishes such as herrings to the more anterior locations termed thoracic or jugular in advanced fishes. It is sometimes called the ventral fin.

Perinasal groove: cleft or furrow around the nasal opening in some sharks. Also called circumnarial groove.

Pharyngeal teeth: opposing patches of teeth which occur on upper and lower elements of the gill arches. Vary from sharp and piercing to nodular or molariform; may be modified into a grooved grinding apparatus (or pharyngeal mill), such as is seen in the parrotfishes.

Phytoplankton: the plants of the plankton.

Plankton: collective term for pelagic animals and plants that drift with ocean currents; many are motile but are too small or swim too feebly or aimlessly to resist the sweep of the current. By contrast, animals of the nekton are independent of water movement.

Polychaete: an animal of Class Polychaeta of Phylum Annelida; a segmented worm with setae (bristles), which may move about freely or live permanently in a tube. Polychaete is from the Greek meaning many hairs or bristles.

Polyp: the sedentary form of coelenterate animals consisting of a tubular body with one external opening (the mouth) rimmed with tentacles; may be one of a colony; the soft part of a living coral.

Precaudal pit: the dorsal depression or notch just in front of the caudal fin of sharks.

Predorsal scales: the series of scales along the middorsal line extending anterior to the origin of the dorsal fin.

Premaxilla: the more anterior bone forming the upper jaw. In the higher fishes it extends backward and bears all of the teeth of the jaw. It is this part of the upper jaw which can be protruded by many fishes.

Preopercle: a boomerang-shaped bone, the edges of which form the posterior and lower margins of the cheek region; it is the most anterior of the bones comprising the gill cover. The upper vertical margin is sometimes called the upper limb, and the lower horizontal edge the lower limb; the two limbs meet at the angle of the preopercle.

Preoral length: measurement used for sharks taken between the snout tip and front of the upper jaw.

Preorbital: the first and usually the largest of the suborbital bones; located along the ventroanterior rim of the eye. Sometimes called the lachrymal bone.

Principal caudal rays: the caudal rays which reach the posterior, terminal border of the fin; in those fishes with branched caudal rays, the count includes the branched rays plus the uppermost and lowermost rays which are unbranched.

Produced: drawn out to a point; lengthened.

Protrusible: capable of projection as in some jaws.

Proximal: toward the centre of the body; the opposite of distal.

Radii: small (often microscopic) grooves on the margin of scales; radiate from the focus (centre of origin) of the scale, hence cut across the circuli (growth rings).

Ray: the supporting bony elements of fins; includes spines and soft rays.

Recurve: to curve backwards (towards the tail).

Retrorse spine: a spine which curves backwards.

Rhomboid: wedge-shaped; refers to a caudal fin in which the middle rays are longest and the upper and lower portions of the terminal border of the fin are more-or-less straight; essentially the opposite of forked. It is an uncommon fin shape.

Rounded: refers to a caudal fin in which the terminal border is smoothly convex.

Rudiment: a structure so deficient in size that it does not perform its normal function; often used in reference to small nodular gill rakers at the ends of the gill arches.

Scute: an external bony plate or enlarged scale.

Segmented rays: the soft rays of the fins which bear cross striations, at least distally.

Serrate: notched along a free margin; like the edge of a saw.

Sessile: permanently attached.

Seta: a bristle or bristle-like structure; the plural is setae.

Sexual dichromatism: a condition wherein the two sexes of the same species are of different colour.

Simple: not branched.

Sipunculid: an unsegmented marine worm of the Phylum Sipunculoidea; commonly called peanut worms.

Snout: the region of the head in front of the eye. Snout length is measured from front of the upper lip to the anterior edge of the eye.

Soft ray: a segmented fin ray which is composed of two closely joined lateral elements. It is nearly always flexible and often branched.

Spatulate: flattened with a rounded end, sometimes used to describe tooth shape.

Species: the fundamental unit in the classification of animals and plants consisting of a population of individuals which freely interbreed with one another. The word "species" is both singular and plural.

Spine: unsegmented bony process consisting of single element, usually rigid and sharply pointed. Those spines which support fins are never branched.

Spinule: a small spine (but not used to refer to the spines in fins).

Spiracle: an opening between the eye and the first gill slit of sharks and rays which leads to the pharyngeal cavity.

Standard length: the straight-line length of a fish from the front of the upper lip to the posterior end of the vertebral column (the last element of which, the hypural plate, is somewhat broadened and forms the bony support for the caudal fin rays).

Stripe: a horizontal straight-sided colour marking.

Subopercle: an elongate flat dermal bone which is one of the four comprising the operculum; lies below the opercle and forms the ventroposterior margin of the operculum.

Suborbital depth: the distance from the lower edge of the eye to the nearest edge of the upper lip.

Suborbital stay: a bony ridge across the cheek found in scorpaeniform fishes.

Subterminal notch: indentation near the tip of the posterior edge of the upper caudal lobe of many sharks.

Supraorbital: the region above the upper edge of the eye.

Supraorbital ridge: bony crest above eye.

Supraorbital tentacle: a slender flap of skin above the eye.

Supratemporal: in reference to the "scale bone" of primitive clupeoid fishes, or to the general region of the head above the operculum (gill cover).

Swimbladder: the hydrostatic organ of fishes, consisting of a tough-walled sac just beneath the vertebral column; also known as the gas bladder.

Symbiosis: the living together in close association by two dissimilar organisms. This term includes commensalism whereby one organism derives benefit from the association but the other does not (though it is not harmed), parasitism where the association is disadvantageous to one of the organisms, and mutualism where both organisms exist to mutual advantage.

Sympatric: in reference to species which live in the same major geographical area; the opposite of allopatric.

Synonym: invalid scientific name of an organism proposed after accepted name.

Tail: that part of an animal posterior to the anus (disregarding the hind limbs of quadrupeds).

Teleost: refers to the Teleostei, the highest superorder of rayfin bony fishes. The other superorders are the Chondrostei (surgeons and paddlefishes are living representatives) and the Holostei (the bowfin and true gars are contemporary forms). Teleosts represent about 96% of extant fishes.

Thermocline: a plane within a body of water separating a warm upper layer from an abruptly and distinctly cooler lower layer.

Tholichthys larva: the pelagic stage of butterflyfishes (Chaetodontidae) characterised by external bony plates covering the head.

Thoracic: referring to the chest region.

Total length: the maximum straight-line length of a fish; generally taken from the front of whichever jaw is most anterior to the end of the longest caudal fin ray.

Transverse scales: series of scales in a vertical row, often counted between the dorsal and anal fin bases.

Truncate: square-ended; used to describe a caudal fin with a vertically straight terminal border and angular or slightly rounded corners.

Tunicate: a marine animal of the Subphylum Tunicata, Phylum Chordata. The subphylum includes the ascidians (commonly called sea squirts), which are bottom-dwelling and occur either as solitary individuals or as colonies of individuals with a common covering; it also includes the pelagic larvaceans and salps.

Uniserial: occurring in a single row.

Upper limb: refers either to the vertical free margin of the preopercle or the upper part of the gill arch

Ventral: toward the lower part of the body; the opposite of dorsal.

Vertebrae: the series of block-like bones that comprise the backbone of vertebrate animals, such as fishes, reptiles, birds and mammals.

Vertical scale rows: see midlateral scales.

Villiform: like the villi of the intestine, hence with numerous small, slender projections. Used to describe bands of small close-set teeth, particularly if slender. If the teeth are short, they are often termed cardiform.

Viviparous: producing living young which develop from nourishment directly from the mother.

Vomer: a median unpaired bone toward the front of the roof of the mouth, the anterior end of which often bears teeth.

Zoantharian: a radially symmetrical benthic animal of the Subclass Zoantharia, Phylum Coelenterata; includes the sea anemones, stony corals and black corals.

Zooplankton: the animals of the plankton.

BIBLIOGRAPHY

Abou-Seedo, F., J.M. Wright, and D.A. Clayton. 1990. Aspects of the biology of *Diplodus sargus kotschyi* (Sparidae) from Kuwait Bay. *Cybium* 14(3): 217-223.

Al-Baharna, W.S. 1986. *Fishes of Bahrain*, 294 pp., Directorate of Fisheries, Ministry of Commerce and Agriculture, Bahrain.

Alcock, A. 1898. *Illustrations of the Zoology of Royal Indian Marine Survey Ship Investigator, under the Command of Commander T.H. Heming, R.N.*, pls. 18-24, Government Printing, Calcutta.

Allen, G.R. 1975. *Anemonefishes*, 2nd ed., 352 pp., T.F.H. Publications, Neptune City, New Jersey.

———. 1978. *Die Anemonenfische*, 104 pp., Mergus, Melle, Germany.

———. 1985. Snappers of the World. *FAO Species Catalogue* 6: vi + 208 pp.

———. 1980. *Butterfly and Angelfishes of the World*, vol. 2: 145-352, John Wiley & Sons, New York (English edition).

———. 1991. *Damselfishes of the World*, 271 pp., Mergus, Melle, Germany.

Allen, G.R. and W.E. Burgess. 1990. A review of the glassfishes (Chandidae) of Australia and New Guinea. *Rec. West. Austral. Mus.*, Suppl. no. 34: 139-206.

Allen, G.R. and R.H. Kuiter. 1978. *Heniochus diphreutes* Jordan, a valid species of butterflyfish (Chaetodontidae) from the Indo-West Pacific. *Jour. Roy. Soc. West. Austral.* 61(1): 11-18.

Allen, G.R. and J.E. Randall. 1977. Review of the sharpnose pufferfishes (subfamily Canthigasterinae) of the Indo-Pacific. *Rec. Austral. Mus.* 30(17): 475-517.

———. 1980. A review of the damselfishes (Teleostei: Pomacentridae) of the Red Sea. *Israel Jour. Zool.* 29: 1-98.

———. 1994. A new species of cardinalfish (Apogon: Apogonidae) from Arabian Seas. *Rev. Franç. Aquariol.* 21(1-2): 24-26.

Allen, G.R. and F.H. Talbot. 1985. Review of the snappers of the genus *Lutjanus* (Pisces: Lutjanidae) from the Indo-Pacific, with the description of a new species. *Indo-Pacific Fishes*, no. 11: 1-87.

Amaoka, K. and T. Kanayama. 1981. Additional specimens of *Minous longimanus* from the western Indian Ocean, distinct from *M. inermis*. *Japan. Jour. Ichth.* 27(4): 330-332.

Annandale, N. 1909. Report on the fishes taken by the Bengal fisheries steamer "Golden Crown." Part I.—Batoidei. *Mem. Indian Mus.* 4: 1-60.

Baranes, A. and D. Golani. 1993. An annotated list of deep-sea fishes collected in the northern Red Sea, Gulf of Aqaba. *Israel Jour. Zool.* 39(4): 299-336.

Bass, A.J., J.D. D'Aubrey, and N. Kistnasamy. 1973. Sharks of the east coast of southern Africa. I. The genus *Carcharhinus* (Carcharhinidae). *Invest. Rep. Oceanogr. Res. Inst.*, no. 33: 1-168.

———. 1975a. Sharks of the east coast of southern Africa. III. The families Carcharhinidae (excluding *Mustelus* and *Carcharhinus*) and Sphyrnidae. *Invest. Rep. Oceanogr. Res. Inst.*, no. 38: 1-100.

———. 1975b. Sharks of the east coast of southern Africa. V. The families Hexanchidae, Chlamydoselachidae, Heterodontidae, Pristiophoridae and Squatinidae. *Invest. Rep. Oceanogr. Res. Inst.*, no. 43: 1-50.

Basson, P.W., J.E. Burchard, Jr., J.T. Hardy, and A.R.G. Price. 1981. *Biotopes of the Western Arabian Gulf*, 2nd ed., 284 pp., Arabian American Oil Company, Dhahran.

Bath, H. 1980. *Omobranchus punctatus* (Valenciennes 1836) neu im Suez-Kanal. *Senckenb. Biol.* 60(5/6): 317-319.

———. 1982. Beitrag zur Revalidation von *Parablennius ruber* (Valenciennes 1836) mit kritischen Bemerkungen zur Gültigkeit der Gattung *Pictiblennius* Whitley 1930 (Pisces: Blenniidae). *Senckenb. Biol.* 62(4/6): 211-224.

———. 1983. Revision der Gattung *Antennablennius* Fowler 1931 mit Beschreibung einer neuen Art und Untersuchung der taxonomischen Stellung von *Antennablennius anuchalis* Springer & Spreitzer 1978. *Senckenb. Biol.* 64(1/3): 47-80.

———. 1989. Die Arten der Gattung *Parablennius* Ribeiro 1915 im Roten Meer, Indischen und NW des Pazifischen Ozeans (Pisces: Blenniidae). *Senckenb. Biol.* 69(4/6): 301-343.

Bauchot, M.L. and G. Bianchi. 1984. *Diplodus cervinus omanensis*, nouvelle sous-espèce de *Diplodus cervinus* (Lowe, 1841), capturée en mer d'Arabie (Pisces, Perciformes, Sparidae).

Beebe, W. and J. Tee-Van. 1933. Nomenclatural notes on the shore fishes of Bermuda. *Zoologica* 13(7): 133-158.

Bellwood, D.R. 1994. A phylogenetic study of the parrotfishes family Scaridae (Pisces: Labroidei), with a revision of genera. *Rec. Austral. Mus.*, Suppl. 20: 1-86.

Bellwood, D.R. and J.H. Choat. 1989. A description of the juvenile phase colour patterns of 24 parrotfish species (family Scaridae) from the Great Barrier Reef, Australia. *Rec. Austral. Mus.* 41: 1-41.

———. 1990. A functional analysis of grazing in parrotfishes (family Scaridae): the ecological implications. *Env. Biol. Fish.* 28: 189-214.

Bigelow, H.B. and W.C. Schroeder. 1953. *Fishes of the Western North Atlantic. Part II. Sawfishes, Guitarfishes, Skates and Rays*, xv + 588 pp., Sears Foundation for Marine Research, Yale University, New Haven.

Bleeker, P. 1865. *Atlas Ichthyologique des Indes Orientales Néêrlandaises*, vol. 4: 132 pp., Fréderic Muller, Amsterdam.

———. 1875. *Atlas Ichthyologique des Indes Orientales Néêrlandaises*, vol. 6: 170 pp., Fréderic Muller, Amsterdam.

———. 1877-1878. *Atlas Ichthyologique des Indes Orientales Néêrlandaises*, vol. 9: 80 pp., Fréderic Muller, Amsterdam.

———. 1983. *Atlas Ichthyologique des Indes Orientales Néêrlandaises*, plates planned for vols. 11-14, Smithsonian Institution Press, Washington, D.C.

Blegvad, H. 1944. *Fishes of the Iranian Gulf*. 247 pp., Einar Munksgaard, Copenhagen.

Bloch, M.E. and J.G. Schneider. 1801. *Systema Ichthyologiae iconibus cx illustratum* ... ix + 584 pp., Sanderiano Commissum, Berlin.

Böhlke, E.B. (ed.). 1989. *Fishes of the Western North Atlantic. Part Nine, Volume One: Orders Anguilliformes and Saccopharyngiformes*, xvii + 655 pp., Sears Foundation for Marine Research, Yale University, New Haven.

Böhlke, E.B. and J.E. Randall. 1995. Description of a new species of moray eel (Anguilliformes: Muraenidae: *Gymnothorax*) from Oman and Somalia, *Not. Nat.*, no. 472: 1-5.

Böhlke, J. E. and C.G. Chaplin. 1957. Oral incubation in Bahaman jawfishes *Opistognathus whitehursti* and *O. maxillosus*. *Science* 125 (3243): 353.

Boulenger, G.A. 1887. An account of the fishes obtained by Surgeon-Major A.S.G. Jayakar at Muscat, east coast of Arabia. *Proc. Zool. Soc. London.* 1887: 653-667.

———. 1889. Second account of the fishes obtained by Surgeon-Major A.S.G. Jayakar at Muscat, east coast of Arabia. *Proc. Zool. Soc. London.* 1889: 236-246.

———. 1892. Third account of the fishes obtained by Surgeon-Major A.S.G. Jayakar at Muscat, east coast of Arabia. *Proc. Zool. Soc. London.* 1892: 134-136.

———. 1895a. Description of a new eagle-ray from Muscat (*Rhinoptera jayakari* n. sp.). *Ann. Mag. Nat. Hist.*, ser. 6, 15: 141.

———. 1895b. *Catalogue of the Fishes of the British Museum*, second edition, xix + 391 pp., British Museum (Natural History), London.

———. 1897. Descriptions of fishes from the Mekran coast, Persia. *Ann. Mag. Nat. Hist.*, ser. 6, 20: 420-422.

———. 1900. Description of a new sea-horse (*Hippocampus*) from Muscat. *Ann. Mag. Nat. Hist.*, ser. 7, 6: 51-52.

———. 1901. On some deep-sea fishes collected by Mr. F.W. Townsend in the Sea of Oman. *Ann. Mag. Nat. Hist.*, ser. 7, 7: 261-263.

Boylan, D.B. and P.J. Scheuer. 1967. Pahutoxin: a fish poison. *Science* 155: 52-56.

Briggs, J.C. 1955. A monograph of the clingfishes (Order Xenopterygii). *Stanford Ichth. Bull.* 6: iv + 224 pp.

Burchmore, J.J., D.A. Pollard, M.J. Middleton, J.D. Bell, and B.C. Pease. 1988. Biology of four species of whiting (Pisces: Sillaginidae) in Botany Bay, New South Wales. *Austral. Jour. Mar. Freshw. Res.* 39: 709-727.

Burgess, W.E. 1974. Evidence for the elevation to family status of the angelfishes (Pomacanthidae), previously considered to be a subfamily of the butterflyfish family, Chaetodontidae. *Pac. Sci.* 28(1): 57-71.

————. 1978. *Butterflyfishes of the World*, 832 pp., T.F.H. Publications, Neptune City, New Jersey.

Cantwell, G.E. 1964. A revision of the genus *Parapercis*, family Mugiloididae. *Pac. Sci.* 18(3): 239-280.

Carpenter, K.E. 1987. Revision of the Indo-Pacific fish family Caesionidae (Lutjanoidea), with descriptions of five new species. *Indo-Pacific Fishes*, no. 15: 1-56.

Carpenter, K.E. and G.R. Allen. 1989. Emperor fishes and large-eye breams of the world. *FAO Species Catalogue*, vol. 9: v + 118 pp.

Chapleau, F. and C.B. Renaud. 1993. *Paraplagusia sinerama* (Pleuronectiformes: Cynoglossidae), a new Indo-Pacific tongue sole with a revised key to species of the genus. *Copeia* 1993(3): 798-807.

Chave, E.H. and H.A. Randall. 1971. Feeding behavior of the moray eel *Gymnothorax pictus*. *Copeia* 1971(3): 570-574.

Clark, E. 1979. Red Sea fishes of the family Tripterygiidae with descriptions of eight new species. *Israel Jour. Zool.* 28: 65-113.

Clark, E. and A. George. 1979. Two toxic soles, *Pardachirus marmoratus* from the Red Sea and *P. pavoninus* from Japan, with notes on other species. *Env. Biol. Fish.* 4(2): 103-123.

Clark, E. and H.A.F. Gohar. 1953. The fishes of the Red Sea: Order Plectognathi. *Publ. Mar. Biol. Sta. Al Ghardaqa (Red Sea)*, no. 8: 1-80 (plus text in Arabic).

Clark, E. and J.F. Pohle. 1992. Monogamy in tilefish. *Natl. Geogr. Res. Explor.* 8(3): 276-295.

Clarke, T.A. 1971. The ecology of the scalloped hammerhead shark, *Sphyrna lewini*, in Hawaii. *Pac. Sci.* 25(2): 133-144.

Cohen, D.M. 1970. How many recent fishes are there? *Proc. Calif. Acad. Sci.*, ser. 4., 38(17): 341-346.

Cole, K.S. and D.R. Robertson. 1988. Protogyny in the Caribbean reef goby *Coryphopterus personatus*: gonad ontogeny and social influences on sex-change. *Bull. Mar. Sci.* 42(2): 317-333.

Cole, K.S. and D.Y. Shapiro. 1990. Gonad structure and hermaphroditism in the gobiid genus *Coryphopterus* (Teleostei: Gobiidae). *Copeia* 1990(4): 996-1003.

Colin, P.L. 1976. Filter feeding and predation on the eggs of *Thalassoma* sp. by the scombrid fish *Rastrelliger kanagurta*. *Copeia* 1976(3): 596-597.

Collette, B.B. 1976. Indo-west Pacific halfbeaks (Hemiramphidae) of the genus *Rhynchorhamphus* with descriptions of two new species. *Bull. Mar. Sci.* 26(1): 72-98.

Collette, B.B. and C.E. Nauen. 1983. Scombrids of the world. *FAO Species Catalogue* 2: vii + 137 pp.

Compagno, L.J.V. 1979. Carcharhinoid sharks: morphology, systematics, and phylogeny. *Dissertation Abstr.* Int. (B) 40(2): 629.

————. 1984. Sharks of the world. *FAO Species Catalogue* 1, Part 1: viii + 249 pp., Part 2: x + 251-655 pp.

————. 1988. *Sharks of the Order Carcharhiniformes*, xxii + 486 pp., Princeton University Press, Princeton, New Jersey.

Compagno, L.J.V. and T.R. Roberts. 1982. Freshwater stingrays (Dasyatidae) of southeast Asia and New Guinea, with description of a new species of *Himantura* and reports of uniden-

tified species. *Env. Biol. Fish.* 7(4): 321-339.

Cressey, R. 1981. Revision of Indo-west Pacific lizardfishes of the genus *Synodus* (Pisces: Synodontidae). *Smiths. Contr. Zool.*, no. 342: iii + 53 pp.

Cressey, R.F. and E.A. Lachner. 1970. The parasitic copepod diet and life history of diskfishes (Echeneidae). *Copeia* 1970(2): 310-318.

Cuvier, G.L. and A. Valenciennes. 1828-1849. *Histoire Naturelle de Poissons*, 22 vols., F.G. Levrault, Ch. Pitois, and P. Bertrand, Paris.

Dawson, C.E. 1985. *Indo-Pacific Pipefishes (Red Sea to the Americas)*, 230 pp., Gulf Coast Research Laboratory, Ocean Springs, Mississippi.

Day, F. 1875-1878. *The Fishes of India*, xx + 778 pp., Bernard Quaritch, London.

De Beaufort, L.F. and W.M. Chapman. 1951. *The Fishes of the Indo-Australian Archipelago*, vol. 9: xi + 484 pp., E.J. Brill, Leiden.

Debelius, H. 1993. *Indian Ocean Tropical Fish Guide*, 321 pp., Aquaprint, Neu Isenburg, Germany.

De la Paz, R.M. 1978. *Diplodus noct* Ehrenberg MS (Valenciennes, 1830) and *D. kotschyi* (Steindachner, 1877) (Pisces: Teleostei: Sparidae) and the origin of *Diplodus*. *Proc. Intern. Symp. Mar. Biogeog. Evol. S. Hemisphere, Auckland, N. Z.* 2: 731-740.

De Sylva, D.P. 1963. Systematics and life history of the great barracuda *Sphyraena barracuda* (Walbaum). *Stud. Trop. Oceanogr. Miami* 1: viii + 179 pp.

Devadoss, P. 1981. On the food of rays, *Dasyatis uranak* (Forskal), *D. alcockii* (Annandale) and *D. sephen* (Forskal). *Indian Jour. Fish.* (1978) 25(1/2): 9-13.

Diamant, A. and M. Shpigel. 1985. Interspecific feeding associations of groupers (Teleostei: Serranidae) with octopuses and moray eels in the Gulf of Eilat (Aqaba). *Env. Biol. Fish.* 13 (2): 153-159.

Dingerkus, G. and T.C. DeFino. 1983. A revision of the orectolobiform shark family Hemiscylliidae (Chondrichthyes, Selachii). *Bull. Amer. Mus. Nat. Hist.* 176(1): 1-93.

Doi, M., M.H.M. Nawi, N.R.N. Lah, and Z. Talib. 1991. Artificial propogation of the grouper, *Epinephelus suillus* at the marine finfish hatchery in Tanjong Demong, Terengganui, Malaysia. *Kertas Pengembancan Perikanan* (Dept. of Fisheries, Ministry of Agriculture, Kuala Lumpur), no. 167: vii + 41 pp.

Dooley, J.K. 1978. Systematics and biology of the tilefishes (Perciformes: Branchiostegidae and Malacanthidae), with descriptions of two new species. *NOAA Tech. Rept., NMFS Circ.* 411: v + 78 pp.

Eschmeyer, W.N. 1990. *Catalog of the Genera of Recent Fishes*, v + 697 pp., California Academy of Sciences, San Francisco.

Eschmeyer, W.N. and K.V. Rama-Rao. 1975. Two new stonefishes (Pisces, Scorpaenidae) from the Indo-west Pacific, with a synopsis of the subfamily Synanceiinae. *Proc. Calif. Acad. Sci.*, 39(18): 337-382.

Eschmeyer, W.N., K.V. Rama-Rao, and L.E. Hallacher. 1979a. The scorpionfish genus *Minous* (Scorpaenidae, Minoinae) including a new species from the Indian Ocean. *Proc. Calif. Acad. Sci.*, ser. 4, 41(20): 453-473.

————. 1979b. Fishes of the scorpionfish sub-

family Choridactylinae from the western Pacific and the Indian Ocean. *Proc. Calif. Acad. Sci.*, ser. 4, 41(21): 475-500.

Fautin, D.G. and G.R. Allen. 1992. *Field Guide to Anemonefishes and their Host Sea Anemones*, vi + 160 pp., Western Australian Museum, Perth.

Fischer, W. and G. Bianchi (eds.). 1984. *FAO Species Identification Sheets for Fishery Purposes, Western Indian Ocean, Fishery Area 51*, 5 vols., no pagination, Food and Agriculture Organization of the United Nations, Rome.

Fishelson, L. 1966. Preliminary observations on *Lepadichthys lineatus* Briggs, a clingfish associated with crinoids. *Bull. Sea Fish. Res. Sta. Haifa* 42: 41-48.

————. 1992. Comparative gonad morphology and sexuality of the Muraenidae (Pisces, Teleostei). *Copeia* 1992(2): 518-520.

Fishelson, L., D. Popper, and A. Avidor. 1974. Biosociology and ecology of pomacentrid fishes around the Sinai Peninsula (northern Red Sea). *Jour. Fish Biol.* 6: 119-133.

Forsskål, P. 1775. *Descriptiones animalium … piscium … in itinere orientali observavit*, 164 pp., Mölleri, Copenhagen.

Fowler, H.W. 1938. Descriptions of new fishes obtained by the United States Bureau of Fisheries steamer "Albatross", chiefly in Philippine seas and adjacent waters. *Proc. U.S. Natl. Mus.* 85(3032): 31-135.

Fraser, T.H. 1972. Comparative osteology of the shallow water cardinal fishes (Perciformes: Apogonidae) with reference to the systematics and evolution of the family. *Ichth. Bull.*, no. 34: 5 + 104 pp.

————. 1973. Evolutionary significance of *Holapogon*, a new genus of cardinal fishes (Apogonidae), with a redescription of its type-species, *Apogon maximus*. *Spec. Publ. J.L.B. Smith Inst. Ichth.*, no. 10: 1-7.

Fraser, T.H. and E.A. Lachner. 1985. A revision of the cardinalfish subgenera *Pristiapogon* and *Zoramia* (genus *Apogon*) of the Indo-Pacific region (Teleostei: Apogonidae). *Smiths. Contr. Zool.*, no. 412: iii + 47 pp.

Fraser-Brunner, A. 1949. On the electric rays of the genus *Torpedo*. *Ann. Mag. Nat. Hist.*, ser. 12, 2: 943-947.

Fricke, R. 1983. *Revision of the Indo-Pacific Genera and Species of the Dragonet Family Callionymidae (Teleostei)*, x + 774 pp., J. Cramer, Braunschweig, Germany.

————. 1994. *Trypterygiid Fishes of Australia, New Zealand and the Southwest Pacific Ocean (Teleostei)*, vii + 585 pp., Koeltz Scientific Books, Königstein, Germany.

Fritzsche, R.A. 1976. A review of the cornetfishes, genus *Fistularia* (Fistulariidae), with a discussion of intrageneric relationships and zoogeography. *Bull. Mar. Sci.* 26(2): 196-204.

Gallotti, A.M. 1971. Intorno all'identità di *Upeneoides doriae* Günther (Pisces, Percoidei). *Doriana* 4(196): 1-3.

Garrick, J.A.F. 1982. Sharks of the genus *Carcharhinus*. *NOAA Tech. Rep., NMFS Circ.* 445: vii + 194 pp.

Gibbs, R.H., Jr. and B.B. Collette. 1959. On the identification, distribution, and biology of the dolphins, *Coryphaena hippurus* and *C. equiselis*. *Bull. Mar. Sci. Gulf. Carib.* 9(2): 117-152.

Gilbert, C.R. 1967. A revision of the hammerhead sharks (family Sphyrnidae). *Proc. U.S. Natl. Mus.* 119(3539): 1-88.

Gill, A.C. and J.K.L. Mee. 1993. Notes on dottyback fishes of the genus *Pseudochromis* of Oman, with description of a new species (Perciformes: Pseudochromidae). *Rev. Franç. Aquariol.* 20(2): 53-60.

Gill, A.C. and J.E. Randall. 1994. *Chlidichthys cacatuoides*, a new species of pseudoplesiopine dottyback from southern Oman, with a diagnosis of the genus *Chlidichthys* Smith, and a new record of *Pseudochromis punctatus* Kotthaus from Oman (Teleostei: Perciformes: Pseudochromidae). *Rev. Franç. Aquariol.* 21 (1/2): 11-18.

Gill, H.S. and P.J. Miller. 1990. A new genus and species of goby from the Swan-Avon Estuary, Western Australia, with a redescription of the genus *Favonigobius* Whitley, 1930. *Rec. West. Austral. Mus.* 14(4): 503-525.

Gloerfelt-Tarp, T. and P.J. Kailola. 1984. *Trawled Fishes of Southern Indonesia and Northwestern Australia*, xvi + 406 pp., ADAB, Australia; DGF, Indonesia; and GTZ, Germany.

Godkin, C.M. and R. Winterbottom. 1985. Phylogeny of the family Congrogadidae (Pisces: Perciformes) and its placement as a subfamily of the Pseudochromidae. *Bull. Mar. Sci.* 36(3): 633-671.

Gohar, H.A.F. and F.M. Mazhar. 1964. The elasmobranchs of the north-western Red Sea. *Publ. Mar. Biol. Sta. Al-Ghardaqa (Red Sea)*, no. 13: 1-144.

Gomon, J.R. and W.R. Taylor. 1982. *Plotosus nkunga*, a new species of catfish from South Africa, with a redescription of *Plotosus limbatus* Valenciennes and key to the species of *Plotosus* (Siluriformes: Plotosidae). *Spec. Publ. J.L.B. Smith Inst. Ichth.*, no. 22: 1-16.

Gon, O. 1986. *Apogon bifasciatus* Rüppell 1838, a junior synonym of *Apogon taeniatus* Ehrenberg 1828, and description of *Apogon pseudotaeniatus* n. sp. (Pisces: Apogonidae). *Senckenb. Biol.* 67(1/3): 5-17.

———. 1993. Revision of the cardinalfish genus *Cheilodipterus* (Perciformes: Apogonidae), with description of five new species. *Indo-Pacific Fishes*, no. 22: 1-59.

———. 1995. Revision of the cardinalfish subgenus *Lepidamia* (Perciformes, Apogonidae, *Apogon*). *Israel Jour. Zool.* 41: 1-22.

Goren, M. 1985. A review of the gobiid fish genus *Monishia* Smith, 1949, from the western Indian Ocean and Red Sea, with description of a new species. *Contr. Sci. Nat. Hist. Mus. Los Angeles County.*, no. 360: 1-9.

Goren, M., A. Miroz, and A. Baranes. 1991. *Callogobius amikami* a new species of goby (Gobiidae) from the Red Sea. *Cybium* 15(4): 299-302.

Greenfield, D.W. 1974. A revision of the squirrelfish genus *Myripristis* Cuvier (Pisces: Holocentridae). *Bull. Nat. Hist. Mus. Los Angeles County*, no. 19: 1-54.

Gubanov, E.P. and N.A. Shleib (eds.). 1980. *Sharks of the Arabian Gulf*, 69 pp., Fisheries Division, Agriculture Department, Ministry of Public Works, Kuwait.

Gunn, J.S. 1990. A revision of selected genera of the family Carangidae (Pisces) from Australian waters. *Rec. Austral. Mus.*, suppl. 12: 1-77.

Günther, A. 1860. *Catalogue of the Acanthopterygian Fishes in the Collection of the British Museum*, vol. 2: xxi + 548 pp., British Museum, London.

Gushiken, S. 1983. Revision of the carangid fishes of Japan. *Galaxea* 2: 135-264.

Haedrich, R.L. 1967. The stromateoid fishes: systematics and a classification. *Bull. Mus. Comp. Zool.* 135(2): 31-139.

Halstead, B.W. 1967. *Poisonous and Venomous Marine Animals of the World*, vol. 2 – Vertebrates, xxxi + 1070 pp., U.S. Government Printing Office, Washington, D.C.

Halstead, B.W. 1970. *Poisonous and Venomous Marine Animals of the World*, vol. 3 – Vertebrates, xxv + 1006 pp., U.S. Government Printing Office, Washington, D.C.

Haneda, Y. and F.H. Johnson. 1958. The luciferin-luciferase reaction in a fish, *Parapriacanthus beryciformis,* of newly discovered luminescence. *Proc. Natl. Acad. Sci.* 44(2): 127-129.

———. 1962. The photogenic organs of *Parapriacanthus beryciformis* Franz and other fish with the indirect type of luminescent system. *Jour. Morph.* 110(2): 187-198.

Haneda, Y. and F.I. Tsuji. 1976. The luminescent systems of pony-fishes. *Jour. Morph.* 150(2): 539-552.

Hansen, P.E.H. 1986. Revision of the tripterygiid fish genus *Helcogramma*, including descriptions of four new species. *Bull. Mar. Sci.* 38(2): 313-354.

Hardy, G.S. 1983a. A revision of the fishes of the family Pentacerotidae (Perciformes). *New Zeal. Jour. Zool.* 10: 177-220.

———. 1983b. A new genus and species of boarfish (Perciformes: Pentacerotidae) from Western Australia. *Rec. West. Austral. Mus.* 10(4): 373-380.

Hare, S. 1990. Sampling manual for data collectors aboard demersal trawlers. *Spec. Rep. Oman Mar. Sci. Fish. Center* 1 (1st revision): iii + 96 pp.

Harmelin-Vivien, M.L. and C. Bouchon. 1976. Feeding behavior of some carnivorous fishes (Serranidae and Scorpaenidae) from Tuléar, (Madagascar). *Mar. Biol.* 37: 329-340.

Heemstra, P.C. 1973. *Anthias conspicuus* sp. nova (Perciformes: Serranidae) from the Indian Ocean, with comments on related species. *Copeia* 1973(2): 200-210.

Heemstra, P.C. and T. Hecht. 1986. Dinopercidae, a new family for the percoid marine fish genera *Dinoperca* Boulenger and *Centrarchops* Fowler (Pisces: Perciformes). *Ichth. Bull.*, no. 51: 1-20.

Heemstra, P.C. and J.E. Randall. 1977. A revision of the Emmelichthyidae (Pisces: Perciformes). *Austral. Jour. Mar. Freshw. Res.* 28: 361-396.

———. 1979. Revision of the anthiine fish genus *Sacura* (Perciformes: Serranidae) with descriptions of two new species. *Spec. Publ. J.L.B. Smith Inst. Ichth.*, no. 20: 1-13.

Helfrich, P. and P.M. Allen. 1975. Observations on the spawning of mullet, *Crenimugil crenilabis* (Forskål) at Enewetak, Marshall Islands. *Micronesica* 11(2): 219-225.

Helfrich, P., T. Piyakarnchana, and P.S. Miles. 1968. Ciguatera fish poisoning. 1. The ecology of ciguateric reef fishes in the Line Islands. *Occ. Pap. B.P. Bishop Mus.* 23: 371-382.

Herre, A.W.C.T. 1923. A review of the eels of the Philippine Archipelago. *Philip. Jour. Sci.* 23(1): 123-236.

Hoese, D.F. 1986. Descriptions of two new species of *Hetereleotris* (Pisces: Gobiidae) from the western Indian Ocean, with discussion of related species. *Spec. Publ. J.L.B. Smith Inst. Ichth.*, no. 41: 1-25.

Hoese, D.F. and H.K. Larson. 1994. Revision of the Indo-Pacific gobiid fish genus *Valenciennea*, with descriptions of seven new species. *Indo-Pacific Fishes*, no. 23: 1-71.

Holleman, W. 1991. A revision of the tripterygiid fish genus *Norfolkia* Fowler, 1953 (Perciformes: Blennioidei). *Ann. Cape Prov. Mus. (Nat. Hist.)* 18(11): 227-243.

Homma, K. and H. Ishihara. 1994. Food habits of six species of rays occurring at Pohnpei (Ponape) Island (E. Caroline Islands), FSM. *Chondros* 5(1): 4-8.

Hora, S.L. 1926. Notes on fishes in the Indian Museum, XIII. On certain new and rare species of "Pipe fish" (Fam. Syngnathidae). *Rec. Indian Mus.* (1925) 27: 460-468.

Hori, K., N. Fusetani, K. Kashimoto, K. Aida, and J.E. Randall. 1979. Occurrence of a grammistin-like mucous toxin in the clingfish *Diademichthys lineatus*. *Toxicon* 17: 418-424.

Hubbs, C.L. 1944. Species of the circumtropical fish genus *Brotula*. *Copeia* 1944(3): 162-178.

———. 1945. Phylogenetic position of the Citharidae, a family of flatfishes. *Misc. Publ. Mus. Zool. Univ. Mich.*, no. 63: 1-38.

Humann, P. 1993. *Reef Fish Identification Galápagos*, 192 pp., New World Publications, Jacksonville, Florida.

Humphreys, R.L., Jr., G.A. Winans, and D.T. Tagami. 1989. Synonymy and life history of the North Pacific pelagic armorhead, *Pseudopentaceros wheeleri* Hardy (Pisces: Pentacerotidae). *Copeia* 1989(1): 142-153.

Hutchins, J.B. 1977. Descriptions of three new genera and eight new species of monocanthid fishes from Australia. *Rec. West. Austral. Mus.* 5(1): 3-58.

Ismail, W.A. and D.A. Clayton. 1990. Biology of *Omobranchus punctatus* (Blenniidae) on rocky shores in Kuwait. *Cybium* 14(4): 285-293.

James, P.S.B.R. 1975. A systematic review of the fishes of the family Leiognathidae. *Jour. Mar. Biol. Assoc. India* 17(1): 138-172.

Jayaram, K.C. and J.R. Dhanze. 1986. Evolution and biogeography of the Indian genera of the family Ariidae. *Proc. Indian Acad. Sci. (Anim. Sci.)* 95(2): 279-288.

Johnson, G.D. 1981. The limits and relationships of the Lutjanidae and associated families. *Bull. Scripps Inst. Oceanogr.* 24: 1-114.

———. 1984. Percoidei: development and relationships. Pp 464-498 *in* H.G. Moser et al. (eds.), *Ontogeny and Systematics of Fishes*. Spec. Publ., American Society of Ichthyologists and Herpetologists, no. 1.

———. 1986. Scombroid phylogeny: an alternative hypothesis. *Bull. Mar. Sci.* 39 (1): 1-41.

Johnson, G.D. and R.H. Rosenblatt. 1988. Mechanisms of light organ occlusion in flashlight fishes, family Anomalopidae (Teleostei: Beryciformes), and the evolution of the group. *Zool. Jour. Linn. Soc.* 94: 65-96.

Johnson, R.H. 1978. *Sharks of Polynesia*, 170 pp., Les Editions du Pacifique, Papeete.

Johnson, R.H. and D.R. Nelson. 1973. Agonistic display in the gray reef shark, *Carcharhinus menisorrah*, and its relationship to attacks on man. *Copeia* 1973(1): 76-84.

Jones, G. 1985. Revision of the Australian species of the fish family Leiognathidae. *Austral. Jour. Mar. Freshw. Res.* 36: 559-613.

Jones, S. and H. Rosa, Jr. 1967. Synopsis of biological data on the fishes of the genus *Rastrelliger* Jordan and Starks 1908, with an annotated bibliography. *Proc. Sympos. Scombroid Fishes, Mar. Biol. Assoc. India* 1(3): 1109-1236.

Jones, S. and E.G. Silas. 1963. Synopsis of biological data on skipjack *Katsuwonus pelamis* (Linnaeus) 1758 (Indian Ocean). *FAO Fish Rep.* (6), 2: 663-694.

Jordan, D.S. and A. Seale. 1907. The fishes of Samoa. *Bull. Bur. Fish.* 25: 175-488.

Kailola, P.J. 1986. Ariidae systematics: comparison of the giant sea catfishes *Arius thalassinus* and *A. bilineatus* of the Indo-Pacific. Pp. 540-549 *in* T. Uyeno, R. Arai, T. Taniuchi, and K. Matsuura (eds.) *Proc. Second Internatl. Conf. Indo-Pacific Fishes Tokyo*

Kanayama, T. and K. Amaoka. 1981. First record of the scorpaenid fish *Brachypterois serrulatus* from Japan, with a key to Japanese genera of the Pteroinae. *Japan. Jour. Ichth.* 28(2): 181-183.

Karplus, I. 1987. The association between gobiid fishes and burrowing alpheid shrimps. *Oceanogr. Mar. Biol. Ann. Rev.* 25: 507-562.

Khalaf, K.T. 1961. *The Marine and Fresh Water Fishes of Iraq*, 164 pp., Ar-Rabitta Press, Baghdad.

Kishimoto, H., M. Hayashi, H. Kohno, and O. Moriyama. 1988. Revision of Japanese batfishes, genus *Platax*. *Sci. Rep. Yokusuka City Mus.*, no. 36: 19-38 (in Japanese, with English abstract).

Klausewitz, W. 1960. Die Typen und Typoide des Naturmuseums Senckenberg, 23: Pisces, Chondrichthyes, Elasmobranchii. *Senckenb. Biol.* 41(5/6): 289-296.

———. 1962. Taxionomische Untersuchungen an der Gattung *Gomphosus* (Pisces, Percomorphi, Labridae). *Senckenb. Biol.* 43(1): 11-16.

———. 1982. Tiefenwasser- und Tiefseefische aus dem Roten Meer. V. Über die vertikale Verbreitung von *Champsodon omanensis* Regan. *Senckenb. Marit.* 14(1/2): 39-45.

———. 1983. Tiefenwasser- und Tiefseefische aus dem Roten Meer. VII. *Harpadon erythraeus* n. sp aus der Tiefsee des zentralen Roten Meeres. *Senckenb. Biol.* 64(1/3): 35-45.

Klausewitz, W. and H. Fricke. 1985. Fische aus dem Roten Meer. XVI. On the occurrence of *Chaetodon jayakari* Norman in the deep water of the Gulf of Aqaba, Red Sea. *Senckenb. Marit.* 17(1/3): 1-13.

Klausewitz, W. and J.G. Nielsen. 1965. On Forsskål's collection of fishes in the Zoological Museum of Copenhagen. *Spolia Zool. Mus. Hauniensis* 22: 1-29.

Klausewitz, W. and T. Wongratana. 1970. Vergleichende Untersuchungen an *Apolemichthys xanthurus* und *xanthotis*. *Senckenb. Biol.* 51(5/6): 323-332.

Klausewitz, W. and C.D. Zander. 1967. *Acentrogobius meteori* n. sp. (Pisces, Gobiidae). 6. Beitrag der Arbeitsgruppe Litoralforschung.

"Meteor" Forschungsergebnisse, Ser. D, 2: 85-87.

Klimley, A.P. 1982. Grouping behavior in the scalloped hammerhead. *Oceanus* 24 (4): 65-71.

Klunzinger, C.B. 1884. *Die Fische des Rothen Meeres*, ix + 133 pp., E. Schweizerbart'sche, Stuttgart.

Knapp, L.W. and T. Wongratana. 1987. *Sorsogona melanoptera*, a new flathead fish from the northern Indian Ocean (Teleostei: Platycephalidae). *Proc. Biol. Soc. Wash.*, 100(2): 381-385.

Kohno, H., M. Duray, and J. Juario. 1988. State of grouper (lapu-lapu) culture in the Philippines. *SEAFDEC Asian Aquacult.* 10(2): 4-9.

Kotlyar, A.N. 1985. Taxonomy and distribution of Monocentridae (Beryciformes). *Jour. Ichth.* 21(3): 9-13.

Kraul, S.A., Jr. 1989. Review and current status of aquaculture potential for the mahimahi, *Coryphaena hippurus*. *Proceedings of Workshop on Advances in Tropical Aquaculture* (Tahiti, February, 1989): 445-459.

Krupp, F. 1983. Fishes of Saudi Arabia: freshwater fishes of Saudi Arabia and adjacent regions of the Arabian Peninsula. *Fauna Saudi Arabia* 5: 568-636.

Kuiter, R.H. 1993. *Coastal Fishes of South-Eastern Australia*, xxxi + 437 pp., Crawford House Press, Bathurst, New South Wales.

Kuiter, R.H. and H. Debelius. 1994. *Southeast Asia Tropical Fish Guide*, 321 pp., IKAN-Unterwasserarchiv, Frankfurt.

Kuiter, R.H. and J.E. Randall. 1981. Three look-alike Indo-Pacific labrid fishes, *Halichoeres margaritaceus*, *H. nebulosus* and *H. miniatus*. *Rev. Franç. Aquariol.* 8(1): 13-18.

Kuronuma, K. and Y. Abe. 1972. *Fishes of Kuwait*, xiv + 123 pp., Kuwait Institute for Scientific Research, Kuwait City.

———. 1986. *Fishes of the Arabian Gulf*, xii + 356 pp., Kuwait Institute for Scientific Research, Kuwait City.

Kuthalingam, M.D.K. and K.K.P. Menon. 1965. A note on the occurrence of *Xiphasia setifer* (Swainson) off Mangalore, west coast of India. *Jour. Mar. Biol. Assoc. India* 7(1): 214-217.

Kyushin, K., K. Amaoka, K. Nakaya, H. Ida, T. Tanino, and T. Senta. 1982. *Fishes of the South China Sea*, 333 pp., Japan Marine Fishery Resource Research Center, Tokyo.

Lachner, E.A. 1954. A revision of the goatfish genus *Upeneus* with descriptions of two new species. *Proc. U.S. Natl. Mus.* 103(3330): 497-532.

Lachner, E.A. and S.J. Karnella. 1980. Fishes of the Indo-Pacific genus *Eviota* with descriptions of eight new species (Teleostei: Gobiidae). *Smiths. Contr. Zool.*, no. 315: iii + 127 pp.

Lachner, E.A. and J.F. McKinney. 1978. A revision of the Indo-Pacific fish genus *Gobiopsis* with descriptions of four new species (Pisces: Gobiidae). *Smiths. Contr. Zool.*, no. 262: iii + 52 pp.

Lal Mohan, R.S. 1968. On a collection of blennies from the Gujarat coast with some new records. *Jour. Mar. Biol. Assoc. India* 10(1): 118-125.

Larson, H.K. 1985. A revision of the gobiid genus *Bryaninops* (Pisces), with a description of six new species. *The Beagle* 2(1): 57-93.

———. 1990. A revision of the commensal gobiid fish genera *Pleurosicya* and *Luposicya* (Gobiidae), with descriptions of eight new species of *Pleurosicya* and discussion of related genera. *The Beagle* 7(1): 1-53.

Larson, H.K. and D.F. Hoese. 1980. Fische des Indischen Ozeans. Ergebnisse der ichthyologischen Untersuchungen während der Expedition des Forschungsschiffes "Meteor" in den Indischen Ozean, Oktober 1964 bis Mai 1965. A. Systematischer Teil, XXIII Gobiidae. *"Meteor" Forsch.-Ergebnisse*, no. 32: 33-43.

Last, P.R. and J.D. Stevens. 1994. *Sharks and Rays of Australia*, 513 pp., CSIRO, Australia.

Leis, J.M. 1978. Systematics and zoogeography of the porcupinefishes (*Diodon*, Diodontidae, Tetraodontiformes), with comments on egg and larval development. *Fishery Bull.* 76(3): 535-567.

Longley, W.H. 1941. Systematic catalogue of the fishes of Tortugas, Florida. *Pap. Tortugas Lab.* 34 (*Carnegie Inst. Wash. Publ.* 535): xiii + 331 pp.

Losey, G.S. 1972. Predator protection in the poison-fang blenny, *Meiacanthus atrodorsalis*, and its mimics, *Ecsenius bicolor* and *Runula laudandus* (Blenniidae). *Pac. Sci.* 26(2): 129-139.

Lloyd, R.E. 1909. A description of deep-sea fish caught by the R.I.M.S. ship "Investigator" since the year 1900, with supposed evidence of mutation in *Malthopsis*. *Mem. Indian Mus.* 2: 139-180.

Lubbock, R. 1975. Fishes of the family Pseudochromidae (Perciformes) in the northwest Indian Ocean and Red Sea. *Jour. Zool., Lond.* 176: 115-157.

Mann, B.Q. and C.D. Buxton. 1992. Diets of *Diplodus sargus capensis* and *D. cervinus hottentotus* (Pisces: Sparidae) on the Tsitsikamma coast, South Africa. *Koedoe* 35(2): 27-36.

Masuda, H., C. Araga, and T. Yoshino. 1975. *Coastal Fishes of Southern Japan*, 379 pp., Tokai University Press, Tokyo.

Masuda, H., K. Amaoka, C. Araga, T. Uyeno, and T. Yoshino (eds.). 1984. *Fishes of the Japanese Archipelago*, text volume: xxii + 437 pp., plate volume: 370 pls., Tokai University Press, Tokyo.

Matsuura, K. 1980. A revision of Japanese balistoid fishes. I. Family Balistidae. *Bull. Natl. Sci. Mus.*, ser. A (Zool.) 6(1): 27-69.

Matsuura, K., K. Sakai, and T. Yoshino. 1993. Records of two diodontid fishes, *Cyclichthys orbicularis* and *C. spilostylus*, from Japan. *Japan. Jour. Ichth.* 40(3): 372-376.

McCosker, J.E. 1977. The osteology, classification, and relationships of the eel family Ophichthidae. *Proc. Cal. Acad. Sci.*, ser. 4, 41(1): 1-123.

McCosker, J.E. and R.H. Rosenblatt. 1987. Notes on the biology, taxonomy, and distribution of flashlight fishes (Beryciformes: Anomalopidae). *Japan. Jour. Ichth.* 34(2): 157-164.

———. 1993. A revision of the snake eel genus *Myrichthys* (Anguilliformes: Ophichthidae) with the description of a new eastern Pacific species. *Proc. Cal. Acad. Sci.* 48(8): 153-169.

McKay, R.J. 1985. A revision of the fishes of the family Sillaginidae. *Mem. Queensl. Mus.* 22(1): 1-73.

———. 1992. Sillaginid fishes of the world (fami-

418

ly Sillaginidae). *FAO Species Catalogue* 14 : vi + 87 pp.

Mee, J.K.L. and S.R. Hare. 1995. *Coris nigrotaenia*, a new wrasse (Perciformes: Labridae) from the northwestern Indian Ocean. *Jour. S. Asian Nat. Hist.* 1(2): 247-254.

Mees, G.F. 1962. A preliminary revision of the Belonidae. *Zool. Verhandl.* no. 54: 1-96.

Menon, A.G.K. 1977. A systematic monograph of the tongue soles of the genus *Cynoglossus* Hamilton-Buchanan (Pisces: Cynoglossidae). *Smiths. Contr. Zool.*, no. 238: iv + 129 pp.

————. 1979. A revision of the fringed-lip tongue soles of the genus *Paraplagusia* Bleeker, 1865 (Family Cynoglossidae). *Matsya* 5: 11-22.

Mohr, E. 1937. Revision der Centriscidae (Acanthopterygii. Centrisciformes). *Dana Rep.*, no. 13: 1-69.

Mooi, R.D. 1995. Revision, phylogeny, and discussion of biology and biogeography of the fish genus *Plesiops* (Perciformes: Plesiopidae). *Life Sci. Contr. Roy. Ontario Mus.*, no. 15: 1-112.

Morgans, J.F.C. 1982. Serranid fishes of Tanzania and Kenya. *Ichth. Bull. J.L.B. Smith Inst. Ichth.*, no. 46: 1-44.

Moser, H.G., W.J. Richards, D.M. Cohen, M.P. Fahay, A.W. Kendall, Jr., and S.L. Richardson (eds.). 1984. *Ontogeny and Systematics of Fishes*, Spec. Publ., American Society of Ichthyologists and Herpetologists, no. 1: ix + 760 pp.

Müller, J. and F.G.J. Henle. 1838-1841. *Systematische Beschreibung der Plagiostomen*, xxii + 200 pp., Von Veit and Co., Berlin.

Murdy, E.O. 1989. A taxonomic revision and cladistic analysis of the oxudercine gobies (Gobiidae: Oxudercinae). *Rec. Austral. Mus.*, suppl. 11: 1-93.

Murdy, E.O. and D.F. Hoese. 1985. Revision of the gobiid fish genus *Istigobius*. *Indo-Pacific Fishes*, no. 4: 1-41.

Myrberg, A.A., Jr., W. L. Montgomery, and L. Fishelson. 1988. The reproductive behavior of *Acanthurus nigrofuscus* (Forskal) and other surgeonfishes (Fam. Acanthuridae) off Eilat, Israel (Gulf of Aqaba, Red Sea). *Ethology* 79: 31-61.

Nakamura, I. 1985. Billfishes of the world. *FAO Species Catalogue* 5: iv + 65 pp.

Nakamura, I. and N.V. Parin. 1993. Snake mackerels and cutlassfishes of the world (families Gempylidae and Trichiuridae). *FAO Species Catalogue* 15: vii + 136 pp.

Nelson, G. and L. McCarthy. 1995. Two new species of gizzard shads of the genus *Nematalosa* (Teleostei, Clupeidae, Dorosomatinae) from the Persian/Arabian Gulf. *Japan. Jour. Ichth.* 41(4): 379-383.

Nelson, G. and M.N. Rothman. 1973. The species of gizzard shads (Dorosomatinae) with particular reference to the Indo-Pacific region. *Bull. Amer. Mus. Nat. Hist.* 150(2): 131-206.

Nelson, J.S. 1994. *Fishes of the World*, 3rd edition, xiii + 600 pp., John Wiley & Sons, New York.

Nemeth, D. 1994. Systematics and distribution of fishes of the family Champsodontidae (Teleostei: Perciformes), with descriptions of three new species. *Copeia* 1994(2): 347-371.

Nishida, K. 1990. Phylogeny of the suborder Myliobatidoidei. *Mem. Fac. Fish. Hokkaido Univ.* 37 (1/2): 1-108.

Norman, J.R. 1926. A synopsis of the rays of the family Rhinobatidae, with a revision of the genus *Rhinobatus*. *Proc. Zool. Soc. London*, no. 62: 941-982.

————. 1927. The flatfishes (Heterosomata) of India, with a list of the specimens in the Indian Museum. Part I. *Rec. Indian Mus.* 29: 7-48.

————. 1928. The flatfishes (Heterosomata) of India, with a list of the specimens in the Indian Museum. Part II. *Rec. Indian Mus.* 30: 173-215 .

————. 1934. *Monograph of the Flatfishes*, viii + 459 pp., British Musum (Natural History), London.

————. 1939. Fishes in *The John Murray Expedition l933-34, Scientific Reports*, vol. 7: 1-116, British Museum (Natural History), London.

Norman, J.R. and F.C. Fraser. 1948. *Giant Fishes, Whales and Dolphins*, xxii + 375 pp., Putnam, London.

Notarbartolo-di-Sciara, G. 1987. A revisionary study of the genus *Mobula* Rafinesque, 1810 (Chondrichthyes: Mobulidae) with description of a new species. *Zool. Jour. Linn. Soc.* 91: 1-91.

Palsson, W.A. and T.W. Pietsch. 1989. Revision of the acanthopterygian fish family Pegasidae (order Gasterosteiformes). *Indo-Pacific Fishes*, no. 18: 1-38.

Parin, N.V. 1967. Review of the marine needle-fishes of the West Pacific and Indian Oceans. *Trudy Okeanol. Inst.* 84: 3-83 (in Russian).

Parin, N.V., B.B. Collette, and Y.N. Shcherbachev. 1980. Preliminary review of the marine halfbeaks (Hemiramphidae, Beloniformes) of the tropical Indo-west Pacific. *Trudy Inst. Okeanol. Adad. Nauk SSSR*, 97: 7-173 (in Russian).

Paxton, J.R., D.F. Hoese, G.R. Allen, and J.E. Hanley. 1989. *Zoological Catalogue of Australia, Volume 7, Pisces, Petromyzontidae to Carangidae*, xii + 665 pp. Australian Government Publishing Service, Canberra.

Pietsch, T.W. and D.G. Grobecker. 1987. *Frogfishes of the World*, xxii + 420 pp., Stanford University Press, Stanford, California.

Poss, S.G., and J.K.L. Mee. 1995. A new species of *Choridactylus* (Pisces: Scorpaenoidei) from southern Oman. *Japan. Jour. Ichth.* 42(1): 1-6.

Prince, E.D., D.W. Lee, C.A. Wilson, and J.M. Dean. 1986. Longevity and age validation of a tag-recaptured Atlantic sailfish, *Istiophorus platypterus*, using dorsal spines and otoliths. *Fishery Bull.* 84(3): 493-502.

Randall, H.A. and G.R. Allen. 1977. A revision of the damselfish genus *Dascyllus* (Pomacentridae) with description of a new species. *Rec. Austral. Mus.* 31(9): 349-385.

Randall, J.E. 1955a. A revision of the surgeon fish genera *Zebrasoma* and *Paracanthurus*. *Pac. Sci.* 9(4): 396-412.

————. 1955b. A revision of the surgeon fish genus *Ctenochaetus*, family Acanthuridae, with descriptions of five new species. *Zoologica* 40(4): 149-166.

————. 1956. A revision of the surgeon fish genus *Acanthurus*. *Pac. Sci.* 10(2): 159-235.

————. 1960. The living javelin. *Sea Frontiers* 6(4): 228-233.

————. 1961a. Observations on the spawning of surgeonfishes in the Society Islands. *Copeia* 1961(2): 237-238.

————. 1961b. A technique for fish photography. *Copeia* 1961(2): 241-242.

————. 1961c. A contribution to the biology of the convict surgeonfish of the Hawaiian Islands, *Acanthurus triostegus sandvicensis*. *Pac. Sci.* 15(2): 215-272.

————. 1963. Review of the hawkfishes (family Cirrhitidae). *Proc. U.S. Natl. Mus.* 114(3472): 389-451.

————. 1964. A revision of the filefish genera *Amanses* and *Cantherhines*. *Copeia* 1964(2): 331-361.

————. 1977. Contribution to the biology of the whitetip reef shark (*Triaenodon obesus*). *Pac. Sci.* 31(2): 143-164.

————. 1978. A revision of the Indo-Pacific labrid fish genus *Macropharyngodon*, with descriptions of five new species. *Bull. Mar. Sci.* 28(4): 742-770.

————. 1980. A survey of ciguatera at Enewetak and Bikini, Marshall Islands, with notes on the systematics and food habits of ciguatoxic fishes. *Fishery Bull.* 78: 201-249.

————. 1983. *Red Sea Reef Fishes*, 192 pp., Immel Publishing, London.

————. 1984. Two new Indo-Pacific mugiloidid fishes of the genus *Parapercis*. *Freshw. Mar. Aquar.* 7(12): 41-49.

————. 1985. On the validity of the tetraodontid fish *Arothron manilensis* (Procé). *Japan. Jour. Ichth.* 32(3): 347-354.

————. 1986. *Sharks of Arabia*, 148 pp., Immel Publishing, London.

————. 1992. Review of the biology of the tiger shark (*Galeocerdo cuvier*). *Austral. Jour. Mar. Freshw. Res.* 43: 21-31.

————. 1994. Twenty-two new records of fishes from the Red Sea. *Fauna Saudi Arabia* 14: 259-275.

————. 1995. *Fusigobius* Whitley, a junior synonym of the gobiid fish genus *Coryphopterus* Gill. *Bull. Mar. Sci.* 56(3): 800-803.

————. 1995. *Zebrias captivus*, a new species of sole (Pleuronectiformes: Soleidae) from the Persian Gulf. *Jour. S. Asian Nat. Hist.* 1(2): 241-246.

————. 1995. A review of the triplefin fishes (Perciformes: Blennioidei: Tripterygiidae) of Oman, with descriptions of two new species of *Enneapterygius*. *Rev. Franç. Aquariol.* 22 (1-2): 27-34.

Randall, J.E., K. Aida, T. Hibiya, N. Mitsuura, H. Kamiya, and Y. Hashimoto. 1971. Grammistin, the skin toxin of soapfishes, and its significance in the classification of the Grammistidae. *Publ. Seto Mar. Biol. Lab.*, 19(2/3): 157-190.

Randall, J.E., K. Aida, Y. Oshima, K. Hori, and Y. Hashimoto. 1981. Occurrence of a crinotoxin and hemagglutinin in the skin mucus of the moray eel *Lycodontis nudivomer*. *Mar. Biol.* 62: 179-184.

Randall, J.E., G.R. Allen, and W.D. Anderson, Jr. 1987. Revision of the Indo-Pacific lutjanid genus *Pinjalo*, with description of a new species. *Indo-Pacific Fishes*, no. 14: 1-17.

Randall, J.E., G.R. Allen, and W.F. Smith-Vaniz. 1978. *Illustrated Identification Guide to Commercial Fishes* (of Arabian Gulf and Gulf of Oman), v + 221 pp., Food and Agriculture Organization of the United Nations and United

Nations Development Programme, Rome.

Randall, J.E. and R.C. Anderson. 1993. An annotated checklist of the epipelagic and shore fishes of the Maldive Islands. *Ichth. Bull.*, no. 59: 1-47.

Randall, J.E. and J.E. Böhlke. 1981. The status of the cardinalfishes *Apogon evermanni* and *A. anisolepis* (Perciformes: Apogonidae) with description of a related new species from the Red Sea. *Proc. Acad. Nat. Sci. Phila.* 133: 129-140.

Randall, J.E. and V.E. Brock. 1960. Observations on the ecology of epinepeline and lutjanid fishes of the Society Islands, with emphasis on food habits. *Trans. Amer. Fish. Soc.* 89(1): 9-16.

Randall, J.E. and R.W. Bruce. 1983. The parrotfishes of the subfamily Scarinae of the western Indian Ocean with descriptions of three new species. *Ichth. Bull.*, no. 47: 1-39.

Randall, J.E. and A. Cea Egaña. 1989. *Canthigaster cyanetron* a new toby (Teleostei: Tetraodontidae) from Easter Island. *Rev. Franç. Aquariol.* 15(3): 93-96.

Randall, J.E., N. Downing, L.J. McCarthy, B.E. Stanaland, and A.B. Tarr. 1994. Fifty-one new records of fishes from the Arabian Gulf. *Fauna Saudi Arabia* 14: 220-258.

Randall, J.E., T.H. Fraser, and E.A. Lachner. 1990. On the validity of the Indo-Pacific cardinalfishes *Apogon aureus* (Lacepède) and *A. fleurieu* (Lacepède), with description of a related new species from the Red Sea. *Proc. Biol. Soc. Wash.*, 103(1): 39-62.

Randall, J.E. and M. Goren. 1993. A review of the gobioid fishes of the Maldives. *Ichth. Bull.*, no. 58: 1-37.

Randall, J.E. and P. Guézé. 1980. The goatfish *Mulloidichthys mimicus* n. sp. (Pisces: Mullidae) from Oceania, a mimic of the snapper *Lutjanus kasmira* (Pisces, Lutjanidae). *Bull. Mus. Natl. Hist. Nat.* 4(2): 603-609.

———. 1981. The holocentrid fishes of the genus *Myripristis* of the Red Sea, with clarification of the *murdjan* and *hexagonus* complexes. *Bull. Nat. Hist. Mus. Los Angeles County*, no. 334: 1-16.

Randall, J.E. and P.C. Heemstra. 1985. A review of the squirrelfishes of the subfamily Holocentrinae from the western Indian Ocean and Red Sea. *Ichth. Bull.*, no. 49: 1-29.

———. 1991. Revision of Indo-Pacific groupers (Perciformes: Serranidae: Epinephelinae), with descriptions of five new species. *Indo-Pacific Fishes*, no. 20: 1-332.

Randall, J.E. and G.S. Helfman. 1973. Attacks on humans by the blacktip reef shark (*Carcharhinus melanopterus*). *Pac. Sci.* 27(3): 226-238.

Randall, J.E. and D.F. Hoese. 1985. Revision of the Indo-Pacific dartfishes, genus *Ptereleotris* (Perciformes: Gobioidei). *Indo-Pacific Fishes*, no. 7: 1-36.

Randall, J.E. and R.H. Kuiter. 1989. The juvenile Indo-Pacific grouper *Anyperodon leucogrammicus*, a mimic of the wrasse *Halichoeres purpurescens* and allied species, with a review of recent literature on mimicry of fishes. *Rev. Franç. Aquariol.* 16(2): 51-56.

Randall, J.E. and R. Lubbock. 1981. Labrid fishes of the genus *Paracheilinus*, with descriptions of three new species from the Philippines.

Japan. Jour. Ichth. 28(1): 19-30.

Randall, J.E. and R. Meléndez C. 1987. A new sole of the genus *Aseraggodes* from Easter Island and Lord Howe Island, with comments on the validity of *A. ramsaii*. *Occ. Pap. B.P. Bishop Mus.* 27: 97-105.

Randall, J.E. and J.T. Millington. 1990. Triggerfish bite – a little-known marine hazard. *Jour. Wilderness Med.* 1: 79-85.

Randall, J.E. and H.A. Randall. 1960. Examples of mimicry and protective resemblance in tropical marine fishes. *Bull. Mar. Sci. Gulf. Carib.* 10(4): 444-480.

Randall, J.E. and M.M. Smith. 1982. A review of the labrid fishes of the genus *Halichoeres* of the western Indian Ocean, with descriptions of six new species. *Ichth. Bull.* 45: 1-26.

Randall, J.E. and G.J. Stroud. 1985. On the validity of the mugiloidid fish *Parapercis robinsoni* Fowler. *Japan. Jour. Ichth.* 32(1): 93-99.

Randall, J.E. and A.B. Tarr. 1994. *Trichonotus arabicus* (Perciformes: Trichonotidae), a new species of sand diver from the Arabian Gulf and Oman. *Fauna Saudi Arabia* 14: 309-316.

Randall, J.E. and K. van Egmond. 1994. Marine fishes from the Seychelles: 108 new records. *Zool. Verhandl.*, no. 297: 43-83.

Ray, C. and C.W. Coates. 1958, A case of poisoning by the lionfish *Pterois volitans*. *Copeia* 1958(3): 235.

Regan, C.T. 1905. On fishes from the Persian Gulf, the Sea of Oman, and Karachi, collected by Mr. F.W. Townsend. *Jour. Bombay Nat. Hist. Soc.* 16: 318-333.

———. 1908. Report on the marine fishes collected by Mr. J. Stanley Gardiner in the Indian Ocean. *Trans. Linn. Soc. London* (Zool.), ser. 2, 12: 217-255.

Rennis, D.S. and D.F. Hoese, 1985. A review of the genus *Parioglossus*, with descriptions of six new species (Pisces: Gobioidei). *Rec. Austral. Mus.* 36: 169-201.

Richards, W.J. and V.P. Saksena. 1974. Fische des Indischen Ozeans. Ergebnisse der ichthyologischen Untersuchungen während der Expedition des Forschungsschiffes "Meteor" in den Indischen Ozean, Oktober 1964 bis Mai 1965. A. Systematischer Teil, XIII. Scorpaeniformes (1) Family Triglidae. *"Meteor" Forsch.-Ergeb.*, ser. D, no. 18: 55-60.

———. 1977. Systematics of the gurnards, genus *Lepidotrigla* (Pisces: Triglidae) from the Indian Ocean. *Bull. Mar. Sci.* 27(2): 208-222.

Robertson, D.R. and G. Justines. 1982. Protogynous hermaphroditism in four Caribbean reef gobies. *Env. Biol. Fish.* 7(2): 137-142.

Robins, C.R., R.M. Bailey, C.E. Bond, J.R. Brooker, E.A. Lachner, R.N. Lea, and W.B. Scott. 1991. *Common and Scientific Names of Fishes from the United States and Canada.* Fifth edition, 183 pp., American Fisheries Society, Bethesda, Maryland.

Rosa, I.L. and R.S. Rosa. 1987. *Pinguipes* Cuvier and Valenciennes and Pinguipedidae Günther, the valid names for the fish taxa usually known as *Mugiloides* and Mugiloididae. *Copeia* 1987 (4): 1048-1051.

Russell, B.C. 1985. Revision of the Indo-Pacific labrid fish genus *Suezichthys*, with descriprions of four new species. *Indo-Pacific Fishes*, no. 2: 1-21.

Russell, B.C. 1990. Nemipterid fishes of the

world. *FAO Species Catalogue* 12: v + 149 pp.

Russell, B.C., G.R. Allen, and H.R. Lubbock. 1976. New cases of mimicry in marine fishes. *Jour. Zool., Lond.* 180: 407-423.

Russell, P. 1803. *Descriptions and Figures of Two Hundred Fishes; Collected at Vizagapatam on the Coast of Coromandel*, vol. 2, 85 pp., W. Bulmer and Co. Shakespeare Press, London.

Sainsbury, K.J., P.J. Kailola, and Guy G. Leyland. 1985. *Continental Shelf Fishes of Northern and North-Western Australia*, viii + 375 pp., Clouston & Hall and Peter Pownall Fisheries Information Service, Canberra.

Salm, R.V. 1993. Coral reefs of the Sultanate of Oman. *Atoll Res. Bull.*, no. 380: 1-85.

Salm, R.V., R.A.C. Jensen, and V.A. Papastavrou. 1993. *Marine Fauna of Oman: Cetaceans, Turtles, Seabirds and Shallow Water Corals.* Marine Conservation and Development Report, vi + 66 pp., IUCN, Gland, Switzerland.

Salm, R.V. and J.K.L. Mee. 1989. *Chaetodon dialeucos* sp. nov. a new species of shallow water butterflyfish from the northwest Indian Ocean. *Freshw. Mar. Aquar.* 12 (3): 8-9,11,131.

Sasaki, K. 1989. Phylogeny of the family Sciaenidae, with notes on its zoogeography (Teleostei, Perciformes). *Mem. Fac. Fish. Hokkaido Univ.* 36(1-2): 1-137.

———. 1994. *Johnius aneus* Bloch, a senior synonym of *Pennahia macrophthalmus* (Bleeker), with comments on the identity and status of an alleged lectotype of *J. aneus* (Sciaenidae: Perciformes). *Japan. Jour. Ichth.* 40(4): 498-499.

Savidge, G., J. Lennon, and A.J. Matthews. 1990. A shore-based survey of upwelling along the coast of Dhofar region, southern Oman. *Continental Shelf Res.* 10(3): 259-275.

Schaefer, M.B., G.C. Broadhead, and C.J. Orange. 1963. Synopsis on the biology of yellowfin tuna *Thunnus* (*Neothunnus*) *albacares* (Bonnaterre) 1788 (Pacific Ocean). *FAO Fish. Rep.* 2: 538-561.

Schultz, E.T. 1986. *Pterois volitans* and *Pterois miles*: two valid species. *Copeia* 1986(3): 686-690.

Schultz, L.P. and collaborators. 1958. Fishes of the Marshall and Marianas Islands, vol. 1, *Bull. U.S. Natl. Mus.* 202: xxxii + 685 pp.

Seigel, J.A. 1982. Median fin-spine locking in the ponyfishes (Perciformes: Leiognathidae). *Copeia* 1982(1): 202-205.

Senou, H. and M. Okiyama. In press. Phylogenetic relationships of the mullets (Pisces: Mugilidae).

Senou, H., T. Yoshino, and M. Okiyama. 1987. A review of the mullets with a keel on the back, *Liza carinata* complex (Pisces: Mugilidae). *Publ. Seto Mar. Biol. Lab.* 32(4/6): 303-321.

Seshagiri Rao, B.V. 1976. Notes on the Indo-west Pacific species of the clupeid fish genus *Ilisha*, with a key to their identification. *Copeia* 1976 (3): 503-509.

Shaklee, J.B. and C.S. Tamaru. 1981. Biochemical and morphological evolution of Hawaiian bonefishes (*Albula*). *Syst. Zool.* 30(2): 125-146.

Shamsul Hoda, S.M. 1980. Blenniid fishes from the Karachi coast. *Proc. 1st Pakistan Congr. Zool.*, B: 437-447.

Shimada, K. and T. Yoshino. 1984. A new trichonotid fish from the Yaeyama Islands, Okinawa Prefecture, Japan. *Japan. Jour. Ichth.* 31(1): 15-19.

Shindo, S. and U. Yamada. 1972. Descriptions of three new species of the lizardfish genus *Saurida*, with a key to its Indo-Pacific species. *UO*, nos. 11 and 12: 13 and 14 pp.

Shpigel, M. and L. Fishelson. 1989. Food habits and prey selection of three species of groupers from the genus *Cephalopholis* (*Serranidae*: *Teleostei*). *Env. Biol. Fish.* 24(1): 67-73.

Sivasubramaniam, K. and M.A. Ibrahim. 1982. *Common Fishes of Qatar*, iii + 172 pp., University of Qatar, Doha.

Smith, J.L.B. 1956. The parrotfishes of the family Calliodontidae of the western Indian Ocean. *Ichth. Bull.* no. 1: 1-23.

————. 1957. Two rapid fatalities from stonefish stabs. *Copeia* 1957(3): 249.

————. 1959a. Gobioid fishes of the families Gobiidae, Periophthalmidae, Trypauchenidae, Taenioididae, and Kraemeriidae of the western Indian Ocean. *Ichth. Bull.* 13: 184-225.

————. 1959b. Fishes of the families Blenniidae and Salariidae of the western Indian Ocean. *Ichth. Bull.* 14: 227-252.

————. 1959c. Fishes of the family Lethrinidae from the western Indian Ocean. *Ichth. Bull.* 17: 283-295.

————. 1960. Coral fishes of the family Pomacentridae from the western Indian Ocean and the Red Sea. *Ichth. Bull.* 19: 315-349.

————. 1962. Fishes of the family Gaterinidae. *Ichth. Bull.* 25: 467-502.

————. 1966. Fishes of the sub-family Nasinae with a synoposis of the Prionurinae. *Ichth. Bull.* 32: 634-682.

Smith, J.L.B. and M.M. Smith. 1963. *The Fishes of Seychelles*, 215 pp., Department of Ichthyology, Rhodes University, Grahamstown.

Smith, M.M. and P.C. Heemstra. 1986. *Smiths' Sea Fishes*, xx + 1047 pp., Macmillan South Africa, Johannesburg.

Smith-Vaniz, W.F. 1976. The saber-toothed blennies, tribe Nemophini (Pisces: Blenniidae). *Monogr. Acad. Nat. Sci. Phila.*, no. 19: vii + 196 pp.

————. 1987. The saber-toothed blennies, tribe Nemophini (Pisces: Blenniidae): an update. *Proc. Acad. Nat. Sci. Phila.* 139: 1-52.

————. 1989. Revision of the jawfish genus *Stalix* (Pisces: Opistognathidae), with descriptions of four new species. *Proc. Acad. Nat. Sci. Phila.* 141: 375-407.

Smith-Vaniz, W.F. and G.D. Johnson. 1990. Two new species of Acanthoclininae (Pisces: Plesiopidae) with a synopsis and phylogeny of the subfamily. *Proc. Acad. Nat. Sci. Phila.* 142: 211-260.

Smith-Vaniz, W.F. and J.E. Randall. 1994. *Scomber dentex* Bloch & Schneider, 1801 and *Caranx lugubris* Poey, 1860 (Pisces, Carangidae) proposed conservation by suppression of *Scomber glaucus* Linnaeus, 1758 and *Scomber adscensionis* Osbeck, 1771, and *Caranx ascensionis* Cuvier, 1833, respectively. *Bull. Zool. Nomen.* 51(4): 1-7.

Smith-Vaniz, W.F. and V.G. Springer. 1971. Synopsis of the tribe Salariini, with description of five new genera and three new species (Pisces: Blenniidae). *Smiths. Contr. Zool.*, no. 732: 1-61.

Smith-Vaniz, W.F. and J.C. Staiger. 1973. Comparative revision of *Scomberoides*, *Oligoplites*, *Parona*, and *Hypacanthus* with comments on the phylogenetic position of *Campogramma* (Pisces: Carangidae). *Proc. Calif. Acad. Sci.*, ser. 4 , 39(13): 185-256.

Springer, S. 1950. A revision of North American sharks allied to the genus *Carcharhinus*. *Amer. Mus. Novit.*, no. 1451: 1-13.

Springer, V.G. 1964. A revision of the carcharhinid shark genera *Scoliodon*, *Loxodon*, and *Rhizoprionodon*. *Proc. U.S. Natl. Mus.* 15(3493): 559-632.

————. 1972. Synopsis of the tribe Omobranchini with descriptions of three new genera and two new species (Pisces: Blenniidae). *Smiths. Contr. Zool.*, no. 130: 1-31.

————. 1981. Notes on blenniid fishes of the tribe Omobranchini, with descriptions of two new species. *Proc. Biol. Soc. Wash.* 94(3): 699-707.

————. 1983. *Tyson belos*, new genus and species of western Pacific fish (Gobiidae, Xenisthminae), with discussions of gobioid osteology and classification. *Smiths. Contr. Zool.* 390: iii + 40 pp.

————. 1988. The Indo-Pacific blenniid fish genus *Ecsenius*. *Smiths. Contr. Zool.*, no. 465: 1-134.

————. 1991. Documentation of the blenniid fish *Parablennius thysanius* from the Hawaiian Islands. *Pac. Sci.* 45(1): 72-75.

————. 1993. Definition of the suborder Blennioidei and its included families (Pisces: Perciformes). *Bull. Mar. Sci.* 52(1): 472-495.

Springer, V.G., C.L. Smith, and T.H. Fraser. 1977. *Anisochromis straussi*, new species of protogynous hermaphroditic fish, and synonymy of Anisochromidae, Pseudoplesiopidae, and Pseudochromidae. *Smiths. Contr. Zool.*, no. 252: 1-15.

Springer, V.G. and M.F. Gomon. 1975. Revision of the blenniid fish genus *Omobranchus* with descriptions of three new species and notes on other species of the tribe Omobranchini. *Smiths. Contr. Zool.*, no. 177: iii + 135 pp.

Springer, V.G. and W.F. Smith-Vaniz. 1972. Mimetic relationships involving fishes of the family Blenniidae. *Smiths. Contr. Zool.*, no. 112: 1-36.

Springer, V.G. and A.E. Spreitzer. 1978. Five new species and a new genus of Indian Ocean blenniid fishes, tribe Salariini, with a key to the genera of the tribe. *Smiths. Contr. Zool.*, no. 268: iii + 20 pp.

Springer, V.G. and J.T. Williams. 1994. The Indo-west Pacific blenniid fish genus *Istiblennius* reappraised: a revision of *Istiblennius*, *Blenniella*, and *Paralticus*, new genus. *Smiths. Contr. Zool.*, no. 565: 193 pp.

Starnes, W.C. 1988. Revision, phylogeny and biogeographic comments on the circumtropical marine percoid fish family Priacanthidae. *Bull. Mar. Sci.* 43(2): 117-203.

Steene, R.C. 1978. *Butterfly and Angelfishes of the World*, vol. l, Australia, 144 pp., Mergus Verlag, Melle, Germany.

Steindachner, F. 1898. Über einige neue Fischarten aus dem Rothen Meere. *Akad. Wiss. Wien* 107: 780-788.

————. 1902. Fische aus Südarabien und Sokótra. *Denkschr. Akad. Wiss. Wien.* 71: 123-168.

Steinitz, H. 1959. Observations on *Pterois volitans* (L.) and its venom. *Copeia* 1959(2): 158-160.

Stepien, C.A., J.E. Randall, and R.H. Rosenblatt. 1994. Genetic and morphological divergence of a circumtropical complex of goatfishes: *Mulloidichthys vanicolensis*, *M. dentatus*, and *M. martinicus*.. *Pac. Sci.* 48(1): 44-56.

Strasburg, D.W. 1958. Distribution, abundance, and habits of pelagic sharks in the central Pacific Ocean. *Fishery Bull.* 58 (138): i-iv + 335-361.

Su, J. and J.C Tyler. 1986. Diagnoses of *Arothron nigropunctatus* and *A. meleagris*, two extremely polychromatic Indo-Pacific pufferfishes (Pisces: Tetraodontidae). *Proc. Acad. Nat. Sci. Phila.* 138(1): 14-32.

Suzuki, K., and S. Hioki. 1979. Spawning behavior, eggs, and larvae of the lutjanid fish, *Lutjanus kasmira*, in an aquarium. *Japan. Jour. Ichth.* 26(2): 161-166.

Suzuki, K., S. Hioki, and H. Kitazawa. 1983. Spawning and life history of *Triacanthus biaculeatus* (Pisces: Triacanthidae) in an aquarium. *Jour. Fac. Mar. Sci. Technol. Tokai Univ.* 17: 131-138 (in Japanese).

Talbot, F.H. 1960. Notes on the biology of the Lutjanidae (Pisces) of the East African coast, with special reference to *L. bohar* (Forskål). *Ann. S. Afr. Mus.* 45: 549-573.

Talwar, P.K. 1977. The rare deep-water scorpionfish *Snyderina guentheri* in Indian Seas. *Copeia* 1977(3): 580-581.

Talwar, P.K. and R.K. Kacker. 1984. *Commercial Sea Fishes of India*, xv + 997 pp., Zoological Survey of India, Calcutta.

Temminck, C.J. and H. Schlegel. 1842-1850. Pisces *in* P.F. von Siebold's *Fauna Japonica*. 323 pp., Lugduni Batavorum, Batavia.

Thomson, D.A. 1964. Ostracitoxin: an ichthyotoxic stress secretion of the boxfish *Ostracion lentiginosus*. *Science* 146: 242-246.

Thresher, R.E., P.L. Colin, and L.J. Bell. 1989. Planktonic duration, distribution, and population structure of western and central Pacific damselfishes (Pomacentridae). *Copeia* 1989 (2): 420-434.

Trewavas, E. 1977. The sciaenid fishes of the Indo-West-Pacific. *Trans. Zool. Soc. Lond.* 33: 253-541.

Trubschenck, C.H., III. 1981. A Synopsis of the Taxonomy and Distribution of the Boxfish Families Aracanidae and Ostraciidae, iv + 210 pp., MS thesis, California State University, Sacramento.

Tucker, D.W. 1956. Studies on the trichiuroid fishes – 3. A preliminary revision of the family Trichiuridae. *Bull. Brit. Mus. Nat. Hist.* 4: 73-130.

Tyler, J.C. 1967. A diagnosis of the two transversely barred Indo-Pacific pufferfishes of the genus *Canthigaster* (*valentini* and *coronatus*). *Proc. Acad. Nat. Sci. Phila.* 119(2): 53-73.

————. 1968. A monograph on plectognath fishes of the superfamily Triacanthoidea. *Monogr. Acad. Nat. Sci. Phila.* 16: 1-364.

Tyler, J.C., G.D. Johnson, I. Nakamura and B.B. Collette. 1989. Morphology of *Luvarus imperialis* (Luvaridae), with a phylogenetic analysis of the Acanthuroidei (Pisces). *Smiths. Contr. Zool.*, no. 485: 1-78.

Uchida, R.N. 1981. Synopsis of biological data on frigate tuna, *Auxis thazard*, and bullet tuna,

A. rochei. NOAA Tech. Rep., NMFS Circ., no. 436: 1-63.

Uchiyama, J.H., R.K. Burch and S.A. Kraul, Jr. 1986. Growth of dolphins, *Coryphaena hippurus* and *C. equiselis*, in Hawaiian waters as determined by daily increments on otoliths. *Fishery Bull.* 84(1): 186-191.

Van der Elst, R. 1981. *A Guide to the Common Sea Fishes of Southern Africa*, 367 pp., C. Struik, Cape Town.

Vari, R.P. 1978. The terapon perches (Perciodei, Teraponidae). A cladistic analysis and taxonomic revision. *Bull. Amer. Mus. Nat. Hist.* 159(5): 175-340.

Waldron, K.D. 1963. Synopsis of biological data on skipjack *Katsuwonus pelamis* (Linnaeus) 1758 (Pacific Ocean). *FAO Fish. Rep.* (6), 2: 695-778.

Wallace, J.H. 1967a. The batoid fishes of the east coast of southern Africa. Part I: sawfishes and guitarfishes. *Invest. Rep. Oceanogr. Res. Inst.,* no. 15: 1-32

———. 1967b. The batoid fishes of the east coast of southern Africa. Part II: manta, eagle, duckbill, cownose, butterfly and sting rays. *Invest. Oceanogr. Res. Inst.,* no. 16: 1-56.

———. 1967c. The batoid fishes of the east coast of southern Africa. Part III: skates and electric rays. *Invest. Oceanogr. Res. Inst.,* no. 17: 1-62.

Walters, V. 1960. Synopsis of the lampridiform suborder Veliferoidei. *Copeia.* 1960(3): 245-247.

Waples, R.S. 1982. A biochemical and morphological review of the lizardfish genus *Saurida* in Hawaii, with the description of a new species. *Pac. Sci.* (1981), 35(3): 217-235.

Waples, R.S., and J.E. Randall. 1988. A revision of the Hawaiian lizardfishes of the genus *Synodus*, with descriptions of four new species. *Pac. Sci.* 42 (3/4): 178-213.

Wass, R.C. 1973. Size, growth, and reproduction of the sandbar shark, *Carcharinus milberti*, in Hawaii. *Pac. Sci.* 27(4): 305-318.

———. 1984. An annotated checklist of the fishes of Samoa. *NOAA Tech. Rep.* SSRF-781: v + 43 pp.

Weber, M., and L.F. de Beaufort. 1936. *The Fishes of the Indo-Australian Archipelago*, vol. 7: xvi + 607 pp., E.J. Brill, Leiden.

Wellington, G.M., and B.C. Victor. 1989. Planktonic larval duration of one hundred species of Pacific and Atlantic damselfishes (Pomacentridae). *Mar. Biol.* 101: 557-567.

Westneat, M.W. 1993. Phylogenetic relationships of the tribe Cheilinini (Labridae: Perciformes). *Bull. Mar. Sci.* 52(1): 351-394.

White, A.W., and M.A. Barwani. 1971. *Common Sea Fishes of the Arabian Gulf and Gulf of Oman*, 170 pp., Trucial States Council, Dubai.

Whitehead, P.J.P. 1962a. The species of *Elops* (Pisces: Elopidae). *Ann. Mag. Nat. Hist.*, ser. 13, 5: 321-329.

———. 1962b. A review of the Indo-Pacific gizzard shad genera *Nematalosa, Clupanodon* and *Konosirus* (Pisces: Dorosomatidae). *Bull. Brit. Mus. (Nat. Hist.).* 9(2): 89-102.

———. 1963. A revision of the recent round herrings (Pisces: Dussumieriidae). *Bull. Brit. Mus. (Nat. Hist.).* 10(6): 307-380.

———. 1973. A synopsis of the clupeoid fishes of India. *Jour. Mar. Biol. Assoc. India.* 14(1): 160-256.

———. 1985. Clupeoid fishes of the world (suborder Clupeoidei). Part 1 – Chirocentridae, Clupeidae and Pristigasteridae. *FAO Species Catalogue* 7: x + 303 pp.

Whitehead, P.J.P., M.L. Bauchot, J.-C. Hureau, J. Nielsen and E. Tortonese (eds). 1986. *Fishes of the North-eastern Atlantic and the Mediterranean*, vol. 3: 1015-1473, UNESCO, Paris.

Whitehead, P.J.P., and W. Ivantsoff. 1983. *Atherina lacunosa* and the fishes described by J.R. Forster. *Japan. Jour. Ichth.* 29(4): 355-364.

Whitehead, P.J.P., G.J. Nelson and T. Wongratana. 1988. Clupeoid fishes of the world (suborder Clupeoidei). Part 2 – Engraulidae. *FAO Species Catalogue*, vol. 7: xiii + 305-579 pages.

Williams, F. 1959. The barracudas (genus *Sphyraena*) in British East African waters. *Ann. Mag. Nat. Hist.*, ser. 13, 2: 92-128.

Williams, J.T. 1988. Revision and phylogenetic relationships of the blenniid fish genus *Cirripectes*. *Indo-Pacific Fishes*, no. 17: 1-78.

Winterbottom, R. 1985. Revision and vicariance biogeography of the subfamily Congrogadinae (Pisces: Perciformes: Pseudochromidae). *Indo-Pacific Fishes*, no. 9: 1-33.

———. 1993. Myological evidence for the phylogeny of recent genera of surgeonfishes (Percomorpha, Acanthuridae) with comments on the Acanthuroidei. *Copeia* 1993(1): 21-39.

Winterbottom, R., and M. Burridge. 1988. A new species of *Priolepis* (Pisces: Gobiidae) from the Pacific plate, with biogeographic comments. *Can. Jour. Zool.* 67: 2398-2402.

Winterbottom, R., and A.R. Emery. 1986. A new genus and two new species of gobiid fishes (Perciformes) from the Chagos Archipelago, central Indian Ocean. *Env. Biol. Fish.* 6(2): 139-149.

Winterbottom, R., A.R. Emery and E. Holm. 1989. An annotated checklist of the fishes of the Chagos Archipelago, central Indian Ocean. *Life Sci. Contr. Roy. Ontario Mus.*, no. 145: vi + 226 pp.

Wongratana, T. 1983. Diagnoses of 24 new species and proposal of a new name for a species of Indo-Pacific clupeoid fishes. *Japan. Jour. Ichth.* 29(4): 385-407.

Woodland, D.W. 1990. Revision of the fish family Siganidae with descriptions of two new species and comments on distribution and biology. *Indo-Pacific Fishes*, no. 19: 1-136.

INDEX

428

435